SWINE SCIENCE
(Animal Agriculture Series)

SWINE SCIENCE
(Animal Agriculture Series)

by

M. E. ENSMINGER, B.S., M.A., Ph.D.

Formerly: Assistant Professor in Animal Science
University of Massachusetts

Chairman, Department of Animal Science
Washington State University

Consultant, General Electric Company
Nucleonics Department (Atomic Energy Commission)

Currently: President
Consultants-Agriservices
Clovis, California

President
Agriservices Foundation

Collaborator
U. S. Department of Agriculture

Distinguished Professor
Wisconsin State University

Fourth Edition

THE INTERSTATE
PRINTERS & PUBLISHERS, INC.
Danville, Illinois

First Edition, 1952

Second Edition, 1957

Third Edition, 1961

Fourth Edition, 1970

Library of Congress
Catalog Card Number
68-21886

Printed in U. S. A.

TO . . .

Professor E. F. Ferrin, formerly Chief of the Department of Animal Science of the University of Minnesota—scholar, gentleman, fine swine specialist, and chairman of my Doctor of Philosophy thesis committee—this book is dedicated.

PREFACE TO THE FOURTH EDITION

Hog producer profits in the years ahead will largely be determined by (1) the economic climate for all agriculture, and (2) the individual swine operator's skill, competitive position, and production methods. Individual producers can do little to change the first force—the economic climate. But the prospects are for a reasonably good climate based on the following: government farm programs will keep hog prices at moderately favorable levels; U. S. human population will increase 1.2 to 1.6 percent per year, and domestic demand for pork will increase 1.5 to 2.0 percent per year; somewhat more pork will be exported, with the result that total demand (domestic and foreign combined) for pork will increase by 2.0 to 2.5 percent per year; and pork prices will work irregularly upward.

The larger and more skilled swine producers can, and will, cope with increased pork production costs by becoming more efficient. They will become larger; more capital will be required—because of sheer size, and because capital for automating will be substituted for labor; skilled managers will be in demand to operate these large, complex, and modern swine production units, and fewer unskilled laborers will be needed; more swine producers will specialize—not only will more of them produce hogs only, but they will specialize in one phase, i.e., some will produce feeder pigs, whereas others will finish hogs; there'll be increased integration—for example, more feed companies and more meat packers will also own hogs, just as has occurred in modern broiler, layer, and turkey production; producers will become more market-oriented; there will be increased confinement production in units that are highly automated and environmentally controlled; manure handling will receive increased consideration; and the business aspects of swine production will become more important.

To make large, high-capital, confinement hog units pay off, a low unit cost (cost per pound or per pig) of production will be essential. Also, there must be continuity of competent management and a strong financial position.

With all the new developments being implemented in swine production, *normality* isn't good enough for tomorrow's hog production. This revision of *Swine Science* was prepared better to serve those students, teachers, and swine producers who are not satisfied with normals or averages.

M. E. Ensminger

Clovis, California
January, 1970

REFERENCES

The following books are by the same author and the same publisher as *Swine Science:*

Animal Science
Beef Cattle Science
Sheep and Wool Science
Horses and Horsemanship
The Stockman's Handbook

Animal Science presents a perspective or panorama of the far-flung livestock industry; whereas the beef, sheep, and horse books each present specialized material pertaining to the respective class of farm animals indicated by the name.

The Stockman's Handbook is a modern "how-to-do-it" book which contains, under one cover, the pertinent things that a stockman needs to know in the daily operation of a farm or ranch. It covers the broad field of animal agriculture, concisely and completely, and, whenever possible, in tabular and outline form.

OTHER SELECTED GENERAL REFERENCES ON SWINE

Title of Publication	Author(s)	Publisher
Approved Practices in Swine Production	G. C. Cook E. M. Juergenson	The Interstate Printers & Publishers, Inc., Danville, Ill., 1962.
Hog Annual, The	Staff	*The Farm Quarterly,* Cincinnati, Ohio, 1952.
Hog Profits for Farmers	W. N. McMillen	Windsor Press, Chicago, Ill., 1952.
Meat Hog, The	C. H. Hinman	*The Daily Sentinel,* Grand Junction, Colo., 1955.
Pigs from Cave to Cornbelt	C. W. Towne E. N. Wentworth	University of Oklahoma Press, Norman, Okla., 1950.
Pork Production	W. W. Smith L. M. Hutchings	The Macmillan Company, New York, N. Y., 1952.
Raising Swine	G. P. Deyoe J. L. Krider	McGraw-Hill Book Co., New York, N. Y., 1952.
Selecting, Fitting and Showing Swine	J. E. Nordby H. E. Lattig	The Interstate Printers & Publishers, Inc., Danville, Ill., 1961.
Swine Enterprises	A. L. Anderson	J. B. Lippincott Co., Philadelphia, Pa., 1931.
Swine Feeding and Nutrition	T. J. Cunha	Interscience Publishers, Inc., New York, N. Y., 1957.
Swine in Bio-medical Research	Leo K. Bustad Roger O. McClellan	Battelle Memorial Institute, Pacific Northwest Laboratory, Richland, Wash.
Swine Production	W. E. Carroll J. L. Krider F. N. Andrews	McGraw-Hill Book Co., New York, N. Y., 1962
Swine Production	C. E. Bundy R. V. Diggins	Prentice-Hall, Inc., Englewood Cliffs, N. J., 1956.

CONTENTS

CHAPTER I

HISTORY AND DEVELOPMENT OF
THE SWINE INDUSTRY[1]

Contents   Page

Nomadic peoples could not move swine about with them as easily as they could cattle, sheep, or horses. Moreover, close confinement was invariably accompanied by the foul odors of the pig sty. For this reason, the early keepers of swine were often regarded with contempt. This may have been the origin of the Hebrew and Moslem dislike of swine, later fortified by religious precept. As swine do not migrate great distances under natural conditions and the early nomadic peoples could not move them about easily, there developed in these animals, more than in most stock, a differentiation into local races that varied from place to place. It also appears that swine were domesticated in several different regions and that each region or country developed a characteristic type of hog.

ORIGIN AND DOMESTICATION OF SWINE

Most authorities agree that two wild stocks contributed to American breeds of swine; namely, the European wild boar

---

[1]In the preparation of Chapter I, the author was especially fortunate in having the valued counsel and suggestions of Mr. Karl P. Schmidt, formerly Chief Curator of the Department of Zoology, Chicago Natural History Museum, Chicago, Ill., who so patiently and thoroughly reviewed this historical material.

(*Sus scrofa*) and the East Indian pig (primarily *Sus vittatus*).[2] Both were gregarious, often forming large herds. Their feed consisted mostly of roots, mast (especially acorns and beechnuts), and such forage as they could glean from the fields and forests. Because of their roving nature, diseases and parasites were almost unknown.

In addition to these two stocks, there exist certain wild types of pig-like animals which, to this day, have never been domesticated. Included in the latter group are the brightly colored tropical river pigs and the giant forest hog of Africa; the hideous wart hog of the African plains; the native American pigs (known as peccaries) ; and the babirussa of Celebes, whose tusks resemble horns more than they do teeth.

Pigs were first domesticated in China in Neolithic times, about 4900 B.C. Biblical writings mention them as early as 1500 B.C., and legendary and historical accounts refer to the keeping of swine in Great Britain as early as 800 B.C. Swine seem to have been especially variable under domestication and especially amenable to human selection. As evidence of this assertion, one need but observe the difference in length of snout and size of ears of modern breeds of hogs.

When given the opportunity, pigs promptly revert within only a few generations to a wild or feral state in which they acquire the body form and characteristics of their wild progenitors many generations removed. The self-sustaining razorback of the United States is an example of this reversion.

European Wild Boar (*Sus scrofa*)

The European wild boar (*Sus scrofa*) still lives in some of the forests of Europe. Although much reduced in numbers in the last few hundred years, it appears unlikely that the famous wild boar will become extinct like the Aurochs (the chief progenitor of domestic cattle). In comparison with the domestic pig, this race of hogs is characterized by its coarser hair (with an almost mane-like crest along the back), larger and longer head, larger feet, longer and stronger tusks, narrower body, and greater ability to run and fight. The color of mature animals is nearly black,

---

[2]Some authorities now hold that the East Indian *Sus vittatus* is actually connected with *Sus scrofa* by a chain of intermediates.

with a mixture of gray and rusty brown on the body. Very young pigs are striped. The ears are short and erect.

These sturdy ancestors of domestic swine are extremely courageous and stubborn fighters and are able to drive off most of their enemies, except man. If attacked, they will use their

Fig. 1-1. European wild boar (*Sus scrofa*). Note the coarse hair, long head and snout, large feet, and long tusks. (Courtesy, New York Zoological Society)

tusks with deadly effect, although normally they are as shy as most animals and prefer to avoid man. The wild boar hunt has been regarded as a noble sport throughout history. Custom decrees that the hunt shall be on horseback and with dogs and that the quarry shall be killed with a spear.

The European wild boar will cross freely with domestic swine, and the offspring are fertile. It was domesticated somewhere around the Baltic Sea in Neolithic times.

East Indian Pig

This broad classification includes a number of wild stocks of swine that were native to the East Indies and southeastern Asia. Though a bewildering number of domestic races are derived from the East Indian pig, including the domestic pig of China, all of them are smaller and more refined than the European wild

Fig. 1-2. Malayan or Philippine pig (*Sus philippinensis*). This animal is rather typical of all East Indian pigs, the wild stock which, along with the European wild boar, contributed to American breeds of swine. In comparison with the European wild boar, East Indian pigs are smaller and more refined. (Courtesy, Chicago Natural History Museum)

boar. The East Indian pig is further distinguished by the absence of the crest of hair on the back and a white streak along the sides of the face. It is thought that *Sus vittatus* was the chief, if not the only, race or species of the East Indian pig that was crossed with the descendants of the European wild boar in founding the American breeds of swine.

POSITION OF THE HOG IN THE ZOOLOGICAL SCHEME

The following outline shows the basic position of the domesticated hog in the zoological scheme:

Kingdom *Animalia:* Animals collectively; the animal kingdom.

Phylum *Chordata:* One of approximately twenty-one phyla of the animal kingdom, in which there is either a backbone (in the vertebrates) or the rudiment of a backbone, the chorda.

Class *Mammalia:* Mammals or warm-blooded, hairy animals that produce their young alive and suckle them for a variable period on a secretion from the mammary glands.

Order *Artiodactyla:* Even-toed, hoofed mammals.

Family *Suidae:* The family of nonruminant, artiodactyl ungulates, consisting of wild and domestic swine but, in modern classifications, excluding the peccaries.

Genus *Sus:* The typical genus of swine, formerly comprehensive but now restricted to the European wild boar and its allies, with the domestic breeds derived from them.

Species *Sus scrofa* and *Sus vittatus: Sus scrofa* is a wild hog of continental Europe from which most domestic swine have been derived. *Sus vittatus* was the chief, if not the only, race or species of the East Indian pig that contributed to present-day domestic swine.

HOW BACON GOT ITS NAME

The word "bacon" is said by one authority to have been derived from the old German word "baec," which means "back." However, others express the opinion that the word may have been derived from the noted Englishman, Lord Bacon, for the reason that the crest of Lord Bacon depicts a pig. In support of the latter story, it can be said that bacon has for many years been a favorite item in the English menu. It has also been suggested that the expression, "bringing home the bacon" is of English origin, having grown out of an ancient English ceremony, which annually took place in a village about 40 miles from London. In this ceremony, it was the custom to award a "flitch

Fig. 1-3. The crest of Lord Bacon (1561-1626)—noted English Viscount, lawyer, statesman, politician. (Courtesy, Picture Post Library, London, England)

of bacon" to each couple who, after a year of married life, could swear that they had been happy and had not wished themselves unwed. This 700-year-old tradition was revived in 1949 (see Fig. 1-4).

INTRODUCTION OF SWINE TO AMERICA

Although many wild animals were widely distributed over the North American continent prior to the coming of the white man, the wild boar was unknown to the native American Indian.

Columbus first brought hogs to the West Indies on his second voyage, in 1493. According to historians, only eight head were landed as foundation stock. However, these hardy animals must

Fig. 1-4. Trial of the Dunmow flitch (or side) of bacon. Custom decreed that the married couple kneel on pointed stones while swearing that they had told the truth about their happy marital life. The traditional English ceremony of Dunmow, Essex, England, is—so the story goes—responsible for the origin of the word "bacon." It was the custom to award a flitch of bacon to each couple who, after a year of marital life, could prove to the satisfaction of a judge and jury (composed of spinsters and bachelors) that they had been happy and had not wished themselves unwed. This homey 700-year-old tradition was started in the twelfth century by a young lord who married a commoner, and, having proved after a year that he was happy with her, was given the flitch of bacon by the Prior of Dunmow. (Courtesy, Picture Post Library, London, England)

have multiplied at a prodigious rate, for, thirteen years later, the settlers of this same territory found it necessary to hunt the ferocious wild swine with dogs; they had grown so numerous that they were killing cattle.

Although swine were taken to other Spanish settlements following the early explorations of Columbus, pigs first saw America when touring the continent with Hernando De Soto. The energetic Spanish explorer arrived in Tampa Bay (now Florida), in 1539. Upon his several vessels (between seven and ten), he had six hundred or more soldiers, some two hundred or three hundred horses, and thirteen head of hogs.

This hardy herd of squealing, scampering pigs traveled with the army of the brave Spanish explorer. The hazardous journey stretched from the Everglades of Florida to the Ozarks of Missouri. In spite of battles with hostile Indians, difficult travel,

and other hardships, the herd thrived so well that at the time of De Soto's death on the upper Mississippi, three years after the landing at Tampa, the hog herd had grown to seven hundred. De Soto's successor, Moscoso, then ordered that the swine be auctioned off among the men.

Fig. 1-5. De Soto discovers the Mississippi. When, in 1539, the Spanish explorer landed at Tampa Bay (now Florida) he brought with him 13 head of hogs. At the time of De Soto's death on the upper Mississippi, three years after the landing at Tampa, the hog herd had grown to 700. (Courtesy, The Bettmann Archive)

It is reasonable to assume, therefore, that the cross-country tour of De Soto's herd of pigs was the first swine enterprise in America. No doubt some of De Soto's herd escaped to the forest, and perhaps still others were traded to the Indians. At any rate, this sturdy stock served as foundation blood for some of our early American razorbacks.

COLONIAL SWINE PRODUCTION IN THE UNITED STATES

The colonists must have imported hogs from the mother country at a very early date, for one of the historical documents

Fig. 1-6. A typical Arkansas razorback. This two-year-old sow weighed 180 pounds. (Courtesy, United Duroc Record Association)

of 1633 refers to their innumerable swine. It is also noted that John Pynchon, an early-day packer of Springfield, Massachusetts, bought and packed (barrelled) great numbers of hogs for the West Indian trade between 1662 and 1683. In general, this pork was exchanged for sugar and rum. Pynchon's records reveal something about the hogs in the early New England Colonies. They were described as black or sandy in color, with razorback build; and they were said to be speedy runners (as might be inferred from the fact that they ranged the woods in a half-wild state). With their huge tusks, the boars were believed to be quite capable of taking care of any wolves that might attack them. Pynchon's book records the weight of one lot of 162 hogs as 27,409 pounds, an average of only 170 pounds per animal. Sixteen of these weighed less than 120 pounds. Twenty-five weighed more than 200 pounds; and the two heaviest tipped the scales at 270 and 282 pounds, respectively. Others followed Pynchon's lead in packing pork, and, in the year of 1790, it was reported that six million pounds of pork and lard were exported from the United States.

Unlike the cattle, sheep, and horses—which were largely

Fig. 1-7. Old-time farm slaughter scene. When nearly all the people lived on the land—prior to the growth of cities and the rise of the town butcher—each family did its own slaughtering and either consumed the fresh meats or dried, smoked, or salted them for later use. (Courtesy, Swift and Company)

confined to the town commons for pasturage—the hogs of early New England roamed the surrounding countryside. Many of them were caught by hound dogs at marketing time. Usually a dog held on to each ear of the hog until the animal could be tied and pitched into a properly enclosed wagon. In order to prevent too much damage from rooting, some of the New England towns designated a "hog ringer," whose duty it was to ring all swine above a certain height (Hadley, Massachusetts, drew the line at fourteen inches). Few hogs were marked, for these animals were so numerous that nobody minded the theft of a pig. The only care ever given the hogs, and then infrequently, was at farrowing

time, at which time the sow might be given the privilege of using a shelter or be allowed to crawl under the barn or house.

THE CREATION OF AMERICAN BREEDS OF SWINE

The most thoroughly American domestic animal is the hog. In no other class of animals have so many truly American breeds been created. These facts probably result from (1) the suitability of native maize or Indian corn as a swine feed, (2) the ease with which pork could be cured and stored prior to the days of refrigeration, and (3) the need for fats and high-energy foods for laborers engaged in the heavy development work of a frontier country.

Unlike the beef and dairy stockmen, who sent their native cattle to slaughter and imported whole herds of blooded cattle from England, the American hog raiser was content to use the mongrel sow descended from colonial ancestry as a base, upon which he crossed imported Chinese, Neapolitan, Berkshire, Tamworth, Russian, Suffolk Black, Byfield, and Irish Grazier boars. These importations began as early as the second quarter of the nineteenth century. Out of the various crosses, which varied from area to area, were created the several genuinely American breeds of swine.

Structurally, the creation of the modern hog has been that of developing an animal that would put flesh on the sides and quarters, instead of running to bone and a big head. Physiologically, breed improvement has resulted in an elongation of the intestine of the hog, thus enabling him to consume more feed for conversion into meat. According to naturalists, the average length of the intestine of a wild boar compared with his body is in the proportion of 9 to 1; whereas, in the improved American breeds, it is in the proportion of 13.5 to 1.

THE RISE OF CINCINNATI AS A
PORK-PACKING CENTER

With the expansion of farming west of the Allegheny Mountains, corn was marketed chiefly through hogs and cattle. At the time of the first United States census, taken in 1840, the important hog-production centers were in what were then the corn growing areas of Tennessee, Kentucky, and Ohio.

Fig. 1-8. Cleaning and dressing hogs in a meat packing plant, 1860.
(Courtesy, The Bettmann Archive)

Cincinnati became the earliest and foremost pork-packing center in the United States. By 1850, it was known throughout the length and breadth of the land as "Porkopolis." Cincinnati originated and perfected the system that packed fifteen bushels of corn into a pig, packed that pig into a barrel, and sent him over the mountains and over the ocean to feed mankind.

Some idea relative to the rapid rise in pork slaughtering in Cincinnati and the price fluctuations of the period may be gained from Table 1-1.

Cincinnati was favored as an early-day, pork-packing center because (1) it was then the center of the finest hog-raising region

TABLE 1-1

NUMBER OF HOGS SLAUGHTERED AND PRICES ON THE
CINCINNATI MARKET, 1833-67

Year	Number of Hogs Slaughtered	Year	Price/Cwt.
1833	85,000	1855	$ 5.75
1838	182,000	1860	6.21
1843	250,000	1862	3.28
1853	360,000	1865	14.62
1863	606,457	1866	11.97
		1867	6.95

in the world, and (2) it was strategically located from the stand-point of shipping, large quantities of cured pork being shipped to southern points in flat boats via the Ohio and Mississippi Rivers. Both pork and lard were exported to the West Indies, England, and France.

The inflated price of 1865 and the slump of two years later were the result of the demands caused by the Civil War. History repeated itself during World Wars I and II.

By 1860, the center of pork production and packing was again shifted westward, and Chicago became the foremost pack-ing center.

GROWTH OF THE UNITED STATES SWINE INDUSTRY

The growth of hog production has paralleled very closely the production of corn in the north central or Corn Belt states, as half of the United States corn crop normally is fed to hogs, and these states produce nearly three-fourths of the corn grown in the country. Thus, when corn yields are down, the price of feed is up, and swine production decreases. The opposite occurs when corn yields are high.

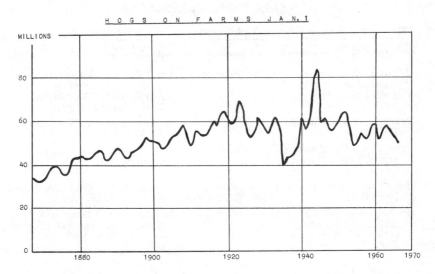

Fig. 1-9. Hogs on farms January 1, 1867 to 1968. Though hog numbers have changed rather sharply from year to year, the long-time trend shows a gradual increase. (Courtesy, USDA, Agricultural Marketing Service)

As shown in Figure 1-9, hog numbers change sharply from year to year. Except for the sharp increase during the war years (with an all-time peak of 83,741,000 head on January 1, 1944), there has been a tendency to decline in numbers in recent years. This change has probably been the result, in part at least, of decreased export demands for pork and pork by-products and of the increased competition that lard has encountered from vegetable oils. Also, beef has moved ahead of pork in per capita consumption.

QUESTIONS FOR STUDY AND DISCUSSION

1. What prompted such early explorers as Columbus and DeSoto to take swine with them?
2. More truly American breeds were created in swine than was the case with cattle, sheep, and horses. How do you explain this situation?
3. Discuss the reasons back of the rise and fall of Cincinnati as an early day pork-packing center.
4. Fig. 1-9 shows that there has been a tendency for hog numbers to level off since 1923. Why has this been so?

SELECTED REFERENCES

Title of Publication	Author(s)	Publisher
Encyclopaedia Britannica		Encyclopaedia Britannica, Chicago, Ill.
History of Livestock Raising in the United States 1607-1860	J. W. Thompson	Agri. History Series No. 5, U. S. Department of Agriculture, Washington, D. C., November, 1942.
Natural History of the Pig, The	I. M. Mellen	Exposition Press, New York, N. Y., 1952.
Our Friendly Animals and Whence They Came	K. P. Schmidt	M. A. Donohue & Co., Chicago, Ill., 1938.
Pigs from Cave to Corn Belt	C. W. Towne E. N. Wentworth	University of Oklahoma Press, Norman, Okla., 1950.
Principles of Classification and a Classification of Mammals, The	G. G. Simpson	Bulletin of the American Museum of Natural History, Vol. 85, New York, N. Y., 1945.

DISTRIBUTION, ADAPTATION, AND THE FUTURE
OF THE SWINE INDUSTRY

Contents   **Page**

Swine are produced most numerously in the temperate zones and in those areas where the population is relatively dense. There is reason to believe that these conditions will continue to prevail.

WORLD DISTRIBUTION OF SWINE

Table 2-1 gives data pertaining to the ten leading swine-producing countries of the world. China has long had the largest hog population, but, because of the large human population, production in that country is largely on a domestic basis, with very negligible quantities of pork entering into world trade. Also, it must be remembered that in China pigs are primarily scavengers and that the value of the manure produced is one of the main incentives for keeping them.

In South America, hog numbers have advanced at a rapid pace since the late 1950's. Brazil accounts for most of the production in that area.

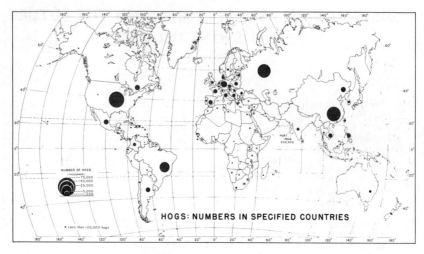

Fig. 2-1. World distribution of swine. (Courtesy, USDA, Office of Foreign Agricultural Relations)

Hog production in the U.S.S.R. has risen sharply in recent years. Today, it ranks third in total hog numbers.

In general, in the European countries, hog numbers are closely related to the development of the dairy industry and the production of barley and potatoes—in much the same manner as the distribution of swine in the United States is closely related to the acreage of corn.

Corn is raised extensively in the La Plata region of South America and in the Danube Basin of southern Europe. In these corn-growing areas, hog production is a dominant type of farming.

Dairy by-products—skim milk, buttermilk, and whey—have long been important swine supplements in northeastern United States and also in Denmark, Holland, Canada, Ireland, Sweden, and Latvia. In Germany and Poland, potatoes have always been extensively used in swine feeding.

Since 1923, except for the increases occurring during World War II, there has been a downward trend in the exports of pork and lard from the United States. This has been due to a marked

CHAPTER II

TABLE 2-1

SIZE AND DENSITY OF HOG POPULATION OF TEN LEADING HOG PRODUCING COUNTRIES OF THE WORLD, BY RANK

Country	Hogs[1] Number	When Estimated[2]	Human Population[3] Number	When Estimated	Size of Country (sq. mi.)	Size of Country (sq. km)	Hogs per Capita[4]	Hogs per (sq. mi.)	Hogs per (sq. km)
China (Mainland)	69,000,000	1963	750,000,000	1964	2,279,134	5,902,957	.09	30.27	11.68
Brazil	63,020,000	1966	78,809,000	1964	3,286,270	8,511,439	.79	19.18	7.40
U.S.S.R.	58,000,000	1967	229,100,000	1965	8,655,890	22,418,755	.25	6.70	2.59
United States	51,035,000	1967	194,600,000	1965	3,548,974	9,191,843	.26	14.38	5.55
Germany (West)	17,668,000	1967	58,290,000	1964	95,931	248,613	.30	184.17	71.07
Poland	14,251,000	1966	31,161,000	1964	120,359	311,730	.45	118.40	45.72
Mexico	9,538,000	1965	39,643,000	1964	758,259	1,963,891	.24	12.58	4.86
Germany (East)	9,312,000	1967	17,011,000	1964	41,645	107,861	.54	223.60	86.33
France	9,239,000	1966	48,492,000	1965	212,659	550,787	.19	43.45	16.77
United Kingdom	7,286,000	1967	54,066,000	1964	94,209	244,001	.13	77.34	29.86
World Total	498,000,000	1967	3,220,000,000	1964	52,403,746	135,725,702	.15	9.50	3.67

[1]Foreign Agriculture Circular, USDA, Livestock and Meats, FLM 2-67, May 1967.
[2]Preliminary for 1966 and 1967.
[3]World Almanac, 1966, New York World-Telegram.
[4]Hogs per capita computed from most recent hog and human census figures reported; in some cases, this necessitated using data for different years.

increase in production in Canada and in the European countries, particularly in Denmark, Germany, and Ireland, and to various trade restrictions imposed by the importing countries. In no sense has this decrease been due to any lack of capacity to produce on the part of the American farmer.

Hog numbers fluctuate rather sharply on the basis of available feed supplies. Also, the annual per capita consumption of pork in different countries of the world varies directly with production and availability, cost, the taste preference of the people, and in some cases with the religious beliefs that bar the use of pork as a food.

SWINE PRODUCTION IN THE UNITED STATES

The contribution of the humble pig to American agriculture is expressed by his undisputed title as the "mortgage lifter." No other animal has been of such importance to the farmer.

On January 1, 1968, there were 54,263,000 head of hogs in the continental United States.[1] Hogs rank third only to beef and dairy cattle in animal population.

Areas of Swine Production

The geographical distribution of swine in the United States coincides closely with the acreage of corn, the principal swine feed. Normally, one half of the corn crop is fed to hogs. It is not surprising, therefore, to find that 66 percent of the hog production is centered in the seven Corn Belt states: Iowa, Illinois, Indiana, Ohio, Missouri, Nebraska, and Kansas.[2] From this it should not be concluded that sections other than the Corn Belt are not well adapted to pork production. As a matter of fact, any area that produces dairy by-products, small grains, and forage is admirably adapted to the production of bacon of the highest quality. Table 2-2 shows swine numbers and percentage distribution by geographical areas in 1967.

Since 1920, there has been a significant increase in pork production in the northwestern Corn Belt and in the northern and western Great Plains area. This has been attributed to the increased corn and barley production in these areas.

---

[1] *Livestock and Poultry Inventory, January 1*, USDA, Statistical Reporting Service, Feb. 13, 1968.
[2] *Ibid.*

TABLE 2-2

SWINE PRODUCTION BY GEOGRAPHICAL AREAS, 1967[1]

	1,000 Head	% of Total Prod.
The Corn Belt and North Central States-----------	40,332	79.1
The South ---	4,907	9.6
The Atlantic Coast ---	4,765	9.4
The West--	964	1.9
Total--------------	50,968	

[1]For the areas of swine production and the states included in each area, see Fig. 7-1 in Chapter 7. Additionally, there were 12,000 hogs in Alaska and 68,000 in Hawaii in 1967. From *Livestock and Meat Statistics*, Supp. for 1966 to Statistical Bul. No. 333, June 1967, p. 4.

The eastern, New England, and western states of the United States are pork deficit areas. Despite the greatly expanded human population of the Pacific Coast, it is noteworthy that hog numbers in this area have remained about the same since 1900.

Many of the live hogs slaughtered in the West Coast plants today are shipped distances of 1,500 to 2,000 miles. They are being transported greater distances on foot than was necessary a century ago when the eastern packers were prompted to move their slaughtering plants from the East Coast to Chicago.

Leading States in Swine Production

The state of Iowa has held undisputed lead in hog numbers since 1880, but the rank of the other states has shifted about considerably. A ranking of the ten leading states, together with total numbers for the United States is given in Table 2-3.

TABLE 2-3

TEN LEADING STATES IN HOG NUMBERS, BY RANK, 1968[1]

State	Number of Hogs
Iowa ---	13,740,000
Illinois --	6,772,000
Missouri ---	4,174,000
Indiana --	4,111,000
Minnesota---	2,867,000
Nebraska --	2,738,000
Ohio--	2,340,000
South Dakota---	1,615,000
Wisconsin ---	1,581,000
Kansas ---	1,541,000
United States Total ---	54,263,000

[1]*Livestock and Poultry Inventory, January 1*, USDA, February 13, 1968. Total includes Alaska and Hawaii.

Growing corn and producing pork have contributed largely toward making the farmers of the upper Mississippi Valley the wealthiest agricultural people on the globe.

RELATION OF SWINE PRODUCTION TO TYPES OF AGRICULTURE

With cattle, and to a lesser extent with sheep, there is considerable two-phase production, in which the young are produced on the ranges of the West and then shipped to the Corn Belt as feeder animals to be finished out on grain. Because of the greater disease and shipping hazards and the fact that all classes of swine—mature breeding stock, the growing pig, and the finishing animal—require much the same kind of feed, the complete process of farrowing and finishing hogs is usually carried out on the same farm. Even so, more and more two-phase swine operations are developing; with some specializing in producing and marketing feeder pigs, and others in finishing hogs for market.

The Corn-Hog Relationship

With the opening of the central Mississippi Valley region, it soon became evident that here was one of the greatest corn countries in the world. The fertile soil, relatively long growing season, ample moisture, and warm nights were ideal for corn production. Also, it was soon realized that corn was unsurpassed as a hog feed. Here appeared to be an invincible combination, but, unfortunately, the early-day hog proved quite incompetent in the efficient conversion of corn into meat and lard. Undaunted, the swine producers of America promptly set about improving the existing swine, eventually developing several new and distinctly American breeds. Thus, "King Corn" and the American hog have played no small part in the development of American agriculture and in the prosperity of our farmers. The hog created a channel of disposal or market for corn and supplied the people of this and other countries with highly palatable and nutritious meat at a moderate price.

The Hog and Beef Combination

Farmers in the central states long ago recognized the advantages of combining beef cattle and hogs. Regardless of the system of beef production—cow and calf proposition, the grow-

ing of stockers and feeders, finishing steers, dual-purpose production, or a combination of two or more of these systems—the beef cattle and swine enterprises complement each other in balanced farming.

The cattle are able to utilize effectively great quantities of roughages, both dry forages (hay, fodder, etc.) and pastures; whereas the pig is fed primarily on concentrates. Moreover, hogs profitably salvage waste grains from the droppings of finishing cattle. In brief, the beef cattle-hog combination makes it possible to market efficiently all the forages and grains through livestock, with the manure being available for application back on the land. Such a combination makes for excellent distribution of labor. The largest labor requirements for both beef cattle and hogs comes in the winter and early spring. During the growing and harvesting seasons, therefore, most of the labor is released for attention to the crops.

The Hog and Dairy Combination

Where whole milk is marketed, it is doubtful if there is any advantage to be gained from combining hog raising with dairying. On the other hand, where cream or butter is sold and the skim milk or buttermilk is available, the hog-dairy cattle combination is usually a very profitable one. No finer protein supplement for pigs can be obtained than that afforded by milk by-products. A swine ration consisting of grain and skim milk or buttermilk produces excellent results when fed to pigs on good pasture; for the green forage provides an abundance of carotene (vitamin A), and the exposure to direct sunlight provides vitamin D requirements.

Swine Production in the South

In recent years, there has been a concerted effort to diversify the agriculture of the South away from the straight cotton, peanut, and tobacco farming traditional to the area. In part, this movement has been motivated by the recognized need for greater attention to improved soil conservation practices and the unprofitable prices often encountered from the sale of cotton, peanuts, and tobacco. Also, vertical integration has speeded the movement through providing necessary capital and know-how.

The southern states are by no means uniform in the crops that they grow. A great variety of suitable swine feeds are pro-

duced from area to area. The common hog feeds of the South include corn, peanuts, soybeans, velvet beans, sweet potatoes, molasses, cottonseed meal, some small grains, and numerous grazing crops. From the standpoint of pastures, the South has the unique advantage of possible year-round grazing, particularly when permanent pastures are properly supplemented with adapted temporary grazing crops.

Swine Production in the Far West

As has already been pointed out, the Far West is a swine deficit area. This is largely due to the fact that other enterprises have been more remunerative; and, over a long period of time, farmers and ranchers do those things which are most profitable to them. Moreover, in the Far West, wheat, the leading grain crop of the area, is frequently too high in price to use profitably as a swine feed. This is due to the fact that wheat has always been considered primarily a human cereal and that it frequently has been federally subsidized.

SUITABILITY OF THE FARM

A swine producer may have one neighbor who is a cattle feeder, a second who operates a dairy, a third who keeps a sizeable farm flock of sheep, a fourth who produces light horses for recreation and sport, and a fifth whose chief source of income is from poultry. All may be successful and satisfied with their respective livestock enterprises. This indicates that several types of livestock farming may be equally well adapted to an area or region. Therefore, the selection of the dominant type of livestock enterprise should be analyzed from the standpoint of the individual farm.

Usually a combination of several factors suggests the livestock enterprise or enterprises best adapted to a particular farm and farmer. Some of the things that characterize successful major swine enterprises are:

1. Swine knowledge, interest, and skill of the operator.

2. A plentiful supply of home-grown grains or other high energy feeds.

3. Available labor skilled in caring for swine, especially at farrowing time.

4. A satisfactory market outlet.
5. Well-drained soil.
6. Adequate and convenient, but not elaborate equipment.
7. Good records.

THE FUNCTIONS OF SWINE

The average person is aware, at least in part, of the basic utility function of swine in contributing food. Few recognize, however, that—because of their added functions—swine are an integral part of a sound, mature, and permanent agriculture.

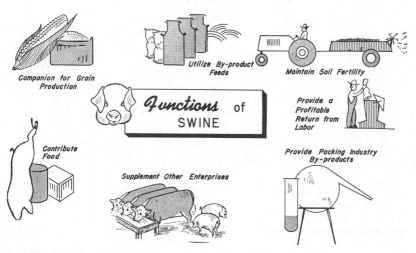

Companion for Grain Production

Utilize By-product Feeds

Maintain Soil Fertility

Functions of SWINE

Provide a Profitable Return from Labor

Contribute Food

Provide Packing Industry By-products

Supplement Other Enterprises

Fig. 2-2. Some of the functions of swine. (Drawing by R. F. Johnson)

Swine Contribute Food

The development of railroads, the perfection of artificial refrigeration, the growth of livestock markets and packing houses, the improvement and extension of highways, and the invention of the motor truck, all enhanced richly man's food supply, especially the quality and quantity of available animal products. Today, nearly half of the total food supply of man is contributed by mammalian, avian, and aquatic life. The list of food products of animal origin includes meat from domestic and wild animals, fowl and eggs from domestic and wild birds, fish of many kinds, and milk from cows, mares, goats, and sheep. Research has given positive proof of the leadership of these animal foods as rich

sources of those nutrients that are so essential for good health and proper nutrition.

In general, the consumption of food products of animal origin is limited by their cost, which in turn is governed by supply and demand. Naturally, the comparative prices of other food products and their competition with each other are also major factors.

Table 2-4 shows the United States per capita consumption of selected food products. It is noteworthy that the U. S. per capita consumption of pork ranks second only to beef.

TABLE 2-4

ANNUAL PER CAPITA CONSUMPTION OF
SELECTED FOOD PRODUCTS, 1965[1]

Product	Per Capita/Year	
	(lbs.)	(kg)
Meats (total red meat)	166.9	75.8
Beef	99.3	45.1
Veal	5.2	2.4
Lamb and mutton	3.7	1.7
Pork (excluding lard)	58.7	26.6
Fish (edible weight)	11.0	5.0
Poultry products		
Eggs, number	(No. 308.0 eggs)	308.0
Chicken (ready-to-cook)	33.3	15.1
Turkey (ready-to-cook)	7.4	3.4
Dairy products		
Cheese	9.4	4.3
Condensed and evaporated milk	10.8	4.9
Fluid milk and cream	302.0	137.1
Ice cream	18.4	8.4
Fats and oils	47.6	21.6
Butter	6.5	3.0
Margarine	9.9	4.5
Lard	6.4	2.9
Shortening	13.9	6.3
Other edible fats and oils	14.2	6.4
Fruits		
Fresh	83.0	37.7
Processed	47.4	21.5
Vegetables (fresh, canned, and frozen)	154.2	70.0
Potatoes and sweet potatoes	115.6	52.5
Sugar (refined)	96.5	43.8

[1]*USDA Report*, NFS-116, Table 5, p. 15, May 1966. (Courtesy, John C. Pierce, Director, Livestock Division, Consumer and Marketing Service, USDA)

Swine Provide Profitable Returns from Available Labor

Consciously or unconsciously, most farmers keep hogs simply because they find them remunerative. Primary factors contributing to a profitable swine enterprise are: (1) a relatively high labor return in comparison with other types of livestock production (see Table 2-5), and (2) a fairly uniform labor requirement throughout the year. Of course, it is recognized that dairy and poultry enterprises require more labor than swine, but they generally do not give as high returns per man hour.

TABLE 2-5

RETURNS PER HOUR OF WORK ON FARMS AND
IN ALL MANUFACTURING INDUSTRIES, 1964[1]

Item	Return/Hour
	($)
Dairy farms	0.61
Egg producing farms, New Jersey	0.15
Broiler farms, Maine	1.19
Hog-dairy, Corn Belt	1.14
Hog-beef finishing, Corn Belt	0.99
Cash grain, Corn Belt	2.13
All U.S. manufacturing industries	2.53

[1]*Organization and Competition in the Dairy Industry*, National Commission on Food Marketing, Tech. Study No. 3, June 1966, Table 2-8, p. 31.

Swine Convert Inedible Feeds into Valuable Products

Much of the feed used by swine is not suited for human consumption. In this category are pastures; certain grains; such by-products as are obtained from mills, packing houses, etc.; damaged grains and foods; and garbage. All these are converted into pork.

Such well-known grains as corn, oats, and barley would have only limited value if restricted solely to direct human consumption, but, because eventually they can ride to market as animal products, their value is immensely greater. A distinction needs to be made, therefore, between food grains for people and feed grains for livestock.

Swine utilize much less roughage than other classes of farm animals, 95.6 percent of their ration coming from concen-

trates.[3] For the most part, however, these concentrates are either not edible or not very palatable to man, or in more abundant supply than needed in their less concentrated form. For example, it is estimated that between 40 and 50 percent of the annual U. S. corn crop is fed to hogs. Also, swine are better adapted than any other class of livestock to utilizing otherwise waste feeds, such as garbage, bakery wastes, and cull or damaged grain, root crops, and fruit. Poultry alone can compete with the pig in the conversion to edible foods of the numerous by-products of the meat packing, fishery, milling, and vegetable oil processing industries. Also, hogs are more expert than any other livestock, except poultry, in selectively separating out the assorted hardware (nails, glass, stones, bolts, wire, etc.) of grains salvaged from elevator fires or the feed of garbage.

Finally, there is a saving in market transportation costs, because the 15 to 20 bushels of grain consumed by the pig in growing to market weight require only about one-fourth the space on the four legs of the pig as would be needed in marketing the grains. Even with animal transportation rates about double that of grain per hundredweight, the cost of marketing the grain through animals is reduced by one-half.

Swine Aid in Maintaining Soil Fertility

Cash crops, whether they be grains or forages, result in the marketing of soil fertility. Although it is possible to use green-manure crops from the standpoint of the retention of soil fertility, usually it is more practical to attain this end through feeding the grains and forages to animals. On the average general farm, with various classes and ages of animals, probably 80 percent of the fertilizing value of the feed is excreted in the feces and urine. With proper conservation, therefore, this fertility value may be returned to the soil (see Chapter XIV for further details).

Under good management conditions, a 200-pound market hog will have consumed from 800 to 850 pounds of grain or other high energy feed equivalent, 40 to 50 pounds of protein supplement, and perhaps some pasture. In general, the protein-rich con-

---

[3] On the average, 95.6 percent of the feed for swine is derived from concentrates and 4.4 percent from roughages. For comparative figures for different classes of livestock, see Table 6-1, Chapter VI of this book.

centrate which is purchased and brought on the farm will provide an equivalent quantity of nutrients to those marketed in the animal.

Swine Serve as an Important Companion of Grain Production

Swine provide a large and flexible outlet for the year-to-year changes in grain supplies. When there is a large production of grain, (1) more sows can be bred to farrow, and (2) market hogs can be carried to heavier weights. On the other hand, when grain prices are high, (1) pregnant sows can be marketed without too great a sacrifice in price, (2) market hogs can be slaughtered at lighter weights, and (3) the breeding herd can be maintained by reducing the grain that is fed and increasing the pasture or ground hay. Thus, swine give stability to grain farming.

Swine Supplement Other Enterprises

Swine supplement other enterprises, including (1) cattle feeding, (2) dairying, and (3) crop farming.

Cattle feeders who have a convenient source of feeder pigs, who are not "allergic" to keeping hogs, and whose cattle lots are fenced hog-tight, can add to their net income by having hogs follow cattle. The following hog-cattle ratio is recommended, using 75 to 150 pound pigs:

	If Whole Shelled Corn Is Fed	If Ground or Rolled Corn Is Fed
	(Pig-Steer Ratio)	(Pig-Steer Ratio)
Calves---	1:3	1:5
Yearlings---	1:2	1:4
Two-year-olds---------------------------------	1:1½	1:3

For every 50 bushels of whole corn fed to yearling cattle, approximately 50 pounds of pork will be produced. Allowing 25 cents for hogs, and subtracting $3.50 per pig for protein and other costs, that's $9.00 per pig. When pigs following cattle do especially well, it's a sure sign that the processing of the grain for the cattle leaves much to be desired and/or the grain is being wasted from the bunks; neither of which condition is a credit to

an economy-conscious cattle feeder. But grain-processing deficiencies and wastage will likely persist for a long time to come, particularly in the smaller feedlots. Accordingly, when one or both conditions prevail, pigs can be used effectively to supplement the cattle enterprise.

Fig. 2-3. Pigs following steers. The cattle feeder should plan for one pig to follow every one to five steers; the proportion of each class of animals varying with the kind and preparation of the feed and the age of the cattle. (Courtesy, American Feed Manufacturers Association, Inc., Chicago, Ill.)

Where cream or butter is marketed, rather than whole milk, and the skim milk or buttermilk is available for feeding, swine supplement the dairy enterprise admirably. No finer protein supplement for swine can be obtained than that afforded by the milk by-products, and they will bring handsome returns.

Swine also supplement crop production through hogging-down certain crops. In addition to doing their own harvesting, the maximum fertility value of the manure is conserved. This contribution of pigs is valuable especially where crops have been

damaged or lodged, where harvesting labor is not available, or where crop prices are disastrous.

Other Functions of Swine

Swine have other values. Every day millions of people use swine products for their health, enjoyment, amusement, beautification, and general happiness. Hogs are not processed for meat and lard alone. The insulin that keeps the diabetic alive (it takes pancreas glands from 7,500 hogs to produce one precious ounce of insulin) and innumerable other by-products which contribute to the welfare of society would not be possible without the swine industry.

FACTORS FAVORABLE TO SWINE PRODUCTION

The important position that the hog occupies in American agriculture is due to certain factors and economic conditions favorable to swine production. These may be enumerated as follows:

1. Swine excel other red-meat-producing animals (beef cattle and sheep) in converting feed to food (see Table 2-6), although they are not as efficient as dairy cattle, fish, or poultry. Historical support of this situation is found in the fact that, despite the predominantly cereal grain diet of the people, China has the largest swine population of any country in the world. Of course, it is recognized that Chinese swine are used primarily as scavengers and for the fertility value of the manure produced.

2. Swine are prolific, commonly farrowing from six to twelve pigs and producing two litters per year.

3. Swine excel in dressing percentage, yielding 65 to 80 percent of their live weight when dressed packer style—with head, leaf fat, kidneys, and ham facings removed. On the other hand, cattle dress only 50 to 60 percent, and sheep and lambs 45 to 55 percent. Moreover, because of the small proportion of bone, the percentage of edible meat in the carcass of the hogs is greater.

4. Pork is most nutritious. Because of the higher content of fat and the slightly lower content of water, the energy value of pork is usually higher than that of beef or lamb.

5. Hogs are efficient converters of wastes and by-products

TABLE

FEED TO FOOD EFFICIENCY

(Based on energy as TDN or DE and crude protein in feed eaten by various kinds

Species	Unit of Production (on foot)	Feed Required to Produce One Production Unit[1]				Dressing Yield	
		Pounds	TDN	DE[2]	Protein	Percent	Net Left
		(lb.)	(lb.)	(kcal)	(lb.)	(%)	(lb.)
Dairy cow----------------------------------1 lb. milk		.85[6]	.60	1,200	.11	100	1.0
Fish--1 lb. fish		1.6[7]	.90	1,800	.57	65[8]	.65
Layer --------------------------------------1 lb. eggs (8 eggs)		4.0[10]	2.96	5,920	.68	100	1.0
Broiler-------------------------------------1 lb. chicken		3.0[10]	2.37	4,740	.66	72[12]	.72
Turkey--------------------------------------1 lb. turkey		5.2[10]	3.95	7,900	1.19	79.7[12]	.797
Hog (birth to 200 lb.) ------------------1 lb. pork		4.9[6]	3.67	7,340	.69	70[15]	.70
Beef steer (yearling finishing period in feedlot) ----------------------1 lb. beef		10.0[17]	6.50	13,000	1.00	58[15]	.58
Lamb (finishing period in feedlot)-1 lb. lamb		9.0[18]	5.58	11,160	.96	47[15]	.47

[1]Includes provision for body maintenance, for the reason that feed energy must be expended in body maintenance before there can be any production; for example, the dairy cow must be maintained before there can be any milk production.
[2]Digestible Energy (DE) in this column given in kcal, which is 1 Calorie (written with a capital C), or 1,000 calories (written with a small c). Kilocalories computed from TDN values in column to immediate left as follows: 1 lb. TDN=2,000 kcal.
[3]From Lessons on Meat, 1965, National Livestock and Meat Board.
[4]Kilocalories in ready-to-eat food ÷ kilocalories in feed consumed, converted to percentage.
[5]Protein in ready-to-eat food ÷ protein in feed consumed, converted to percentage.
[6]Computations made by the author.
[7]Data from Feedstuffs, April 15, 1967, report by Dr. Phillip J. Schaible, Michigan State University.
[8]Industrial Fishery Technology, ed. by Maurice E. Stansby, Reinhold Pub. Corp., 1963, Ch. 26, Table 26.1.
[9]Ibid. Reports that "Dressed fish averages about 73% flesh, 21% bone, and 6% skin." In limited experiments conducted by A. Ensminger, it was found that there was a 22% cooking loss on filet of sole. Hence, these values—73% flesh from dressed fish, plus 22% cooking losses—give 57% yield of edible fish after cooking, as a percent of the raw, dressed product.

into pork. This includes grain wasted by finishing cattle, garbage, garden waste, and such dairy by-products as skim milk.

6. Since hogs are well adapted to the practice of self-feeding, labor is kept to a minimum.

7. Swine require a small investment for buildings and equipment.

8. The pig is adapted to both diversified and intensified agriculture.

9. The initial investment in getting into the business is small, and the returns come quickly. A gilt may be bred at eight months of age, and the pigs can be marketed six months after farrowing.

10. The spread in price in market hogs is relatively small—much smaller, for example, than the spread which usually exists between the price of Prime steers and Canner cows. Hogs may be sold at weights ranging from 150 to 300 pounds without any great penalty in price. Also, old sows and stags that have outlived their usefulness in the breeding herd may be disposed of without difficulty.

2-6

RATING BY SPECIES OF ANIMALS

of animals converted into Calories and protein content of ready-to-eat human food)

Ready-to-Eat; Yield of Edible Product (meat and fish deboned and after cooking)				Efficiency Rating		Total Score	Rank
As % of Raw Product (carcass)	Amount Remaining From One Unit of Production	Calories[3]	Protein[3]	Calorie Efficiency[4]	Protein Efficiency[5]	(calories + protein)	(calories & protein)
(%)	(lb.)	(kcal)	(lb.)	(%)	(%)		
100	1.0	309	.037	25.8	33.6	59.4	1
57[9]	.37	285	.093	15.8	16.3	32.1	2
100[11]	1.0[11]	616	.106	10.4	15.6	26.0	3
54[13]	.39	274	.11	5.8	16.7	22.5	4
57[14]	.45	446	.146	5.6	12.3	17.9	5
44[16]	.31	341	.088	4.6	12.7	17.3	6
49[16]	.28	342	.085	2.6	8.5	11.1	7
40[16]	.19	225	.052	2.1	5.4	7.5	8

[10]*Handbook of Agriculture Charts 1965*, Agric. Handbook No. 300, p. 53, USDA, Oct. 1965.
[11]Calories and protein computed basis per egg; hence, the values herein are 100% and 1.0 lb., respectively.
[12]*Marketing Poultry Products*, p. 147.
[13]*Factors Affecting Poultry Meat Yields*, Univ. of Minn. Sta. Bul. 476, Table 11 (fricassee), p. 29, 1964.
[14]*Ibid*. Table 10, p. 28, 1964.
[15] *The Stockman's Handbook*, 4th Ed., Sec. XII.
[16]Allowance made for both cutting and cooking losses following dressing. Thus, values are on a cooked, ready-to-eat basis of lean and marbled meat, exclusive of bone, gristle, and fat. Values provided by National Live Stock and Meat Board (personal communication of June 5, 1967, from Dr. Wm. C. Sherman, Director, Nutrition Research to the author; and based on data from *The Nutritive Value of Cooked Meat*, by Ruth M. Leverton and George V. Odell, Misc. Pub. MP-49, Appendix C, March 1958).
[17]*Beef Cattle Science*, 4th Ed., Ch. 14, Table 14-21.
[18]*Sheep and Wool Science*, 3rd Ed., p. 250.

11. Hogs are unexcelled as a source of farm meats. This is due to their ease of dressing and the superior curing and keeping qualities of pork.

12. The hog excels all other farm animals in fat storing ability, and pork fat is more valuable than fats produced by other domestic animals with the exception of the dairy cow.

FACTORS UNFAVORABLE TO SWINE PRODUCTION

It is not recommended that hogs be raised under any and all conditions. There are certain limitations that should receive consideration if the venture is to be successful. Some of these reservations are as follows:

1. Because of the nature of the digestive tract, the growing-finishing pig must be fed a maximum of concentrates and a minimum of roughages. Where or when grains are scarce and high in price, this may result in high production costs.

2. Because of the nature of their diet and their rapid

growth rate, hogs are extremely sensitive to unfavorable rations and to careless management.

3. Swine are very susceptible to numerous diseases and parasites.

4. Fences of a more expensive kind are necessary in hog raising.

5. Sows should have skilled attention at farrowing time.

6. Because of their rooting and close-grazing habits, hogs are hard on pasture.

7. Hogs are not adapted to a frontier type of agriculture where grazing areas are extensive and vegetation is sparse. Neither are they best suited to the utilization of permanent-pasture areas.

THE FUTURE OF THE AMERICAN SWINE INDUSTRY

Some of the factors that will determine the future of the American swine industry are:

1. **Foreign competition.**—Denmark is the world's largest pork exporter, followed some distance behind by the Netherlands and Poland. Combined, these three account for approximately 70 percent of world exports. The United Kingdom—unrivaled top-ranking pork importer—takes 55 to 60 percent of total world imports. The United States ranks second as a pork importer.

Some of the South American countries are potential pork-producing and pork-exporting nations, an encouraging market being the only needed incentive. Canada is making great progress in swine production, in both quality and quantity. Only tariffs, quotas, and embargoes enacted by our federal government can prevent future and serious competition from foreign imports. However, with our huge corn production and improved swine-production methods, it is not anticipated that pork will ever have the potential foreign competition that exists with beef.

Table 2-7 shows the tariff rates (duties) on imported pork and live hogs.

There are no quotas on pork or live hogs.

The potential pork-export situation is not encouraging.

2. **The lard situation.**—Lard was a drug on the market prior to 1941 and soon after World War II this status returned. Satisfactory vegetable oils can now be produced at lower cost.

TABLE 2-7

TARIFF RATES ON IMPORTED PORK AND LIVE HOGS[1]

Item	Prior Rate	1968 Rate	1969 Rate	1970 Rate	1971 Rate	1972 Rate
	(¢/lb.)	(¢/lb.)	(¢/lb.)	(¢/lb.)	(¢/lb.)	(¢/lb.)
Pork; fresh, chilled, or frozen	1.25	1.0	1.0	0.8	0.7	0.5
Cured hams, shoulders, bacon, or other	2.0	2.0	2.0	2.0	2.0	2.0
Canned, boned and cooked hams, shoulders, bacon, or other	3.0	3.0	3.0	3.0	3.0	3.0
Sausage: Fresh	3.25	2.9	2.5	2.2	1.9	1.6
Live hogs	1.0	0.9	0.8	0.7	0.6	0.5

[1]From: Tariff Schedules of the United States Annotated (1968), Staged Rates and Historical Notes, provided to the author by James P. Hartman, Livestock and Meat Products Division, USDA, Foreign Agricultural Service, Washington, D.C. These duties, graduated downward (staged rates), were established as a result of the Kennedy Round discussions concluded in 1967.

LARD: U.S. PRODUCTION AND EXPORTS

Fig. 2-4. Production and exports of lard from the United States, 1900 to 1965. Note that lard exports increased sharply during both World War I and World War II, but they were very small between 1935 and 1940. Most authorities agree that future lard exports will be negligible. (Courtesy, USDA, Agricultural Marketing Service)

When processed lard sells for less than the price of hogs on foot, it should be perfectly evident that the product is lacking in demand. In order to alleviate the surplus lard situation, the soundest approach consists of: (a) breeding a type of hog that is less lardy in conformation, (b) feeding so as to produce

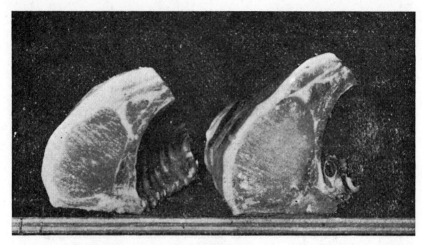

Fig. 2-5. Breeding made the difference! These are cuts between 10th and 11th ribs. The hogs received the same ration and were slaughtered at the same weight. Note the difference in the amount of lean meat, with the cut on the right being superior. (Courtesy, Washington State University)

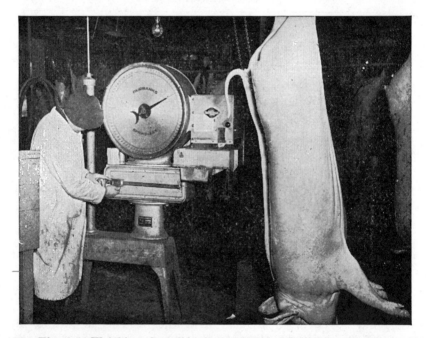

Fig. 2-6. Weighing Canadian hog carcasses. Selling on the basis of carcass grade and weight is the most common method of marketing hogs in Denmark, Sweden, and Canada. (Courtesy, Department of Agriculture, Ottawa, Canada)

less excess fat, (c) marketing at lighter weights, and (d) purchasing hogs on a quality basis (preferably rail-graded).

3. **Increased human consumption.**—Without doubt some increased human consumption of pork could be brought about through the production of a higher quality product. Many folks, for example, would relish more high quality breakfast bacon. It is not anticipated, however, that any considerable opportunity for increased demand for hogs will come from any marked increase in per capita consumption of pork. Rather, such increases as occur will accrue from our expanding population.

4. **Competition from other farm animals and between areas.**—Hogs must continue to compete with all classes of animals for the available concentrates. For the nation as a whole, it appears, however, that there exists a fair balance of production with consumption of the several products of domestic animals. Thus, no immediate or sizeable shift that would be either favorable or unfavorable to increased pork production is anticipated. On the other hand, certain minor shifts in production from area to area may be expected.

QUESTIONS FOR STUDY AND DISCUSSION

1. What factors will continue to keep out or discourage more foreign imports of pork, or of hogs on foot?

2. Discuss the factors which account for each of the five leading swine producing countries (see Table 2-1) holding their respective ranks.

3. How do you account for the fact that 66 percent of the hog production is centered in the seven Corn Belt states?

4. In cattle production, cow-and-calf operations predominate on the range and cattle are finished primarily in Corn Belt feedlots or in the irrigated areas of the West and Southwest. Why does not swine production lend itself to two-phase production, as is true with cattle?

5. Select a certain farm or ranch (your home farm or ranch, or one with which you are familiar). Then, (a) discuss the relation of swine production on this farm or ranch to the type of agriculture, and (b) list the factors favorable and unfavorable to swine production on this particular farm or ranch.

6. Assuming that a young man had no "roots" in a particular

location, in what area of the United States would you recommend that he establish a swine enterprise? Justify your answer.

7. When processed lard sells for less than the price of hogs on foot, it should be perfectly evident that the product is lacking in demand. How may we alleviate the surplus lard situation?

8. On the whole, do you feel that the future of U.S. swine production warrants optimism or pessimism? Justify your answer.

SELECTED REFERENCES

Title of Publication	Author(s)	Publisher
Pork Production	W. W. Smith L. M. Hutchings	The Macmillan Company, New York, N. Y., 1952.
Swine Production	C. E. Bundy R. V. Diggins	Prentice-Hall, Inc., Englewood Cliffs, N. J., 1956.
Swine Production	W. E. Carroll J. L. Krider F. N. Andrews	McGraw-Hill Book Co., New York, N. Y., 1962.

TYPES AND BREEDS OF SWINE[1]

Contents   **Page**

In the hands of skilled livestock men, swine are the most plastic of any species of farm animals. This is due to their early maturity, multiple rate of reproduction, and the short time between generations. A farmer who produces a total of one hundred spring-farrowed pigs yearly needs only fourteen gilts to raise a crop of the same size the following spring. There will be approximately fifty gilts from which he may select the fourteen brood sows needed. He has a wide choice of keeping the lardy and more early maturing gilts or of picking others of a meaty form. Con-

---

[1] Sometimes folks construe the write-up of a breed of livestock in a book or in a U. S. Department of Agriculture bulletin as an official recognition of the breed. Nothing could be further from the truth, for no person or office has authority to approve a breed. The only legal basis for recognizing a breed is contained in the Tariff Act of 1930, which provides for the duty-free admission of purebred breeding stock provided they are registered in the country of origin. But the latter stipulation applies to imported animals only.

In this book, no *official* recognition of any breed is intended or implied. Rather, the author has tried earnestly, and without favoritism, to present the factual story of the breeds in narrative and picture. In particular, such information relative to the new and/or less widely distributed breeds is needed, and often difficult to come by.

tinued selection each year with emphasis upon the same characteristics and the purchase of boars of the same type can completely alter the conformation of the hogs in a herd in the short
period of four to five years. Despite this fact, progress in producing meat type hogs was often slow and painful throughout the
thirties and forties. As a result, (1) pork gradually lost its place
as the preferred meat, with beef taking the lead in the early
fifties, and (2) a number of new American breeds of swine
evolved, most of them carrying some Landrace breeding.

Pork may never regain the lead that it once enjoyed, and
many of the newer breeds of swine may not survive. However, it
is to the everlasting credit of the new breeds that they shook
their older counterparts out of their lethargy. They more than
justified the effort and cost back of them. Likewise, it is to the
credit of the established breeds that they met the challenge and
speeded up the transition in type. As a result, pork that satisfies
consumer demands is once again being produced throughout
America.

THE TYPES OF HOGS

Swine types are the result of three contributing factors:
(1) the demands of the consumer, (2) the character of the available feeds, and (3) the breeding and pursuit of type fads by
breeders.

Historically, three distinct types of hogs have been recognized; namely (1) lard type, (2) bacon type, and (3) meat type.
At the present time, however, the goal for all U. S. swine breeds
is for a meat type hog, although it is obvious that some breeds
have more nearly achieved this than others.

The Lard Type

Originally, breeders of hogs stressed immense size and scale
and great fattening ability. This general type persisted until the
latter part of the nineteenth century. Beginning about 1890,
breeders turned their attention to the development of early maturity, great refinement, and a very thick finish. In order to obtain
these desired qualities, animals were developed that were smaller
in size, thick, compactly built, and very short of leg. In the Poland China breed, this fashionable fad was carried to the extreme. It finally culminated in the development of the "hot

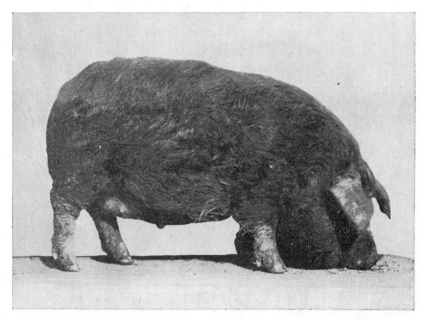

Fig. 3-1. A Poland China gilt of the chuffy type. Small, refined animals of this type dominated the American show ring from 1890 to 1910. (Courtesy, University of Illinois)

bloods." Hogs of this chuffy type were notoriously lacking in prolificacy. They often farrowed twins and triplets; and, when they were carried to weights in excess of 200 pounds, their gains were very expensive. Small refined animals of this type dominated the show ring from about 1890 to 1910.

In order to secure increased utility qualities, breeders finally, about 1915, began the shift to the big-type strains. Before long, the craze swept across the nation, and again the pendulum swung too far. Breeders demanded great size, growthiness, length of body, and plenty of bone. The big-type animal was rangy in conformation and slow in maturity. Many champions of the show ring included as their attributes long legs, weak loins, and "cat hams." One popular champion of the day was advertised as being "so tall that it makes him dizzy to look down." Inasmuch as this type failed most miserably in meeting the requirements of either the packer or the producer—being too slow to reach maturity and requiring a heavy weight in order to reach market finish—another shift in ideals became necessary.

Fig. 3-2. A Poland China boar pig of the rangy type. Long legged, weak loined, "cat hammed" animals of this type dominated the American show ring from 1915 to 1925. (Courtesy, H. M. Meneough, Editor, *Poland China World*, Grimes, Ia.)

Since about 1925, swine breeders have been striving to develop the medium or meat type. Although much real progress has been made, the present lack of uniformity within breeds bears evidence of the difficulties encountered in correcting such radical shifts. The best specimens of the meat type combine size, balance, and smoothness with feeding capacity and the ability to finish during the growing period. Moreover, the present market trend is in the direction of a type that is less pronounced in lard character. In recognition of this change in consumer demand and in the consequent shift in type, most swine authorities now consider the term "meat type" as far more applicable than lard type.

The Bacon Type

Bacon type hogs are more common in those areas where the available feeds consist of dairy by-products, peas, barley, wheat, oats, rye, and root crops. As compared with corn, such feeds are not so fattening. Thus, instead of producing a great amount of lard, they build sufficient muscle for desirable bacon. The countries of Denmark, Canada, and Ireland have long been noted for

the production of high-quality bacon. In the past, the surplus pork produced in these countries has found a ready market in England, largely selling as Wiltshire sides.

In emphasizing the importance of character of feeds as a factor influencing the production of bacon type hogs, it is not to be inferred that there is no hereditary difference. That is to say, when bacon type hogs are taken into the Corn Belt and fed largely on corn, they never entirely lose their bacon qualities.

The Meat Type

Since about 1925, American swine breeders have been striving to produce meat type hogs—animals that are intermediate between the lard and bacon types. The best specimens of the meat type combine muscling, length of body, balance, and the ability to reach market weight and finish without excess fat. In achieving the meat type, the selection and breeding programs of producers have been stoutly augmented by meat certification programs, livestock shows, and swine type conferences.

THE BREEDS OF HOGS IN THE UNITED STATES

The breeds of hogs in the United States include the following:

American Landrace	Minnesota No. 1
Beltsville No. 1	Minnesota No. 2
Berkshire	Minnesota No. 3
Chester White	Montana No. 1
CPF No. 1	OIC
CPF No. 2	Palouse
Duroc	Poland China
Hampshire	Spotted
Hereford	Tamworth
Kentucky Red Berkshire	Wessex Saddleback
Lacombe	Yorkshire
Maryland No. 1	

With the exception of the American Landrace, Berkshire, Lacombe, Tamworth, Wessex Saddleback, and Yorkshire, the breeds of swine common to the United States are strictly American creations. This is interesting in view of the fact that only one of our breeds of draft horses and few of our better known breeds

sheep and beef cattle were American creations. With the exception of the Hereford breed and some of the newer crossbred breeds of swine, the American breeds came into being in the period from 1800 to 1880—an era which was characterized by the production of an abundance of corn for utilization by hogs and by consumer demand for fat, heavy cuts of pork. The European breeds did not seem to meet these requirements.

It must be remembered, however, that the American breeds of swine were not developed without recourse to foreign stock. Prior to De Soto's importation, no hogs were found on the continent. The offspring of De Soto's sturdy razorbacks, together with subsequent importations of European and Oriental hogs, served as the foundation stock for the American breeds which followed. Out of these early-day, multiple-colored and conglomerate types of swine, the swine producers of different areas of the United States, through the tools of selection and controlled matings, gradually molded uniform animals, later to be known as breeds. It is to be noted, however, that these foundation animals carried a variable genetic composition. This made them flexible in the hands of man and accounted for the radical subsequent shifts in swine types that have been observed within the pure breeds.

RELATIVE POPULARITY OF BREEDS OF SWINE

Table 3-1 shows the 1968 and total registrations to date of the common breeds of hogs. Although trends are not shown in this table, the 1968 registrations are indicative of the current popularity of each of the breeds.

Although there are many breed differences and most breed associations are constantly extolling the virtues of their respective breeds, it is perhaps fair to say that there is more difference within than between breeds from the standpoint of efficiency of production and carcass quality. Without doubt, the future and enduring popularity of each breed will depend upon how well it fulfills these two primary requisites.

American Landrace

As was originally true of Spain with its Merino Sheep, Denmark long held a monopoly on the Landrace breed of swine. In

TABLE 3-1
1968 AND TOTAL REGISTRATIONS OF SWINE IN
UNITED STATES BREED ASSOCIATIONS

Breed	1968 Registrations	Total Registrations
Hampshire	63,496	1,965,154
Duroc[1]	48,075	4,024,140
Yorkshire	40,033	565,000
Poland China	19,512	2,680,011
Chester White	17,115	116,739
Spotted	12,367	1,001,667
Berkshire	8,502	947,921
American Landrace	8,123	889,275
Tamworth	1,775	185,563
Hereford	697	111,287
Incrosses[2]	172	3,837
CPF No. 2[2]	168	598
Minnesota No. 3[2]	151	1,978
CPF No. 1[2]	105	449
Large Black	78	1,511
Minnesota No. 2[2]	27	5,968
Minnesota No. 1[2]	13	22,122
Beltsville No. 1[2]	8	4,555
Palouse[2]	0	1,902
Maryland No. 1[2]	0	1,299
Hybrids[1][2]	0	694

[1]1965 figures.
[2]Registered by the Inbred Livestock Registry Association, Augusta, Ill. Hybrids are crosses of two or more inbred lines or breeds of swine registered by the Inbred Livestock Registry Association.

1934, Landrace hogs were shipped to the United States and Canada, but, by government agreement, for several years thereafter they could not be released as purebreds; their use being restricted to crossbreeding. Subsequently, an agreement was reached with Denmark whereby surplus purebred Landrace swine could be released. Thereupon (in 1950), the American Landrace Association, Inc., was organized, and the breed became known as the American Landrace in this country.

The Landrace is also of considerable importance in this country because of the many new strains of hogs that are based on a crossbred foundation with this breed as one of the parents.

ORIGIN AND NATIVE HOME

The Landrace breed of hogs is native to Denmark, where it has been bred and fed to produce the highest quality bacon in the

Fig. 3-3. Landrace boar, 6 months old. (Courtesy, American Landrace Association)

world. With the aid of government testing stations, the Landrace breed has long been selected for improved bacon carcass quality and efficiency of pork production. In addition to improved breeding, the feeds common to Denmark—small grains and dairy by-products—are also conducive to the production of high-quality bacon. For many years, the chief outlet for the surplus pork of Denmark has been the London market, where it is sold primarily in the form of Wiltshire sides.

EARLY AMERICAN IMPORTATIONS

The United States Department of Agriculture made an importation of Danish Landrace swine from Denmark in 1934. Under the terms of the original agreement, purebred Landrace stock could not be raised by private individuals; only by certain experiment stations. Subsequently, Denmark approved of the release of surplus breeding stock that was already in the United States. Then, in 1954, 38 head of boars and gilts were imported from Norway by four individual breeders. The latter animals carried Norwegian, Danish, and Swedish Landrace blood. Other importations followed.

AMERICAN LANDRACE CHARACTERISTICS

The Landrace breed is white in color, although black skin spots or freckles are rather common. The breed is characterized by its very long side, square ham, relatively short legs, trim jowl, and medium lop ears. It is noted for prolificacy and for efficiency of feed utilization.

The breed registry association lists the following disqualifications: black in the hair coat; fewer than six teats on either side; and erect ears, with no forward break.

Berkshire

The Berkshire is one of the oldest of the improved breeds of swine. The striking style and carriage of the Berkshire has made it known as the aristocrat among the breeds of swine.

ORIGIN AND NATIVE HOME

The native home of the Berkshire is in south central England, principally in the counties of Berkshire and Wiltshire. The old English hog, a descendant of the wild boar, served as foundation stock; and these early animals were improved by introducing Chinese, Siamese, and Neopolitan blood. In 1789, the Berkshire was described as follows: reddish brown in color; with black spots, large drooping ears, short legs, fine bone, and the disposition to fatten at an early age.

EARLY AMERICAN IMPORTATIONS

The earliest importation of Berkshire hogs into the United States, of which there is authentic record, was made by John Brentnall of New Jersey, in 1823. This importation was followed by those of Bagg and Wait, of Orange County, New York, in 1839, and A. B. Allen of Buffalo, New York, in 1841.

Although there have been many constructive Berkshire breeders in this country, certainly the name of N. H. Gentry, of Sedalia, Missouri, is among the immortals. Few breeders either here or abroad have achieved the success which was his. He was truly a master breeder. The majority of the best Berkshires of today trace to Gentry breeding, particularly to the great and prepotent boar, Longfellow.

BERKSHIRE CHARACTERISTICS

The distinct peculiarity of the Berkshire breed is the short, and sometimes upturned nose. The face is dished, and the ears are erect but inclined slightly forward. The color is black with six white points—four white feet, some white in the face, and a white switch on the tail.

Fig. 3-4. Champion Berkshire boar at the Louisville Show. Owned and exhibited by Milo Wolrab, Mt. Vernon, Iowa. Note the upturned nose, erect ears, and white points which are characteristic of the breed. (Courtesy, American Berkshire Association)

The conformation of the Berkshire may be described as excellent meat type. Fortunately, the big-type craze did not gain great momentum among Berkshire breeders. Thus, there seems to be pronounced uniformity within the breed at the present time.

The typical Berkshire is long-bodied, with a long, deep side; moderately wide across the back; smooth throughout; well balanced and medium in length of leg. The meat is exceptionally fine in quality, well streaked with lean, and has no heavy covering of fat. The breed has established an enviable record in the barrow and carcass contests of the country.

There was a time when Berkshire sows were considered lacking in prolificacy. Judicious breeding and selection, however, have largely eliminated this criticism.

The Berkshire is not as large as most of the other breeds. However, because of its great length, depth, and balance, it is likely to be underestimated in weight. When in good show condition, mature boars weigh from 600 to 850 pounds and the sows from 450 to 650 pounds.

Animals possessing more than 10 percent white or having swirls are disqualified from registry.

Chester White

The Chester White breed is very popular on the farms of the northern part of the United States, and barrows of this breed have an enviable reputation in the barrow classes of the Chicago International Livestock Show.

ORIGIN AND NATIVE HOME

The Chester White had its origin in the fertile agricultural section of southeastern Pennsylvania, principally in Chester and Delaware counties. Both of these counties border on Lancaster County, one of the most noted agricultural and livestock counties in the United States. The breed seems to have originated early in the nineteenth century from the amalgamation of several breeds, most of which were white in color. The foundation stock included imported pigs of English Yorkshire, Lincolnshire, and Cheshire breeding. In 1818, Captain James Jeffries of Chester County imported a pair of white pigs from Bedfordshire, England. The boar in this importation was destined to exert a marked refining influence on the foundation stock of the Chester White breed. By 1848, the breed had reached such a degree of uniformity and purity that it was named Chester County White. The word county was soon dropped, and the present name became established.

CHESTER WHITE CHARACTERISTICS

As the name indicates, the breed is white in color. Although small bluish spots, called freckles, are sometimes found on the skin, such spots are to be discriminated against.

Fig. 3-5. Chester White gilt. Illinois Junior Champion and National Barrow Show Champion. Bred by KOK Farms, Sullivan, Ill.; sold to Chester Home Farms, Waterloo, Wisc. (Courtesy, Chester White Swine Record Association)

In general, type changes within this breed have followed those of the Poland China and the Duroc, although they have been less radical in nature. No doubt, some Yorkshire blood was infused into certain herds during the big-type craze. If so, perhaps it can be added that this blood brought real improvement and benefit to the breed.

Chester White sows are very prolific and are exceptional mothers. The pigs are good feeders and grazers; they mature early; and the finished barrows are very popular on the market.

Any of the following are disqualifications: Not two-thirds big enough for age; upright ears; off colored hair; spots on hide larger than a silver dollar; cryptorchidism in males; hernia in males or females; or swirls on body above the flanks.

Duroc

The Duroc is the leading breed of swine in America, registering more purebreds annually than any other breed.

ORIGIN AND NATIVE HOME

The Duroc breed of swine originated in the northeastern section of the United States. Although several different elements composed the foundation stock, it is reasonably certain that the Durocs, of New York, and the Jersey Reds, of New Jersey, contributed most to the ancestry.

The Jersey Reds were large, coarse, prolific red hogs that were bred in New Jersey early in the nineteenth century. The Durocs were smaller in size, more compact, and possessed great refinement. The red hogs of uncertain origin, which were found in New York, were named after the famous stallion, Duroc, a noted horse of that day. Beginning about 1860, these two strains of red hogs were systematically blended together, and thus there was formed the breed that is known at the present time as the Duroc.

DUROC CHARACTERISTICS

The Duroc is red in color, with the shades varying from light to dark. Although a medium cherry red is preferred by the majority of breeders, there is no particular discrimination against lighter or darker shades so long as they are not too extreme.

During the big-type era, the Duroc also had its change in type. The show ring was dominated by tall, rangy individuals—animals possessing narrow loins, light hams, shallow bodies, and slow maturity. Although some lack of uniformity still exists within the breed as a result of this radical shift, today the best representatives are of the most approved meat type. The popularity of the breed may be attributed to the valuable combination of size, feeding capacity, prolificacy, and hardiness.

In show condition, aged Duroc boars weigh from 750 to 1,100 pounds and mature sows from 600 to 850 pounds.

Any of the following are disqualifications for registry: white feet or white spots on any part of the body; any white on the end of the nose; black spots larger than 2 inches in diameter on the body; swirls on upper half of the body or neck; or ridgeling (one testicle) boars or fewer than six udder sections on either side.

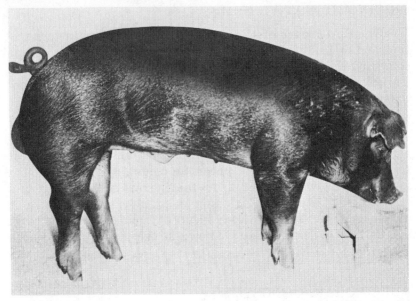

Fig. 3-6. Mr. 66, the Grand Champion Duroc boar at the 1966 Southwestern Duroc Congress; bred and shown by Bilt Rite Farms, Happy, Texas; sold to Robert Johnson, Cash, Arkansas, for $6,600. (Courtesy, United Duroc Swine Registry)

Hampshire

The Hampshire is one of the youngest breeds of swine, but its rise in popularity has been rapid. It is widely distributed throughout the Corn Belt and the South.

ORIGIN AND NATIVE HOME

The Hampshire breed of swine originated in Boone County, Kentucky, just across the Ohio River from Cincinnati. The foundation stock consisted of fifteen head of belted hogs, generally known as Thin Rinds and Ring Middles. This original herd was purchased in Pennsylvania in 1835 by Major Joel Garnett, who had the animals driven to Pittsburgh and then sent by boat to Kentucky. Years later, in 1893, six Boone County (Kentucky) farmers organized the Thin Rind Association, which, in 1904, became the Hampshire Swine Association.

The origin of the foundation herd purchased by Major Garnett is clouded in obscurity. However, belted hogs were re-

ported in Massachusetts and New York between 1820 and 1830. Moreover, the Essex and Wessex Saddleback breeds of England possess the same color pattern as the present-day Hampshire.

HAMPSHIRE CHARACTERISTICS

The most striking characteristic of the Hampshire is the white belt around the shoulders and body, including the front legs. The black color with the white belt constitutes a distinctive trademark; breed enthusiasts refer to it as the million dollar trademark.

Hampshire breeders have always stressed great quality and smoothness. The jowl is trim and light, the head refined, the ears erect, the shoulders smooth and well set, and the back well arched. An effort is now being made to secure more length of body and greater fullness of hams. In general, the breed has not been subjected to radical type fads. The trimness and freedom from excess lardiness give promise of a bright future for the Hamp-

Fig. 3-7. Bankers Dream, 1966 All American January Hampshire boar. The most striking characteristic of the Hampshire breed is the white belt around the shoulders and body, including the front legs. (Courtesy, Hampshire Swine Registry)

shire. Animals of this breed are active, and the sows have a reputation of raising a high percentage of the pigs farrowed.

As a rule, Hampshires are not so heavy as the other breeds. In show condition, mature boars weigh from 700 to 900 pounds and mature sows in similar condition from 550 to 750 pounds.

The Hampshire Swine Registry lists the following disqualifications, except that color markings do not apply to market barrows: any white on the head other than the front of the snout; white on the hind legs higher than the bottom of the ham; more than two-thirds of the body white; solid black; white from belt running back on underline to meet white on hind quarters; an incomplete belt; one or both front legs black; a swirl; boar with one testicle; more than two-thirds undersize; or any animal showing signs of having been tampered with in any way to conceal faults of conformation or color markings.

Hereford

The Hereford is one of the newer and less widely distributed breeds of swine. Among many swine growers, it has enjoyed a special attraction because the color markings emulate those of Hereford cattle.

ORIGIN AND NATIVE HOME

The Hereford breed of hogs was founded by R. U. Webber, of LaPlata, Missouri. He conceived the idea of producing a white-faced hog with a cherry-red body color that would resemble the markings of Hereford cattle. The foundation stock included Chester Whites, OIC's, Durocs, and pigs of unknown origin. By inbreeding and selection, the breed was further developed over a period of twenty years. In 1934, the National Hereford Hog Association was organized, under the sponsorship of the Polled Hereford Cattle Registry Association.

HEREFORD CHARACTERISTICS

The most distinctive characteristic of the Hereford breed of hogs is their color marking, which is similar to that of Hereford cattle. In order to be eligible for registry, animals must be at least two-thirds red in color, either light or dark, and must

have white faces; and white must appear on at least two feet and extend at least an inch above the hoof. The ideal colored Hereford has a white head and ears, four white feet, white switch, and white markings on the underline.

In size, the Hereford is smaller than the other breeds of swine. At the present time, many specimens of the breed are considered too lardy, heavy shouldered, and rough; but great improvement is being made through selection.

Any of the following disqualify an animal from registry or exhibiting: a white belt extending over the shoulders, back,

Fig. 3-8. Junior and Reserve Grand Champion Hereford gilt at the Iowa State Fair, and Senior and Grand Champion at the same show the next year. Bred and shown by Herbert Schulte, Norway, Ia. (Courtesy, National Hereford Hog Record Association)

or rump; more than one-third white markings; no white markings on the face; less than two white feet; a swirl; no marks of identification (ear notches or tattoo required); boar with one testicle; or permanent deformities of any kind.

OIC

Although the OIC (commonly but now incorrectly referred

to as Ohio Improved Chester) and Chester White breeds stemmed
from the same parent stock in Chester County, Pennsylvania,
they are now distinct and separate breeds. Today, their chief
resemblance is in color only, both being white.

ORIGIN AND NATIVE HOME

The OIC was originated by L. B. Silver of Salem, Ohio. While
traveling through the eastern states in 1865, for the purpose of
studying the pure breeds of swine, he selected the foundation
stock in Chester County, Pennsylvania. In subsequent years, Mr.
Silver and his son, Carl, are reputed to have wrought much improvement in their herd, developing white hogs that were larger
and more prolific than the common run of Chester Whites of the
day. Although Mr. Silver had long maintained private facilities
for recording his hogs, he was instrumental in organizing the
OIC Swine Breeders' Association in 1897.

After the death of Mr. Silver, the OIC suffered from lack of
promotion.

OIC CHARACTERISTICS

The OIC is white in color; the head is rather short and wide;
the face is slightly dished; and the ears are slightly drooping.

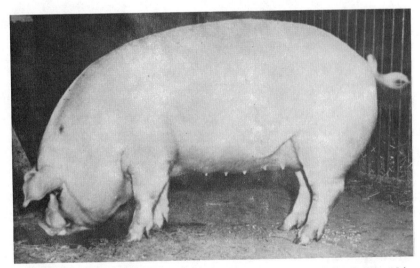

Fig. 3-9. OIC senior gilt; owned by Merlyn G. Oates, Bellville, Ohio.
(Courtesy, OIC Swine Breeders' Association)

The OIC breed escaped the big type craze, in vogue in most of the breeds of swine from 1915 to 1925. They clung to the chuffy type.

Progressive breeders have made strides in the production of OIC hogs of approved meat type, but even ardent breed enthusiasts recognize that further improvement along these lines must come.

Animals possessing any of the following characteristics are ineligible for registration: swirls on the upper half of the body, hernia, cryptorchidism, spots on the skin with other than white hair, or inverted nipples.

Poland China

No other breed of swine has been subjected to such radical shifts in type as the Poland China. Likewise, no other breed has swung from such heights of popularity or fallen so low in disrepute.

ORIGIN AND NATIVE HOME

The Poland China breed of swine originated in southwestern Ohio in the fertile area known as the Miami Valley, particularly in Warren and Butler Counties. In the early part of the nineteenth century, the Miami Valley was the richest corn-producing section of the United States. Moreover, prior to the Civil War, Cincinnati was the pork-packing metropolis of America. Thus, the conditions were ideal for the development of a new breed of hogs.

The common stock kept by the early settlers of the Miami Valley were described as being of mixed color, breeding, and type. The foundation animals were crossed with the Russian and Byfield hogs that were introduced into the valley early in the nineteenth century. In 1816, the Shaker Society, a religious sect, introduced the Big China breed. This breeding and improvement gave rise to the so-called Warren County hog, which gained considerable prominence as a result of its huge size and great fattening ability. Later, hogs of Berkshire and Irish Grazier breeding were introduced into the area and were crossed with the Warren County hogs. This improved the quality and refinement of the stock and resulted in earlier maturity. It is generally agreed that no outside blood was brought into the Miami Valley after about 1845.

The name, Poland China, was established in 1872 by the National Swine Breeders in convention at Indianapolis, Indiana. In view of the fact that it seems to be definitely established that no breed known as Poland hogs was ever used as foundation stock, it is of interest to know how the name, Poland China, was selected. A Mr. Asher, a prominent Polish farmer in the Valley, was supposedly responsible for the word Poland. As China hogs had been introduced by the Shaker Society, the name of Poland China was adopted.

POLAND CHINA CHARACTERISTICS

Modern Poland Chinas are black in color with six white points—the feet, face, and tip of tail—but prior to 1872, they were generally mixed black and white and spotted. Absence of one or two of the six white points is of small concern, and a small white spot on the body is not seriously criticized.

Until the latter part of the nineteenth century, Poland China hogs were noted for their immense size and scale. Beginning

Fig. 3-10. The Grand Champion Poland China Boar at the Illinois State Fair, pictured as a two-year-old, weighing 900 pounds. He was from a Certified Litter that weighed 200 pounds at 165 days of age, and that cut 29.45 inches in carcass length, 1.37 inches backfat, and 4.79 square inches of loin-eye. (Courtesy, The Poland China Record Association)

about 1890, breeders turned their attention to the development of greater refinement, earlier maturity, and smaller size. This fashionable fad finally culminated in the development of the "hot bloods," an extremely small, compact, short-legged type which dominated the show ring from 1900 to 1910.

Finally, in order to secure increased utility qualities, breeders began the shift to the big-type strains. The craze swept across the nation, and again the pendulum swung too far. However, since 1925, the efforts of breeders have been toward development of the more conservative meat type.

Mature Poland China boars in show condition weigh from 850 to 1,000 pounds and mature sows from 650 to 900 pounds.

The following disqualify an animal from registry: less than six teats on a side, a swirl on the upper half of the body, hernia, or cryptorchidism.

Spotted

The popularity of the "Spots" is chiefly attributed to the success of breeders in preserving the utility value of the old Spotted Polands while making certain improvements in the breed.

ORIGIN AND NATIVE HOME

The Spotted was developed in the north central part of the United States, principally in the state of Indiana. As has been indicated, the foundation stock of the Miami Valley Poland Chinas was frequently of a black and white spotted color. Moreover, they had a reputation for size, ruggedness, bone, and prolificacy. During the era of the "hot bloods," many breeders forsook the Poland China breed and attempted to revive the utility qualities of the original spotted hogs of the Miami Valley. Thus, the Spotted was established. In addition to utilizing selected strains of the Poland China, breeders introduced, in 1914, the blood of the Gloucester Spotted hog of England. Although the Spotted breed had its official beginning with the organization of record associations in 1914, liberal infusion of big-type Poland China blood was continued until ten years later.

SPOTTED CHARACTERISTICS

At the present time, there is no great difference between the most approved type of Poland China and the Spotted. The former

has a little more size, but in general the conformation is much alike.

The most desired color in the Spotted is spotted black and white—50 per cent of each. Females must have at least six prominent teats on each side to be eligible for show or sale.

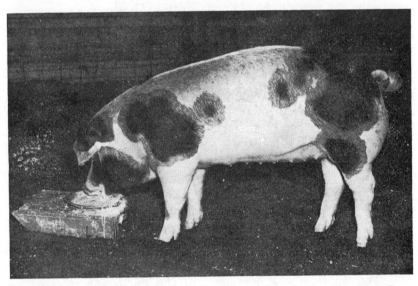

Fig. 3-11. Standout Miss, Champion Spotted gilt at the Spot Type Conference. Shown by Kenneth Hoing, Marshalltown, Ia.; sold to Charles Ausfahl, New Bloomfield, Mo. (Courtesy, The National Spotted Poland China Record)

Boars in show condition weigh from 750 to 1,000 pounds and sows from 600 to 800 pounds.

The following constitute disqualifications and bar animals from registry: brown or sandy spots; less than 20 percent or more than 80 percent white on body; boar with a swirl; small upright ears; not over half normal size; cramped or deformed feet; seriously diseased, barren, or blind; or if scoring less than 60 points.

Tamworth

The Tamworth is one of the oldest and probably one of the purest of all breeds of hogs. It is also recognized as the most extreme bacon type of any breed.

ORIGIN AND NATIVE HOME

The native home of the Tamworth is in central England in the counties of Stafford, Leicester, Warwick, and Northampton. The breed derives its name from the town of Tamworth, which is located on the river Thames.

Although little is known concerning the early history and development of the breed, it is probably safe to assume that it is descended from the Old English Hog which resulted from domestication of the wild boar.

There is no evidence to indicate that any breed improvement was attempted through crossing with other breeds. On the other hand, there is record of pure breeding and careful selection dating back more than one hundred years.

Fig. 3-12. Mary Lee, Grand Champion Tamworth sow at the Ohio State Fair. (Courtesy, Tamworth Swine Association)

EARLY AMERICAN IMPORTATIONS

The earliest importation of Tamworths into the United

States, of which there is authentic record, was made by Thomas Bennett, of Rossville, Illinois, in 1882. Numerous importations were made to Canada soon thereafter. Owing to its extreme bacon type, the breed never became popular in the United States.

TAMWORTH CHARACTERISTICS

The color of the breed is red, varying from light to dark. The conformation may be described as that of extreme bacon type. The individuals are rather long-legged; with long, smooth sides, and strong backs. The head is wide between the ears, the snout is moderately long and straight, the jowl is neat, and the ears are medium sized and erect. The Tamworth carcass produces bacon of the finest quality. The sows are prolific and careful mothers, and the pigs are excellent foragers.

Mature boars weigh from 700 to 900 pounds and mature sows from 550 to 700 pounds.

Yorkshire

In its native home, England, the Yorkshire breed is known as the Large White. Since World War II, there has been a pronounced interest in raising more Yorkshire hogs in the United States.

ORIGIN AND NATIVE HOME

The Yorkshire is a popular English bacon breed which had its origin nearly a century ago in Yorkshire and neighboring counties in northern England. The foundation stock consisted of large, coarse white hogs with black or bluish spots on the skin. They were direct descendants of the Old English Hogs. Subsequent improvement in this stock was effected through the infusion of blood of the Leicester pig, a creation of Robert Bakewell. However, the Yorkshire breed was not crossed with foreign blood to any great extent. Rather, its improvement is a tribute to careful breeding and judicious selection.

EARLY AMERICAN IMPORTATIONS

Although Yorkshires were probably first brought to the United States early in the nineteenth century, representatives of

the modern type were first introduced by Wilcox and Liggett, of Minnesota, in 1893. A great many importations were made into Canada at an early date, and the breed has always enjoyed a position of prominence in that country.

YORKSHIRE CHARACTERISTICS

Yorkshires should be entirely white in color. Although black pigment spots, called "freckles," do not constitute a defect, they are frowned upon by breeders. The face is slightly dished, and the ears are erect.

Fig. 3-13. Champion Yorkshire boar at the 1965 Type Conference. (Courtesy, American Yorkshire Club)

Yorkshire sows are noted as good mothers. They not only farrow and raise large litters, but they are great milkers. The pigs are excellent foragers and compare favorably with those of any other breed in economy of gains.

Yorkshire hogs are smooth; the body is long and deep, with an especially long, deep side; the loins are large; but sometimes

the hams lack depth and plumpness. Slaughter animals yield a high dressing percentage and produce carcasses of the finest quality. The present surplus of lard in this country is causing breeders and promoters of the meat breeds to change their ideal in type more in keeping with that of the most approved Yorkshires. Moreover, Yorkshires are becoming very popular, even in the Corn Belt.

The following disqualify animals from registry: the presence of swirls on the upper third of the body, hernia, hair color other than white, cryptorchidism, hermaphrodite, blind or inverted teats, total blindness, or less than six teats on each side.

NEW AND/OR LESS WIDELY DISTRIBUTED BREEDS

In addition to the more widely distributed swine breeds that have already been discussed, some of the other breeds of importance in different sections of the United States and Canada are listed in Table 3-2. The several breeds carrying Landrace breeding are registered in the Inbred Livestock Registry Association, which was organized in 1946.

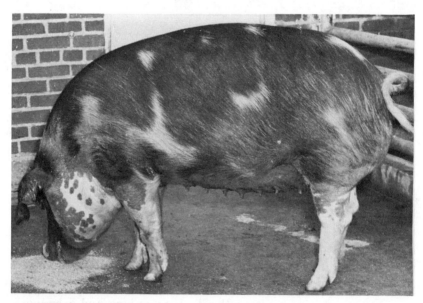

Fig. 3-14. Beltsville No. 1 gilt. They are black with white spots. (Courtesy, Inbred Livestock Registry)

TABLE 3-2

BREEDS OF SWINE AND THEIR CHARACTERISTICS

Breed	Place of Origin	Color	Distinctive Head Characteristics	Other Distinguishing Characteristics
Beltsville No. 1 (75% Landrace & 25% Poland China)	United States by the USDA at Beltsville, Maryland, beginning in 1934.	Black with white spots.	Fairly long, narrow head with trim, light jowl, and moderately large, drooping ears.	
CPF No. 1 (Developed from San Pierre X Beltsville No. 1)	Conner Prairie Farm, Noblesville, Ind.; 1956, accepted in 1964.	Black and white.	Fairly long snout, trim jowl, moderate size, drooping ears.	Moderately long and well muscled.
CPF No. 2 (25% Yorkshire, 25% Beltsville No. 1, 50% Maryland No. 1)	Conner Prairie Farm, Noblesville, Ind.; beginning in 1959, accepted for registry in 1964.	Black and white.	Fairly short snout, small ears that jot forward.	Fairly long body and length of leg; trim middle.
Kentucky Red Berkshire	United States; in Kentucky.	Red	Short upturned nose, dished face, and erect ears.	
Lacombe (55% Landrace, 23% Berkshire, and 22% Chester White)	Canada; at the Experimental Farm, Lacombe, Alberta, beginning in 1947.	White	Medium-sized flop ears and a medium length, slightly dished face.	Of the three parent breeds, it resembles the Landrace most closely.
Maryland No. 1 (62% Landrace X 38% Berkshire)	United States; by the USDA and the U. of Maryland, beginning in 1941.	Black and white spotted.	The ears are erect or slightly drooping and intermediate in size.	

(Continued)

TABLE 3-2 (Continued)

Breed	Place of Origin	Color	Distinctive Head Characteristics	Other Distinguishing Characteristics
Minnesota No. 1 (48% Landrace X 52% Tamworth)	United States; by the USDA and the U. of Minnesota, beginning in 1936.	Red with occasional small black spots.	Long face, trim jowls, and fairly erect ears.	Long-bodied, short-legged, light shoulders, and a relatively straight back.
Minnesota No. 2 (40% Yorkshire and 60% Poland China)	United States; by the U. of Minnesota, beginning in 1941.	Black and white.	Ears of medium size, with erect carriage. Snout is shorter than Minnesota No. 1.	
Minnesota No. 3 (From following 8 lines or breeds: Gloucester Old Spot, Welsh, Large White, C-Line Poland, Beltsville No. 2, Minnesota No. 1, Minnesota No. 2, and San Pierre)	Rosemount Experiment Station, Rosemont, Minn.; breeding stock first released in 1957.	Black and red spotted; or black and white.	Moderately dished face, trim jowl, ears tilted forward and slightly erect.	Noted for rapid growth and ruggedness.
Montana No. 1 (55% Landrace X 45% Hampshire)	United States; in Montana, by the USDA and Montana State University, beginning in 1936.	Black	Drooping ears.	
Palouse (65% Landrace and 35% Chester White)	United States; by Washington State University, beginning in 1945.	White	Head is moderate in length; the ears are somewhat erect but inclined forward.	

(Continued)

TABLE 3-2 (Continued)

Breed	Place of Origin	Color	Distinctive Head Characteristics	Other Distinguishing Characteristics
Wessex Saddleback	Hampshire, England.	Black, with a white belt around the shoulders and body including the front legs.	Fairly long snout; medium sized ears with forward pitch; trim jowl.	

Fig. 3-15. A Lacombe gilt. (Courtesy, J. G. Stothart, Director, Canada Department of Agriculture, Research Branch, Lacombe, Alberta)

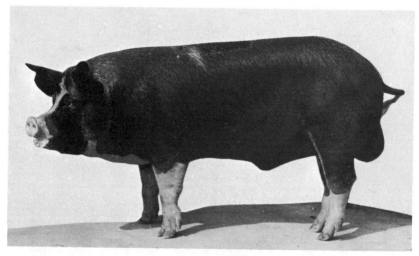

Fig. 3-16. Maryland No. 1 boar. They are black and white spotted. (Courtesy, Conner Prairie Farm, Noblesville, Ind.)

Fig. 3-17. A Minnesota No. 1 boar; owned by the University of Minnesota. They are red with occasional small black spots. Note the long face and trim jowl which characterize the breed. (Courtesy, Inbred Livestock Registry Association)

Fig. 3-18. A Minnesota No. 2 boar; bred and owned by Conner Prairie Farms, Noblesville, Ind. They are black and white in color. The ears are of medium size and carried erect, and the snout is shorter than that of the Minnesota No. 1. (Courtesy, Inbred Livestock Registry Association)

Fig. 3-19. A Minnesota No. 3 gilt; owned by the University of Minnesota. (Courtesy, Inbred Livestock Registry Association)

Fig. 3-20. A Montana No. 1 boar; owned by George Slater, Augusta, Ill. They are black in color and have drooping ears. (Courtesy, Inbred Livestock Registry Association)

Fig. 3-21. A Palouse sow at 17 months of age. Note her deep full ham; long, level rump; and high tail set. She has 14 teats. This great sow raised 11 pigs in her first litter, and 12 in the second. The second litter averaged 43.9 pounds at 56 days. (Courtesy, Washington State University)

QUESTIONS FOR STUDY AND DISCUSSION

1. Trace shifting of swine types throughout the years, including the factors that prompted such shifts.
2. Why have U. S. swine types shifted more rapidly and more radically than cattle and sheep types?
3. Most American-created breeds of swine evolved during two periods; namely (a) 1800 to 1880, and (b) since 1940. What is the explanation of this?
4. List the (a) distinguishing characteristics and (b) disqualifications of each breed of swine. Discuss the importance of each of the listings.
5. Obtain breed registry association literature and a sample copy of a magazine of your favorite breed of swine. Evaluate the soundness and value of the material that you receive. (See Tables VI-1 and VII-1 in the Appendix for addresses.)
6. Justify any preference that you may have for one particular breed of swine.
7. Must a new breed of swine be approved by someone, or can anyone start a new breed?

SELECTED REFERENCES

Title of Publication	Author(s)	Publisher
Breeds of Livestock, The	C. W. Gay	The Macmillan Company, New York, N. Y., 1918.
Breeds of Livestock in America	H. W. Vaughan	R. G. Adams and Company, Columbus, Ohio, 1937.
Breeds of Swine	Animal Husb. Res. Div., ARS	Farmers' Bul. 1263, U. S. Department of Agriculture, Washington, D. C., 1966.
Modern Breeds of Livestock	H. M. Briggs	The Macmillan Company, New York, N. Y., 1958.
Pigs from Cave to Corn Belt	C. W. Towne E. N. Wentworth	University of Oklahoma Press, Norman, Okla., 1950.
Stockman's Handbook, The	M. E. Ensminger	The Interstate Printers & Publishers, Inc., Danville, Ill., 1970.
Story of Durocs, The	B. R. Evans G. G. Evans	United Duroc Record Assoc., Peoria, Ill., 1946.
Study of Breeds in America, The	Thomas Shaw	Orange Judd Company, New York, N. Y., 1912.
Types and Breeds of Farm Animals	C. S. Plumb	Ginn and Company, Boston, Mass., 1920.
Word Dictionary of Breeds Types and Varieties of Livestock, The	I. L. Mason	Commonwealth Agricultural Bureaux, Farnham House, Farnham Royal, Slough, Bucks, England, 1951.

Also, breed literature pertaining to each breed may be secured by writing to the respective breed registry associations (see Sec. VI, Appendix, for the name and address of each association).

CHAPTER IV

ESTABLISHING THE HERD; SELECTING
AND JUDGING SWINE

Contents   Page

The problems encountered and the principles employed in establishing the swine herd and in selecting and judging hogs are very similar to those for beef cattle and sheep. In general, however, one can establish a swine herd at a lower cost and more quickly than is possible with other classes of farm animals. Until recently, hog markets were less discriminating than cattle or sheep markets, with the result that the average commercial producer gave far less attention to becoming proficient in selecting and judging swine.

FACTORS TO CONSIDER IN ESTABLISHING THE HERD

At the outset, it should be recognized that the vast majority of the swine producers of this nation keep hogs simply because they expect them to be profitable. That hogs have usually lived up to this expectation is attested by their undisputed claim to the title of the "mortgage lifter." For maximum profit and satis-

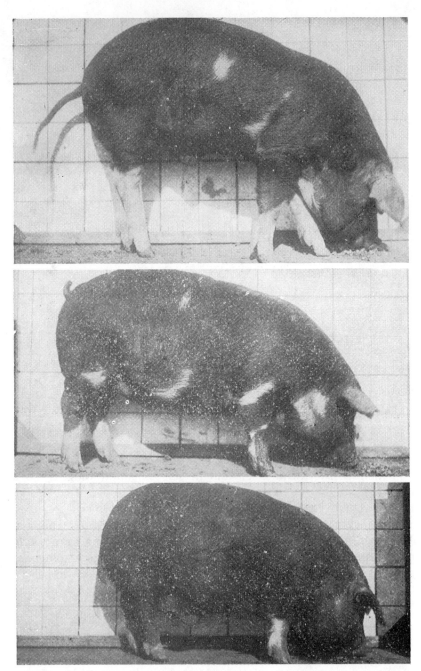

Fig. 4-1. From top to bottom: (1) very rangy type, (2) intermediate type, and (3) very chuffy type hogs. These animals were among those used in the classic swine type studies conducted by the University of Illinois. While there was little difference between types in rate and economy of gains, the intermediate type produced the most desirable carcass. (Courtesy, University of Illinois)

faction in establishing the herd, the individual swine producer must give consideration to the type, breeding, and individual merit of each foundation animal, and to the size of the herd.

Type: Meat vs. Bacon; and Large, Medium, or Small

With reference to hogs, the word "type" is used in a dual capacity: (1) to denote whether breeds are of meat type or bacon type, and (2) to denote the difference in form and general conformation within a breed on the basis of large, medium, or small type.

In the United States, the difference in the general conformation and form between the modern meat and bacon types is less pronounced than formerly, primarily because of a shift of ideals within both types toward bred-in meat qualities. With lard becoming a drug on the market, often selling for less per pound than the price of slaughter hogs on foot, breeders of meat type breeds are stressing the maximum cut-out value of primal cuts together with a minimum of lard. Likewise, breeders of bacon breeds are selecting for more muscling and thickness. Thus, the most desirable specimens of all U. S. breeds—the former (1) lard type breeds and (2) bacon type breeds—are now meat type breeds, with similar goals; although some breeds more closely approach this objective than others. In Canada, on the other hand, bacon type hogs prevail. Perhaps there is little difference in efficiency of production between the best specimens of the meat and bacon type breeds. Accordingly, consumer demand and market returns should be the determining factors as to the type of hogs produced.

As approximately 95 percent of U. S. market hogs of the present day are of the so-called meat type breeds, further discussion relative to possible variations of types within these breeds may be appropriate; for not all of these animals within breeds are of the true meat type. Over the years, most of these breeds have run the gauntlet in types, producing animals of the chuffy, rangy, and medium types. It is evident even today that these breeds possess the necessary store of genes through which such shift in types may be made by breeding and selection. Even so, most pork producers prefer the medium or intermediate type to either the chuffy or rangy types. Chuffy type animals lack in prolificacy and rapidity of gains, whereas the rangy hog must be carried to too heavy a weight in order to reach market

finish. The packer and consumer object to the chuffy animals because of their excess lardiness and to the rangy ones because of
their large cuts that lack plumpness. It may be concluded, therefore, that most successful swine producers of the present day
favor a medium type or meat type hog.

Purebreds, Grades, or Crossbreds

Generally speaking, only the experienced breeder should
undertake the production of purebreds with the intention of
eventually furnishing foundation or replacement stock to other
purebred breeders or purebred boars to the commercial producer.
However, in many cases the spread in price between purebred
and grade gilts is so small as to warrant the purchase of the
former, even for commercial production. In any event, the use of
a purebred boar is always to be advocated.

Crossbreeding of swine is fully discussed in Chapter V. At
this point, it is sufficient to say that this type of breeding program
is more widely used in the production of hogs than with any other
class of livestock, with the possible exception of sheep, and that
under certain conditions it may be advantageous.

Selection of the Breed

No one breed of hogs can be said to excel others in all points
of swine production and for all conditions. It is true, however,
that particular breed characteristics may result in a certain
breed being better adapted to given conditions; for example, hogs
of light color are subject to sun scald in the deep South. Usually,
however, there is a greater difference among individuals within
the same breed than between the different breeds; this applies
both to type and efficiency of production. In the end, therefore,
the selection of a particular breed is most often a matter of personal preference, and usually the breed that the individual producer likes is the one with which he will have the greatest degree
of success. Where no definite preference exists, however, it is well
to choose the breed that is most popular in the community. This
consideration allows for greater latitude in the choice of foundation stock and makes the problem of securing herd boars less difficult. The producer should also give some thought to the local
market demands and initial costs.

Size of Herd

Hogs multiply more rapidly than any other class of farm animals. They also breed at an early age, produce twice each year, and bear litters. It does not take long, therefore, to get into the hog business.

The eventual size of the herd is best determined by the following factors: (1) size of farm, (2) available grains and pastures, (3) kind and amount of labor, (4) the disease and parasite situation, (5) the probable market, and (6) comparative profits from hogs and other types of enterprises.

Uniformity

Uniformity of type and ancestry gives assurance of the production of high-quality pigs that are alike and true to type. This applies both to the purebred and the grade herd. Uniform offspring sell at a premium at any age, whether they are sold as purebreds for foundation stock, as feeder pigs, or as slaughter hogs. With a uniform group of sows, it is also possible to make a more intelligent selection of the herd boar.

Health

Breeding animals that are in a thrifty, vigorous condition and that have been raised under a system of swine sanitation (by breeders who have exercised care in the control of diseases and parasites) should have a decided preference. Tests should be made to make certain of freedom from swine brucellosis or contagious abortion. In fact, all purchases should be made subject to the animals being free from contagious diseases.

Age

In establishing the herd, the beginner may well purchase a few bred gilts that are well grown, uniform in type, and of good ancestry and that have been mated to a proved sire. Although less risk is involved in the purchase of tried sows, the cost is likely to be greater in relation to the ultimate value of the sows on the market.

Then, too, with limited capital, it may be necessary to consider the purchase of a younger boar. Usually a wider selection

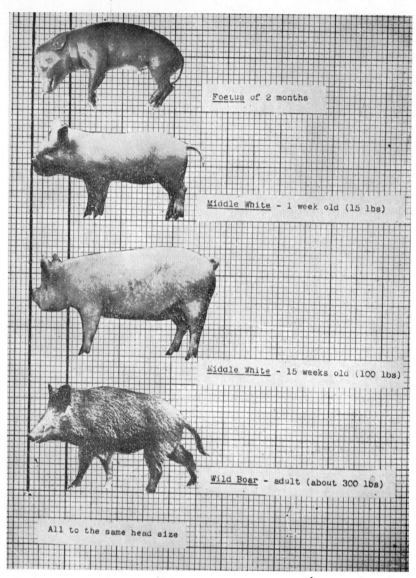

Fig. 4-2. This figure illustrates how years of selection have changed the conformation of the pig to meet market requirements. Each animal is reduced to the same head size. As shown, as an improved breed matures, the proportion of loin to head and neck increases greatly; but an unimproved type such as the wild boar matures without much change in body proportions.

Top: Fetus at 2 months.
2nd: Yorkshire pig, 1 week old, 15 lbs. wt.
3rd: Yorkshire pig, 15 weeks old, 100 lbs. wt.
Bottom: Wild boar, adult, about 300 lbs. wt.

(From *Farm Animals*, by John Hammond; published by Edward Arnold & Co., London; courtesy, Sir John Hammond)

is afforded with this procedure, and, in addition, the younger animal has a longer life of usefulness ahead.

Price

The beginner should always start in a conservative way. However, this should never be cause for the purchase of poor individuals—animals that are high at any price.

SELECTION AND ITS BASES

Generally, the selection of foundation hogs is made on the basis of one or more of the following considerations: (1) type or individuality, (2) pedigree, (3) show-ring winnings, or (4) Production Testing.

Selection Based on Type or Individuality

In addition to choosing between (1) meat type and bacon type animals and (2) rangy-, medium-, and chuffy-type individuals, selection based on type or individuality implies the selection of those animals that approach the ideal or standard of perfection most closely and the culling out of those that fall short of these standards.

Selection Based on Pedigree

In the selection of breeding animals, the pedigree is a record of the individual's heredity or inheritance. If the ancestry is good, it lends confidence in projecting how well young animals may breed. It is to be emphasized, however, that mere names and registration numbers are meaningless. A pedigree may be considered as desirable only when the ancestors close up in the lineage—the parents and grandparents—were superior individuals and outstanding producers. Too often, purebred hog breeders are prone to play up one or two outstanding animals back in the third or fourth generations. If pedigree selection is to be of any help, one must be familiar with the individual animals listed therein.

The boar should always be purebred, which means that he is of known ancestry. This alone is not enough, for he should also be a good representative of the breed selected; and his pedigree

should contain an impressive list of noted animals. Likewise, it is important that the sows be of good ancestry, regardless of whether they are purebreds, grades, or crossbreds. Such ancestry and breeding give more assurance of the production of high-quality pigs that are uniform and true to type.

Selection Based on Show-Ring Winnings

Swine producers have long looked favorably upon using show-ring winnings as a basis of selection. Purebred breeders have been quick to recognize this appeal and to extol their champions through advertising. In most instances, the selection of foundation or replacement hogs on the basis of show-ring winnings and standards has been for the good. On many occasions, however, purebred and commercial breeders alike have come to regret selections based on show-ring winnings. This was especially true during the eras when the chuffy or rangy types were sweeping shows from one end of the country to the other. This would indicate that some scrutiny should be given to the type of animals winning in the show, especially to ascertain whether such animals are of a type that are efficient from the standpoint of the producer, and whether, over a period of years, they will command a premium on a discriminating market.

Perhaps the principal value of selections based on show-ring winnings lies in the fact that shows direct the attention of the amateur to those types and strains of hogs that at the moment are meeting with the approval of the better breeders and judges.

Selection Based on Production Testing

Production Testing includes (1) Performance Testing (sometimes called Individual Merit Testing), and (2) Progeny Testing. The definitions and relative merits of each system are presented in Chapter V. Also suggested record forms are reproduced in the same chapter.

No criterion that can be used in selecting an animal is so accurate or important as past performance. It is recommended, therefore, that one purchase tried sows and a proved herd boar when such animals of the right kind can be secured at reasonable prices. Unfortunately, breeding animals of known merit are not usually available at a figure that a beginner can afford to pay. Sometimes, however, established breeders make the error of

sacrificing brood sows of proved performance in favor of younger sows or find it necessary to sell proved boars because they can no longer be used in the breeding program. Animals of this kind constitute one of the soundest purchases that a young breeder can make.

Several of the purebred swine registry associations now have (1) Production Registry and/or (2) Meat Certification programs. Although these programs are not perfect, they do represent a progressive step in the right direction. Without doubt, both pure-bred and commercial swine producers of the future will make increasing use of such records as a basis for selection.

In selecting swine on the basis of production records, it is recognized that the amount of emphasis placed on each of the traits should vary from herd to herd and area to area. For example, where high-quality bacon is being produced for a dis-criminating market, it is logical that greater emphasis should be placed on body type, or, better yet, that carcasses of near relatives be studied.

HERD IMPROVEMENT THROUGH SELECTION

Constructive breeders are those who effect improvement through breeding and selection, and this applies to both purebred and commercial producers. Such selection must be based on pro-duction factors of economic importance and market price as determined by carcass quality on a discriminating market.

Good standards to keep in mind when selecting gilts and re-placement boars are:

1. **Litter size.**—The ability to produce large litters is in-herited to some extent. Hence, select prospective breeding animals from a litter of at least eight, and preferably ten, pigs.

2. **Weaning weight.**—Heavy weaning weight is an indicator of the sow's nursing ability. Select pigs from gilt litters that weigh 24 pounds or more at 6 weeks, and 35 pounds or more at 8 weeks; and pigs from sow litters that weigh 27 pounds or more at 6 weeks, and 40 pounds or more at 8 weeks.

3. **Age at 200 pounds.**—Weight for age is another index of gaining ability. Gilts for the breeding herd should reach 200 pounds at 165 days or less of age; and boars at 150 days or less.

4. **Conformation.**—Select meaty animals that have good length of body and heavy bone.

5. **Mammary development.**—There should be at least 12 well-spaced, well-developed teat sections on both boars and gilts.

6. **Feed conversion.**—Prospective breeding hogs should not consume more than 325 pounds of feed per 100 pounds of gain from weaning to 200 pounds.

7. **Carcass quality.**—A backfat probe or ultrasonic equipment may be used as a means of eliminating "lardy" animals. Backfat thickness at 200 pounds weight should not exceed 1.4 inches in gilts and 1.25 inches in boars. Littermates that go to market should average 29 inches in body length and have at least 4 square inches of loin-eye, with less than 1.6 inches of backfat.

8. **Freedom from diseases.**—Buy from herds known to be free from atrophic rhinitis and virus pneumonia, and other diseases.

9. **Absence of abnormalities and heritable defects.**—Select breeding animals that are free from such abnormal conditions as shakes, hernia, and cryptorchidism.

JUDGING SWINE

As previously indicated, until recently the small price spread in market classes and grades of swine offered little incentive to commercial swine producers to become proficient in judging. It is to the everlasting credit of purebred swine breeders, however, that they have been very progressive in this respect. The swine-type conferences sponsored by the various breed associations have made a unique contribution. Through bolstering live-animal work with a liberal amount of carcass data, these contests have soundly set fashions for both the producer and the packer.

The discussion that follows represents a further elucidation of the first point discussed under selection—individuality. In addition to individual merit, the word judging implies the comparative appraisal or placing of several animals.

Judging swine, like all livestock judging, is an art, the rudiments of which must be obtained through patient study and long practice. The master breeders throughout the years have been competent livestock judges. Shrewd traders have also been masters of the art, even to the point of deception.

The essential qualifications that a good judge of swine must

possess, and the recommended procedure to follow in the judging assignment are as follows:

1. **Knowledge of the parts of an animal.**—This consists of mastering the language that describes and locates the different parts of an animal (see Fig. 4-3). In addition, it is necessary to

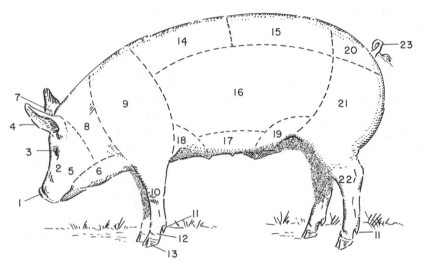

Fig. 4-3. Parts of a hog. The first step in preparation for judging hogs consists in mastering the language that describes and locates the different parts of the animal. (Drawing by R. F. Johnson)

1. Snout	5. Cheek	10. Fore leg	15. Loin	20. Rump
2. Face	6. Jowl	11. Dew claw	16. Side	21. Ham
3. Eye	7. Poll	12. Pastern	17. Belly	22. Rear leg
4. Ear	8. Neck	13. Toes	18. Fore flank	23. Tail
	9. Shoulder	14. Back	19. Rear flank	

know which of these parts are of major importance; that is, what comparative evaluation to give to the different parts.

2. **A clearly defined ideal or standard of perfection.**—The successful swine judge must know for what he is looking; that is, he must have in mind an ideal or standard of perfection.

3. **Keen observation and sound judgment.**—The good judge possesses the ability to observe both good conformation and defects, and to weigh and evaluate the relative importance of the various good and bad features.

4. **Honesty and courage.**—The good judge of any class of

livestock must possess honesty and courage, whether it be in making a show-ring placing or conducting a breeding and marketing program. For example, it often requires considerable courage to place a class of animals without regard to: (a) placings in previous shows, (b) ownership, and (c) public applause. It may take even greater courage and honesty to discard from the herd a costly animal whose progeny has failed to measure up.

5. **Logical procedure in examining.**—There is always great danger of the beginner making too close an inspection; he oftentimes gets "so close to the trees that he fails to see the forest." Good judging procedure consists of the following three separate steps: (a) observing at a distance and securing a panoramic view where several animals are involved, (b) using close inspection, and (c) moving the animal in order to observe action.

Since a pig will neither stand still nor remain in the same vicinity long, it is not possible to arrive at a set procedure for

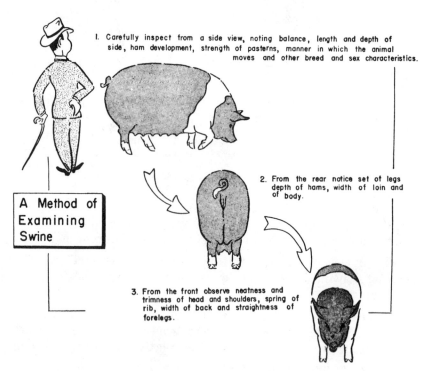

1. Carefully inspect from a side view, noting balance, length and depth of side, ham development, strength of pasterns, manner in which the animal moves and other breed and sex characteristics.

A Method of Examining Swine

2. From the rear notice set of legs depth of hams, width of loin and of body.

3. From the front observe neatness and trimness of head and shoulders, spring of rib, width of back and straightness of forelegs.

Fig. 4-4. A good procedure for examining a hog and some of the things for which to look. (Drawing by R. F. Johnson)

examining swine. In this respect, the judging of hogs is made more difficult than the judging of other classes of livestock. Where feasible, however, the steps for examining as illustrated in Fig. 4-4 are very satisfactory, and perhaps as good as any.

6. **Tact.**—In discussing either (a) a show-ring class, or (b) animals on a stockman's farm or ranch, it is important that the judge be tactful. The owner is likely to resent any remarks that imply that his animal is inferior.

Having acquired this knowledge, long hours must be spent in patient study and practice in comparing animals. Even this will not make expert and proficient judges in all instances, for there may be a grain of truth in the statement that "the best judges are born and not made." Nevertheless, training in judging and selecting animals is effective when directed by a competent instructor or experienced stockman.

Ideal Type and Conformation

The next requisite in judging or selection is to have clearly in mind a standard or ideal. Presumably, this ideal should be based on a combination of (1) the efficient performance of the animal from the standpoint of the producer, and (2) the desirable carcass characteristics of the market animals as determined by the consumer.

The most approved meat-type breeding animals combine size, smoothness, and quality, and the offspring possess the ability to finish during the growing period without producing an excessive amount of lard. The head and neck should be trim and neat; the back well arched and of ample width; the sides long, deep, and smooth; and the hams well developed and deep. The legs should be of medium length, straight, true, and squarely set; the pasterns should be short and strong; and the bone should be ample and show plenty of quality. With this splendid meat type, there should be style, balance, and symmetry and an abundance of quality and smoothness.

The most approved bacon type breeding hogs differ from meat type animals chiefly in that greater emphasis is placed on length of side and the maximum development of the primal cuts with the minimum of lard. Also, bacon type hogs generally have less width over the back and have a squarer type of ham, and show more trimness throughout.

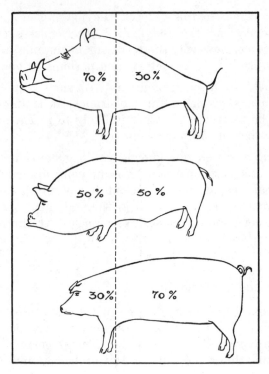

Fig. 4-5. Sir John Hammond, Cambridge, England, accompanied the above line drawing with this caption: "The object of breeders should be to strive for a light fore-end." According to Sir John, "The wild boar, which was one of the ancestors of our improved pigs, has a very heavy fore-end and light hams, and so unless constant selection is carried out for these characters there tends to be reversion to the primitive type." (From: "The Growth of the Pig," printed in *Pig Progress*, July, 1957)

With both meat and bacon type animals, the brood sows should show great femininity and breediness; and the udder should be well developed, carrying from ten to twelve teats. The herd boar should show great masculinity as indicated by strength and character in the head, a somewhat crested neck, well-developed but smooth shoulders, a general ruggedness throughout, and an energetic disposition. The reproductive organs of the boar should be clearly visible and well developed. A boar with one testicle should never be used.

Figure 4-6 shows the ideal meat type hog versus some of the common faults. Since no animal is perfect, the proficient swine judge must be able to recognize, weigh, and evaluate both the

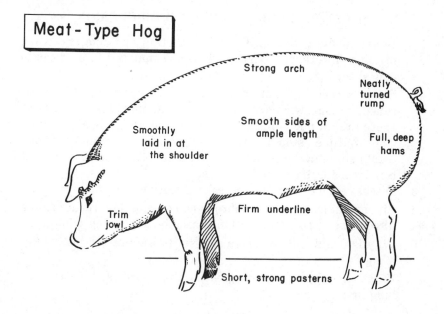

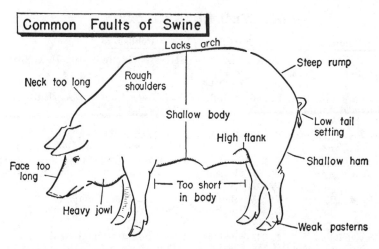

Fig. 4-6. Ideal meat type vs. common faults. The successful hog judge must know for what he is looking and be able to recognize and appraise both the good points and the common faults. (Drawing by R. F. Johnson)

good points and the common faults. In addition, he must be able to arrive at a decision as to the degree to which the given points are good or bad.

QUESTIONS FOR STUDY AND DISCUSSION

1. In establishing the herd and in selecting and judging, what primary differences exist in swine as compared to beef cattle and sheep?
2. Select a certain farm or ranch (either your home farm or ranch, or one with which you are familiar). Assume that there are no hogs on this establishment at the present time. Then outline, step by step, (a) how you would go about establishing a herd, and (b) the factors that you would consider. Justify your decisions.
3. Discuss each of the four bases of selection of swine.
4. Cite examples of how purebred and commercial breeders alike have come to regret selections based on show-ring winnings.
5. Why is it difficult to arrive at a set procedure for examining a pig?
6. What are the disadvantages to the score-card system of judging?

SELECTED REFERENCES

Title of Publication	Author(s)	Publisher
Breeding Better Livestock	V. A. Rice F. N. Andrews E. J. Warwick	McGraw-Hill Book Co., New York, N. Y., 1953.
Determining the Age of Farm Animals by Their Teeth	Farmers' Bul. 1721	U. S. Department of Agriculture, Washington, D. C.
Elements of Livestock Judging, The	W. W. Smith	J. B. Lippincott Co., Philadelphia, Pa., 1930.
Livestock Judging Handbook	J. E. Nordby W. M. Beeson D. L. Fourt	The Interstate Printers & Publishers, Inc., Danville, Ill., 1962.
Pork Production	W. W. Smith L. M. Hutchings D.V.M.	The Macmillan Company, New York, N. Y., 1952.
Selecting, Fitting and Showing Swine	J. E. Nordby H. E. Lattig	The Interstate Printers & Publishers, Inc., Danville, Ill., 1961.
Stockman's Handbook, The	M. E. Ensminger	The Interstate Printers & Publishers, Inc., Danville, Ill. 1970.

Chapter V

BREEDING SWINE[1]

[1]The author gratefully acknowledges the authoritative review and helpful suggestions of Dr. S. H. Fowler, Animal Breeding Specialist, Mississippi State University, who reviewed this chapter.

Contents   Page

PART I—SOME PRINCIPLES OF SWINE GENETICS

The laws of heredity apply to swine breeding exactly as they do to all classes of farm animals. But the breeding of swine is more flexible in the hands of man because: (1) hogs normally breed at an earlier age, thus making for a shorter interval between generations, and (2) they are litter-bearing animals. Because of these factors, together with the available feeds and the type of pork products demanded by the consumer, the American farmer has created more new breeds and made more rapid shifts in type in hogs than in any other class of farm animals.

Until very recent times, the general principle that like begets like was the only recognized law of heredity. That the application of this principle over a long period of time has been effective in modifying animal types in the direction of selection is evident from a comparison of present-day types and breeds of swine.

There can be little doubt that men like Bakewell, the English patriarch, and other eighteenth-century breeders had made a tremendous contribution in pointing the way toward livestock improvement before Mendel's laws became known to the world in the early part of the twentieth century. Robert Bakewell's use of progeny testing through his ram letting was truly epoch making, and his improvement of Shire horses and Longhorn cattle was equally outstanding. He and other pioneers had certain ideals in mind, and, according to their standards, they were able to develop some nearly perfect specimens. These men were intensely practical, never overlooking the utility value or the market requirements. No animal met with their favor unless such favor was earned by meat upon the back, milk in the pail, weight and quality of wool, pounds gained for pounds of feed consumed, draft ability, or some other performance of practical value. Their ultimate goal was that of furnishing better animals for the market and/or lowering the cost of production. It must be just so with the master breeders of the present and future.

Others took up the challenge of animal improvement where Bakewell and his contemporaries left off, slowly but surely molding animal types. Thus, during the past hundred years, remarkable progress has been made in breeding better meat animals—animals that are more efficient and, at the same time, that produce cuts of meat more nearly meeting the exacting requirements of the consuming public. The wild boar and the Arkansas razorback have been replaced by the modern meat and bacon types of swine.

Despite the remarkable progress of the past, much remains to be done. A casual glance at the daily receipts of any public stockyards is convincing evidence of the task ahead. The challenge is primarily that of improving the great masses of animals in order that more of them may approach the too few nearly perfect specimens. Moreover, in this space age, there must be greater efficiency of production; and this means more rapid growth, less feed to produce one hundred pounds of meat, and lifting of the percentage pig crop well above the present United States average. With the experience of the pioneers to guide us and with our present knowledge of genetics and physiology of reproduction, progress should now be much more certain and rapid. In the past, animal breeding has been an art. In the future, it is likely to be both an art and a science.

MENDEL'S CONTRIBUTION TO GENETICS

Modern genetics was really founded by Gregor Johann Mendel, a cigar-smoking Austrian monk, who conducted breeding experiments with garden peas from 1857 to 1865, during the time of the Civil War in the United States. In his monastery at Brünn (now Brno, in Czechoslovakia), Mendel applied a powerful curiosity and a clear mind to reveal some of the basic principles of hereditary transmission. In 1866, he published in the proceedings of a local scientific society a report covering eight years of his studies, but for thirty-four years his findings went unheralded and ignored. Finally, in 1900, sixteen years after Mendel's death, three European biologists independently duplicated his findings, and this led to the dusting off of the original paper published by the monk thirty-four years earlier. It is of further interest to note that W. J. Spillman, of the U. S. Department of Agriculture, who was stationed at Washington State

Fig. 5-1. Gregor Johann Mendel
(1822-1884), a cigar-smoking Austrian
monk, whose breeding experiments with
garden peas founded modern genetics.
(Courtesy, The Bettmann Archive)

University, Pullman, Washington, rediscovered some of Mendel's principles and published his results in 1901, without prior knowledge that they had been rediscovered by the European biologists the previous year.

The essence of Mendelism is that inheritance is by particles or units (called genes), that these genes are present in pairs—one member of each pair having come from each parent—and that each gene maintains its identity generation after generation. Thus, Mendel's work with peas laid the basis for two of the general laws of inheritance: (1) the law of segregation, and (2) the independent assortment of genes. Later genetic principles have been added; yet all the phenomena of inheritance, based upon the reactions of genes, are generally known under the collective term, Mendelism.

Thus, modern genetics is really unique in that it was founded by an amateur who was not trained as a geneticist and who did his work merely as a hobby. During the years since the redis-

covery of Mendel's principles (in 1900), many additional genetic principles have been added, but the fundamentals as set forth by Mendel have been proved correct in every detail. It can be said, therefore, that inheritance in both plants and animals follows the biological laws discovered by Mendel.

SOME FUNDAMENTALS OF HEREDITY IN SWINE

The author has no intention of covering all of the diverse field of genetics and animal breeding. Rather, he will present a condensation of a few of the known facts in regard to the field and briefly summarize their application to swine.

The Gene as the Unit of Heredity

Genes determine all the hereditary characteristics of animals, from the body type to the color of the hair. They are truly the fundamental unit of genetics.

The bodies of all animals are made up of millions or even billions of tiny cells, microscopic in size. Each cell contains a nucleus in which there are a number of pairs of bundles called

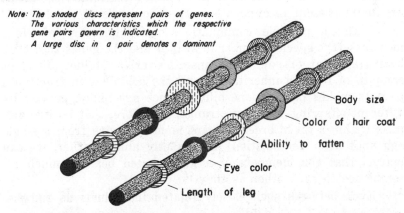

Schematic Drawing of a Pair of Chromosomes

Note: The shaded discs represent pairs of genes. The various characteristics which the respective gene pairs govern is indicated. A large disc in a pair denotes a dominant

Body size
Color of hair coat
Ability to fatten
Eye color
Length of leg

Fig. 5-2. A pair of bundles, called chromosomes, carrying minute particles, called genes. The genes determine all the hereditary characteristics of living animals, from length of leg to body size. (Drawing by R. F. Johnson)

chromosomes. In turn, the chromosomes carry pairs of minute particles, called genes, which are the basic hereditary material. The nucleus of each body cell of swine contains forty pairs of chromosomes[2] or a total of eighty, whereas there are perhaps thousands of pairs of genes. These genes determine all the hereditary characteristics of living animals. Thus, inheritance goes by units rather than by the blending of two fluids, as our grandfathers thought.

The modern breeder knows that the job of transmitting qualities from one generation to the next is performed by the germ cells—a sperm from the male and an ovum or egg from the female. All animals, therefore, are the result of the union of two such tiny cells, one from each of its parents. These two germ cells contain all the anatomical, physiological, and psychological characters that the offspring will inherit.

In the body cells of an animal, each of the chromosomes is duplicated; whereas in the formation of the sex cells, the egg and the sperm, a reduction division occurs and only one chromosome and one gene of each pair goes into a sex cell. This means that only half the number of chromosomes and genes present in the body cells of the animal go into each egg and sperm, but each sperm or egg cell has genes for every characteristic of its species. As will be explained later, the particular half that any one germ cell gets is determined by chance. When mating and fertilization occur, the single chromosomes from the germ cell of each parent unite to form new pairs, and the genes are again present in duplicate in the body cells of the embryo.

With all possible combinations in forty pairs of chromosomes (the species number in swine) and the genes that they bear, any boar or sow can transmit over one billion different samples of its own inheritance; and the combination from both parents makes possible one billion times one billion genetically different offspring. It is not strange, therefore, that no two animals within a given breed (except identical twins from a single egg split after fertilization) are exactly alike. Rather, we can marvel that the members of a given breed bear as much resemblance to each other as they do.

Even between such closely related individuals as full sis-

---

[2]Cattle and horses have thirty pairs of chromosomes; sheep have fifty-four.

ters, it is possible that there will be quite wide differences in size, growth rate, temperament, conformation, and in almost every conceivable character. Admitting that many of these differences may be due to undetected differences in environment, it is still true that in such animals much of the variation is due to hereditary differences. A boar, for example, will sometimes transmit to one offspring much better inheritance than he does to most of his get, simply as the result of chance differences in the genes that go to different sperm at the time of the reduction division. Such differences in inheritance in offspring have been called both the hope and the despair of the livestock breeder.

If an animal gets similar determiners or genes from each parent, it will produce uniform germ cells; because any half of its inheritance is just like any other half. For example, regardless of what combination of chromosomes go into a particular germ cell, it will be just like any other egg or sperm from the same individual. Such animals are referred to as being homozygous. Few, if any, of our animals are in this hereditary state at the present time. Instead of being homozygous, they are heterozygous. This explains why there may be such wide variation within the offspring of any given sire or dam. The wise and progressive breeder recognizes this fact, and he insists on the production records of all get rather than that of just a few meritorious individuals.

Variation between the offspring of animals that are not pure or homozygous, to use the technical term, is not to be marveled at, but is rather to be expected. No one would expect to draw exactly twenty sound apples and ten rotten ones every time he took a random sample of thirty from a barrel containing forty sound ones and twenty rotten ones, although on the average—if enough samples were drawn—he would expect to get about that proportion of each. Individual drawings would of course vary rather widely. Exactly the same situation applies to the relative number of "good" and "bad" genes that may be present in different germ cells from the same animal. Because of this situation, the mating of a sow with a fine show record to a boar that on the average transmits relatively good offspring will not always produce pigs of merit equal to that of their parents. The pigs could be markedly poorer than the parents or, happily, they could in some cases be better than either parent.

Selection and close breeding are the tools through which the

swine producer can obtain boars and sows whose chromosomes and genes contain similar hereditary determiners—animals that are genetically more homozygous.

Genes Seldom Change

Gene changes are technically known as mutations. *A mutation may be defined as a sudden variation which is later passed on through inheritance and that results from changes in a gene or genes.* Mutations are not only rare, but they are prevailingly harmful. For all practical purposes, therefore, the genes can be thought of as unchanged from one generation to the next. The observed differences between animals are usually due to different combinations of genes being present rather than to mutations. Each gene probably changes only about once in each 100,000 to 1,000,000 animals produced.

Once in a great while a mutation occurs in a farm animal, and it produces a visible effect in the animal carrying it. These animals are commonly called "sports." Such "sports" are occasionally of practical value. The occurrence of the polled characteristic within the horned Hereford and Shorthorn breeds of cattle is an example of a mutation or "sport" of economic importance. Out of this has arisen the Polled Hereford and Polled Shorthorn breeds.

Gene changes can be accelerated by exposure to X rays, radium, and ultraviolet light. Such changes may eventually be observed in the offspring of both people and animals of Japan who were exposed to the atom bombs unleashed in World War II.

Simple Gene Inheritance (Qualitative Traits)

In the simplest type of inheritance, only one pair of genes is involved. Thus, a pair of genes is responsible for erect and lop ears in swine. This situation is illustrated by Fig. 5-3, showing the inheritance of erect ears and lop ears in certain breeds of swine. As noted, all first cross progeny from such matings are hybrid lop eared. When the latter animals are mated together, the ears of the offspring occur in the proportion of 1 pure erect eared pig, 2 impure lop eared pigs, and 1 pure lop eared pig.

It should be borne in mind that the various gene combinations shown in Fig. 5-3, occur at random and that the ears will appear in the offspring in the proportions indicated only when

relatively large numbers are concerned. The possible gene combinations, therefore, are governed by the laws of chance, operating in much the same manner as the results obtained from flip-

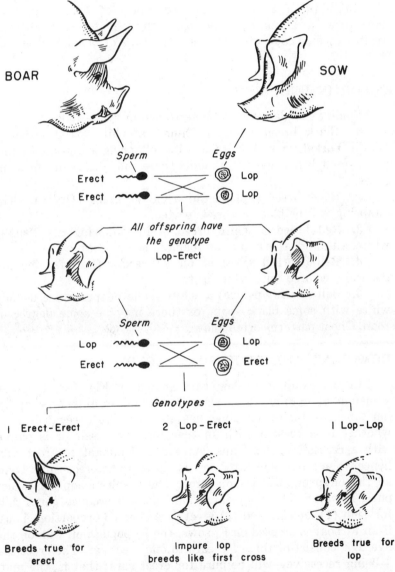

Fig. 5-3. Diagram showing how erect ears and lop ears in certain breeds of swine are inherited. (Drawing by R. F. Johnson)

ping coins. For example, if a penny is flipped often enough, the number of heads and tails will come out about even. However, with the laws of chance in operation, it is possible that out of any four tosses one might get all heads, all tails, or even three to one.

In addition to ears, other examples of simple gene inheritance in animals (sometimes referred to as qualitative traits) include color of hair, eye color, type of blood, and lethals.

COLOR INHERITANCE

Some examples of color inheritance in swine follow:

1. **Black breed (Poland China) x white breed (Chester White, Yorkshire, or Landrace.**—The offspring are usually white with small black spots, although there may be roans in some cases.

2. **Black breed (Poland China) x red breed (Duroc).**—The offspring will be black-and-red-spotted.

3. **Red breed x white breed.**—The offspring are usually white, although there may be roans in some cases.

4. **Belted breed x red or black breed.**—The offspring are generally colored with white belts.

5. **Belted (Hampshire) x white**—The offspring are usually white with some black spots, or there may be some degree of roan. Ghost patterns often show.

DOMINANT AND RECESSIVE FACTORS

In the example of hog ears shown in Fig. 5-3, the phenomenon of dominance is also illustrated. In this type of inheritance, a factor or gene has its full effect regardless of whether it is present with another just like itself or is paired with a recessive gene. Thus, lop ear is dominant to erect ear; hence when a pure lop-eared sow is mated to an erect-eared boar, all the offspring will be lop-eared. The resulting lop ear is not pure, however. These lop-eared animals will produce germ cells for each (1) lop ears and (2) erect ears in equal proportion. Thus, if an F_1 boar is crossed on F_1 sows, the F_2 population will, on the average, consist of three lop ears to one erect ear. The erect ear —being recessive—will be pure for erect ears; that is, the mating of two erect-eared pigs will always produce erect-eared off-

spring. Of the three lop-eared pigs, however, only one is pure for lop ears. The other two will be heterozygous (impure) in genetic constitution, and will produce germ cells carrying erect ears and lop ears in equal proportion. Also, in swine white is dominant to colored hair, with the result that when white hogs are crossed on colored hogs, the first crosses are white (although the colored breeds sometimes transmit some of their skin pigmentation). Thus, a Chester White x Poland China produces white pigs.

It is clear, therefore, that a dominant character will cover up a recessive. Hence a hog's breeding performance cannot be recognized by its phenotype (how it looks), a fact which is of great significance in practical breeding.

As can be readily understood, dominance often makes the task of identifying and discarding all animals carrying an undesirable recessive factor a difficult one. Recessive genes can be passed on from generation to generation, appearing only when two animals both of which carry the recessive factor happen to mate. Even then, only one out of four offspring produced will, on the average, be homozygous for the recessive factor and show it.

Examples of undesirable recessives in animals are: scrotal hernia and inverted nipples (blind teats) in pigs. When these conditions appear, one can be very certain that both the sire and dam contributed equally to the condition and that each of them carries the recessive gene therefor. This fact should be given consideration in the culling program.

Assuming that a hereditary defect or abnormality has occurred in a herd and that it is recessive in nature, the breeding program to be followed to prevent or minimize the possibility of its future occurrence will depend somewhat on the type of herd involved—especially on whether it is a commercial or purebred herd. In an ordinary commercial herd, the breeder can usually guard against further reappearance of the undesirable recessive simply by using an outcross (unrelated) sire within the same breed or by crossbreeding with a sire from another breed. With this system, the breeder is fully aware of the recessive being present, but he has taken action to keep it from showing up.

On the other hand, if such an undesirable recessive appears in a purebred herd, the action should be more drastic. A reputable purebred breeder has an obligation not only to himself but to his customers among both the purebred and commercial

herds. Purebred animals must be purged of undesirable genes and lethals. This can be done by:

1. Eliminating those sires and dams that are known to have transmitted the undesirable recessive character.

2. Eliminating both the abnormal and normal offspring produced by these sires and dams (approximately half of the normal animals will carry the undesirable character in the recessive condition).

3. By, in some instances, breeding a prospective herd sire to a number of females known to carry the factor for the undesirable recessive, thus making sure that the new sire is free from the recessive.

Such action in a purebred herd is expensive, and it calls for considerable courage. Yet it is the only way in which the purebred livestock of the country can be freed from such undesirable genes.

Multiple Gene Inheritance (Quantitative Traits)

Relatively few characters of economic importance in farm animals are inherited in as simple a manner as the ears described. Important characters—such as meat production, milk and butterfat production, egg production, and wool production—are due to many genes; thus they are called multiple-factor characters or multiple-gene characters. Because such characters show all manner of gradation—from high to low performance, for example— they are sometimes referred to as quantitative traits.

In quantitative inheritance, the extremes (either good or bad) tend to swing back to the average. Thus, the offspring of a grand champion boar and a grand champion sow are not apt to be as good as either parent. Likewise, and happily so, the progeny of two very mediocre parents will likely be superior to either parent.

Estimates of the number of pairs of genes affecting each economically important characteristic vary greatly, but the majority of geneticists agree that for most such characters ten or more pairs of genes are involved. Growth rate in swine, therefore, is affected by: (1) the animal's appetite or feed consumption; (2) the efficiency of assimilation—that is, the proportion of the feed eaten that is absorbed into the blood stream; and (3) the use to which the nutrients are put after assimilation—

for example, whether they are used for growth or finishing. This example should indicate clearly enough that such a characteristic as growth rate is controlled by many genes and that it is difficult to determine the mode of inheritance of such characters.

Heredity and Environment

A sleek hog, bedded deep in straw and with a trough full of feed before him, is undeniably the result of two forces—heredity and environment. If turned to the forest, a littermate to the sleek pig would present an entirely different appearance. By the same token, optimum environment could never make a champion out of a pig with scrub ancestry, but it might well be added that "fat and hair will cover up a multitude of sins."

These are extreme examples, and they may be applied to any class of farm animals; but they do emphasize the fact that any particular animal is the product of heredity and environment. Stated differently, heredity may be thought of as the foundation, and environment as the structure. Heredity has already made its contribution at the time of fertilization, but environment works ceaselessly away until death.

Admittedly, after looking over an animal, a breeder cannot with certainty know whether it is genetically a high or a low producer; and there can be no denying the fact that environment—including feeding, management, and disease—plays a tremendous

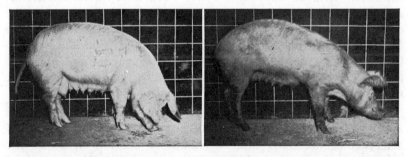

Fig. 5-4. Feed made the difference! The two sows were of the same age and breeding, but the sow shown in the picture at left received all she could eat from birth, whereas the gaunt sow shown in the picture at right was limited to 70 percent of the ration consumed by the better fed animal. This 10-year experiment, conducted at Washington State University, was designed to study the effect of plane of nutrition on meat animal improvement. (Courtesy, Washington State University)

part in determining the extent to which hereditary differences that are present will be expressed in animals.

Experimental work has long shown conclusively enough that the vigor and size of animals at birth is dependent upon the environment of the embryo from the minute the ovum or egg is fertilized by the sperm, and now we have evidence to indicate that newborn animals are affected by the environment of the egg and sperm long before fertilization has been accomplished. In other words, perhaps due to storage of factors, the kind and quality of the ration fed to young, growing females may later affect the quality of their progeny. Generally speaking, then, environment may inhibit the full expression of potentialities from a time preceding fertilization until physiological maturity has been attained.

It is generally agreed, therefore, that maximum development of characters of economic importance—growth, body form, milk production, etc.—cannot be achieved unless there are optimum conditions of nutrition and management. However, the next question is whether a breeding program can make maximum progress under conditions of suboptimal nutrition (such as is often found under some farm conditions). One school of thought is that selection for such factors as body form and growth rate in animals can be most effective only under nutritive conditions promoting the near maximum development of those characters of which the animal is capable. The other school of thought is that genetic differences affecting usefulness under suboptimal conditions will be expressed under such suboptimal conditions, and that differences observed under forced conditions may not be correlated with real utility under less favorable conditions. Those favoring the latter thinking argue, therefore, that the production and selection of breeding animals for suboptimal nutritive conditions should be under less favorable conditions and that the animals should not be highly fitted.

In general, the results of a long-time experiment[3] conducted at Washington State University support the contention that selection of breeding animals should be carried on under the same environmental conditions as those under which commercial animals are produced.

Within the pure breeds of swine—managed under aver-

---

[3]Washington Agricultural Experiment Station Bul. 34, January 1961.

age or better than average conditions—it has been found that, in general, only 15 to 30 percent of the observed variation in a characteristic is actually brought about by hereditary variations. To be sure, if we contrast animals that differ very greatly in heredity—for example, a champion hog and a scrub—90 percent or more of the apparent differences in type may be due to heredity. The point is, however, that extreme cases such as the one just mentioned are not involved in the advancement within improved breeds of livestock. Here the comparisons are between animals of average or better than average quality, and the observed differences are often very minor.

The problem of the progressive breeder is that of selecting the very best animals available genetically—these to be parents of the next generation of offspring in his herd. The fact that only 15 to 30 percent of the observed variation is due to differences in inheritance and that environmental differences can produce misleading variations make mistakes in the selection of breeding animals inevitable. However, if the purebred breeder has clearly in mind a well-defined ideal and adheres rigidly to it in selecting his breeding stock, very definite progress can be made, especially if mild inbreeding is judiciously used as a tool through which to fix the hereditary material.

How Sex Is Determined

On the average, and when considering a large population, approximately equal numbers of males and females are born in all common species of animals. To be sure, many notable exceptions can be found in individual herds or flocks.

The most widely accepted theory of sex determination at the present time is that sex is determined by the chromosomal make-up of the individual. One particular pair of the chromosomes is called the sex chromosomes. In farm animals, the female has a pair of similar chromosomes (usually called X chromosomes), whereas the male has a pair of unlike sex chromosomes (usually called X and Y chromosomes). In the bird, this condition is reversed, the female having the unlike pair and the male having the like pair.

The pairs of sex chromosomes separate out when the germ cells are formed. Thus, each of the ova or eggs produced by the sow contains the X chromosome; whereas the sperm of the

boar are of two types, one-half containing the X chromosome and the other one-half the Y chromosome. Since, on the average, the eggs and sperm unite at random, it can be understood that half

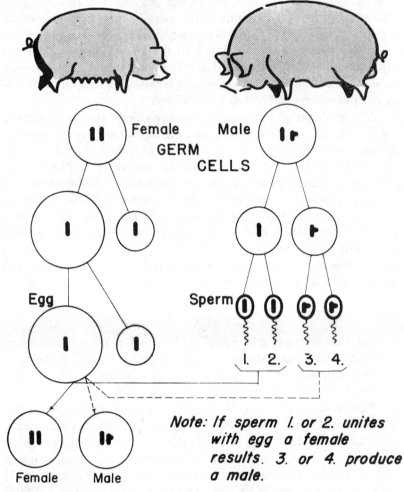

Note: If sperm 1. or 2. unites with egg a female results. 3. or 4. produce a male.

❙ = female chromosome
r = male

Fig. 5-5. Diagrammatic illustration of the mechanism of sex determination in hogs, showing how sex is determined by the chromosomal make-up of the individual. The sow has a pair of like sex chromosomes, whereas the boar has a pair of unlike sex chromosomes. Thus, if an egg and sperm of like sex chromosomal make-up unite, the offspring will be a gilt whereas if an egg and sperm of unlike sex chromosomal make-up unite, the offspring will be a boar. (Drawing by R. F. Johnson)

of the progeny will contain the chromosomal make-up XX (females)[4] and the other one-half XY (males).[5]

Lethals and Other Hereditary Defects in Swine

The term lethal refers to a genetic factor that causes death of the young, either during prenatal life or at birth. Other defects occur which are not sufficiently severe to cause death but which do impair the usefulness of the affected animals. Some of the lethals and other abnormalities that have been reported in swine are summarized in Table 5-1.

Many such abnormal animals are born on the nation's farms and ranches each year. Unfortunately, the purebred breeder, whose chief business is that of selling breeding stock, is likely to "keep mum" about the appearance of any defective animals in his herd because of the justifiable fear that it may hurt his

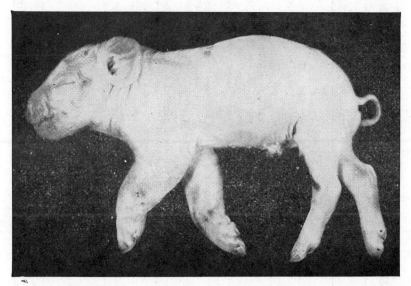

Fig. 5-6. Pig with "thick forelegs," a lethal condition caused by a simple recessive genetic factor. (Courtesy, Department of Veterinary Pathology and Hygiene, College of Veterinary Medicine, University of Illinois)

---

[4] The scientists' symbols for the male and female, respectively, are:
 ♂ (the sacred shield and spear of Mars, the Roman god of war), and
 ♀ (the looking glass of Venus, the Roman goddess of love and beauty).
[5] See Footnote 4.

TABLE 5-1

SOME HEREDITARY LETHALS AND OTHER HEREDITARY ABNORMALITIES WHICH HAVE BEEN REPORTED IN SWINE

Type of Abnormality	Description of Abnormality	Probable Mode of Inheritance
A. Lethals		
Atresia ani	No anal opening. Pigs born alive.	Undetermined
Bent legs	Legs bent at right angle and stiff.	Recessive
Brain hernia	Pigs usually born alive but skull openings present involving frontal and parietal bones.	Probably recessive
Catlin mark	Incomplete development of the skull.	Recessive
Cleft palate	Pigs born alive but unable to nurse.	Recessive
Excessive fatness	Pigs become excessively fat at 70 to 150 lbs. and die.	Undetermined
Fetal mortality	Born dead or are reabsorbed.	Recessive
Hydrocephalus	Fluid on the brain, head enlarged; often accompanied by short tail.	Recessive
Legless	Pigs born alive but without legs.	Recessive
Muscle contracture	Usually only forelegs affected, but sometimes hindlegs are involved. Forelegs rigid. Animals usually stillborn or live only short time.	Recessive
Paralysis	Complete paralysis of hindlegs. Born alive but starve unless given special care.	Recessive
Split ears	Ears split usually associated with cleft palate and deformed hindlegs.	Probably recessive
Thickened forelimbs	Thickening of forelegs caused by infiltration of connective tissues which replace the muscle fibers. Pigs usually born alive.	Recessive
B. Non Lethals		
Cryptorchidism	One or both testicles retained in body cavity.	Recessive
Hair whorls (swirls)	Hair at a given point in back region flanges out in all directions.	Mode of inheritance not certain but probably due to complementary action of two dominant factors.
Hairlessness	Animals born with little or no hair (not to be confused with hairlessness caused by an iodine deficiency).	Recessive
Hemophilia	Blood fails to clot promptly when wounds are inflicted.	Recessive.

(Continued)

TABLE 5-1 (Continued)

Type of Abnormality	Description of Abnormality	Probable Mode of Inheritance
Inverted nipples (blind teats)	Teats inverted and nonfunctional.	Undetermined
Kinky tail	Rigid angles in the tail at birth.	Recessive
Polydactyl	Extra toes on forefeet.	Undetermined
Red eyes	Observed in Hampshires. Affected animals also have light brown hair coat.	Probably recessive
Scrotal hernia	Ruptured; intestines extending into scrotum.	Result of two pairs of recessive factors.
Syndactyl (Mule foot)	Only one toe instead of two.	Dominant
Umbilical hernia	Weakness at umbilicus; intestines protrude.	Dominant
Wattles	Skinlike flaps hanging from throat near lower jaw.	Dominant
Wooly	Kinky hair.	Dominant

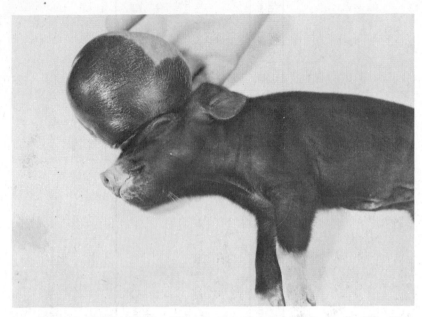

Fig. 5-7. Hydrocephalic (literally meaning "water in the head"). Pigs affected with this condition die soon after birth. It is inherited as a simple recessive. (Courtesy, Purdue University)

Fig. 5-8. A six-legged Duroc gilt. Perhaps this condition can best be described as an "accident of development."

sales. With the commercial producer, however, the appearance of such lethals is simply so much economic loss, with the result that he generally, openly and without embarrassment, admits the presence of the abnormality and seeks correction.

The embryological development—the development of the young from the time that the egg and the sperm unite until the animal is born—is very complicated. Thus, the oddity probably is that so many of the offspring develop normally rather than that a few develop abnormally.

Many such abnormalities (commonly known as monstrosities or freaks) are hereditary, being caused by certain "bad" genes. Moreover, the bulk of such lethals are recessive and may, therefore, remain hidden for many generations. The prevention of such genetic abnormalities requires that the germ plasm be purged of the "bad" genes. This means that, where recessive lethals are involved, the stockman must be aware of the fact that both parents carry the gene. For the total removal of the lethals, test matings and rigid selection must be practiced. The best test mating to use for a given sire consists of mating him to some of his own daughters. Thus, where there is suspicion of scrotal hernia, it is recommended that a boar be bred back to some of his daughters.

In addition to hereditary abnormalities, there are certain abnormalities that may be due to nutritional deficiencies, or to accidents of development—the latter including those which appear to occur sporadically and for which there is no well-defined reason. When only a few defective individuals occur within a particular herd, it is often impossible to determine whether their occurrence is due to: (1) defective heredity, (2) defective nutrition, or (3) accidents of development. If the same abnormality occurs in any appreciable number of animals, however, it is probably either hereditary or nutritional. In any event, the diagnosis of the condition is not always a simple matter.

The following conditions would tend to indicate a hereditary defect:

1. If the defect had previously been reported as hereditary in the same breed of livestock.

2. If it occurred more frequently within certain families or when there had been inbreeding.

3. If it occurred in more than one season and when different rations had been fed.

The following conditions might be accepted as indications that the abnormality was due to a nutritional deficiency:

1. If previously it had been reliably reported to be due to a nutritional deficiency.

2. If it appeared to be restricted to a certain area.

3. If it occurred when the ration of the mother was known to be deficient.

4. If it disappeared when an improved ration was fed.

If there is suspicion that the ration is defective, it should be improved, not only from the standpoint of preventing such deformities, but from the standpoint of good and efficient management.

If there is good and sufficient evidence that the abnormal condition is hereditary, the steps to be followed in purging the herd of the undesirable gene are identical to those already outlined for ridding the herd of an undesirable recessive factor. An inbreeding program, of course, is the most effective way in which to expose hereditary lethals in order that purging may follow.

The Relative Importance of the Boar and the Sow

As a boar can have so many more offspring during a given season or a lifetime than a sow, he is from a hereditary standpoint a more important individual than any one sow so far as the whole herd is concerned, although both the boar and the sow are of equal importance so far as concerns any one offspring. Because of their wider use, therefore, boars are usually culled more rigidly than sows, and the breeder can well afford to pay more for an outstanding boar than for an equally outstanding sow.

Experienced swine producers have long felt that boars often resemble their daughters more closely than their sons, whereas sows resemble their sons. Some boars and sows, therefore, enjoy a reputation based almost exclusively on the merit of their sons, whereas others owe their prestige to their daughters. Although this situation is likely to be exaggerated, any such phenomenon that may exist is due to sex-linked inheritance which may be explained as follows: The genes that determine sex are carried on one of the chromosomes. The other genes that are located on the same chromosome will be linked or associated with sex and will be transmitted to the next generation in combination with

sex. Thus, because of sex linkage, there are more color-blind men than color-blind women. In poultry breeding, the sex-linked factor is used in a practical way for the purpose of distinguishing the pullets from the cockerels early in life, through the process known as "sexing" the chicks. Thus, when a black cock is crossed with barred hens, all the cocks come barred and all the hens come black. It should be emphasized, however, that under most conditions it appears that the influence of the sire and dam on any one offspring is about equal. Most breeders, therefore, will do well to seek excellence in both sexes of breeding animals.

Prepotency

Prepotency refers to the ability of the animal, either male or female, to stamp its own characteristics on its offspring. The offspring of a prepotent boar, for example, resemble both their sire and each other more closely than usual. The only conclusive and final test of prepotency consists of the inspection of the get.

From a genetic standpoint, there are two requisites that an animal must possess in order to be prepotent: (1) dominance and (2) homozygosity. Every offspring that receives a dominant gene or genes will show the effect of that gene or genes in the particular character or characters which result therefrom. Moreover, a perfectly homozygous animal would transmit the same kind of genes to all of its offspring. Although entirely homozygous animals probably never exist, it is realized that a system of inbreeding is the only way to produce animals that are as nearly homozygous as possible.

Popular beliefs to the contrary, there is no evidence that prepotency can be predicted by the appearance of an animal. To be more specific, there is no reason why a vigorous, masculine-appearing boar will be any more prepotent than one less desirable in these respects.

It should also be emphasized that it is impossible to determine just how important prepotency may be in animal breeding, although many sires of the past have enjoyed a reputation for being extremely prepotent. Perhaps these animals were prepotent, but there is also the possibility that their reputation for producing outstanding animals may have rested upon the fact that they were mated to some of the best females of the breed.

In summary, it may be said that if a given boar or sow

possesses a great number of genes that are completely dominant for desirable type and performance and if the animal is relatively homozygous, the offspring will closely resemble the parent and resemble each other, or be uniform. Fortunate, indeed, is the breeder who possesses such an animal.

Nicking

If the offspring of certain matings are especially outstanding and in general better than their parents, breeders are prone to say that the animals nicked well. For example, a sow may produce outstanding pigs to the service of a certain boar, but when mated to another boar of apparent equal merit as a sire, the offspring may be disappointing. Or sometimes the mating of a rather average boar to an equally average sow will result in the production of a most outstanding individual both from the standpoint of type and performance.

So-called successful nicking is due, genetically speaking, to the fact that the right combination of genes for good characters are contributed by each parent, although each of the parents within itself may be lacking in certain genes necessary for excellence. In other words, the animals "nicked" well because their respective combinations of good genes were such as to complement each other.

The history of animal breeding includes records of several supposedly favorable nicks. Because of the very nature of successful nicks, however, outstanding animals arising therefrom must be carefully scrutinized from a breeding standpoint; because, with their heterozygous origin, it is quite unlikely that they will breed true.

Family Names

In animals, depending upon the breed, family names are traced through either the males or females. Unfortunately, the value of family names is generally grossly exaggerated. Obviously, if the foundation boar or sow, as the case may be, is very many generations removed, the genetic superiority of this head of a family is halved so many times by subsequent matings that there is little reason to think that one family is superior to another. The situation is often further distorted by breeders placing a premium on family names of which there are few mem-

bers, little realizing that, in at least some cases, there may be
unfortunate reasons for the scarcity in numbers.

Such family names have about as much significance as
human family names. Who would be so foolish as to think that
the Joneses as a group are alike and superior to the Smiths?
Perhaps, if the truth were known, there have been many individuals with each of these family names who have been of no
particular credit to the clan, and the same applies to all other
family names.

Family names lend themselves readily to speculation. Because of this, the history of livestock breeding has often been
blighted by instances of unwise pedigree selection on the basis
of not too meaningful family names. Fortunately, for swine producers, there has been less worshipping of family names in
hogs than in certain other classes of livestock.

Of course, certain linebred families—linebred to a foundation sire or dam so that the family is kept highly related to it—
do have genetic significance. Moreover, if the programs involved
have been accompanied by rigid culling, many good individuals
may have evolved, and the family name may be in good repute.

SYSTEMS OF BREEDING

The many diverse types and breeds among each class of
farm animals in existence today originated from only a few wild
types within each species. These early domesticated animals
possessed the pool of genes, which, through controlled matings
and selection, proved flexible in the hands of man. In swine,
for example, through various systems of breeding, there evolved
the lard and bacon breeds of swine.

Perhaps at the outset it should be stated that there is no
one best system of breeding or secret of success for any and all
conditions. Each breeding program is an individual case, requiring
careful study. The choice of the system of breeding should be determined primarily by the size and quality of the herd, by the
finances and skill of the operator, and by the ultimate goal ahead.

Purebreeding

*A purebred animal may be defined as a member of a breed,
the animals of which possess a common ancestry and distinctive
characteristics; and it is either registered or eligible for regis-*

try in that breed. The breed association consists of a group of breeders banded together for the purposes of: (1) recording the lineage of their animals, (2) protecting the purity of the breed, and (3) promoting the interest of the breed.

The term purebred refers to animals whose entire lineage, regardless of the number of generations removed, traces back to the foundation animals accepted by the breed or to animals which have been subsequently approved for infusion. The term Thoroughbred is applied properly only to the breed of running race horses developed originally in England; and should not be confused with nor used synonymously with the designation purebred.

It should be emphasized that being a purebred animal does not necessarily guarantee superior type or high productivity. That is to say, the word purebred is not, within itself, magic, nor is it sacred. Many a person has found to his sorrow that there are such things as purebred scrubs. Yet, on the average, pure-bred animals are superior to non-purebreds.

For the man with experience and adequate capital, the breeding of purebreds may offer unlimited opportunities. It has been well said that honor, fame, and fortune are all within the realm of possible realization of the purebred breeder; but it should also be added that only a few achieve this high calling.

Purebred breeding is a highly specialized type of production. Generally speaking, only the experienced breeder should under-take the production of purebreds with the intention of furnish-ing foundation or replacement stock to other purebred breeders. Although we have had many constructive swine breeders and great progress has been made, it must be remembered that only a few achieve sufficient success to classify as master breeders.

Inbreeding or Closebreeding

Inbreeding or closebreeding is rarely practiced among present-day swine producers, though it was common in the foun-dation animals of most of the breeds.

Inbreeding or closebreeding is that system of breeding in which closely related animals are mated. This includes the mating of: (1) sire to daughter, (2) son to dam, and (3) brother to sis-ter; and the minimum number of different ancestors. In the re-

peated mating of a brother with his full sister, there are only two grandparents instead of four, only two great-grandparents instead of eight, and only two different ancestors in each generation farther back—instead of the theoretically possible 16, 32, 64, 128, etc. In certain plants, self-fertilization still more rapidly reduces the number of different ancestors, but none of the domestic animals are self-fertilized.

The **reasons** for practicing inbreeding or closebreeding are:

1. It increases the degree of homozygosity within animals, making the resulting offspring pure or homozygous in a larger proportion of their gene pairs than in the case of linebred or outcross animals. In so doing, the less desirable recessive genes are brought to light so that they can be more readily culled. Thus, inbreeding, together with rigid culling, affords the surest and quickest method of fixing and perpetuating a desirable character or group of characters.

2. If carried on for a period of time, it tends to create lines or strains of animals that are uniform in type and in other characteristics.

3. It keeps the relationship to a desirable ancestor highest.

4. Because of the greater homozygosity, it makes for greater prepotency. That is, selected inbred animals are more homozygous for desirable genes (genes which are often dominant), and they, therefore, transmit these genes with greater uniformity.

5. Through the production of inbred lines or families by inbreeding and the subsequent crossing of certain of these lines, it affords a modern approach to livestock improvement. Moreover, the best of the inbred animals are likely to give superior results in outcrosses.

6. Where a breeder is in the unique position of having his herd so far advanced that to go on the outside for seed stock would merely be a step backward, it offers the only sound alternative for maintaining existing quality or making further improvement.

The **precautions** in inbreeding may be summarized as follows:

1. As inbreeding greatly enhances the chances that recessives will appear during the early generations in obtaining homozygosity, it is almost certain to increase the proportion of

worthless breeding stock produced. This may include such so-
called degenerates as reduction in size, fertility, and general
vigor. Lethals and other genetic abnormalities often appear with
increased frequency in inbred animals.

2. Because of the rigid culling necessary in order to avoid
the fixing of undesirable characters, especially in the first
generations of an inbreeding program, it is almost imperative
that this system of breeding be confined to a relatively large
herd and to instances when the owner has sufficient finances to
stand the rigid culling that must accompany such a program.

3. It requires skill in making planned matings and rigid
selection, thus being most successful when applied by master
breeders.

4. It is not adapted for use by the man with average or
below average stock because the very fact that his animals are
average means that a goodly share of undesirable genes are
present. Inbreeding would merely make the animals more homozygous for undesirable genes and therefore worse.

Judging from outward manifestations alone, it might appear
that inbreeding is predominantly harmful in its effects—often
leading to the production of defective animals lacking in the vi-
tality necessary for successful and profitable production. But
this is by no means the whole story. Although inbreeding often
leads to the production of animals of low value, the resulting
superior animals can confidently be expected to be homozygous
for a greater than average number of good genes and thus more
valuable for breeding purposes. Figuratively speaking, therefore, inbreeding may be referred to as "trial by fire," and the
breeder who practices it can expect to obtain many animals that
fail to measure up and that have to be culled. On the other hand,
if inbreeding is handled properly, he can also expect to secure
animals of exceptional value.

Although inbreeding has been practiced less during the
past century than in the formative period of the different pure
breeds of livestock, it has real merit when its principles and
limitations are fully understood. Perhaps inbreeding or closebreeding had best be confined to use by the skilled master breeder
who is in a sufficiently sound financial position to endure rigid
and intelligent culling and delayed returns and whose herd is
both large and above average in quality.

Linebreeding

From a biological standpoint, inbreeding and linebreeding are the same thing; differing merely in intensity. In general, inbreeding has been frowned upon by swine producers, but linebreeding (the less intensive form) has been looked upon with favor in some quarters.

Linebreeding is that system of breeding in which the degree of relationship is less intense than in inbreeding, and in which the matings are usually directed toward keeping the offspring closely related to some highly admired ancestor. In a linebreeding program, therefore, the degree of relationship is not closer than half-brother and half-sister or matings more distantly related; cousin matings, grandparent to grand offspring, etc.

Linebreeding may be practiced in order to conserve and perpetuate the good traits of a certain outstanding boar or sow. Because such descendants are of similar lineage, they have the same general type of germ plasm and therefore exhibit a high degree of uniformity in type and performance.

In a more limited way, a linebreeding program has the same advantages and disadvantages of an inbreeding program. Stated differently, linebreeding offers fewer possibilities both for good and harm than inbreeding. It is a more conservative and safer type of program, offering less probability to either hit the jackpot or sink the ship. It is a middle-of-the-road program that the vast majority of average and small breeders can follow safely to their advantage. Through it, reasonable progress can be made without taking any great risk. A greater degree of homozygosity of certain desirable genes can be secured without running too great a risk of intensifying undesirable ones.

Usually a linebreeding program is best accomplished through breeding to an outstanding sire rather than to an outstanding dam because of the greater number of offspring of the former. If a swine breeder found himself in possession of a great boar—proved great by the production records of a large number of his get—a linebreeding program might be initiated in the following way: Select two of the best sons of the noted boar and mate them to their half-sisters, balancing all possible defects in the subsequent matings. The next generation matings might well consist of breeding the daughters of one of the boars to the

son of the other, etc. If, in such a program, it seems wise to secure some outside blood (genes) to correct a common defect or defects in the herd, this may be done through selecting a few outstanding proved sows from the outside—animals whose get are strong where the herd may be deficient—and then mating these sows to one of the linebred boars with the hope of producing a son that may be used in the herd.

The small operator—the owner of a few sows—can often follow a linebreeding program by breeding his sows to a boar purchased from a large breeder who follows such a program—thus in effect following the linebreeding program of the larger breeder.

Naturally, a linebreeding program may be achieved in other ways. Regardless of the actual matings used, the main objective in such a system of breeding is that of rendering the animals homozygous—in desired type and performance—to some great and highly regarded ancestor, while at the same time weeding out homozygous undesirable characteristics. The success of the program, therefore, is dependent upon having desirable genes with which to start and an intelligent intensification of these good genes.

"Uncle" Nick Gentry of Sedalia, Missouri—whose name is among the immortals as a Berkshire swine breeder—linebred and inbred with great skill and success to his outstanding boar, Longfellow. That Mr. Gentry was very cautious, however, is attested by the fact that he often spent an hour walking back and forth between his herd boars before deciding which one to mate to a particular sow.

It should be emphasized that there are some types of herds that should almost never inbreed or linebreed. These include herds of only average quality.

The owner of a grade or commercial herd runs the risk of undesirable results, and, even if successful as a commercial breeder, he cannot sell his stock at increased prices for breeding purposes.

With purebred herds of only average quality, more rapid progress can usually be made by introducing superior outcross sires. Moreover, if the animals are of only average quality they must have a preponderance of "bad" genes that would only be intensified through an inbreeding or linebreeding program.

Outcrossing

Outcrossing is the mating of animals that are members of the same breed, but which show no relationship close up in the pedigree (for at least the first four to six generations).

Most of our purebred animals of all classes of livestock are the result of outcrossing. It is a relatively safe system of breeding, for it is unlikely that two such unrelated animals will carry the same "undesirable" genes and pass them on to their offspring.

Perhaps it might well be added that the majority of purebred breeders with average or below average herds had best follow an outcrossing program, because, in such herds, the problem is that of retaining a heterozygous type of germ plasm with the hope that genes for undesirable characters will be counteracted by genes for desirable characters. With such average or below average herds, an inbreeding program would merely make the animals homozygous for the less desirable characters, the presence of which already makes for their mediocrity. In general, continued outcrossing offers neither the hope for improvement nor the hazard of retrogression of linebreeding or inbreeding programs.

Judicious and occasional outcrossing may well be an integral part of linebreeding or inbreeding programs. As closely inbred animals become increasingly homozygous with germ plasm for good characters, they may likewise become homozygous for certain undesirable characters even though their general overall type and performance remains well above the breed average. Such defects may best be remedied by introducing an outcross through an animal or animals known to be especially strong in the character or characters needing strengthening. This having been accomplished, the wise breeder will return to the original inbreeding or linebreeding program, realizing full well the limitations of an outcrossing program.

Grading Up

Grading up is that system of breeding in which a purebred sire of a given breed is mated to a native or grade female. Its purpose is to impart quality and to increase performance in the offspring.

Many breeders will continue to produce purebred stock.

However, the vast majority of animals in the United States—
probably more than 97 percent—are not eligible for registry.
In general, however, because of the obvious merit of using well-
bred sires, farm animals are sired by purebreds. In comparison
with the breeding of purebreds, such a system requires less outlay of cash, and less experience on the part of the producer. However, even with this type of production, grading up of the herd
through the use of purebred sires is generally practiced. Thus,
one of the principal functions of the purebred breeder is that
of serving as a source of seed stock—particularly of sires—for
the commercial producer. In brief, it is hoped that concentrated
doses of "good" genes may be secured through the use of purebred sires. As the common stock is improved, this means that
still further improvement and homozygosity for good genes is

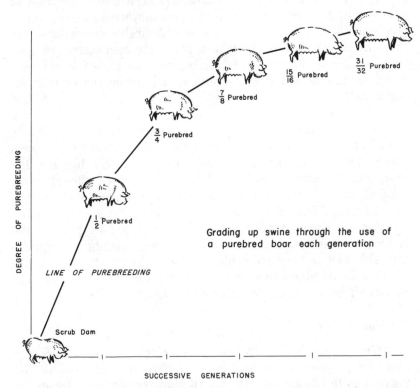

Fig. 5-9. Diagrammatic illustration of grading up a scrub sow with a
purebred boar, showing how the hereditary material is changed with each
generation. (Drawing by R. F. Johnson)

necessary in the purebreds, if they are to bring about further advancement in any grading-up program.

Naturally, the greatest single step toward improved quality and performance occurs in the first cross. The first generation from such a mating results in offspring carrying 50 percent of the hereditary material of the purebred parent (or 50 percent of the "blood" of the purebred parent, as many stockmen speak of it). The next generation gives offspring carrying 75 percent of the "blood" of the purebred breed, and in subsequent generations the proportion of inheritance remaining from the original scrub parent is halved with each cross. Later crosses usually increase quality and performance still more, though in less marked degree. After the third or fourth cross, the offspring compare very favorably with purebred stock in conformation, and only exceptionally good sires can bring about further improvement. This is especially so if the boars used in grading up successive generations are derived from the same strain within a breed.

After some experience, the commercial producer who has successfully handled grade animals may add a few purebreds to the herd and gradually build into the latter, provided that his experience and his market for seed stock justifies this type of production.

Crossbreeding

Crossbreeding is the mating of two animals which are members of different breeds. In a broad sense, crossbreeding also includes the mating of purebred sires of one breed with high grade females of another breed.

Today, there is renewed interest in crossbreeding swine, and increased research is underway on the subject. Crossbreeding is being used by swine producers to (1) increase productivity over straightbreds, because of the resulting hybrid vigor or heterosis, just as is being done by commercial corn and poultry producers; (2) produce commercial hogs with a desired combination of traits not available in any one breed; and (3) produce foundation stock for developing new breeds.

Perhaps in the final analysis all would agree that *any merits that crossbreeding may possess are and will continue to be based on improved "seed stock."* Certainly, from a genetic standpoint,

it should be noted that crossbred animals generally possess greater heterozygosity than outcross animals—with the added virtue of hybrid vigor. It may also be added that, as in outcrossing, the recessive and undesirable genes are more apt to remain hidden in the crossbred animal.

On purely theoretical grounds, it would appear that crossbreeding should result in some increase in vigor because the desirable genes from both breeds would be combined and the undesirable genes from each would tend to be overshadowed as recessives.

Crossbreeding is one of the three tools through which animal improvement may be brought about; the other two are selection and inbreeding. Genetically speaking, crossbreeding promotes the pairing of unlike genes by mating of animals that belong to different species (the horse and the ass cross produces mules or hinnys), to different breeds (a Duroc x Poland China cross), or to different families (crossing two families within a breed).

Crossbreeding has been more widely applied in swine than in any other class of livestock, with the possible exception of sheep. Yet no system of breeding has been the object of greater controversy or of more heated arguments. In the discussion that follows, the writer will attempt to explain the different methods and point out some of the advantages and disadvantages, with the hope that the reader may be better able to arrive at an independent evaluation of merits or demerits of the system.

It is important that crossbreeding be well planned—that there be a systematic approach. The four common crossbreeding systems followed in swine are:

1. **Crossing two different breeds.**—This consists of mating purebred boars to purebred or high-grade sows of another breed.

Where this system is held to first crosses only, the breeder is faced with the problem of sooner or later breeding the females back to a purebred boar of the same breed in order to secure replacement females. Under these conditions, he is prone to make little or no selection and to keep all of the females for replacement purposes. In such a program, it is usually found that the producer does well to maintain the quality of the female herd.

2. **Crisscrossing (a two-breed rotation).**—In which boars of two different breeds are used in alternate generations. Cross-

bred sows are retained each generation and bred to boars of the same breed as the grandsire on the dam's side. Figure 5-10 shows crisscrossing programs.

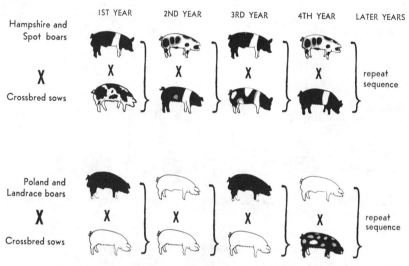

Fig. 5-10. Two examples of crisscrossing—two-breed rotation. (From: Iowa State University, Pamphlet 286, Fig. 4, p. 5.)

Under this system, both sows and pigs are crossbred after the first crossing. Boars are purebred and should be from a herd with proven high performance. Crossbred vigor usually results in an increase in litter size, livability, and growth rate.

3. **Triple crossing (a three-breed rotation).**—In which first cross gilts are mated to a boar of the third breed. The program is then continued through rotating the sires among the three breeds. Figure 5-11 shows triple crossing programs.

4. **Type-crossing.**—This system involves the use of boars of several breeds, but, at such intervals as necessary to keep away from lardiness, boars of either the bacon or the new Landrace crossbred strains are used. Both hybrid vigor and approved type are secured in this manner.

Although somewhat conflicting results have been reported, it seems reasonable to expect that crossbreds obtained through any of these methods will possess some advantage over purebreds in terms of rate and efficiency of gains.

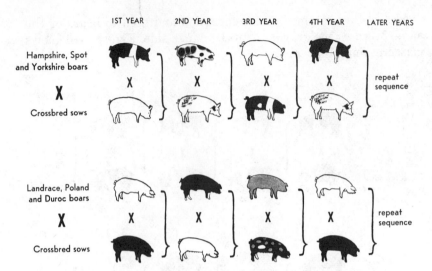

Fig. 5-11. Two examples of triple crossing—three-breed rotation. (From: Iowa State University, Pamphlet 286, Fig. 5, p. 6.)

The chief **reasons for crossbreeding** in swine, or in any other class of farm animals, are:

1. It brings about an increase in vigor, commonly known as hybrid vigor or heterosis. In this connection, the term vigor is broadly used to cover such things as rate of gain, economy of gain, fertility, and general strength.

2. It constitutes the most rapid system of breeding through which new genes may be introduced in order to secure improved qualities. As undesirable qualities are generally recessive, crossbreeding offers the best way in which to improve certain characteristics merely by hiding them with dominants.

3. It creates new breeds. It must be remembered that there is nothing sacred about present existing purebreds. They will stand or fall on their own merits. There is no need to create a new breed, however, unless the combination of characters that the breed possesses fulfills a specific need better than any existing breed.

4. It may be used to produce market animals. It must be realized, however, that the continued improvement in any class of farm animals will always rest on superior purebreds.

Crossbreeding does, however, possess certain **disadvantages,** some of which follow:

1. Generally speaking, a crossbred hog lacks the uniformity in color and general attractiveness of purebreds.

2. Desirable boars of the two or three breeds must be located and purchased.

3. Unless all the breeding is on a gilt basis, more than one boar must be maintained at all times.

4. If the young sows go to market after farrowing only one litter, little constructive selection can be practiced.

Before entering upon a crossbreeding program, the producer should become thoroughly acquainted with the advantages and disadvantages that may be expected therefrom. Also, crossbreeding should not be looked upon as a panacea for neglect of sound practices of breeding, feeding, management, and sanitation. Neither should it be assumed that the virtues of crossbreeding are sufficiently powerful to alleviate the necessity of selecting an outstanding boar rather than a scrub.

It should be understood that the disadvantages of crossing two breeds do not generally apply to the systems of crossbreeding between families or to the creation of a new breed when that seems desirable.

In summary, it can be said that crossbreeding has a place, particularly from the standpoint of increased vigor, growth rate, and efficiency of production; but pure breeding will continue to control the destiny of further improvement in any class of livestock and furnish the desired homozygosity and uniformity which many stockmen insist is a part of the art of breeding better livestock.

PRODUCTION TESTING SWINE

Production Testing embraces both (1) Performance Testing (sometimes called Individual Merit Testing) and (2) Progeny Testing. The distinction between and the relationship of these terms is set forth in the following definitions:

1. *Performance Testing (Individual Merit Testing)—is the practice of evaluating and selecting animals on the basis of their individual merit or performance.*

2. *Progeny Testing—is the practice of selecting animals on the basis of the merit of their progeny.*

3. *Production Testing—is a more inclusive term, including Performance Testing and/or Progeny Testing.*

Production Testing involves the taking of accurate records rather than casual observation. Also, in order to be most effective, the accompanying selection must be based on characteristics of economic importance (see Table 5-2), and an objective measure or yardstick (such as pounds, inches, etc.) should be placed upon each of the traits to be measured. Finally, those breeding animals that fail to meet the high standards set forth must be removed from the herd promptly and unflinchingly.

In comparison with that of chickens, production testing of swine is slow, and, like most investigational work with large animals, it is likely to be expensive. Even so, in realization that such testing is absolutely necessary if maximum improvement is to be made, the progressive purebred swine breeder will wish to make a start.

Table 5-2 lists the economically important characters in swine. That swine show variations in these characteristics is generally recognized. The problem is to measure these differences

Fig. 5-12. Production testing facilities for litters on a purebred establishment. Each litter is on test from weaning to 200 pounds. The owner obtains (1) for each pig a daily grain record and a probed backfat reading and (2) for each litter the feed consumed. (Courtesy, Harold Boucher, Executive Secretary, Hampshire Swine Registry)

from the standpoint of discovering the most desirable genes and then increasing their concentration, and, at the same time, to purge the herd of the less desirable characters.

Certainly, from the ultimate experimental standpoint, the pigs should be individually weighed at weaning and approximately at marketing time (112- or 154-day weights are preferred by some), and feed efficiency records should be kept by litters. If litter feed records are impractical, as may be the case under farm conditions, at least the weight records should be obtained.

Body-type scores—based on the demands and prices of a *discriminating* market as projected into the future—had best be

Fig. 5-13. Measuring backfat on a boar by use of the electronic lean meter. The meter records the passage of a current through fat tissue (a poor conductor) until it reaches the lean (a good conductor). The dial translates the conductivity measurement into inches of fat through which the current passed. (Courtesy, University of Connecticut)

TABLE 5-2

ECONOMICALLY IMPORTANT CHARACTERS OF SWINE, AND THEIR HERITABILITY[1]

Economically Important Characters	Estimated Heritability	Comments
	(average %)	
Performance characters:		Sow production traits are of low heritability; hence, improvement of these traits by selection is low.
No. pigs farrowed	15	On the average, a sow will have consumed a total of ¾ to 1 ton of feed during the period between breeding and the date her litter is weaned. Thus, if this quantity of feed must be charged against a litter of 4 or 5 pigs, the chance of eventual profit is small.
Birth weight of pigs	5	Very light pigs usually lack vigor.
No. pigs weaned	15	Although greatly influenced by herdsmanship, litter survival to weaning is a measure of the mothering ability of the sow.
Weight of litter at weaning	15	Litter weight at weaning is important, for it has been shown that the pigs that are the heaviest at weaning time reach market weight more quickly. Also, litter weight at weaning is a reflection of the fertility of the sow, her mothering and milking ability, the vigor and growing ability of the pigs, and the general over-all health of the litter.
Weight of pigs at 5 months	23	Weight for age is indicative of both rate of gain and feed efficiency.
Daily rate of gain from weaning to (1) 154 days or (2) 200 lbs.	30	Daily rate of gain from weaning to marketing is important because: (1) it is highly correlated with efficiency of gain and (2) it makes for a shorter time in reaching market weight and condition, thus effecting a saving in labor, making less exposure to risk and disease, and allowing for more rapid turnover in capital. Rate of gain and lardiness may be correlated to some degree; thus, one should not let this be the only factor upon which selection is based.
Feed efficiency from weaning to (1) 154 days or (2) 200 lbs.	30	Where convenient, accurate feed records should be kept, for the most profitable animals generally require less feed to make 100 pounds of gain. Individual feeding is expensive, and probably not justified except for a few promising herd boar prospects. If individual feed efficiency cannot be obtained, the next best thing is to obtain litter records or records for four pigs per litter.

(Continued)

Footnote on last page of table.

TABLE 5-2 (Continued)

Economically Important Characters	Estimated Heritability	Comments
	(Average %)	
Items of conformation:		
Length of body	60	Conformation is important if it reflects productive efficiency and carcass quality.
Length of leg	65	
No. of nipples	60	
Conformation score	27	This heritability figure is likely to be considerably higher in a herd of low quality.
Items of carcass:		
	60	Carcass characteristics are more highly hereditary than the other economically important traits. This is demonstrated by the rapid progress made by progressive breeders in developing meat type hogs.
Length	60	Carcass length is perhaps the most highly hereditary trait in hogs. This accounts for the rapid shifts that frequently have been observed; for example, in changing from chuffy to rangy hogs.
Backfat thickness	50	Backfat taken at three positions along the animal's back on prospective breeding animals may be measured with (1) a small calibrated rod or probe, (2) an electronic meter, or (3) ultrasonic equipment.
Loin eye area	48	Loin lean area is an indication of muscling or red meat.
Percent of fat cuts (based on carcass weight)	60	
Percent of lean cuts (based on carcass weight)	34	
Percent of ham (based on carcass weight)	59	

[r]These heritability estimates apply to within herd and within breed variations. Variations between breeds are much higher in heritability than the variations within.

Individual Sow Record

Breed _____

Date Farrowed _____

Bred by _____

Name and Registration No. _____

Identification _____ (ear notch, tattoo)

_____ (Name and address)

Sow's pedigree:

_____ (Sire)

_____ (Dam)

Record of litter of which the sow was a member:

No. in litter _____ No. of pigs weaned _____

Weaning wt. at _____ days of age:

_____ (fill in)

Her own wt. _____ Av. wt. of litter _____

Litter mate carcass record, if any:

No. carcasses _____ ; Av. back fat _____ (in.) ; loin eye _____ (sq. in.) ; length _____ (in.)

Number of teats _____

Fig. 5-14a. Individual Sow Record. (See next page for lower half of form.)

Production Record of Sow

	1	2	3	4	5	6	7	8
Litter No.								
Sire								
No. services								
Farrowing data:								
Date								
Temperament of sow:								
(Gentle; nervous; cross)								
No. pigs born:								
Alive								
Dead								
Mummies								
Total								
Av. birth weight								
No. functioning teats								
Weaning data:								
Age								
No. Weaned								
Av. weaning wt.								
Offspring saved for breeding:								
No. gilts								
No. boars								

DISPOSAL OF SOW

Reasons.

(Name and address)

Date

Sold to

Price $

Litter Record

Breed _____

Litter No. _____ (notch, tattoo)

Data on Dam:

Pedigree: _____ (Sire)

{ (name, reg. no., and ear notch) } _____ (Dam)

Birth date _____
(date and year)

Litter mate carcass data, if any:

No. carcasses _____ ; Av. back fat _____ (in.) ; loin eye _____ (sq. in.) ; length _____ (in.)

Sow's _____ Litter.
(1st, 2nd, etc.)

Data on Sire:

Pedigree: _____ (Sire)

{ (name, reg. no., and ear notch) } _____ (Dam)

Birth date _____

Litter mate carcass data, if any:

No. carcasses _____ ; Av. back fat _____ (in.) ; loin eye _____ (sq. in.) ; length _____ (in.)

Health Services:

Date cholera vaccinated _____
Date erysipelas vaccinated _____
Date wormed _____
Other, including iron pills or shots (list) _____
_____
_____

Date of birth _____

No. pigs born:

Alive _____
Dead _____
Mummies _____

Total _____

No. pigs weaned _____

Fig. 5-14b. Litter Record. (See next page for lower half of form.)

Individual Pig Record

Pig's No.	Sex	No. Teats	Birth Wt.	Off Color Markings	Defects & Abnormalities	Weaning Wt. ___ days (fill in)	Date Castrated	Date & Cause of Death	Disposal Date & To Whom	Remarks

taken at a standard age,[6] being evaluated in terms of either a numerical score or a letter. It is important that all animals be evaluated and that their scores be made a part of the permanent record. Consistently good production is to be desired. It should be realized that it is all too easy for a breeder to remember the good individuals produced by a given sow or boar and to forget those which are mediocre or culls.

Finally, it should be recognized that swine are raised primarily for profit, and profit is dependent upon efficiency of production and market price. Fortunately, the factors making for efficiency of production—including litter size and survival, growth rate, and feed efficiency—do not change with type fads. For this reason, emphasis should be placed on proper balance of the production factors. It might be added that type changes, quite likely, would not be so radical as in the past if they were guided by market demands based on carcass values. These facts show clearly enough that Production Testing will lend stability to swine breeding operations, from the standpoint of both efficiency of production and type.

A prerequisite for any production data is that each animal be positively identified—by means of ear notches. For purebred breeders, who must use a system of animal identification anyway, this does not constitute an additional detail. But the taking of weights and grades does require additional time and labor—an expenditure which is highly worth while, however.

In order not to be burdensome, the record forms should be relatively simple. Figure 5-14a is an Individual Sow Record, designed for use in recording the lifetime production record of one sow; whereas Fig. 5-14b is a Litter Record form for use in recording detailed information on one litter.

Information on the productivity of *close relatives* (the sire and the dam and the brothers and sisters) can supplement that on the animal itself and thus be a distinct aid in selection. The production records of more distant relatives are of little significance, because individually, due to the sampling nature of inheritance, they contribute only a few genes to an animal many generations removed.

A good plan in progeny testing boars consists of retaining

---

[6] The author prefers that the type or conformation score be taken at 154 days of age.

and mating one or more boar pigs—the numbers depending upon the size of the herd—to a limited number of females during their first season of breeding. The progeny are then tested and evaluated, and only those boars that prove to be best on the basis of their progeny are retained for further breeding purposes. If boar pigs are each mated to 6 or 8 sows, pigs should be born 114 days later, and the progeny can be tested. Thus, with good fortune, it is possible to have progeny data on a boar when he is approximately twelve months of age. With dairy bulls, whose daughters must be in lactation in order to make the test, it is not possible to make an evaluation until the animal is six to seven years of age.

Animals too young to progeny test may be evaluated by Performance Testing.

How to Use Herd Records in Selection

Herd records have little value unless they are intelligently used in culling operations and in deciding upon replacements. Also, most stockmen can and should use production records for purposes of estimating the rate of progress and for determining the relative emphasis to place on each character.

APPRAISING PERCENT OF CHANGES IN CHARACTERS DUE TO (1) HEREDITY, AND (2) ENVIRONMENT

Swine producers are well aware that there are differences in litter size, in weaning weight, in body type, etc. If those animals which excel in the desired traits would, in turn, transmit without loss these same improved qualities to their offspring, progress would be simple and rapid. Unfortunately, this is not the case. Such economically important characters are greatly affected by environment (by feeding, care, management, etc.). Thus, only part of the apparent improvement in certain animals is hereditary, and can be transmitted on to the next generation.

As would be expected, improvements due to environment are not inherited. This means that if most of the improvement in an economically important character is due to an improved environment, the heritability of that character will be low and little progress can be made through selection. On the other hand, if the character is highly heritable, marked progress can be made through selection. Thus, color of hair in swine is a highly heri-

table character, for environment appears to have little or no part in determining it. On the other hand, such a character as weight per pig at weaning is of low heritability because, for the most part, it is affected by environment (by the nursing ability of the sow).

There is need, therefore, to know the approximate amount or percentage of change in each economically important character which is due to heredity and the amount which is due to environment. Table 5-2 gives this information for swine in terms of the approximate percentage heritability of each of the economically important characters. The heritability figures given therein are averages based on large numbers; thus some variations from these may be expected in individual herds. Even though the heritability of many of the economically important characters listed in Table 5-2 is disappointingly small, it is gratifying to know that much of it is cumulative and permanent.

ESTIMATING RATE OF PROGRESS

For purposes of illustrating the way in which the heritability figures in Table 5-2 may be used in practical breeding operations, the following example is given:

In a certain herd of swine, the litters in a given year average 7 pigs each, with a range of 4 to 15 pigs. There are available sufficient of the larger litters (averaging 12 pigs) from which to select replacement breeding stock. What amount of this larger litter size (5 pigs above the average) is likely to be transmitted to the offspring of these pigs?

Step by step, the answer to this question is secured as follows:

1. $12 - 7 = 5$ pigs, the number by which the selected litter size exceeds the average from which they arose.

2. By referring to Table 5-2, it is found that number of pigs farrowed is 15% heritable. This means that 15% of the 5 pigs can be expected to be due to the superior heredity of the stock saved as breeders, and that the other 85% is due to environment (feed, care, management, etc.).

3. $5 \times 15\% = 0.75$ pig; which means that for litter size the stock saved for the breeding herd is 0.75 pig per litter superior, genetically, to the stock from which it was selected.

4. $7 + 0.75 = 7.75$ pigs per litter; which is the expected performance of the next generation.

It is to be emphasized that the 7.75 pigs per litter is merely the expected performance. The actual outcome may be altered by environment (feed, care, management, etc.) and by chance. Also, it should be recognized that where the heritability of a character is lower less progress can be made. The latter point explains why the degree to which a character is heritable has a very definite influence on the effectiveness of mass selection.

Using the heritability figures given in Table 5-2, and assuming certain herd records, the progress to be expected from one generation of selection in a given herd of swine might appear somewhat as summarized in Table 5-3. Naturally, the same procedure can be applied to each of the traits listed in Table 5-2.

APPRAISING FACTORS INFLUENCING RATE OF PROGRESS

Swine producers need to be informed relative to the factors which influence the rate of progress that can be made through selection. They are:

1. **The heritability of the character.**—When heritability is high, much of that which is selected for will appear in the next generation, and marked improvement will be evident.

2. **The number of characters selected for at the same time.** —The greater the number of characters selected for at the same time, the slower the progress in each. In other words, greater progress can be attained in one character if it alone is selected for. For example, if selection of equal intensity is practiced for 4 independent traits, the progress in any one will be only one-half of that which would occur if only one trait were considered; whereas selection for 9 traits will reduce the progress in any one to one-third. This emphasizes the importance of limiting the traits in selection to those which have greatest importance as determined by economic value and heritability. At the same time, it is recognized that it is rarely possible to select for one trait only, and that income is usually dependent upon several traits.

3. **The amount of heritable variation measured in such specific units as pounds, inches, numbers, etc.**—If the amount of heritable variation—measured in such specific units as pounds, inches, or numbers—is small, the animals selected cannot vary

TABLE 5-3

ESTIMATING RATE OF PROGRESS IN SWINE

Economically Important Characters	Average of Herd	Selected Individuals for Replacements	Average Selection Advantage	Heritability Percent	Expected Performance Next Generation
1. No. pigs farrowed	7	12	5	15	7.75
2. No. pigs weaned	6	10	4	15	6.6
3. Weight of litter at weaning	180	400	220	15	213
4. Daily rate of gain from weaning to marketing	1.2	1.6	0.4	30	1.32
5. Feed efficiency from weaning to marketing	450	375	75	30	427.5
6. Conformation score[1]	3	7	4	27	4.08

[1]The type grades used herein are as follows: Excellent = 9, Good = 7, Medium = 5, Fair = 3, and Inferior = 0. Naturally, the principle herewith illustrated may be applied to any measurable system of grading.

much above the average of the entire herd, and progress will be slow. For example, there is much less spread, in pounds, in the birth weights of pigs than in the 154-day weights (usually there is less than 2 pounds spread in weights at birth, whereas a spread of 30 to 40 pounds is common at 154 days of age). Therefore, more marked progress in selection can be made in the older weights than in birth weights of pigs, when measurements at each stage are in pounds.

4. **The accuracy of records and adherence to an ideal.**—It is a well established fact that a breeder who maintains accurate records and selects consistently toward a certain ideal or goal can make more rapid progress than one whose records are inaccurate and whose ideals change with fads and fancies.

5. **The number of available animals.**—The greater the number of animals available from which to select, the greater the progress that can be made. In other words, for maximum progress, enough animals must be born and raised to permit rigid culling. For this reason, more rapid progress can be made with swine than with animals that have only one offspring, and more rapid progress can be made when a herd is either being maintained at the same numbers or reduced than when it is being increased in size.

6. **The age at which selection is made.**—Progress is more rapid if selection is practiced at an early age. This is so because more of the productive life is ahead of the animal, and the opportunity for gain is then greatest.

7. **The length of generation.**—Shorter generation lengths will result in greater progress per year, provided the same proportion of animals is retained after selection.

Usually it is possible to reduce the length of the generation of sires, but it is not considered practical to reduce materially the length of the generation of females. Thus, if progress is being made, the best young males should be superior to their sires. Then the advantage of this superiority can be gained by changing to new generations as quickly as possible. To this end, it is recommended that the breeder change to younger sires whenever their records equal or excel those of the older sires. In considering this procedure, it should be recognized, however, that it is very difficult to compare records made in different years or at different ages.

8. The calibre of the sires.—Since a much smaller proportion of males than of females is normally saved for replacements, it follows that selection among the males can be more rigorous and that most of the genetic progress in a herd will be made from selection of males. Thus, if 2 percent of the males and 50 percent of the females in a given herd become parents, then about 75 percent of the hereditary gain from selection will result from the selection of males and 25 percent from the selection of females, provided their generation lengths are equal. If the generation lengths of males are shorter than the generation lengths of females, the proportion of hereditary gain due to the selection of males will be even greater.

DETERMINING RELATIVE EMPHASIS TO PLACE ON EACH CHARACTER

A replacement animal seldom excels in all of the economically important characters. The stockman must decide, therefore, how much importance shall be given to each factor. Thus, the swine producer will have to decide how much emphasis shall be placed on litter size, litter survival, efficiency of feed utilization, etc.

Perhaps the relative emphasis to place on each character should vary according to the circumstances. Under certain conditions, some characters may even be ignored. Among the factors which determine the emphasis to place on each character are the following:

1. The economic importance of the character to the producer.—Table 5-2 lists the economically important characters in swine, and summarizes (see comments column) their importance to the producer.

By economic importance is meant their dollars and cents value. Thus, those characters which have the greatest effect on profits should receive the most attention.

2. The heritability of the character.—It stands to reason that the more highly heritable characters should receive higher priority than those which are less heritable, for more progress can be made thereby.

3. The amount of variation in each character.—Obviously, if all animals were exactly alike in a given character, there could

be no selection for that character. Likewise, if the amount of variation in a given character is small, the selected animals cannot be very much above the average of the entire herd, and progress will be slow.

4. **The level of performance already attained.**—If a herd has reached a satisfactory level of performance for a certain character, there is not much need for further selection for that character.

SYSTEMS OF SELECTION

Finally, the swine producer needs to follow a system of selection which will result in maximum total progress over a period of several years or animal generations. The three common systems are:

1. **Tandem selection.**—This refers to that system in which there is selection for only one trait at a time until the desired improvement in that particular trait is reached, following which selection is made for another trait, etc. This system makes it possible to make rapid improvement in the trait for which selection is being practiced, but it has two major disadvantages: (a) usually it is not possible to select for one trait only, and (b) generally income is dependent on several traits.

Tandem selection is recommended only in those rare herds where one character only is primarily in need of improvement; for example, where a certain herd of swine needs improving primarily in litter size.

2. **Establishing minimum standards for each character, and selecting simultaneously but independently for each character.** —This system, in which several of the most important characters are selected for simultaneously, is without doubt the most common system of selection. It involves establishing minimum standards for each character and culling animals which fall below these standards. For example, it might be decided to cull all pigs in litters of less than 7 pigs, or weighing less than 40 pounds at weaning, or grading *five* or less. Of course, the minimum standards may have to vary from year to year if environmental factors change markedly (for example, if pigs average light at weaning time due to a disease).

The chief weakness of this system is that an individual

may be culled because of being faulty in one character only, even though he is well nigh ideal otherwise.

3. **Selection index.**—Selection indexes combine all important traits into one overall value or index. Theoretically, a selection index provides a more desirable way in which to select for several traits than either (a) the tandem method or (b) the method of establishing minimum standards for each character and selecting simultaneously but independently for each character.

Selection indexes are designed to accomplish the following:
a. To give emphasis to the different traits in keeping with their relative importance.
b. To balance the strong points against the weak points of each animal.
c. To obtain an over-all total score for each animal, following which all animals can be ranked from best to poorest.
d. To assure a constant and objective degree of emphasis on each trait being considered, without any shifting of ideals from year to year.
e. To provide a convenient way in which to correct for environmental effects, such as age of dam, etc.

Despite their acknowledged virtues, selection indexes are not perfect. Among their weaknesses are the following:
f. Practical indexes are not available for all classes of animals.
g. Their use may result in covering up or masking certain bad faults or defects.
h. They do not allow for year to year differences.

Production Testing by Swine Record Associations

Several of the swine registry associations of the United States have a system of production testing known as Production Registry (PR). The rules governing these registries are very similar in the breeds and generally include the following:

1. The registries are available only to registered purebreds not possessing any outstanding faults.

2. Litters must be ear-notched at farrowing.

3. Production registry (PR) litters consist of eight (some specify a minimum of 9 pigs for a sow) or more live pigs far-

rowed, with minimum litter weights to be met. There is a good deal of variation between breed registry associations as to when litter weights are taken; some take them at birth, whereas others take them at 21-, 35-, or 56-days of age. Weights must be witnessed by an agricultural college representative, extension worker, cow tester, vocational agricultural instructor, veterinarian, or other person acceptable to the registry office.

4. To qualify, a sow must produce a PR litter; some registry associations require that a sow produce two PR litters in order to qualify.

5. A boar becomes a "PR Boar" when he has sired a specified number of PR qualifying litters (anywhere from 5 to 15, depending on the registry association) ; or a specified number of PR daughters (anywhere from 2 to 10, depending on the registry association) ; or a combination of the two.

6. Breed associations urge testing of whole herds of sows rather than a selected few.

Thus, in addition to pedigreeing, protecting, and promoting, the swine record associations of America are now adding proving to the list of services rendered. Swine Production Testing as now followed in this country is relatively simple, and, where it has been tried, the breeders are convinced of its merits. It merely involves marking the pigs in each litter—a practice followed by purebred breeders, anyway—then weighing them at a specified age and recording the weights. If the pigs in a litter do not measure up to a certain standard, they and their parents should be discarded from the breeding herd. In a purebred herd, the pigs must also measure up to the standards of the breed. One hundred and fifty-four-day weights plus records of feed consumption would be desirable, but these are more difficult to obtain.

The purpose of Production Registry in swine is to emphasize practical utility points and to enable breeders to coordinate outstanding individuality (type) with equally outstanding production ability. In addition to providing a basis for more intelligent selection of breeding stock, such production records furnish valuable information for advertising purposes.

MEAT CERTIFICATION PROGRAM OF
SWINE RECORD ASSOCIATIONS

The National Association of Swine Records adopted a uni-

form program relative to *Certified Meat Hogs*. This program adds carcass evaluation to Production Registry.

A *Certified Litter* must meet the following standards in order to qualify:

1. It must first qualify for Production Registry in its own breed registry association.

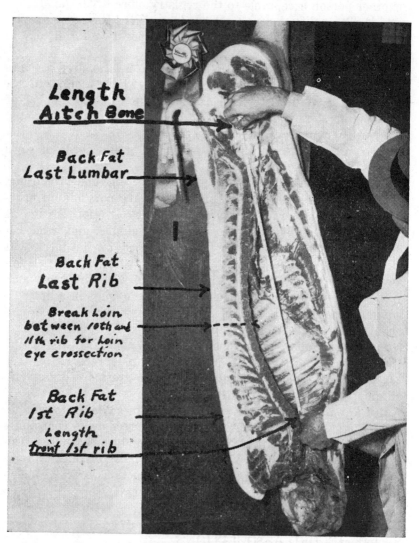

Fig. 5-15. Where and how to measure for meat certification. (Courtesy, The Chester White Swine Record Association)

2. At approximately 175 days of age and a maximum weight of 220 pounds (when weighed off the truck for slaughter), two gilts or barrows from the litter must be delivered to a cooperating slaughter station. At the time of delivery, they will be individually tattooed.

A weight of 200 pounds at 175 days is required; but equivalent 175-day weights may be calculated by adding 2 pounds for each day under 175 days, or by deducting 2 pounds for each day over 175 days.

3. The carcass from these two pigs must meet the following standards, which the slaughtering station must report officially to the registry association of the breed represented.[7]

Weight	Loin Area (minimum)	Length [1] (minimum)	Fat-back Thickness [2] (maximum)
(lbs.)	(sq. in.)	(in.)	(in.)
220 or less	4.0	29.0	1.6

[1]Some breeds have a minimum length of 0.5 inch less than given.
[2]Some breeds have a maximum fat-back thickness of 0.1 inch less than given.

4. The carcass measurements are obtained as follows:

   a. The loin is broken at the tenth rib, and the loin area is calculated by means of a planimeter from tracings of loin eye made on parchment paper.

   b. The carcass length is calculated from the front of the first rib, where it joins the vertebra, to the front of the aitch bone (see Fig. 5-15).

   c. The fat back is an average of three measurements taken opposite (1) the first rib, (2) the last rib, and (3) the last lumbar vertebra. Actual fat back thickness is measured to the outside of the skin and at a right angle to the back (see Fig. 5-15).

A Certified Boar is one that has sired five Certified Litters; each litter of which is out of a different sow, not more than two of which are full sisters or dam and daughter.

A Certified Mating is the repeat mating of a boar and sow that have produced a Certified Litter.

---

[7] Some breed registry associations give additional and special recognition for meeting higher standards.

The Danish System of Production Testing Swine

Without doubt, the outstanding example of production testing work with meat animals is the swine breeding work of Denmark. This work was started in 1907, and since then, it has
operated continuously, except for three years during World War
I when shortage of feed forced the suspension of all testing. In
the Danish system, the registration of swine is supervised by a
national committee in charge of swine breeding. Only animals
bred at organized swine-breeding centers are eligible for registration, because these are the farms where the breeders have
complied with certain regulations, including sending each year to
the testing stations half as many litters as they have sows in
their herd. At the testing stations, these test litters of four pigs
each are fed under standard conditions, and the rates and econ-
omies of gain are recorded. When each pig reaches a weight of

Fig. 5-16. Interior view of the world's first swine production testing station established in 1907 at Elsesminde, Denmark. In Denmark four pigs
of each litter are tested under standard conditions, with evaluation based on
(1) rate and economy of gain and (2) carcass quality at two hundred
pounds weight. The most outstanding example in the world of production
testing meat animals is, without doubt, the swine breeding work of Denmark. (Courtesy, Danish Embassy)

two hundred pounds, it is slaughtered at a nearby bacon factory, and its dressing percentage and the type, conformation, and quality of its carcass are measured and scored. Twice annually, each breeding center is inspected by a committee that scores it for: (1) management and general appearance of the farm, (2) conformation of breeding animals, (3) fertility of the breeding animals, (4) efficiency in the use of feed by the test pigs from this center, and (5) slaughter quality of the test pigs. The advance made in the carcass qualities (body length, belly and backfat thickness), plus efficiency of feed utilization, have been phenomenal. Swine selection in Denmark is strictly based on utility considerations.

PART II—SOME PHYSIOLOGICAL ASPECTS OF REPRODUCTION IN SWINE

Swine producers have many reproductive problems, a reduction of which calls for a full understanding of reproductive physiology and the application of scientific practices therein. In fact, it may be said that reproduction is the first and most important requisite of swine breeding, for if animals fail to reproduce the breeder is soon out of business.

Many outstanding individuals, and even whole families, are disappointments because they are either sterile or reproduce poorly. Twenty percent of all sows fail to breed; from 5 to 30 percent of the fertilized eggs do not develop normally, resulting in embryonic mortality or death; and from 10 to 30 percent of the live pigs farrowed die within the first seven to ten days of life. The subject of physiology of reproduction is, therefore, of great importance.

THE REPRODUCTIVE ORGANS OF THE BOAR

The boar's functions in reproduction are: (1) to produce the male reproductive cells, the *sperm* or *spermatozoa,* and (2) to introduce sperm into the female reproductive tract at the proper time. In order that these functions may be fulfilled, swine breeders should have a clear understanding of the anatomy of the reproductive system of the boar and of the functions of each of its parts. Figure 5-18 is a schematic drawing of the reproductive organs of the boar. A description of each part follows:

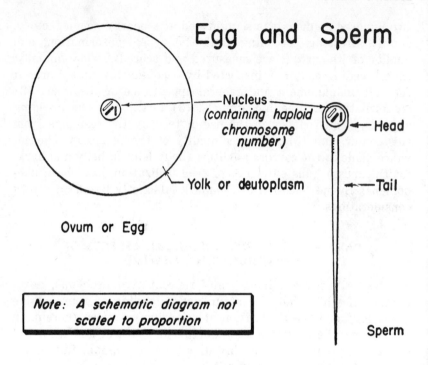

Fig. 5-17. Egg and sperm. The parent germ cells, the egg from the female and the sperm from the male, unite and transmit to the offspring all the characters that it will inherit. (Drawing by R. F. Johnson)

1. **Testicles.**—The primary function of the testicles is to produce sperm. They are enclosed in the *scrotum,* a diverticulum of the abdomen.

The chief function of the scrotum is thermoregulatory; to maintain the testicles at temperatures several degrees lower than that of the body proper.

Cryptorchids are males one or both of whose testicles have not descended to the scrotum. The undescended testicle(s) is usually sterile because of the high temperature in the abdomen.

The testicles communicate through the inguinal canal with the pelvic cavity, where accessory organs and glands are located. A weakness of the inguinal canal, which is heritable in swine, sometimes allows part of the vicera to pass out into the scrotum —a condition called *scrotal hernia.*

2. **Seminiferous tubule.**—This is the germinal portion of the testis, in which are situated the spermatogonia (sperm-pro-

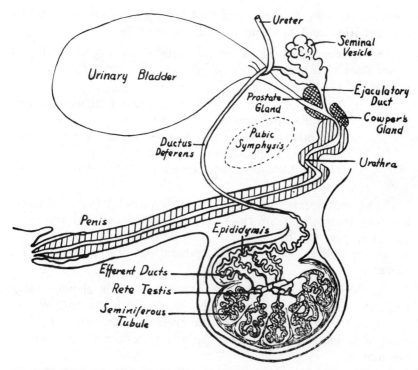

Fig. 5-18. Diagram of the reproductive organs of the boar. The testes and their ducts up to the entrance of the ejaculatory ducts into the urethra are paired, but, for simplicity, only those on the left side have been reproduced. (Drawing by Steve Allured)

ducing cells). If laid end to end, it has been estimated that the seminiferous tubules of one testicle of the boar would be nearly two miles long.

Around and between the seminiferous tubules are the *interstitial cells,* which produce the male sex hormone, *androgen* or *testosterone.* Androgen is necessary for the mature development and continued function of the reproductive organs, for the development of the male secondary sexual characteristics, and for sexual drive.

3. **Rete testis.**—The rete testis is formed from the union of several seminiferous tubules.

4. **Efferent ducts (Ductuli efferentes).**—The efferent ducts carry the sperm cells from the rete testis to the head of the

epididymis. Also, it is thought that their secretions are vital to the nutrition and ripening of the sperm cells.

5. **Epididymis.**—The efferent ducts of each testis unite into one duct, thus forming the epididymis. This greatly coiled tube consists of three parts:

    a. **The head.**—Which includes several tubules that are grouped into lobules.

    b. **The body.**—The part of the epididymis which passes down along the sides of the testis.

    c. **The tail.**—The part located at the bottom of the testis.

The epididymis has four functions; namely, (a) as a passage way for sperm from the seminiferous tubules, (b) the storage of sperm, (c) the secretion of a fluid which probably nourishes the sperm, and (d) the maturation or ripening of the sperm.

6. **Vas deferens (Ductus deferens).**—This slender tube, which is lined with ciliated cells, leads from the tail of the epididymis to the pelvic part of the urethra in the penis. Its primary function is to move sperm into the urethra at the time of ejaculation.

The vas deferens—together with the longitudinal strands of smooth muscle, blood vessels, and nerves; all encased in a fibrous sheath—make up the spermatic cord (two of them) which pass up through an opening in the abdominal wall, the inguinal canal, into the pelvic cavity.

The cutting or closing off of the ductus deferens, known as *vasectomy,* is the most usual operation performed to produce sterility, where sterility without castration is desired.

7. **Seminal vesicle (or vesiculae seminales).**—This pair of glands flanks the vas deferens near its point of termination. They are the largest of the accessory glands of reproduction in the male, and are located in the pelvic cavity.

The seminal vesicle secretes a fluid which provides a medium of transport of the spermatozoa. It is not a store house for sperm, some opinions to the contrary.

8. **Prostate gland.**—This gland is located at the neck of the bladder, surrounding or nearly surrounding the urethra and ventral to the rectum. The secretion of the prostate gland is thick

and rich in proteins and salts. It is alkaline, and it has a characteristic odor.

It cleanses the urethra prior to and during ejaculation, and provides bulk and a suitable medium for the transport of sperm.

9. **Cowper's gland (Bulbo-urethral gland).**—These two glands, which often reach a diameter of 1½ inches in the boar, are located on either side of the urethra in the pelvic region. They communicate with the urethra by means of a small duct.

It is thought that these glands produce an alkaline secretion for the purpose of neutralizing or cleansing the urethra prior to the passage of semen.

10. **Urethra.**—This is a long tube which extends from the bladder to the glans penis. The vas deferens and seminal vesicle open to the urethra close to its point of origin.

The urethra serves for the passage of both urine and semen.

11. **Penis.**—This is the boar's organ of copulation. It is composed essentially of erectile tissue, which, at the times of erection, becomes gorged with blood.

In total, the reproductive organs of the boar are designed to produce semen and to convey it to the female at the time of mating. The semen consists of two parts; namely (1) the sperm which are produced by the testes, and (2) the liquid portion, or semen plasma, which is secreted by the seminiferous tubules, the epididymis, the vas deferens, the seminal vesicles, the prostate, and the Cowper's glands. Actually, the sperm make up only a small portion of the ejaculate. On the average, at the time of each service, a boar ejaculates 240 to 250 milliliters (about 8 ounces), with a range from less than 100 to well over 500 milliliters; and the average ejaculate contains 40 to 45 billion normal, live sperm.

THE REPRODUCTIVE ORGANS OF THE SOW

The sow's functions in reproduction are: (1) to produce the female reproductive cells, the *eggs* or *ova*, (2) to develop the new individual, the *embryo*, in the uterus, (3) to expel the fully developed young at the time of *birth* or *parturition*, and (4) to produce milk for the nourishment of the young. Actually, the part played by the sow in the generative process is much more complicated than that of the boar. It is imperative, therefore,

that modern swine producers have a full understanding of the anatomy of the reproductive organs of the sow and the functions of each part. Figure 5-19 shows the reproductive organs of the sow, and a description of each part follows:

1. **Ovaries.**—The two irregular-shaped ovaries of the sow are suspended in the abdominal cavity near the backbone and just in front of the pelvis.

The ovaries have three functions: (a) to produce the female reproductive cells, the *eggs* or *ova*, (b) to secrete the female sex hormone, *estrogen,* and (c) to form the *corpora lutea.* The ovaries may alternate somewhat irregularly in the performance of these functions.

The ovaries differ from the testes in that eggs are produced in very limited numbers (10 to 20 in the sow) and at intervals, during or shortly after heat. Each miniature egg is contained in

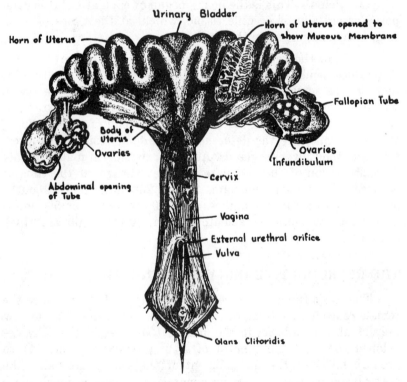

Fig. 5-19. The reproductive organs of the sow. (Drawing by Steve Allured)

a sac, called *Graafian follicle,* a large number of which are scattered throughout the ovary. Generally, the follicles remain in an unchanged state until the advent of puberty, at which time some of them begin to enlarge through an increase in the follicular liquid within. Toward the end of heat, the follicles (which at maturity measure about one-third of an inch in diameter) rupture and discharge the eggs, which process is known as *ovulation.* As soon as the eggs are released the corpora lutea make their appearance. The corpora lutea secrete a hormone called *progesterone,* which (a) acts on the uterus so that it implants and nourishes the embryo, (b) prevents other eggs from maturing and keeps the animal from coming in heat during pregnancy, (c) maintains the animal in a pregnant condition, and (d) assists the female hormone in the development of the mammary glands. If the eggs are not fertilized, however, the corpora lutea atrophy and allow new follicles to ripen and a new heat to appear. Occasionally, cystic ovaries develop, thus inducing temporary sterility. Actually, there are three different types of disturbed conditions which are commonly called cystic ovaries; namely (a) cystic follicles, (b) cystic corpus luteum, and (c) persistent corpus luteum. All three conditions prevent normal ovulation and constitute major causes of sterility in sows.

The egg-containing follicles also secrete into the blood the female sex hormone, *estrogen.* Estrogen is necessary for the development of the female reproductive system, for the mating behavior or *heat* of the female, for the development of the mammary glands, and for the development of the secondary sex characteristics, or femininity, in the sow.

From the standpoint of the practical hog breeder, the ripening of the first Graafian follicle in a gilt generally coincides with puberty, and this marks the beginning of reproduction.

2. **Fallopian tubes (or oviducts).**—These small, cilia-lined tubes or ducts lead from the ovaries to the horns of the uterus. They are about 10 inches long in the sow and the end of each tube nearest the ovary, called *infundibulum,* flares out like a funnel. They are not attached to the ovaries but lie so close to them that they seldom fail to catch the released eggs.

At ovulation, the eggs pass into the infundibulum where, within a few minutes, the ciliary movement within the tube, assisted by the muscular movements of the tube itself, carries

them down into the oviduct. If mating has taken place, the union of the sperm and eggs usually takes place in the upper third of the fallopian tube. Thence the fertilized eggs move into the uterine horn. All this movement from the ovary to the uterine horn takes place in 3 to 4 days.

3. **Uterus.**—The uterus is the muscular sac, connecting the fallopian tubes and the vagina, in which the fertilized eggs attach themselves and develop until expelled from the body of the sow at the time of parturition. The uterus consists of the two horns, the body, and the neck or cervix of the womb. In the sow, the horns are about 4 or 5 feet long, the body about 2 inches long, and the cervix about 6 inches long.

In swine, the fetal membranes that surround the developing embryo are in contact with the entire lining of the uterus; and there are no *buttons* or *cotyledons* as in the cow and ewe.

4. **Vagina.**—The vagina admits the penis of the boar at the time of service and receives the semen. At the time of birth, it expands and serves as the final passageway for the fetus.

5. **Vulva (or urogenital sinus).**—The vulva is the external opening of both the urinary and genital tracts. It is about three inches in length. During sexual excitement, the vulva of the sow becomes swollen, thus producing one of the signs of heat.

MATING

Mating is a prolonged process in swine, varying from 3 to 25 minutes, in which waves of high and low sperm concentration exist in the flow of the ejaculate. For this reason, it is important that copulation take place without disturbance.

An ejaculation consists of the following three phases:

1. The first, or pre-sperm phase, which lasts 1 to 5 minutes, consists of a watery fluid in which there are tapioca-like pellets but no sperm, and comprises 5 to 20 percent of the ejaculate.

2. The second, or sperm-containing phase, which lasts 2 to 5 minutes, consists of a whitish, uniform fluid which contains the sperm, and comprises 30 to 50 percent of the ejaculate.

3. The last phase, which lasts 3 to 8 minutes, contains very few sperm, helps form a gelatinous plug in the female tract, and comprises 40 to 60 percent of the total volume.

FERTILIZATION

It is believed that the eggs are usually liberated on the second day of heat. Unfortunately, there is no reliable way of predicting the length of heat nor the time of ovulation.

The sperm (or male germ cells) are deposited in the vagina and cervix at the time of service and from there ascend the female reproductive tract. Under favorable conditions, they meet the eggs, and one of them fertilizes each egg in the upper part of the oviduct near the ovary.

A series of delicate time relationships must be met, however, or the eggs will not be fertilized. The sperm cells live only twenty-four to forty-eight hours in the reproductive tract of the female, and it probably requires four to six hours for them to ascend the female reproductive tract. Moreover, the eggs are viable for an even shorter period of time; probably for not more than twenty-four hours after ovulation. For conception, therefore, breeding must take place at the right time.

As sows usually stay in heat from two to three days, perhaps the highest conception rate may be obtained by serving the sow early on the second day during the heat period. Sows that have a record of staying in heat three days should be bred on the afternoon of the second day.

NORMAL BREEDING HABITS OF SWINE

The pig lends itself very well to experimental study in confined conditions. It is reasonable to expect, therefore, that we should have a considerable store of knowledge relative to the normal breeding habits of swine, perhaps more than we have of any other class of farm animals.

Age of Puberty

The age of puberty in swine varies from four to seven months. This rather wide range is due to difference in breeds and lines, sex, and environment—especially nutrition. In general, boars do not reach puberty quite so early as gilts.

Age to Breed Gilts

Reasonably early breeding has the advantages of establish-

ing regular and reliable breeding habits and reducing the cost of the pigs at birth.

Gilts that are well developed may, as a general rule, be bred to farrow at twelve to fourteen months of age. It is to be emphasized, however, that this depends primarily upon development rather than age; thus, it is recommended that gilts weigh at least 225 pounds before breeding. Proper development is essential in order that animals may be able to withstand the strain of lactation, the demands of which are much more rigorous than gestation.

The breeding of show gilts is often delayed until after the show season. This practice frequently results in difficult conception and temporary, if not permanent, sterility. This is attributed to (1) the fatty tissue around the ovaries that prevents release of the eggs, or (2) the fat around the oviducts that "chokes" off the meeting of sperm and ova. Permanent sterility may result if fatty infiltration of the ovary tissue occurs and remains over a long period of time.

Heat Periods

The heat period—the time during which the sow will accept the boar—lasts from 1 to 5 days, with an average of 2 to 3 days. Older sows generally remain in heat longer than gilts.

Ovulation probably occurs on the second day of heat, although evidence on the latter point is not too conclusive. As in females of all species, sows bred approximately at the time of ovulation are more likely to conceive than if bred at any other time. The first mating of gilts should be on the first day of estrus, and the first mating of sows on the second day of estrus. In each case, a second service should follow the first by 24 hours. If not bred, the heat period normally recurs at intervals of eighteen to twenty-four days, with an average of twenty-one days.

The external signs of heat in the sow are restless activity, swelling or enlargement of and discharge from the vulva (although these signs are not always present), frequent mounting of other sows, frequent urination, and occasional loud grunting.

Gestation Period

The average gestation period of sows is 114 days, although extremes of 98 to 124 days have been reported.

Breeding After Farrowing

Sows will often come in heat during the first few days after farrowing, but they rarely conceive if bred at this time— for the reason that they fail to ovulate.

Following the early postfarrowing heat period, sows normally will not come in heat again until near the end of the suckling period. However, they may be brought into heat during the lactation period by removing the pigs for several consecutive nights. Some producers follow this practice and rebreed about the fifth week after farrowing. Nevertheless, it is common practice first to wean the litter and to let the animals have a few days rest before rebreeding. Normally, sows will come in heat 3 to 10 days, with an average of about 7 days after weaning.

When the pigs are weaned under two weeks of age, it is recommended that sows be bred on the second heat period after weaning. However, when the pigs are weaned at three or more weeks of age, it is generally satisfactory to breed on the first heat period following weaning.

The most natural breeding season for sows seems to be in the early summer and late autumn, although they will breed any time of the year.

FERTILITY AND PROLIFICACY IN SWINE

Under domestication and conditions of good care, a high degree of fertility is desired. The cost of carrying a litter of ten pigs to weaning time is little greater than the cost of producing a litter of only five or six. In other words, the maintenance costs on both the sow and the boar remain fairly constant. It must be remembered, however, that in the wild state high fertility may not have been characteristic of swine. Survival and natural selection were probably in the direction of smaller litters, but nature's plan has been reversed through planned matings and selection.

Low fertility in swine is most commonly attributed to hereditary and environmental factors. Maximum prolificacy depends upon having a large number of eggs shed at the time of estrus, upon adequate viable sperm present for fertilization at the proper time, and upon a minimum of fetal atrophy.

It is a well-known fact that some breeds and strains of swine

Fig. 5-20. Prolificacy in swine is much desired, for the cost of keeping a pregnant sow and of carrying a litter of ten or twelve pigs to weaning time is little greater than the cost of producing a litter of only five or six. (Courtesy, Maple Leaf Mills Ltd., Toronto, Ontario, Canada)

are much more prolific than others. We are told that litters of twelve are considered normal rather than exceptional among Chinese swine. Also, through selection, more prolific strains of swine can be developed. As shown in Table 5-2, however, the heritability of litter size is low. Yet, because such gains are cumulative, they are highly worthwhile.

The number of pigs produced increases with the age of the sow. Also it appears that flushing or conditioning of sows exerts an influence on the number of eggs shed. All in all, it appears that more can be accomplished through proper management and environment to increase litter size than can be done through selection.

Practical swine producers generally associate type with prolificacy. To substantiate their theory, they point out that the fat, chuffy hogs in vogue during the early part of the present century

were not prolific but were prone to farrow twins and triplets. Experimental work substantiates this opinion.

Even though many eggs may be shed and fertilized, the size of the litter may be affected materially by fetal atrophy, which ranges from 5 to 30 percent. Usually this condition is attributed to (1) hereditary factors, perhaps recessive lethals; (2) overcrowding resulting from a large number of pigs and a consequent limited uterine surface area available for the nourishment of the individual embryos; (3) nutritionally incomplete rations prior to and during gestation; (4) excessive fatness or a thin run-down condition; (5) diseases or parasites; or (6) accidents or injuries. Additional studies need to be made relative to the cause and prevention of fetal atrophy.

Litter size is affected little, if any, by the boar. In fact, research work indicates that fertilization in swine is very much an all or none phenomenon. Perhaps an exception exists in boars that are on the borderline of sterility, when insufficient viable sperm are present to fertilize the eggs. Certainly, the boar cannot affect the number of eggs shed and, therefore, cannot increase litter size. It has been observed that litter size may be slightly increased if two services are used instead of one. Also, it is recommended that, in advance of the regular breeding sea-

TABLE 5-4

ANALYSIS OF REASONS FOR SLAUGHTERING SOWS IN ENGLAND[1]

Reasons for Slaughter	Percent of Total
	(%)
Failure to breed	21.4
Piglet mortality	17.8
Old age	15.0
Low fertility	10.1
Disease	7.5
Milk failure and udder troubles	6.1
Uneven or unthrifty litters	4.6
Foot-and-mouth disease restrictions	3.2
Injury	2.6
Giving up pig breeding	2.6
Too fat or too big	2.1
Labor difficulties	2.0
Miscellaneous	5.0
Total	100.0

[1]Pomeroy, R. W., "Infertility and Neonatal Mortality in the Sow," *Journal of Agricultural Science*, Vol. 54, No. 1, 1960.

son, the boar be mated to a few market gilts; thereby providing for fresh viable sperm in the epididymis when the boar is placed in service in the breeding herd.

An English study revealed that infertility—failure to breed —is the chief reason given by producers for the disposal of sows (Table 5-4).

FLUSHING SOWS

The practice of feeding sows more liberally so that they gain in weight from 1 to 1½ pounds daily from one to two weeks before the opening of the breeding season until they are safely in pig is known as flushing. This is usually accomplished by increasing the concentrate ration by about 2 pounds per sow per day. Some of the beneficial effects attributed to this practice are: (1) more eggs are shed, and this results in larger litters; (2) the sows come in heat more promptly; and (3) conception is more certain.

If sows are already overfat, the best preparation for breeding consists of conditioning by providing plenty of exercise and access to a lush pasture, while decreasing the heavy grain ration.

THE BREEDING PROCEDURE; HAND-MATING; THE BREEDING CRATE

Hand-mating is more generally practiced in swine than with either cattle or sheep. In fact, it is almost the universal procedure in purebred swine herds, and many commercial producers follow the same practice.

When a mature, heavy boar is to be bred to gilts or when a boar pig is to be bred to big, rangy sows, the use of a breeding crate is recommended. Animals that have formed the habit of breeding without the crate may be rather obstinate in accepting the new method, or may refuse service altogether. Commercial swine producers usually use active, young boars; in many instances they allow the boar to run with the sows to be bred. Where field mating is practiced, two methods are recommended: (1) split the sow or gilt herd so as to have one boar per group, or (2) alternate boars in the sow or gilt herd—that is, use one boar or set of boars one day and another boar or set of boars the next day.

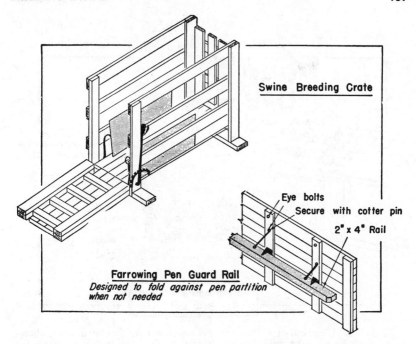

Fig. 5-21. Two handy pieces of swine equipment: the breeding crate (top), and the guard rail (bottom). (Drawing by R. F. Johnson)

CARE AND MANAGEMENT OF THE BOAR

Proper care and management of the herd boar is most essential for successful swine production. Too frequently the boar is looked upon as a necessary evil and is neglected. Under such conditions, he is usually confined to a small, filthy pen—a typical pigsty—exercise is discouraged; and the feeding practices are anything but intelligent.

Feed, Shelter, and Exercise

Outdoor exercise throughout the year is one of the first essentials in keeping the boar in a thrifty condition and virile. This may be accomplished by providing a well-fenced pasture. Even then, the herdsman may find it necessary to walk old boars or boars that are being fitted for the shows. In addition to the valuable exercise that is obtained in the pasture lot, green succulent pasture furnishes valuable nutrients for the herd boar. The amount of feed provided should be such as to keep the boar

Fig. 5-22. Diagram of a desirable arrangement for the herd boar; showing a good fence, a portable house, shade, water, and sufficient area for
pasture and exercise. (Drawing by R. F. Johnson)

in a thrifty, vigorous condition at all times. He should be neither
overfat nor in a thin, run-down condition. The concentrate allowance should be varied with the age, development, and temperament of the individual; breeding demands; roughage consumed,
etc. Feeding the boar is more fully covered in Chapter VI.

A satisfactory but inexpensive shelter should be provided
for the boar, and he should be allowed to run in and out at choice.

Boars of the same age or size can be run together during the
off-breeding season, but boars of different ages should not be
kept together.

Ranting

Some boars pace back and forth along the fence, often
chopping their jaws and slobbering. Such action is called ranting. Young boars that take to excessive ranting may go off feed,
become "shieldy," and fail to develop properly. Although this
condition will not affect their breeding ability, it is undesirable
from the standpoint of appearance. Isolation from other boars or
from the sow herd is usually an effective means of quieting such

boars. Should the boar remain off feed, placing a barrow or a bred sow in the pen with him will help to get him back on feed.

AGE AND SERVICE OF THE BOAR

The number of services allowed will vary with the age, development, temperament, health, breeding condition, distribution of services, and system of mating (hand-coupling or pasture breeding). No standard number of services can be recommended for any and all conditions. Yet the practices followed by good swine producers are not far different. Such practices are summarized in Table 5-5.

TABLE 5-5

HANDY BOAR MATING GUIDE

| Age | Number of Matings/Yr. | | Comments |
	Hand-mating	Pasture-mating	
8 to 12 months of age	24	12	Boar pigs should be limited to one service/day; older boars to two services/day.
Yearling or older	50	35-40	A boar should remain a vigorous and reliable breeder up to 6 to 8 yrs. of age.

For best results, the boar should be at least eight months old and well grown before being put into service. Even then, he should be limited to one service per day and a maximum total of two dozen services during his first breeding season, unless the mating period covers more than one month.

When fed and cared for by an experienced herdsman, a strong, vigorous boar from one to four years of age (the period of most active service) may serve two sows per day during the breeding season provided that a system of hand-coupling is practiced. Excessive service will result in the release of a decreased concentration of sperm as well as immature sperm. With pasture mating, fewer sows can be bred.

A boar should remain a vigorous and reliable breeder up to six or eight years of age or older, provided that he has been managed properly throughout his lifetime.

CARE OF THE PREGNANT SOW

Without attempting to duplicate the discussion on feeding the gestating sow as found in Chapter VI, it may be well to emphasize that there are two cardinal principles which the producer should keep in mind when feeding sows during the pregnancy period. These are: (1) to provide a ration which will insure the complete nourishment of the sow and her developing fetal litter, and (2) to choose the feeds and adopt a method of feeding which will prove economical and adaptable to local farm conditions.

In addition to having proper nutrition, the pregnant sow should have regular and careful exercise. During periods of inclement weather and when feed is brought into the house, sows quite often exercise too little. As a result, they become sluggish; and the blood circulation is poor. Forced exercise may be brought about by feeding some distance from the house or by driving the animals at a moderate walk. Sows that have had plenty of exercise during the gestation period generally encounter less difficulty at farrowing time and produce stronger pigs.

The shelter for bred sows need not be elaborate or expensive. Less labor is involved when several sows of the same age, size, and condition are run together. The chief requirements are that the shelter be tight overhead, that it afford protection from inclement weather, that it is well drained and dry, and that it is of sufficient size to allow the animals to move about and lie down in comfort. Except during the most inclement weather, the sows should be encouraged to run outdoors where they will get exercise, fresh air, and sunshine.

As previously mentioned, to date there has been great emphasis on the importance of exercise and inexpensive shelters for gestating sows. Nevertheless, an increasing number of hog producers are confining bred sows throughout gestation—primarily as a means of lessening labor and automating, freeing land for crops, and controlling environment. Some are confining sows in groups, others are handling them individually. With confinement, less exercise and more expensive buildings are inevitable than in the older, more conventional method. As is true of most developments, the future of confinement handling of gestating sows will be determined by experiments and experiences, some of which are now in progress.

CARE OF THE SOW AT FARROWING TIME

The careful and observant herdsman realizes the importance of having everything in readiness for farrowing time. If the pregnant sows have been so fed and managed as to give birth to a crop of strong, vigorous pigs, the next problem is that of saving the pigs at farrowing time.

It has been conservatively estimated that from 30 to 35 percent of the pigs farrowed never reach weaning age, and an additional loss of 5 to 10 percent occurs after weaning. This means that only 60 percent of the pig crop reaches market age.

Signs of Approaching Parturition

The immediate indications that the sow is about to farrow are extreme nervousness and uneasiness, an enlarged vulva, and a possible mucus discharge. She usually makes a nest for her young, and milk is present in the teats.

Preparation for Farrowing

About three or four days prior to farrowing, the sow should be isolated from the rest of the herd. It is important, however, that moderate exercise be continued while the animal is in the farrowing quarters.

SANITARY MEASURES

Before being moved into the farrowing quarters, the sow should be thoroughly scrubbed with soap and warm water, especially in the region of the sides, udder, and undersurface of the body. This removes adhering parasite eggs (especially the eggs of the common round worm) and disease germs.

The house should be thoroughly cleaned to reduce possible infection. This may be done by scrubbing the walls and floors with boiling-hot lye water made by using one can of lye to 15 gallons of water. If the farrowing house has dirt floors, the top 2 or 3 inches of soil should be replaced by an equal quantity of clean clay soil. The sow should then be placed in her new quarters.

Fig. 5-23. Washing the sow prior to moving her into the farrowing quarters. This removes adhering parasite eggs (especially the eggs of the common round worm) and disease germs. (Courtesy, Washington State University)

THE QUARTERS

Hogs are sensative to extremes of heat and cold and require more protection than any other class of farm animals. This is especially true at the time of parturition. It is recommended that the farrowing house temperature be maintained at 60° to 70° F., and that it not go below 40° F. or above 85° F. Along with this temperature, there should be adequate ventilation at all times. In cold areas and during the winter months, use heat lamps or pig brooders when the farrowing house temperature falls below 65° F. (see Chapter X).

The main requirements for satisfactory housing are that the quarters be dry, sanitary, and well ventilated and that they provide good protection from heat, cold, and winds. The buildings should be economical and durable.

THE GUARD RAIL

A guard rail around the farrowing pen is an effective means of preventing sows from crushing their pigs. The importance of

this simple protective measure may be emphasized best by pointing out that approximately one-half of the young pig losses are accounted for by those pigs that are over-laid by their mothers. The rail should be raised 8 to 10 inches from the floor and should be 8 to 12 inches from the walls. It may be constructed of two-by-fours, two-by-sixes, or strong poles or steel pipe (see Fig. 5-21).

BEDDING

The farrowing quarters should be lightly bedded with clean, fresh material. Any good absorbent that is not too long and coarse is satisfactory. Wheat, barley, rye, or oat straw; short or chopped hay; ground corn cobs; peanut hulls; cottonseed hulls; shredded corn fodder; and shavings are most commonly used.

The Attendant

The herdsman should be on the job, especially during times of inclement weather. It may be necessary to free the newborn pigs from the enveloping membrane and to help them reach the mother's teat. In cold weather the young should be dried off and other precautions taken to avoid chilling.

If the sow has labored for some time with little progress or is laboring rather infrequently, assistance should be given. This usually consists of inserting the hand and arm in the vulva and gently correcting the condition preventing delivery. Before doing this, the fingernails should be trimmed closely, and the hands and arm should be thoroughly washed with soap and warm water, disinfected, and then lubricated with petroleum jelly or linseed oil.

As soon as the afterbirth is expelled, it should be removed from the pen and burned or buried in lime. This prevents the sow from eating the afterbirth and prevents the development of bacteria and foul odors. Many good swine producers are convinced that eating the afterbirth encourages the development of the pig-eating vice. Dead pigs should be removed for the same reason.

It is also well to work over the bedding; remove wet, stained, or soiled bedding and provide clean fresh material.

Chilled and Weak Pigs

Pigs arriving during cold weather are easily chilled. Under such conditions, it may be advisable to take the pigs from the mother as they are born and to place them in a half-barrel or basket lined with straw or rags. In extremely cold weather, a few hot bricks or a jug of warm water (properly wrapped to prevent burns) may be placed in the barrel or basket; or the pigs may be taken to a warm room until they are dry and active.

One of the most effective methods of reviving a chilled pig is to immerse the body, except the head, in water as warm as one's elbow can bear. The pig should be kept in this for a few minutes, then removed and rubbed vigorously with cloths.

Orphan Pigs

Pigs may be orphaned either through sickness or death of their mother. In either event, the most satisfactory arrangement for the orphans is to provide a foster mother. When it is impossible to transfer the pigs to another sow, they may be raised on cow's milk or milk replacer. The problem will be simplified if the pigs have received a small amount of colostrum (the first milk) from their mother.

If cow's milk is used, it is preferable that it be from a low-testing cow. Do not add cream or sugar; however, skim milk powder, at the rate of a tablespoonful to a pint of fluid milk may be added, if available. Milk replacer should be mixed according to the directions found on the container. The first two or three days the orphans should be fed regularly every two hours, and the milk should be at 100° F. Thereafter, the intervals may be spaced farther apart. All utensils (pan feeding or a bottle and nipple may be used) should be clean and sterilized.

Orphan pigs should be started on a prestarter or starter ration when they are one week old. Also, a source of iron should be provided (in keeping with instructions given in Chapter VI).

Artificial Heat

During times of inclement weather, artificial heat usually must be provided, especially for pigs farrowed in the northern United States. Most large central hog houses are equipped with a heating unit for use in winter farrowing, designed to maintain the temperature at 55° to 65° F.

Individual houses may be insulated by banking with straw and other insulating materials. Then a lantern or oil burner may be suspended from the top of the house. It must be remembered, however, that there is considerable fire hazard with this practice. The electric pig brooder is a much safer heating unit for either the central or the movable hog house. The principles involved are identical to those of the electric chick brooder.

THE SOW AND LITTER

The care and management given the sow and litter should be such as to get the pigs off to a good start. As is true of other young livestock, young pigs make more rapid and efficient gains than older hogs. Strict sanitation and intelligent feeding are especially important for the well being of the young pig.

The successful swine producer, consciously or unconsciously, follows the principles of the McLean County System of Swine Sanitation. This and other management practices pertinent to the well being of young pigs—including grouping [(1) adjusting litter size, and (2) running sows and litters together], removal of the needle teeth, ear notching, castrating, etc.—are fully covered in Chapter XIV. Sows and litters may be kept either in the dry lot or placed on pasture.

Feed Requirements of the Nursing Sow

Until the pigs are about three days old, limit the sow's intake and feed plenty of bran. Thereafter, gradually increase the feed allowance so as to arrive at full feeding ten days to two weeks later. Throughout the lactation period, she should be fed liberally with feeds that will stimulate milk production. The most essential ingredients fed in the brood sow's ration during this period are an ample amount of protein, vitamin, and mineral substances.

NORMAL BREEDING SEASON AND
TIME OF FARROWING

The season in which the sows are bred and the question of raising one or two litters a year or multiple farrowing, depend primarily on the facilities at hand. The location of the producer (particularly the weather conditions in the area), availability and price of feeds, condition and growth of the sows, equipment

for handling pigs during the winter months, available labor, and
the type of production (purebred or commercial) should be taken
into consideration. No positive advice can be given, therefore, for
any and all conditions. Sows will breed any time of the year, but
as in other farm animals the conception rate is much higher during those seasons when the temperature is moderate and the nutritive conditions are good. For the country as a whole, spring
pigs are preferred, as is shown by the size of the spring pig crop
in comparison with the fall pig crop.

Show-yard Classifications May Determine Farrowing Dates

The purebred breeder who exhibits breeding hogs should
plan the breeding program so that the maximum advantage will
be taken of the various age groups. These are given in
Chapter XVI.

ARTIFICIAL INSEMINATION OF SWINE

Artificial insemination is, by definition, *the deposition of
spermatozoa in the female genitalia by artificial rather than by
natural means.*

Artificial insemination of swine in the United States is still
in the experimental stage, but there is great interest in its potential. Without doubt, its wide-scale use only awaits the time
when a few of the remaining problems are overcome. In Norway,
15 to 20 percent of the sows are bred artificially. The Norwegians
report a 56 percent conception rate, based on number of farrowing sows, and no significant difference in litter size resulting from
artificial insemination and from natural matings.

Before wide use can be made of artificial insemination of
swine in this country, the following problems need to be solved:

1. **We need to be able to breed more sows per boar.**—At the
present time, too few sows can be bred per boar in any one breeding period or season. For example, it is possible to breed 600
cows from one collection of a bull, compared to 10 to 12 for the
boar.

2. **We need to be able to store boar semen longer.**—Boar
semen cannot be stored sufficiently long to allow semen from a
certain boar to be available from one collection to the next. Over
a long period, semen collection from a boar should not be made

more often than three times a week. Efforts are now underway to freeze boar semen as is done for cattle. While not yet a reality, there is every reason to believe frozen swine semen will be available for routine use in the years ahead.

3. **We need to be able to detect when sows are ready for breeding.**—It is sometimes difficult to determine exactly when a sow or gilt is ready for breeding. If a sow is not bred at the proper time (during the first 12 to 24 hours of the heat period), litter size and conception rate are likely to be reduced.

4. **We need estrus control in gilts so as to synchronize farrowings.**—Some control may be obtained in sows through manipulating the pattern of weaning among a group of sows. But there is need for estrus control in gilts so as to synchronize farrowings.

Without doubt, in due time these barriers will be overcome, and artificial insemination of swine will expand just as it has in the American dairy industry.

QUESTIONS FOR STUDY AND DISCUSSION

1. Why is swine breeding more flexible in the hands of man than cattle and sheep breeding?
2. What unique circumstances surrounded the founding of genetics by Mendel?
3. Under what conditions might a theoretically completely homozygous state in hogs be undesirable and unfortunate?
4. Give two examples each of (a) dominance and (b) recessive phenomena in swine.
5. In order to make intelligent selections and breed progress, is it necessary to full feed or place hogs in show condition?
6. Explain how sex is determined.
7. When abnormal pigs are born, what conditions tend to indicate each: (a) a hereditary defect, or (b) a nutritional deficiency?
8. The "sire is half the herd"! Is this an under- or over-statement?
9. What system of breeding do you consider to be best adapted to your herd, or to a herd with which you are familiar? Justify your choice.

10. Which of the four common crossbreeding systems would you recommend, and why?

11. Discuss the advantages and the disadvantages of crossbreeding swine.

12. Based on (a) heritability and (b) dollars and cents value, what characteristics should receive greatest emphasis in a swine production testing program?

13. How would you go about Production Testing a herd of hogs? List and discuss each step.

14. Why do not more swine producers buy and use Production Tested boars?

15. What system of selection—(a) tandem, (b) minimum culling levels, or (c) selection index—would you recommend and why?

16. What standards must a litter meet in order to be "a certified litter" under the Meat Certification Program as adopted by the National Association of Swine Records?

17. Twenty percent of all sows fail to breed; from 5 to 30 percent of the fertilized eggs do not develop normally, resulting in embryonic mortality or death; and from 10 to 30 percent of the live pigs farrowed die within the first seven to ten days of life. Discuss the causes and economics of this situation.

18. Diagram and label the reproductive organs of the boar.

19. Diagram and label the reproductive organs of the sow.

20. In order to synchronize ovulation and insemination, when should sows be bred with relation to the heat period?

21. What advantages could accrue from the practical and extensive use of artificial insemination in swine? Is it likely that artificial insemination will come to be as widely practiced in swine as it is with dairy cattle?

SELECTED REFERENCES

Title of Publication	Author(s)	Publisher
Animal Breeding	A. L. Hagedoorn	Crosby Lockwood & Son, Ltd., London, England, 1950.
Animal Breeding	L. M. Winters	John Wiley & Sons, Inc., New York, N. Y., 1948.
Animal Breeding Plans	J. L. Lush	Collegiate Press, Inc., Ames, Ia., 1963.

Title of Publication	Author(s)	Publisher
Animal Science	M. E. Ensminger	The Interstate Printers & Publishers, Inc., Danville, Ill., 1969.
Artificial Insemination in Livestock Breeding	A. H. Frank	U. S. Department of Agriculture Circ. 567, Washington, D. C., 1952.
Artificial Insemination of Farm Animals	W. W. Green L. M. Winters	Agri. Expt. Sta. Bul. 335, University of Minnesota, St. Paul, Minn., 1946.
Breeding and Improvement of Farm Animals	V. A. Rice F. N. Andrews E. J. Warwick J. E. Legates	McGraw-Hill Book Co., New York, N. Y., 1967.
Breeding Better Livestock	V. A. Rice F. N. Andrews E. J. Warwick	McGraw-Hill Book Co., New York, N. Y., 1953.
Breeding Livestock Adapted to Unfavorable Environments	R. W. Phillips	Food and Agriculture Organization of the United Nations, Washington, D. C., 1949.
Developmental Anatomy	L. B. Arey	W. B. Saunders Co., Philadelphia, Pa.
Elements of Genetics, The	C. D. Carlington K. Mather	The Macmillan Company, New York, N. Y., 1950.
Embryology of the Pig, The	B. M. Patten	P. Blakiston's Son & Co., Inc., Philadelphia, Pa., 1931.
Farm Animals	John Hammond	Edward Arnold & Co., London, England, 1952.
Fifty Years of Progress in Swine Breeding	W. A. Craft	*Journal of Animal Science,* Vol. 17, No. 4, November, 1958.
Genetic Basis of Selection, The	I. Michael Lerner	John Wiley & Sons, Inc., New York, N. Y., 1958.
Genetic Resistance to Disease in Domestic Animals	F. B. Hutt	Comstock Publishing Associates, Cornell University Press, Ithaca, N. Y., 1958.
Genetics and Animal Breeding	E. J. Warwick	Agri. Expt. Sta. Popular Bul. 189, Washington State University, Pullman, Wash., 1948.
Genetics of Livestock Improvement	John F. Lasley	Prentice-Hall, Inc., Englewood Cliffs, N. J., 1963.
Highlights of Breeding Systems	V. A. Rice	Holstein-Friesian Assn. of America, Brattleboro, Vt.
Improvement of Livestock	Ralph Bogart	The Macmillan Company, New York, N. Y., 1959.
Livestock Improvement	J. E. Nichols	Oliver and Boyd, Edinburgh, Tweeddale Court, 1957.
Modern Developments in Animal Breeding	I. Michael Lerner H. P. Donald	Academic Press, London and New York, 1966.

Title of Publication	Author(s)	Publisher
Reproductive Physiology	A. V. Nalbandov	W. H. Freeman & Co., San Francisco, Calif., 1958.
Results of Swine Breeding Research	W. A. Craft	Circ. 916, U. S. Department of Agriculture, Washington, D. C.
Tables for Coefficients of Inbreeding in Animals	C. D. Mueller	Agri. Expt. Sta. Tech. Bul. 80, Kansas State University, Manhattan, Kan.

FEEDING SWINE[1]

Contents   **Page**

[1] The author gratefully acknowledges the helpful suggestions of Dr. Wilton W. Heinemann, Washington State University, who reviewed this chapter.

In the natural state, the wild boar roved through the forests gleaning the feeds provided by nature; whereas on a modern farm the area is restricted and sometimes entirely devoid of vegetation. Domestic swine have less choice in their selection of feed than any other class of livestock. For the most part they are able to consume only what the caretaker provides. This consists largely of concentrated feeds with only a small proportion of roughage (see Table 6-1). These conditions are made more critical because hogs grow much faster in proportion to their body

TABLE 6-1

PERCENTAGE OF FEED FOR DIFFERENT CLASSES OF LIVESTOCK DERIVED FROM (1) CONCENTRATES AND (2) ROUGHAGES INCLUDING PASTURE, AVERAGES FOR THE FEEDING YEARS, 1962, 1963, AND 1964[1]

Class of Animal	Concentrates	Roughages
	(%)	(%)
Swine	95.6	4.4
Beef cattle	21.2	78.8
Dairy cattle	31.3	68.7
Sheep and goats	10.2	89.8
Horses and mules	22.9	77.1
Poultry	98.2	1.8
All livestock	45.2	54.8

[1]Unpublished data provided to the author from Earl F. Hodges, Agricultural Economist, Economic Research Service, USDA.

weight than the larger farm animals, and they produce young at an earlier age; factors which have been accentuated under modern forced production. Thus, a knowledge of the nutritional needs of swine is especially important.

Extensive surveys indicate that about 25 percent of all pigs farrowed fail to live to weaning age. Although these heavy losses are due to many and variable factors, certainly nutritional deficiencies play a major role.

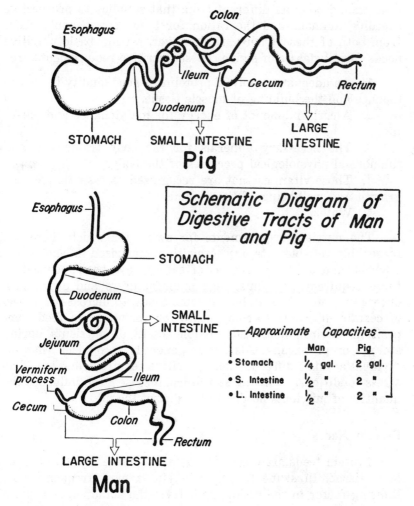

Fig. 6-1. Because of their similar digestive tracts and body sizes, the nutritive requirements of the pig and of man are much alike. Note that both have a simple monogastric stomach. (Drawing by R. F. Johnson)

Knowledge of feeding swine is also important from an economic standpoint, because feed accounts for approximately 75 percent of the total cost of producing pork.

SPECIFIC NUTRITIVE NEEDS OF SWINE

The feed requirements of swine vary according to the purpose for which the animals are kept. The ration for finishing hogs should be quite different from that supplied to prospective breeding animals, and the ration for brood sows should differ from both of these. There are, however, certain basic nutritive needs for all classes of swine. These nutritive requirements are:

1. An adequate supply of proteins of good quality for maintenance and the building of muscle tissue.
2. A certain amount of energy for maintenance and finishing.
3. The necessary minerals for the body framework and the normal physiological processes of the body.
4. Those vitamins that are recognized as essential for the growth and well-being of the animal.
5. Water.

The nutrient requirements for swine for which there are reasonably reliable data are herewith summarized in Tables 6-2, 6-3, 6-4, and 6-5.[2] No margins of safety have been included in these requirements. Thus, feed manufacturers and swine producers may find it desirable, in some cases, to increase the level of certain nutrients to compensate for variations in feed composition, environment, and possible losses of nutrients during storage or processing. Also, it is generally recognized that individual animals differ in their nutritive requirements, and that stress conditions, including subclinical disease level, influence the quantity of nutrients needed in the diet of the pig.

Protein Needs

Protein feeds are essential for maintenance and building of body tissue. In swine feeding, protein is most frequently the limiting factor in the ration, both from the standpoint of quan-

---

[2]From *Nutrient Requirements of Swine*, 1968, NRC Pub. 1599.

NUTRIENT REQUIREMENTS OF GROWING AND FINISHING SWINE[1]
(Amounts per animal per day)

		Full-fed on Cereal Grains						Full-fed on Corn				Full-fed on Wheat, Barley, Oats[2]			
		(lb.)	(kg)	(lb.)	(kg)	(lb.)	(kg)	(lb.)	(kg)	(lb.)	(kg)	(lb.)	(kg)	(lb.)	(kg)
Live weight range		11-22	5-10	22-44	10-20	44-77	20-35	77-132	35-60	132-220	60-100	77-132	35-60	132-220	60-100
Total air dry feed[3]		1.32	0.60	2.75	1.25	3.74	1.70	5.50	2.50	7.70	3.50	5.50	2.50	7.26	3.30
Expected daily gain[3]		.66	0.30	1.10	0.50	1.32	0.60	1.65	0.75	1.98	0.90	1.54	0.70	1.76	0.80
Protein and energy:															
Crude protein	(oz.)/(g)	5	132	8	225	10	272	12	350	16	455	13	375	16	462
Digestible energy[4]	(kcal)	2,100		4,370		5,610		8,250		11,550		7,750		10,230	
TDN[5]	(lb.)/(g)	1.05	477	2.18	993	2.81	1,275	4.13	1,875	5.78	2,625	3.87	1,761	5.12	2,325
Inorganic nutrients:															
Calcium	(g)	4.8		8.1		10.2		12.5		17.5		12.5		16.5	
Phosphorus	(g)	3.6		6.3		8.5		10.0		14.0		10.0		13.2	
Sodium	(g)	—		1.3		1.7		—		—		—		—	
Chlorine	(g)	—		1.6		2.2		—		—		—		—	
Vitamins:															
b-Carotene[6]	(mg)	2.6		4.4		4.4		6.5		9.1		6.5		8.6	
Vitamin A[6]	(IU)	1,300		2,200		2,200		3,250		4,550		3,250		4,300	
Vitamin D	(IU)	132		250		340		312		437		312		412	
Thiamine	(mg)	0.8		1.4		1.9		2.8		3.9		2.8		3.6	
Riboflavin	(mg)	1.8		3.8		4.4		5.5		7.7		5.5		7.3	
Niacin[7]	(mg)	13.2		22.5		23.8		25.0		35.0		25.0		33.0	
Pantothenic acid	(mg)	7.8		13.8		18.7		27.5		38.5		27.5		36.3	
Vitamin B 6	(mg)	0.9		1.9		1.9		—		—		—		—	
Choline	(mg)	660		1,125		1,275		—		—		—		—	
Vitamin B 12	(mcg)	13.2		18.8		18.7		27.5		38.5		27.5		36.3	

[1]From Bul. No. 2, *Nutrient Requirements of Swine*, Revised 1968, NRC Pub. 1599, with avoirdupois added by author.

[2]Barley, oats, and wheat are usually higher in protein than corn, and thus a higher total protein level is needed in the final diet to balance the amino acid requirements.

[3]From 35 to 100 kg live weight, barrows will eat more, and gain more rapidly than gilts.

[4]Digestible energy was calculated on the assumption that one kg of DE has 4400 kcal of digestible energy.

[5]TDN estimated basis that 4.4 kcal of DE contain one gram (or .0022 lb.) of TDN.

[6]Carotene and vitamin A values are based on 1 mg of b-carotene equals 500 IU of biologically active vitamin A. Vitamin A requirements can be met by either carotene or vitamin A or both.

[7]It is assumed that all the niacin in the cereal grains and their by-products is in a bound form and thus is largely unavailable.

TABLE 6-3

NUTRIENT REQUIREMENTS OF GROWING AND FINISHING SWINE[1]
(Expressed in percentage or amount per (1) lb. or (2) kilogram of diet)

	Full-fed on Cereal Grains						Full-fed on Corn				Full-fed on Wheat, Barley, Oats			
	(lb.)	(kg)	(lb.)	(kg)	(lb.)	(kg)	(lb.)	(kg)	(lb.)	(kg)	(lb.)	(kg)	(lb.)	(kg)
Live weight range	11-22	5-10	22-44	10-20	44-77	20-35	77-132	35-60	132-220	60-100	77-132	35-60	132-220	60-100
Expected daily gain	0.66	0.30	1.10	0.50	1.32	0.60	1.65	0.75	1.98	0.90	1.54	0.70	1.76	0.80
Protein and energy:														
Crude protein (%)	22		18		16		14		13		15		14	
Digestible energy (kcal)	3,500		3,500		3,300		3,300		3,300		3,100		3,100	
TDN[2] (%)	79.5		79.5		75.0		75.0		75.0		70.5		70.5	
Inorganic nutrients:														
Calcium (%)	0.80		0.65		0.65		0.50		0.50		0.50		0.50	
Phosphorus (%)	0.60		0.50		0.50		0.40		0.40		0.40		0.40	
Sodium (%)	—		0.10		0.10		—		—		—		—	
Chlorine (%)	—		0.13		0.13		—		—		—		—	
Vitamins:	(per)		(per)		(per)		(per)		(per)		(per)		(per)	
	(lb.)	(kg)	(lb.)	(kg)	(lb.)	(kg)	(lb.)	(kg)	(lb.)	(kg)	(lb.)	(kg)	(lb.)	(kg)
b-Carotene (mg)	2.0	4.4	1.6	3.5	1.2	2.6	1.2	2.6	1.2	2.6	1.2	2.6	1.2	2.6
Vitamin A (IU)	1,000	2,200	795	1,750	590	1,300	590	1,300	590	1,300	590	1,300	590	1,300
Vitamin D (IU)	100	220	91	200	91	200	57	125	57	125	57	125	57	125
Thiamine (mg)	0.6	1.3	0.5	1.1	0.5	1.1	0.5	1.1	0.5	1.1	0.5	1.1	0.5	1.1
Riboflavin (mg)	1.4	3.0	1.4	3.0	1.2	2.6	1.0	2.2	1.0	2.2	1.0	2.2	1.0	2.2
Niacin (mg)	10.0	22.0	8.2	18.0	6.4	14.0	4.5	10.0	4.5	10.0	4.5	10.0	4.5	10.0
Pantothenic acid (mg)	5.9	13.0	5.0	11.0	5.0	11.0	5.0	11.0	5.0	11.0	5.0	11.0	5.0	11.0
Vitamin B6 (mg)	0.7	1.5	0.7	1.5	0.5	1.1	—	—	—	—	—	—	—	—
Choline (mcg)	500	1,100	409	900	—	—	—	—	—	—	—	—	—	—
Vitamin B12 (mcg)	10.0	22.0	6.8	15.0	5.0	11.0	5.0	11.0	5.0	11.0	5.0	11.0	5.0	11.0

[1] From Bul. No. 2, *Nutrient Requirements of Swine*, Revised 1968, NRC Pub. 1599, with avoirdupois added by author.

[2] TDN estimated basis that 4.4 kcal of DE contain one gram (or .0022 lb.) of TDN. Hence, 3500 kcal DE ÷ 4.4 = 795 gm TDN/1000 gm of diet, or 79.5% TDN.

TABLE 6-4

NUTRIENT REQUIREMENTS OF BREEDING SWINE[1]
(Amounts per animal per day)

	Bred				Lactating				Boars			
	Gilts		Sows		Gilts		Sows		Young		Adult	
	(lb.) 242-352	(kg) 110-160	(lb.) 352-550	(kg) 160-250	(lb.) 308-440	(kg) 140-200	(lb.) 440-550	(kg) 200-250	(lb.) 242-396	(kg) 110-180	(lb.) 396-550	(kg) 180-250
Live weight range ----	242-352	110-160	352-550	160-250	308-440	140-200	440-550	200-250	242-396	110-180	396-550	180-250
Total air dry feed----	4.4[2]	2.0[2]	4.4[2]	2.0[2]	11.0[3]	5.0[3]	12.1[3]	5.5[3]	5.5	2.5	4.4	2.0
Expected daily gain----	.77-.99	.35-.45	.33-.66	.15-.30	—	—	—	—	.55-.99	.25-.45	—	—
Protein and energy:												
Crude protein----(oz.)	10		10		27		29		12		10	
----(gm)	280		280		750		825		350		280	
Digestible energy----(kcal)	6,600		6,600		16,500		18,150		8,250		6,600	
TDN[4]----(lb.)	3.30		3.30		8.25		9.07		4.13		3.30	
----(gm)	1,500		1,500		3,750		4,125		1,875		1,500	
Inorganic nutrients:												
Calcium----(gm)	15.0		15.0		30		33		18.8		15.0	
Phosphorus----(gm)	10.0		10.0		20		22		12.5		10.0	
NaCl (salt)----(gm)	10		10		25		27.5		12.5		10.0	
Vitamins:												
b-Carotene----(mg)	16.4		16.4		33		36.3		20.5		16.4	
Vitamin A----(IU)	8,200		8,200		16,500		18,150		10,250		8,200	
Vitamin D----(IU)	550		550		1,100		1,210		690		550	
Thiamine----(mg)	2.8		2.8		5.5		6.0		3.5		2.8	
Riboflavin----(mg)	8.2		8.2		16.5		18.2		10.3		8.2	
Niacin----(mg)	44.0		44.0		88.0		96.8		55.0		44.0	
Pantothenic acid----(mg)	33.0		33.0		66.0		72.6		41.3		33.0	
Vitamin B_{12}----(mcg)	27.6		27.6		55.0		60.5		34.5		27.6	

[1] From Bul. No. 2, Nutrient Requirements of Swine, Revised 1968, NRC Pub. 1599, with avoirdupois added by author.
[2] Environmental conditions and length of lactation will influence the amount of feed needed during gestation.
[3] Feed intake should be related to the number of young pigs suckling the sow.
[4] TDN estimated basis that 4.4 kcal of DE contain one gram (or .0022 lb.) of TDN.

TABLE 6-5

NUTRIENT REQUIREMENTS OF BREEDING SWINE[1]

(Expressed in percentage or amount per (1) lb. or (2) kilogram of diet)

| | Breeding Swine | | | | Boars—Young and Adult | |
	Bred Gilts and Sows		Lactating Gilts and Sows			
Live weight, range ————————(lb.)	242-352		308-440		242-396	
————————(kg)	110-160		140-200		110-180	
Protein and energy:						
Crude protein ————————(%)	14		15		14	
Digestible energy————————(kcal)	3,300		3,300		3,300	
TDN[2] ————————(%)	75.0		75.0		75.0	
Inorganic nutrients:						
Calcium————————(%)	0.75		0.6		0.75	
Phosphorus————————(%)	0.50		0.4		0.50	
NaCl (salt)————————(%)	0.5		0.5		0.5	
Vitamins:	(per lb.)	(per kg)	(per lb.)	(per kg)	(per lb.)	(per kg)
b-Carotene————————(mg)	3.7	8.2	3.0	6.6	3.7	8.2
Vitamin A————————(IU)	1,864	4,100	1,500	3,300	1,864	4,100
Vitamin D————————(IU)	125	275	100	220	125	275
Thiamine————————(mg)	0.6	1.4	0.5	1.1	0.6	1.4
Riboflavin————————(mg)	1.9	4.1	1.5	3.3	1.9	4.1
Niacin————————(mg)	10.0	22.0	8.0	17.6	10.0	22.0
Pantothenic acid————————(mg)	7.5	16.5	6.0	13.2	7.5	16.5
Vitamin B12————————(mcg)	6.3	13.8	5.0	11.0	6.3	13.8

[1]From Bul. No. 2, *Nutrient Requirements of Swine,* Revised 1968, NRC Pub. 1599, with avoirdupois added by author.

[2]TDN estimated basis that 4.4 kcal of DE contain one gram (or .0022 lb.) of TDN.

tity and quality. This is due to the fact that the common farm grains and their by-products—which constitute the chief diet of pigs—are low in protein content, and their proteins are lacking in the essential amino acids. Moreover, the digestive tract of the pig is not adapted to the synthesis of proteins by microorganisms as is the paunch of ruminants. Also, since protein supplements are the most expensive, there is a temptation to feed too little. The protein in the ration is of special importance for young, growing pigs and for gestating-lactating sows—the critical periods in swine production.

Improvement in the quality of proteins in a ration composed of cereal grains and their by-products can usually be achieved by using combinations of feeds. Also, it is recommended that corn, barley, wheat, oats, or milo not be used to provide more than 65 percent of the total dietary protein needs. Although the protein supplements are higher in price than the carbohydrate feeds, the cash outlay usually yields greater returns in increased rate of gain and better utilization of feed.

Young pigs require a much greater proportion of protein in the ration than do those that are approaching market weight. Accordingly, for most economical results the ration of the pig should be changed at different stages. Also, the protein requirements of gestating and lactating sows differ from each other and from those of growing-finishing pigs. The recommended protein levels, average rate of gain, and feed consumption of swine are given in Table 6-6.

If the pigs are being self-fed, the protein supplements may be provided free choice. Fortunately, pigs show a remarkable ability to balance their own rations when allowed to choose from several feeds cafeteria style. (See section entitled "Pointers in Formulating Rations and Feeding Swine," points 9 and 10.)

Young, lush pastures and early-cut, green, leafy alfalfa are sources of good quality proteins. However, the fiber content of roughages is too great and the stomach of the pig is too small to rely upon pastures or ground alfalfa as the sole source of proteins.

The amino acid needs of swine are given in Table 6-7. The essential amino acids, of which there are ten (see Table 6-7), are needed for the normal physiological processes of swine—for maintenance, growth, reproduction, and lactation. It is noteworthy, for example, that a deficiency of protein or of any one of the essential amino acids in the diet of the growing pig will

TABLE 6-6

RECOMMENDED PROTEIN LEVELS, AVERAGE RATE OF GAIN, AND FEED CONSUMPTION FOR SWINE

Description of Animal			Protein Content of Ration (%)	Average Daily Gain (lb.)	(kg)	Average Daily Feed Intake (lb.)	(kg)	Total Feed Needed to Attain Weight[3] (lb.)	(kg)
Breeding stock									
Gestation:									
Gilts			14	.60	.27	5.0	2.27		
Sows			14	.50	.23	5.0	2.27		
Lactation:									
Gilts and Sows			15			12.0	5.44		
Boars			14			6.0	2.72		

						Lb. or Kg Needed per Lb. or Kg Gain[2]			
Grower-finishing pigs[1]									
Pig Weight (lb.)	(kg)	Age, Days							
Birth									
10	4.5	0	17-20 (creep)	—	—	—		110	50.0
30	13.6	14	22 (early weaned)	.50	.23	1.5		130	59.1
		48		1.00	.45	1.9		165	75.0
40	18.2	56	18	1.20	.55	2.2		185	84.1
80	36.4	85	14	1.65	.75	2.8		285	129.5
100	45.4	96	14	1.80	.82	3.1		345	156.8
120	54.5	108	14	1.90	.86	3.3		410	186.4
160	72.7	128	13	2.00	.91	3.5		545	247.7
200	90.9	145	13	2.10	.95	4.1		700	318.1
220	100.0	155	13	2.15	.98	4.4		785	356.8

[1]From Ill. Circ. 866, 1966, with permission of Dr. D. E. Becker; except for "protein content of ration," which the author adapted from NRC Pub. 1599, Rev. 1968.

[2]Based on feeding fortified corn-soybean rations. Where other feeds are used, quantity of feed needed per pound of gain will vary inversely with the calorie density of the diet fed.

[3]Includes feed for sows starting 30 days prior to mating and for breeding boars. Based on feeding fortified corn-soybean rations. Where other feeds are used, quantity of feed needed will vary inversely with the caloric density of the diet fed.

Fig. 6-2. Pigs require the amino acid tryptophan. These two littermate pigs received the same ration, except that 0.4% DL-Tryptophan was added to the diet of the pig in the upper picture.

Upper: Pig gained 25.5 pounds in 21 days.

Lower: Tryptophan-deficient pig lost 8.0 pounds in 21 days.

(Courtesy Dr. W. M. Beeson, Purdue University)

result in slowed or arrested growth, depressed appetite, and inefficient feed utilization. Thus, both the quantity and quality of protein must receive attention when formulating swine rations.

TABLE 6-7

ESSENTIAL AMINO ACID REQUIREMENTS OF SWINE[1]
(Expressed as percentage of diet)

	Growing Pigs		Finishing Pigs	
	5-10 kg 11-22 lb.	20-35 kg 44-77 lb.	60-100 kg 132-220 lb.	Bred Sows and Gilts
Protein --------------------(%)	22	16	13	14
Dig. energy-----(kcal/kg)	3,500	3,300	3,300	3,300
TDN[2] --------------------(%)	79.5	75.0	75.0	75.0
Amino acids: (%)				
Arginine --------------	—	0.20[3]	—	—
Histidine -------------	0.27	0.18	—	0.20[3]
Isoleucine ------------	0.76	0.50	0.35	0.43
Leucine ---------------	0.90	0.60	—	0.66[3]
Lysine -----------------	1.20	0.70	0.50	0.49
Methionine[4] ---------	0.80	0.50	—	0.35
Phenylalanine[5] -----	—	0.50	—	0.52[3]
Threonine -------------	0.70	0.45	—	0.42
Tryptophan----------	0.18	0.13	0.09[3]	0.08[3]
Valine -----------------	0.65	0.50	—	0.46

[1]From Bul. No. 2, *Nutrient Requirements of Swine*, Revised 1968, NRC Pub. 1599, with avoirdupois added by the author.
[2]TDN estimated basis that 4.4 kcal of DE contain one gram (or .0022 lb.) of TDN.
[3]This level is adequate but the minimum requirement has not been established.
[4]Cystine can satisfy 40% of the need for methionine.
[5]Tyrosine can satisfy 30% of the need for phenylalanine.

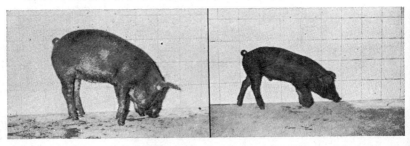

Fig. 6-3. Pigs require the amino acid isoleucine. The weanling pig on the left was fed a ration with adequate isoleucine, whereas the pig on the right was fed an isoleucine-deficient diet for 28 days. Note the marked difference in growth. (Courtesy, Dr. D. E. Becker, University of Illinois)

Energy Needs

Energy is the first essential for the necessary life processes of the animal. After these requirements are met, surplus energy may be stored as body fat.

Practical swine rations contain adequate amounts of fat. However, it has been shown that a semi-purified ration containing

0.06 percent fat will produce fat-deficiency symptoms in swine, manifested by scaly dandruff-like dermatitis, loss of hair, necrotic areas on the skin around the neck and shoulders; and an unthrifty appearance (Fig. 6-4).

The chief sources of heat and energy in swine rations are the carbohydrates and fats of available feeds. Protein-rich supplements seldom are used for this purpose because of their relatively high cost and inefficiency for such use. Carbohydrates, which make up 75 percent of the dry matter in most plants, are the most abundant nutrients of all common feeds and are especially abundant in the cereal grains and their by-products. Fats, which are abundant in such common hog feeds as peanuts and soybeans, have an energy value about 2.25 times as great as carbohydrates and proteins. It is to be emphasized, however, that liberal quantities of either soybeans or peanuts will produce soft pork.

Adding up to 10 percent fat to swine rations increases rate of gain, feed efficiency, and back fat thickness. Two factors should be used as a basis for determining if fat additions to the ration are practical; namely, (1) the margin of return over cost, from adding fat, and (2) the quality of the carcass produced.

Because of the more restricted size of the digestive tract of hogs in comparison with that of ruminants, only limited quantities of roughages are contained in normal swine rations. Roughages (pastures or ground legume hays) are added to the ration because of their vitamins, minerals, and quality proteins, rather than for their energy purposes.

For young pigs, a high energy diet is recommended. For the production of relatively lean bacon carcasses, there should be a reduction in the digestible energy intake during the last few weeks of finishing, starting at a weight of 100 to 125 pounds.

Also, gestating sows on a high energy ration will get too fat. Therefore, their energy intake should be limited by (1) hand-feeding smaller quantities of feed, (2) limiting their access to self-feeders to 24 hours out of each 72 hours, and/or (3) incorporating low-energy feeds such as ground alfalfa or corncobs in the ration.

The amount of feed consumed daily by self-fed, growing-finishing swine is controlled principally by the energy content of the diet, provided it is balanced with all the essential nutrients. Hence, swine tend to eat less feed per unit bodyweight on a high-energy than on a low-energy diet.

Fig. 6-4. Pigs require some fat, as shown by these two littermate pigs.
Upper: Pig received fat in the ration (5.0% ether extract).
    Lower: Pig received little fat in the ration (only 0.06% ether extract).
Note loss of hair, scaly dandruff-like dermatitis, especially on feet and
tail. (Courtesy, Dr. W. M. Beeson, Purdue University)

METHODS OF MEASURING ENERGY[3]

Scientists generally agree that the units used to measure the nutritive requirements of animals and to evaluate feeds should be one and the same. But, there is considerable disagreement as to what units, or system, to use. Generally speaking, there are two schools of thought; and each is inclined to be militant and uncompromising. On the one hand, there are those who will fight for a continuation of the total digestible nutrient system (TDN), rather than switch to the calorie system. Most of them recognize the weaknesses of the TDN system, but they favor a "let well enough alone" policy because, so they argue, folks are generally using it, whereas a change would confuse them. On the other hand, those who champion the adoption of the calorie system are usually impatient; they want to dump the TDN system and move on.

The author favors a gradual transition from the TDN system to the calorie system. For this reason, both systems are presented in this book, and both TDN and digestible energy values are given.

THE TOTAL DIGESTIBLE NUTRIENT (TDN) SYSTEM

Total digestible nutrients (TDN) is the sum of the digestible protein, fiber, nitrogen-free extract, and fat X 2.25.

Back of TDN values are the following steps:

1. **Digestibility.**—The digestibility of a particular feed for a specific class of stock is determined by a digestion trial. It is made by determining the percentage of each nutrient in the feed through chemical analysis; giving the feed to the test animal for a preliminary period, so that all residues of former feeds will pass out of the digestive tract; giving weighed amounts of the feed during the test period; collecting, weighing, and analyzing the feces; determining the difference between the amount of the nutrient fed and the amount found in the feces; and computing the percentage of each nutrient digested. The latter figure is known as the *digestion coefficient* for that nutrient in the feed.

2. **Computation of % digestible nutrients.**—Digestible nutrients are computed by multiplying the percentage of each nutrient in the feed (protein, fiber, nitrogen-free extract—NFE—

---

[3] The author gratefully acknowledges the authoritative help of Dr. Lorin E. Harris, Utah State University, in the preparation of this section.

and fat) by its digestion coefficient. The result is expressed as digestible protein, digestible fiber, digestible NFE, and digestible fat. Thus, for corn the digestible nutrients could be estimated as shown in Table 6-8.

TABLE 6-8

COMPUTATION OF DIGESTIBLE NUTRIENTS OF CORN

Total % of Nutrient in Feed	X	Digestion Coefficient / 100	=	% Digestible Nutrient	
				Digestible nutrient (%)	(lb.)
9.3% protein	X	$\frac{67}{100}$	=	6.2 (protein)	6.2
1.9% fiber	X	$\frac{39}{100}$	=	0.7 (fiber)	0.7
70.1% nitrogen-free extract (NFE)	X	$\frac{85}{100}$	=	59.6 (NFE)	59.6
3.9% ether extract (fat)	X	$\frac{85}{100}$	=	3.3 (fat)	3.3

3. **Computation of total digestible nutrients.**—To approximate the greater energy value of fat, the percentage of digestible fat is multiplied by 2.25. Hence, for the sample of corn, the TDN may be calculated as follows:

```
                              %          %
Digestible protein_____ 6.2 × 1  =  6.2
Digestible crude fiber_____ 0.7 × 1  =  0.7
Digestible NFE_____59.6 × 1  = 59.6
Digestible ether ex-
    tract (fat) _____ 3.3 × 2.25 =  7.4
                                          73.9% lbs. TDN, or
                                          73.9   lbs. TDN/100 lbs. corn.
```

4. **Animal requirements or feeding standards.**—In the TDN system, the feed requirements (energy) of farm animals are given as pounds of total digestible nutrients.

Advantages and Disadvantages of the TDN System

The main **advantage** of the TDN system is that it has been used a long time and many people are acquainted with it.

The main **disadvantages** of the TDN system are:

1. It is based on physiological fuel values for humans and dogs. These do not apply to ruminants. The factors of 1 for protein, crude fiber, and nitrogen-free extract, and 2.25 for fat are not always constant.

2. It over-evaluates high-fiber feeds (roughages) in relation to low-fiber feeds (concentrates) when fed for high rates of production, due to the higher heat loss per pound of TDN in the case of high-fiber feeds.

3. It does not measure energy in energy units.

4. It does not measure all losses of energy from the body.

THE CALORIE SYSTEM

Energy is used in many forms—as light, electricity, atomic force, work, or heat; and it is measured by several units such as candle power, kilowatts, feet, pounds, joules, and calories. In animals, energy is expended as work and/or heat or stored as products. It would appear, therefore, that it should be measured in units suitable for these purposes. Thus, heat unit is an excellent way in which to measure the potential energy of feeds, the energy of animal products, and the heat that results from body processes. The heat unit used by animal nutritionists is the calorie.

A calorie (cal/always written with a small c), is the amount of heat required to raise the temperature of 1 gram of water 1 degree Centigrade. To measure this heat, an instrument known as the bomb calorimeter is used, in which the feed (or other substance) to be tested is placed and burned with the aid of oxygen (see Fig. 6-5).

It is noteworthy that the determination of the heat of combustion with a bomb calorimeter is not as difficult or time consuming as the chemical analyses used in arriving at TDN values. Briefly stated, the procedure is as follows: An electric wire is attached to the material being tested, so that it can be ignited by remote control; 2,000 grams of water are poured around the bomb; 25 to 30 atmospheres of oxygen are added to the bomb; the material is ignited; the heat given off from the burned material warms the water; and a thermometer registers the change in temperature of the water. For example, if 1 gram of material is burned and the temperature of the water is raised 1 degree Centigrade, 2,000 cal are given off. Hence, the material contains 2,000 cal per g, or 907,200 cal per pound. This value is known as

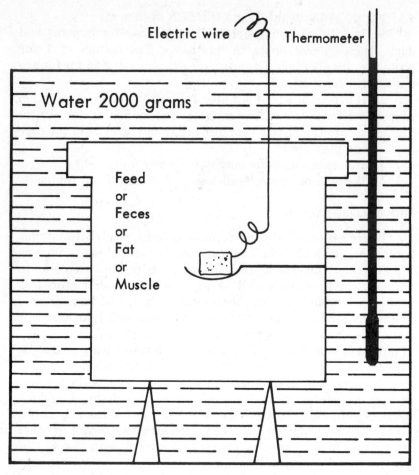

Fig. 6-5. Diagrammatic sketch of a bomb calorimeter used for the determination of the gross energy value (caloric content) of various materials. (Courtesy, Dr. Lorin E. Harris, Utah State University)

the gross energy (GE) content of the material.

Definitions of terms pertinent to the use of the energy system as used herein follow:

Gross energy (GE) (or heat of combustion) is the amount of heat, measured in calories, that is released when a substance is completely oxidized in a bomb calorimeter containing 25 to 30 atmospheres of oxygen. The gross energy of a feed, feces, urine, tissue, eggs, or other materials is determined by burning them in the bomb calorimeter as previously described.

Digestible energy (DE) is the gross energy of the food intake minus fecal energy.

Metabolizable energy (ME) is the gross energy of the food intake minus fecal energy, minus urinary energy, minus energy in the gaseous products of digestion.

Mineral Needs

Of all common farm animals, the pig is most likely to suffer from mineral deficiencies. This is due to the following peculiarities of swine husbandry:

1. Hogs are fed principally upon cereal grains and their by-products, all of which are relatively low in mineral matter, particularly in calcium.

2. The skeleton of the pig supports greater weight in proportion to its size than that of any other farm animal.

3. As hogs do not normally consume great amounts of roughage (pasturage or dry forage), it is not always easy to balance mineral deficiencies.

4. Hogs grow more rapidly than other classes of livestock, and they produce young when less mature.

5. Hogs are forced for an early market, before they are mature.

In addition to the brief narrative that follows, the mineral needs of and recommendations for swine are presented in Tables 6-2 to 6-5, and in Table 6-9.

SALT (SODIUM AND CHLORINE)

Although swine require less salt than other classes of farm animals, it is generally advantageous to supply them with it, particularly if the protein supplement is not derived from tankage or fish meal (two feeds which supply salt). Salt may be added to the ration at the rate of 0.25 to 0.5 percent of the total feed; or it may be provided alone or in a mineral mix in a suitable box or trough to which the animals are allowed free access. When salt is fed free choice, pigs will consume from 0.03 to 0.12 ounce per head daily, the amount depending upon the size of the animal and the type of ration fed.

Swine may suffer from salt poisoning as a result of con-

Minerals Which May Be Deficient Under Normal Conditions	Conditions Usually Prevailing Where Deficiencies Are Reported	Function of Mineral	Some Deficiency Symptoms
Salt (sodium and chlorine)	Salt deficiencies may exist when the protein supplement is all or chiefly of plant origin; although herbivorous animals require more salt than swine.	Sodium chloride helps maintain osmotic pressure in body cells, upon which depends the transfer of nutrients to the cells, the removal of waste materials, and the maintenance of water balance among the tissues. Also, sodium is important in making bile, which aids in the digestion of fats and carbohydrates, and chlorine is required for the formation of hydrochloric acid in the gastric juice so vital to protein digestion. It is noteworthy that when salt is omitted, sodium expresses its deficiency first.	Loss of appetite an poor growth, lack thrift, and a deprave appetite includin tail-biting.
Calcium	When the protein supplements are all or chiefly of plant origin and little forage is used. When swine are raised in confinement without vitamin D added to the ration. When feed intake is restricted during gestation.	Essential for development and maintenance of normal bones and teeth. Important in blood coagulation and lactation. Enables heart, nerves, and muscles to function. Regulates permeability of tissue cells. Affects availability of phosphorus and zinc.	Loss of appetite an poor growth, lack c thrift, lameness an stiffness, weakene bone structure, an impaired reproductio with pigs weak and/o stillborn. Severe case may show reduce serum calcium an tetany. Rickets ma develop in young pigs and osteoporosis i older animals.
Phosphorus	Rations containing only plant ingredients; late gestation; lactation; high calcium rations; swine in confinement without Vitamin D added to the ration; poor calcium to phosphorus ratio.	Essential for sound bones and teeth, and for the assimilation of carbohydrates and fats. A vital ingredient of the proteins in all body cells. Necessary for enzyme activation. Acts as a buffer in blood and tissue. Occupies a key position in biologic oxidation and reactions requiring energy.	Loss of appetite and poor growth, lameness and stiffness weakened bone structure, reduced inorganic blood phosphorus, depraved appetite breeding difficulties rickets, and osteomalacia.
Iodine	Iodine-deficient areas or soils (in northwestern U.S. and in the Great Lakes region) when iodized salt is not fed. Where feeds come from iodine-deficient areas.	Iodine is needed by the thyroid gland in making thyroxin (an iodine-containing hormone which controls the rate of body metabolism or heat production).	Poor hair and skin con dition, impaired re production, dead o weak offspring a birth, birth of hairles pigs, and goiter.
Iron	Suckling pigs kept off soil.	Necessary for formation of hemoglobin, an iron containing compound which enables the blood to carry oxygen. Iron is also important to certain enzyme systems.	Deficiency of iron and, or copper or vitamir B_{12} produces anemi in young pigs; characterized by a swoller condition around the head and shoulders, paleness inside of eyelids, reduced appetite unthriftiness and slow growth. Reproductior may also be impaired

Footnote on last page of table.

Nutrient Requirements[2] (*From NRC Pub. 1599)		Recommended Allowances[2] (*From NRC Pub. 1599)	Practical Sources of the Mineral	Comments
Daily trients/animal	Percentage of Rations			
e Tables 6-2 nd 6-4)	(See Tables 6-3 and 6-5)	*0.25 to 0.5% in the ration, or give hogs free access to salt alone or in a mineral mixture.	Salt in loose form.	When pigs are salt starved, precaution should be taken to prevent overeating of it. In iodine deficient areas, stabilized iodized salt should be used.
e Tables 6-2 nd 6-4)	(See Tables 6-3 and 6-5)	Self-feed suitable mineral, or add Ca to the ration as required to bring level of total ration slightly above requirements.	Ground limestone or oyster shell flour. Where both Ca and P are needed, use bone meal, dicalcium phosphate or defluorinated phosphate.	Because cereal grains (which largely form the diet of swine) are low in Ca, swine are more apt to suffer from Ca deficiencies than from any of the other minerals except salt. Most favorable Ca:P ratio is between 1:1 and 1.5:1. Sows milk contains a Ca:P ratio of 1.3:1.
e Tables 6-2 nd 6-4)	(See Tables 6-3 and 6-5)	Self-feed suitable mineral, or add P to the ration as required to bring level of total ration slightly above requirements.	Monosodium phosphate. Where both Ca and P are needed, use bone meal, dicalcium phosphate, or defluorinated phosphate.	One-half to 2/3 of P in grains is in phytate form, which is not well utilized by swine; although fairly good utilization of phytate P is achieved through action of phytases (enzymes) in the intestine.
or pregnant ows, 4.4 mcg odine/kg body wt. daily, and omewhat less or growing wine.	*0.09 mg/lb. feed (0.2 mg/kg feed)	*Use stabilized, iodized salt containing 0.007% iodine incorporated at 0.5% of the ration or fed free choice.	Stabilized iodized salt containing 0.007% iodine.	
wborn pigs re- ire 7 mg of ab- rbed iron daily r normal growth.	*36.4 mg/lb. feed (80 mg/kg feed) for baby pigs.	Suitable iron preparations, injected at levels of 150 to 200 mg into baby pigs at 1 to 3 days of age, will prevent anemia due to iron deficiency.	Any one of the following: (1) access to sod; (2) swab sow's udder with iron solution; (3) give iron-copper pill; (4) injectable iron compound; or (5) access to oral iron preparations.	Milk is deficient in iron and copper. Pigs should be encouraged to eat grain ration as soon as old enough.

(Continued)

Minerals Which May Be Deficient Under Normal Conditions	Conditions Usually Prevailing Where Deficiencies Are Reported	Function of Mineral	Some Deficiency Symptoms
Copper	Suckling pigs kept off soil.	Copper, along with iron and vitamin B_{12}, is necessary for hemoglobin formation, although it forms no part of the hemoglobin molecule (or red blood cells). Copper is essential in enzyme systems, hair development and pigmentation, bone development, reproduction, and lactation.	Same as with an iron deficiency; see above)
Zinc	High levels of calcium in relation to zinc levels.	Skin, hair and bone, development; reproduction.	Parakeratosis or swine dermatitis, pigs have a mangy look, reduced appetite, unthrifty, and poor growth rate, diarrhea, and there may be vomiting. It affects swine of all ages.
Magnesium		Essential in many enzyme systems.	Hyperirritability, muscular twitching, reluctance to stand, weak pasterns, loss of equilibrium, and tetany followed by death.
Manganese		Bone formation, coordination of muscular movements, and cofactor of some enzyme systems.	Weak pigs and poor sense of balance at birth; increased fat deposition in older swine; lameness and stiffness; and irregular estrus cycles.
Potassium			
Selenium	A selenium deficient diet.	Has a vitamin E relationship.	Death, marked necrosis of the liver, and yellowish-brown discoloration of body fat

Under natural conditions, no evidence of deficiencies in swine have been observed of the following mineral elements: magnesium, manganese, potassium, cobalt, and selenium.

Mineral recommendations for swine:

Allow free access to a two-compartment mineral box with (1) salt (iodized in iodine-deficient areas) in one side and (2) dicalcium phosphate, defluorinated phosphate, or a mixture of 1/3 salt (salt added for purposes of palatability) and 2/3 steamed bone meal in the other side.

Nutrient Requirements[2] (*From NRC Pub. 1599)		Recommended Allowances[2] (*From NRC Pub. 1599)	Practical Sources of the Mineral	Comments
(Daily nutrients/animal	Percentage of Rations			
0.1 to 0.15 mg/ kg body weight.	*2.7 mg/lb. feed (6 mg/kg feed) for baby pigs.		(1) iron-copper pill, (2) access to clean sod; (3) swab udder with copperas	
	*22.7 mg/lb. feed (50 mg/kg feed). When Ca level of ration is 1½ to 2%, double the zinc allowance.		Zinc carbonate, zinc sulfate, or zinc oxide.	It has been shown that parakeratosis is caused by zinc and calcium forming an unavailable complex.
	*181.8 mg/lb. feed (400 mg/kg feed)	Practical rations contain adequate magnesium. Supplementation is not necessary.	Magnesium oxide or magnesium sulfate.	Practical rations adequate in magnesium.
		*9 mg/lb. feed (20 mg/kg feed)	Manganous oxide.	
etween 2.5 and .0 gm daily for 00 lb. pig.	Percent potassium of diet: *0.26% for 10-lb. pig. *0.23 to 0.28% for 35-lb. pig.		Corn contains 0.27% potassium, and other cereals contain 0.42 to 0.49% potassium.	Deficiency of potassium not observed in practical rations.
	*0.10 mg/kg feed.		Practical rations have adequate selenium.	Vitamin E will also prevent symptoms listed; thus indicating a vitamin E-selenium relationship. Caution: Toxic level of selenium is in range of 5 to 8 mg/kg of feed.

the mineral supplement is incorporated in the concentrate ration, follow the directions given in Tables 6-3, 6-5, and 6-11.
so, provide iron and copper to young pigs (through access to soil or sod, by swabbing daily the sow's udder with a solution of ferrous sulfate, or by using an injectable compound).
so, a good commercial mineral may be used, either on a free-choice basis or by incorporating it in the ration.

[2]As used herein, the distinction between "nutrient requirements" and "recommended allowances" is as follows: nutrient requirements, no margins of safety are included intentionally; whereas in "recommended allowances" argins of safety are provided in order to compensate for variations in feed composition, environment, and possible sses during storage or processing.

suming (1) brine or salted fish meal, or (2) as little as 2 percent salt in the ration *when the water intake is restricted.*

CALCIUM AND PHOSPHORUS

Calcium and phosphorus are of importance for skeletal growth and strength of bones. They make up about three-fourths of the mineral matter of the entire body and over 90 percent of that in the skeleton. Also, the role of vitamin D, along with calcium and phosphorus, in normal skeletal development has been long established.

Recommended levels of calcium and phosphorus are given in Tables 6-2 to 6-5. Also, it is noteworthy that the most favorable ratio of calcium to phosphorus appears to be between 1:1 and 1.5:1. Sow's milk contains a calcium-phosphorus ratio of approximately 1.3:1.

It is recognized that the forms in which calcium and phosphorus exist in the ration may influence the efficiency of their utilization; for example, phytase phosphorus and some forms of inorganic phosphates may be poorly utilized. Since one-half to two-thirds of the phosphorus of cereal grains, and an even higher proportion in plant protein supplements, is in the phytate form, this fact merits consideration. Also, it is known that phytase phosphorus utilization is (1) affected by the phytases (enzymes) present in varying levels in corn and other cereal grains and in the intestinal tract, and (2) closely related to vitamin D, calcium, alimentary tract pH, zinc, calcium-phosphorus ratio, and other factors. The percentage values shown in Tables 6-3 and 6-5 take into account the possibility of incomplete utilization of phytate phosphorus.

A deficiency of calcium and phosphorus (or a lack of vitamin D) retards normal skeletal development and gain in live weight. The bones become fragile and are easily broken, and depraved appetites may be observed. In brood sows, a pronounced lack of these minerals may prevent normal reproduction, and the young may be born weak or even dead. If the deficiency persists with pigs, rickets will develop. This nutritional disease is characterized by a stiffness of the legs and a general unthriftiness; and it may even result in a paralysis of the hind legs.

Feeding steamed bone meal or dicalcium phosphate, which furnish both calcium and phosphorus, are common supplements when these two minerals are needed for swine. When calcium

Fig. 6-6. Calcium made the difference! The pig on the left received an adequate calcium ration, whereas the one on the right received a low calcium ration. Note the difference in the size of the animals, though they are of the same age. (Courtesy, Washington State University)

Fig. 6-7. Calcium deficiency (rickets). The young pig on the right was fed a ration seriously deficient in calcium. Note weakened and deformed bone structure of hind legs, depressed growth, and general lack of thriftiness. Fractured vertebrae and subsequent loss of control of hind legs is a common characteristic of calcium deficiency. Normal littermate is at left. (Courtesy, Dr. D. E. Becker, University of Illinois)

alone is needed, ground limestone or ground oyster shell flour
(or other calcium supplement) may be used. When phosphorus
alone is needed, monosodium phosphate may be used. Calcium
and phosphorus supplements may be fed free-choice, as recom-

Fig. 6-8. Phosphorus deficiency. A typical phosphorus-deficient pig is
shown on the left, characterized by weak and crooked leg bones. The pig
on the right received the same ration adequate in available phosphorus.
(Courtesy, M. P. Plumlee and W. M. Beeson, Purdue University)

mended in the section on "Mineral Feeding Recommendations"
which follows; and/or the needed supplements may be added to
the daily ration in keeping with the recommendations given in
Tables 6-2 to 6-5.

IODINE

Hogs require a small amount of iodine. A deficiency of this
mineral results in poor hair and skin condition, impaired re-
producton, dead or weak offspring at birth, and birth of hairless
pigs.

Wherever goiter is detected in livestock, or in inland areas
where natural feedstuffs are deficient in iodine, some supplemental source of iodine should be added.

Adequate iodine may be provided by using stabilized salt
containing 0.007 percent iodine; either (1) incorporating it in
the ration at 0.5 percent of the grain diet and/or (2) feeding the
salt free-choice.

Fig. 6-9. Hairlessness in pigs caused by a deficiency of iodine. In iodine-deficient areas, farm animals should receive iodized salt throughout the year. (Courtesy, Department of Veterinary Pathology and Hygiene, College of Veterinary Medicine, University of Illinois)

IRON AND COPPER

If suckling pigs are confined to paved pens or lots with no access to soil or forage (a common condition with pigs farrowed in the late winter or early spring months, and standard conditions in confinement rearing), serious losses from anemia (lack of red blood cells) are likely to be encountered. This anemia is due to a deficiency of iron and copper in the milk. Sow's milk has been reported to contain an average of 3 mg of iron per liter

TABLE 6-10

COPPER COMPOUNDS AND LEVELS IN SWINE RATIONS

Copper Compound	Percent of Copper	Amount to Add/Ton of Complete Ration to Furnish Copper at Required Level of 2.7 mg /lb. of Diet (6 mg /kg diet)[1]
	(%)	(grams)
Cupric carbonate ($CuCO_3$)-------------------	50	10.8
Cupric oxide (CuO)------------------------------	80	6.75
Cupric sulfate ($CuSO_4 . 5H_2O$) -------------	25	21.6

[1]For supplements, add copper at 4½ times the rate used for complete rations.

Fig. 6-10. Suckling pig with nutritional anemia, caused by a lack of iron, characterized by swollen condition about the head and paleness of the mucus membranes. (Courtesy, College of Veterinary Medicine, University of Illinois)

(1.056 quarts). Moreover, the feeding of various levels of different iron compounds to gestating and/or lactating sows has not proven effective in increasing the iron content of the milk.

Nutritional anemia in swine is characterized by labored breathing, a swollen condition especially around the head and shoulders, and a general weakened condition. This deficiency disease may be prevented or treated by following any one of the preventive measures given in Table 6-9. In addition, the pigs should be encouraged to eat a grain ration as soon as they are old enough.

Beyond the suckling period, normal rations usually contain sufficient quantities of iron and copper to supply the daily needs of swine. The iron and copper requirements of swine are given in Table 6-11, and sources of copper are given in Table 6-10.

ZINC

Zinc deficiency in swine rations produces parakeratosis or dermatosis, a non-contagious ailment. The dietary level of zinc

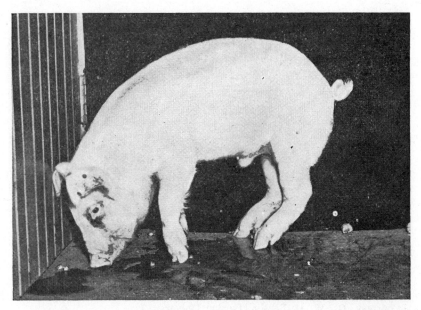

Fig. 6-11. Copper deficiency. Note the drawing under of the rear legs and crookedness of the forelegs. (Courtesy of H. S. Teague and L. E. Carpenter, Hormel Institute)

TABLE 6-11

TRACE MINERALS FOR SWINE[1]

Mineral Element	Recommended Level of Total Feed (Dry Basis)		Toxic Levels
	(ppm)	(g/ton)	(g/ton feed)
Magnesium[2] ------------	400.0	362.9	——
Iron[2] ----------------------	80.0	72.64	4,544
Zinc[3] ----------------------	50.0	45.40	1,818
Manganese--------------	20.0	18.14	3,636
Copper[2] -------------------	6.0	5.44	227
Iodine-------------------	0.2	.272	——
Selenium[4] --------------	0.1	0.18	4
Molybdenum[4]----------	0.01	.009	9

[1]From Bul. No. 2, *Nutrient Requirements of Swine,* Revised 1968, NRC Pub. 1599, p. 12, Table 6, with conversions by the author.
[2]Baby pig requirement.
[3]Higher levels may be needed if excess calcium is fed.
[4]The addition of selenium and molybdenum is not approved by FDA.

required to prevent this syndrome is given in Table 6-11; and recommended zinc compounds are given in Table 6-12. However, it is recognized that the zinc requirement is related to the level of calcium (high levels of calcium usually accentuate paraker-

Fig. 6-12. Zinc made the difference! These two pigs received the same ration for 74 days, except the pig on the left received only 17 ppm (7.7 mg/lb.) of zinc, whereas the pig on the right received 67 ppm (30 mg/lb.) of zinc.
Left: Zinc-deficient pig gained only 3 pounds. Note severe dermatosis or "mangy look."
Right: Pig gained 111 pounds.
(Courtesy, Dr. W. M. Beeson, Purdue University)

TABLE 6-12

RECOMMENDED ZINC COMPOUNDS AND LEVELS IN SWINE RATIONS

Zinc Compound	Zinc Content	Add/Ton of Complete Feed to Furnish Zinc at Level of 22.7 mg/lb. of Diet (50 mg/kg) [1]
	(%)	(grams)
Zinc carbonate (ZnCO₃)	56	81.0
Zinc oxide (ZnO)	80	56.8
Zinc sulfate (ZnSO₄ . 7H₂O)	23	197.3

[1]For protein supplements, add the zinc at 4½ times the rate for complete rations.

atosis and increase the dietary zinc requirement), source and level of protein, source of corn, and the phytic acid present in plant proteins.

OTHER MINERAL NEEDS

Under natural conditions, no evidence of deficiencies in swine have been observed of the following mineral elements: magnesium, manganese, potassium, cobalt, and selenium. Thus, there appears to be no need to supplement practical rations with them.

Fig. 6-13. Magnesium deficiency. Although there is no need to supplement practical swine rations with magnesium, a magnesium deficiency can be produced experimentally. Pig on left was fed 413 ppm (188 mg/lb.) magnesium for 3 weeks and pig on right received 70 ppm (32 mg/lb.) of magnesium for the same period. Note extreme leg weakness, arched back, and general unthriftiness of pig on the right. (Courtesy, M. P. Plumlee and W. M. Beeson, Purdue University)

The recommendations relative to certain trace minerals for swine are given in Table 6-11.

COMPLEX MINERAL MIXTURES

Most animal husbandmen favor the use of simple mineral mixtures. Providing either an excessive amount of minerals or a complex mineral mixture when it is not necessary is expensive and wasteful, and any imbalances may actually be injurious to animals. In general, the wise policy consists in knowing the mineral content of the available feeds and providing, in proper amounts, only those essential minerals which are deficient.

VALUE AND ECONOMY OF COMMERCIAL MINERAL MIXTURES

Commercial mineral mixtures are just what the name implies—minerals mixed by manufacturers who specialize in the commercial mineral business, either handling minerals alone or a combination feed and mineral business. Most commercial minerals are very good.

The commercial mineral manufacturer has the distinct advantages over farm- or ranch-mixing of (1) purchase of minerals in quantity lots, thereby obtaining price advantages, (2) econom-

ical and controlled mixing, (3) the hiring of scientifically trained personnel for use in determining the formulations, and (4) quality control. Additionally, most farmers and ranchers do not have the equipment with which to mix minerals properly. Besides, mineral mixes have become more complicated with recognition of the increasing importance of trace elements and interrelationships. For these reasons, commercial minerals are finding a place of increasing importance in all livestock feeding.

How to Select and Buy Commercial Mineral Mixes

The informed stockman will know what constitutes the best commercial mineral mix for his needs, and how to determine the best buy. Here are the factors to consider when buying a commercial mineral:

1. **The reputation of the manufacturer.**—This can be determined by (a) checking on who is back of it, (b) conferring with other stockmen who have used the particular product, and (c) checking on whether the product under consideration has consistently met its guarantees. The latter can be determined by reading the bulletins or reports published by the respective state departments in charge of enforcing feed laws.

2. **Determining your needs.**—The mineral requirements of the respective classes of livestock are much the same everywhere, although it is recognized that age, pregnancy, and lactation make for differences in mineral needs within a given herd. Additionally, there are some area differences.

3. **Choose method of supplying minerals.**—The daily mineral allowance for swine can be met by either (a) adding the minerals to the ration and/or (b) self-feeding.

4. **What's on the tag?**—Stockmen should study, and be able to interpret, what's on the tag. Does it contain what you need?

5. **Determine the best buy.**—When buying a mineral, the price should be checked against value received. For example, let's assume that the main need is for phosphorus, and that we wish to compare two minerals, which we shall call Brands X and Y. Brand X contains 12 percent phosphorus and sells at $170.00 per ton or $8.50/cwt; whereas Brand Y contains 10 percent phosphorus and sells at $160.00 per ton or $8.00/cwt. Which is the better buy?

COMPARATIVE VALUE OF BRANDS "X" AND "Y"
(based on phosphorus content alone)

Brand	Phosphorus	Price/cwt.	Cost/lb. Phosphorus
	(%)	($)	(cents)
X	12	8.50	71
Y	10	8.00	80

Hence, Brand X is the better buy, even though it costs 50 cents more per hundred, or $10.00 per ton more.

One other thing is important. As a usual thing, the more scientifically formulated mineral mixes will have plus values in terms of (1) trace mineral (needs and balance) and (2) palatability (animals will eat just the right amount of a good mineral, but they won't overdo it—due to appetizers, rather than needs).

FEEDS AS A SOURCE OF MINERALS

The most satisfactory source of minerals for hogs is in the feed consumed. It is important to know, however, whether the minerals in the ration are of the right kind and sufficient in amount. Certain general characteristics of feeds in regard to calcium and phosphorus (the two predominating mineral elements of the body) are worth noting:

1. The cereal grains and their by-products and protein supplements of plant origin are low in calcium but fairly high in phosphorus.

2. The protein supplements of animal origin (skim milk, buttermilk, tankage, meat scraps, fish meal), legume forage (pasturage and hay), and rape are rich in calcium.

3. Most protein-rich supplements are high in phosphorus.

With the possible exception of common salt, the mineral requirements of swine can often be met through the proper selection of feeds. This may not hold true, however, in feeding young pigs and gestating-lactating sows.

MINERAL FEEDING RECOMMENDATIONS[4]

The mineral feeding recommendations for swine are:

---

[4]Generally speaking, the recommendations given herein can be followed on a nation-wide basis. However, it is recognized that area differences do exist. Therefore, for more specific recommendations, the stockman should always obtain the counsel of his county agricultural agent (farm advisor) or state college of agriculture.

1. When supplements of animal or marine origin constitute ⅓ or more of the source of proteins, allow free access to a two-compartment mineral box with (1) salt (iodized salt in iodine-deficient areas) in one side, and (2) a mixture of ⅓ salt (salt added for purposes of palatability) and ⅔ bone meal (or other phosphorus supplement) in the other side.

2. When supplements of plant origin constitute most of the source of proteins, add a third compartment to the mineral box and place in it a mixture of ⅓ salt and ⅔ ground limestone or oyster shell flour (or other calcium supplement).

In addition, iron and copper should be provided to young pigs (see Table 6-9 for methods).

When the calcium content of the ration exceeds 0.8 per cent, add 0.4 pound of zinc carbonate or 0.9 pound of zinc sulfate per ton of feed.

Most authorities prefer that minerals be self-fed free choice. Then the animal consumes them according to need. However,

TABLE 6-13

RECOMMENDED MINERALS AND ALLOWANCES FOR
INCORPORATION (1) IN ENTIRE RATION, AND (2)
IN PROTEIN SUPPLEMENT ONLY

| | Kind and Amounts of Minerals Required | |
Kind of Protein Supplement	When Mixed with Ration Containing All Concentrates	When Mixed with Protein Supplement Only
	(lbs./100 lbs. mix)	(lbs./100 lbs. supplement)
1. Tankage, meat meal, fish meal, and/or dried milk constituting 1/3 or more of the source of proteins	0.25—0.5 salt	1.5 salt
2. Linseed, soybean, cottonseed, and/or peanut meal constituting most of the source of proteins	0.5 salt 0.75 ground lime-stone or oyster shell flour	1.5 to 2.0 salt 4.0—5.0 limestome or oyster shell flour

the mineral supplement may be incorporated in the ration in keeping with the recommended allowances given in Tables 6-3, 6-5, and 6-11. For the entire ration, usually 1 percent by weight will prove adequate; for the protein concentrate only, 5 to 6 pounds of mineral mixture should be added to each 94 to 95 pounds of high-protein feed (see Table 6-13).

Vitamin Needs

Because of the greater prevalence of confinement feeding, swine are more likely to suffer from nutritional deficiencies, especially lack of vitamins, than any other class of farm animals. The vitamin requirements are especially important in young pigs (from birth to 30 pounds) and in gestating-lactating sows.

In addition to the narrative that follows, the vitamin requirements for swine are presented in Tables 6-2 to 6-5 and Table 6-14. As noted, vitamin A and D requirements are in terms of I.U. (International Unit). One I.U. is equal to one U. S. P. unit.

Sometimes vitamins are classified according to method of extraction as (1) fat-soluble, which includes vitamins A, D, E, and K; and (2) water-soluble, which includes the B vitamins and vitamin C.

VITAMIN A

The vitamin A requirements of swine (see Tables 6-2 to 6-5) can be met either by vitamin A or *B*-carotene. However, the pig is a relatively inefficient converter of *B*-carotene to vitamin A as compared to the rat. One mg. of *B*-carotene is equal to approximately 500 I.U. of vitamin A in the pig as compared to 1,667 I.U. of vitamin A in the rat.

The vitamin A and provitamin A in feeds are readily destroyed. Hence, it is usually necessary that a vitamin A supplement be added to swine rations.

In the absence of green forages, in periods of drought, and

Fig. 6-14. Vitamin A deficiency. Litter of pigs born blind and with other abnormalities as the result of maternal vitamin A deficiency. (Courtesy, Prof. Fred Hale, Texas Agricultural Experiment Station)

Vitamins Which May Be Deficient Under Normal Conditions	Conditions Usually Prevailing Where Deficiencies Are Reported	Function of Vitamin	Some Deficiency Symptoms
A	Absence of green forages, either pasture or green hay—especially under confinement conditions. Where the ration consists chiefly of white corn, milo, barley, wheat, oats, or rye; or by-products of these grains; or yellow corn that has been stored in excess of a year.	Essential for normal maintenance and functioning of the epithelial tissues, particularly of the eyes and the respiratory, digestive, reproductive, nerve, and urinary systems.	Night and day bl ness, very irrita poor appetite slow growth, lame and impaired re duction with dea weak offspring birth. Low resistance to piratory infection
D	Limited sunlight and/or limited quantities of sun-cured hay in confinement rations.	Aids in assimilation and utilization of calcium and phosphorus, and necessary in the normal bone development of animals—including the bone of the fetus.	Rickets in young or osteomalacia ir ture hogs. Both ditions result in l joints and weak bc
E (tocopherol)	Diets containing excessive amounts of highly unsaturated fatty acids or oxidized fats.		Increased embryc mortality and mus lar incoordinatior suckling pigs fi sows fed vitamin deficient diets dur gestation and la tion.
B Vitamins, including the following: (The underlined B vitamins are the most limiting for swine during growth and reproduction):	Absence of green forages, either pasture or green hay—especially under confinement conditions. Where good quality animal proteins are missing from or limited in the ration.	In general, the B vitamins are needed as tools for energy metabolism in the body. (See function of each B vitamin.)	Deficiency sympt vary according to specific B vitamir volved (see below

VITAMIN CHART

Nutritive Requirements[1] (*From NRC Pub. 1599)		Recommended Allowances[1] (*From NRC Pub. 1599)	Practical Sources of the Vitamin	Comments
Daily nutrients/animal	Amount per lb. of feed			
(See Table 6-2 and 6-4)	(See Table 6-3 and 6-5)	Add vitamin A to the ration to bring level of total ration slightly above requirements.	Stabilized vitamin A	Confinements and winter swine rations should contain a quantity of high quality ground alfalfa or other suitable forage (5 to 10% for growing-finishing pigs, and 15 to 35% for brood sows). Meals from artificially dehydrated forages are much higher in carotene than sun-cured products. One mg. of beta-carotene from natural feedstuffs is equal to approximately 500 I.U. of vitamin A activity for swine.
(See Table 6-2 and 6-4)	(See Table 6-3 and 6-5)	Add vitamin D to the ration to bring level of total ration slightly above requirements.	Exposure to sunlight. Sun-cured hay (10% alfalfa in the total ration will normally supply sufficient D). Fortified fish oils, irradiated sterols. Crystalline D_2 or D_3, which are similar in biological activity for swine.	The vitamin D requirement is less when a proper balance of calcium and phosphorus exists in the ration. When animals are exposed to direct sunlight, the ultraviolet light produces vitamin D from traces of cholesterol in the skin.
Unknown				
		Add each of the B vitamins to the ration to bring level of total ration slightly above requirements.	Green pastures and green hays are excellent sources of most B vitamins. When neither pasture nor high quality roughage is available, the essential B vitamins may be provided by adding to the ration yeast (2 to 4%), distillers' solubles, animal or marine products, or other B vitamin sources.	The swine producer can usually meet the B vitamin requirements of the pig by (1) making the maximum use of pastures throughout the grazing season and (2) feeding generous quantities (5 to 10% for growing-finishing pigs and 15 to 35% for brood sows) of high quality ground alfalfa or other suitable forage during the winter or under confinement conditions. During the critical periods —(1) young, growing pigs under 75 lbs. in wt., (2) gestation, and (3) lactation—especially under confinement conditions, some animal protein supplement and/or vitamin premixes should also be included in the ration in order to assure sufficient B vitamins and unidentified factors.

(Continued)

Vitamins Which May Be Deficient Under Normal Conditions	Conditions Usually Prevailing Where Deficiencies Are Reported	Function of Vitamin	Some Deficiency Symptoms
Thiamine		Promotes appetite and growth, required for normal carbohydrate metabolism, and aids reproduction.	Loss of appetite and poor growth, diarrhea, dead or weak offspring, slow pulse, low body temperature, and flabby heart.
Riboflavin		Promotes growth, and important in carbohydrate and amino-acid metabolism.	Poor growth, rough hair coat, diarrhea, and abnormal gait in the young pig; reproductive failure in the sow.
Niacin		Required by all living cells, and an essential component of important metabolic enzyme systems involved in glycolysis and tissue respiration.	Loss of appetite and decreased gain, followed by diarrhea, occasional vomiting, dermatitis, and loss of hair.
Pantothenic Acid		Part of co-enzyme A, a necessary factor for intermediary metabolism.	A goose-stepping gait, poor growth, some loss of hair, and diarrhea.
Pyridoxine (B₆)		Basic in amino-acid and fat metabolism.	Loss of appetite and poor-growth, unsteady gait, and epileptic-like fits.
Choline		Functions in amino-acid and fat metabolism and necessary for normal reproduction in swine.	Gestating sows farrow large number of weak pigs. Pigs unthrifty with muscular incoordination and heavy mortality.
B₁₂		Stimulates appetite, increases the rate of growth and the efficiency of feed utilization and necessary for normal reproduction.	Loss of appetite, poor growth and lowered reproduction.
Biotin	Pigs fed (1) dried, raw egg white or (2) sulfathalidine. Also, when very young pigs are fed a diet lacking in biotin.		Alopecia, spasticity of the hind legs, cracks in the feet and a dermatosis.
Either there is sufficient intestinal synthesis or the pig does not need the following B vitamins: inositol, para-aminobenzoic acid, and folic acid (folacin).			

(Continued)

Nutritive Requirements[1] (*From NRC Pub. 1599)		Recommended Allowances[1] (*From NRC Pub. 1599)	Practical Sources of the Vitamin	Comments
Daily nutrients/animal	Amount per lb. of feed			
(See Table 6-2 and 6-4)	(See Table 6-3 and 6-5)			Thiamine content of normal feeds is usually sufficient.
(See Table 6-2 and 6-4)	(See Table 6-3 and 6-5)		Dried skim milk is an excellent source of riboflavin. Synthetic riboflavin.	Riboflavin is apt to be lacking in swine rations.
(See Table 6-2 and 6-4)	(See Table 6-3 and 6-5)			Niacin occurs in corn, wheat and milo in bound form; hence, may be unavailable to the pig. Also, the tryptophan level affects the niacin requirement, because of the conversion of tryptophan to niacin.
(See Table 6-2 and 6-4)	(See Table 6-3 and 6-5)		Fish solubles are an excellent source of pantothenic acid.	Grain is very deficient in pantothenic acid. Thus, it is apt to be lacking in swine rations.
(See Table 6-2 and 6-4)	(See Table 6-3 and 6-5)			Pyridoxine content of normal feeds is usually sufficient.
(See Table 6-2 and 6-4)	(See Table 6-3 and 6-5)	*For baby pigs, 0.1% of the diet; for sows, 20 mg per kg of body weight.		Choline content of normal feeds is usually sufficient.
(See Table 6-2 and 6-4)	(See Table 6-3 and 6-5)		Protein supplements of animal origin.	Vitamin B_{12} is apt to be lacking in normal swine rations. B_{12} contains cobalt.
				Very young pigs do not produce enough biotin until they develop an intestinal flora capable of synthesizing it.

(Continued)

TABLE

Vitamins Which May Be Deficient Under Normal Conditions	Conditions Usually Prevailing Where Deficiencies Are Reported	Function of Vitamin	Some Deficiency Symptoms
Under ordinary conditions, swine never have deficiencies of vitamins K, or C (ascorbic acid).			
Unidentified factors. Both organic and inorganic.		Contribute factor or factors or correct imbalances.	

in various parts of the world where pig diets consist of materials low in carotene—such as white corn, barley, wheat, oats, rye, and feeds made from the by-products of these grains—serious vitamin A losses have occurred. Under these conditions, stabilized vitamin A should be added to the ration.

VITAMIN D

A lack of vitamin D (or of calcium or phosphorus) in swine rations will cause rickets in young pigs or osteomalacia in mature hogs. Both conditions result in large joints and weak bones.

Fig. 6-15. A pig with rickets caused by a vitamin D deficiency. (Courtesy, Ohio Agricultural Experiment Station)

ontinued)

Nutritive Requirements[1] (*From NRC Pub. 1599)		Recommended Allowances[1] (*From NRC Pub. 1599)	Practical Sources of the Vitamin	Comments
Daily nutrients/animal	Amount per lb. of feed			
			Dehydrated alfalfa and grass, dried whey, distillers' solubles, dried fish sholubles, antibiotic fermentation residue.	Unidentified factors contribute other than known nutrients of benefit to growing pigs and gestating-lactating sows.

[1]As used herein, the distinction between "nutrient requirements" and "recommended allowances" is as follows: nutrient requirements, no margins of safety are included intentionally; whereas in nutrient allowances margins safety are provided in order to compensate for variations in feed composition, environment, and possible losses ring storage or processing.

Grains, grain by-products, and high protein feedstuffs are practically devoid of vitamin D. Therefore, in the northern latitudes, a combination of limited and not too effective sunlight, plus limited quantities of sun-cured hay in the ration, cannot always be relied upon to supply ample quantities of vitamin D to hogs. Likewise, this situation applies to hogs kept in confinement. Under these conditions, the addition of vitamin D is cheap and effective protection. Either D_2 (irradiated ergosterol) or D_3 (irradiated 7-dehydrocholesterol) may be used, since they are similar in biological activity for swine. The vitamin D requirements of different classes and weights of swine are given in Tables 6-2 to 6-5. It should be noted, however, that the vitamin-D requirement is less when a proper balance of calcium and phosphorus exists in the ration.

THE B VITAMINS

Young growing pigs and gestating-lactating sows may not obtain optimum amounts of certain of the B vitamins, particularly under confinement conditions. It is considered good practice, therefore, to include them in swine rations during these critical periods. Experimental work has indicated that the following B vitamins are required by the pig: thiamine, riboflavin, niacin, pantothenic acid, pyridoxine (B_6), choline, B_{12}, and biotin.

Fig. 6-16. Contrast in growth of littermates due to level of thiamine intake. The one on the right received no thiamine while the one on the left received the equivalent of 2 mg of thiamine per 100 lbs. liveweight. (Courtesy, N. R. Ellis, USDA Research Center)

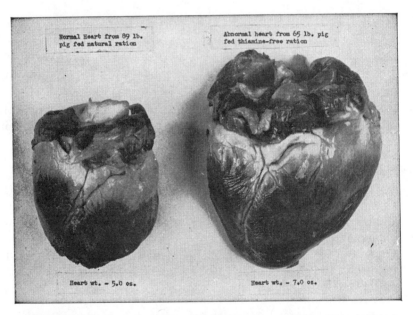

Fig. 6-17. Enlargement of the heart of a pig caused by a B_1 or thiamine deficiency. (Courtesy, Washington State University)

Either there is sufficient intestinal synthesis or the pig does not need the following B vitamins: inositol, para-aminobenzoic acid, and folic acid (folacin).

See Tables 6-2 to 6-5 relative to the nutritive requirements of the B vitamins.

Fig. 6-18. All pigs from sows that received a riboflavin deficient ration during gestation were either born dead or died within 48 hours. (Courtesy, Washington State University)

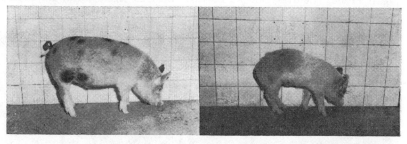

Fig. 6-19. Niacin, or nicotinic acid, deficiency. The weanling pig on the left was fed a high corn ration adequate in niacin or nicotinic acid. The pig on the right was fed a high corn ration without supplementary niacin or nicotinic acid. The latter pig grew slowly, exhibited a rough hair coat, and had intermittent diarrhea. Upon autopsy, the intestinal tract was found to be ulcerated. (Courtesy, Dr. D. E. Becker, University of Illinois)

UNKNOWN FACTOR OR FACTORS

Optimum results with swine during the critical periods (early growth and gestation-lactation) appear to be dependent upon providing an unidentified factor or factors through feeding one or more of the following: distillers' dried solubles, fish

Fig. 6-20. Pantothenic acid deficiency. Locomotor incoordination (goose-stepping) produced by feeding of a pantothenic acid-low corn-soybean meal ration. (Courtesy, R. W. Luecke, Michigan Agricultural Experiment Station)

Fig. 6-21. Vitamin B$_6$ deficiency. This pig is having an epileptic-like fit. (Experimental work, University of California; photo courtesy, Dr. T. J. Cunha, University of Florida)

Fig. 6-22. Pigs from a sow that received a choline-deficient ration during the gestation period. Note the weak, spraddle-legged condition of the pigs. (Courtesy, Washington State University)

Fig. 6-23. Biotin made the difference! Both pigs received the same ration, except that biotin was added to the ration of the pig on the right. The biotin-deficient pig exhibited cracked feet, dryness of the skin, loss of hair, and spasticity of the hind legs. (Courtesy, Washington State University)

solubles, dried whey, grass juice concentrate, soil, high quality alfalfa meal, brewer's dried yeast, pasture, or liver.

BODY STORAGE

Work at both the Wisconsin and Washington stations showed that the ration gilts receive during growth influences their performance during reproduction three to five months later. This means that growing gilts, provided that they are fed a well-balanced ration which supplies these factors, store up certain of these factors which are later required in reproduction. This phenomenon is referred to as the residual effects of previous nutrition. This means that the ration of prospective breeding gilts should receive more attention than may be necessary to give to the ration of growing-finishing hogs to be placed on the market.

Work at the Washington Agricultural Experiment Station also showed a positive relationship between thiamine intake and the deposition of this vitamin in the tissues of hogs. It was found that one pork chop from the pigs consuming the thiamine-enriched ration contained sufficient of this factor to meet the daily requirement of a human. However, it would have required ten pork chops from the pigs on a low-thiamine ration to meet this same need. This suggests the possibility of increasing the nutritive qualities of pork through the ration.

SUMMARY OF VITAMIN NEEDS OF SWINE

The limiting factor in the use of most vitamin supplements is their high price. For economy reasons, therefore, any vitamin fortification of the ration should be in keeping with the nutrient requirements and/or recommended allowances (see Table 6-2 to 6-5).

Anti-microbial Agents[5]

Most swine producers are familiar with, or have used, one or more of the antibiotics or other anti-microbial agents. In 1949, it was discovered that antibiotics were something new to be added

---

[5] This section was authoritatively reviewed by the following persons: Dr. D. E. Becker, Professor and Swine Specialist, Department of Animal Science, University of Illinois, Urbana, Ill.; and Dr. E. R. Barrick, Head, Animal Husbandry Section, North Carolina State University, Raleigh, North Carolina.

to livestock feeds; and soon the race was on with a long list of feed additives. Among them are arsenicals, nitrofurans, sulfonamides, and copper compounds. These chemicals have a specialized role in swine feeding and should be used according to their specific purpose and in keeping with the manufacturer's directions. Some of their functions are similar to those of the antibiotics.

Today, many of these additives are being incorporated in practical swine rations for purposes of stimulating liveweight gains, improving feed efficiency, and lessening disease.

Despite some glowing reports to the contrary, there is no evidence to indicate that the use of these additives can or will alleviate the need for vigilant sanitation, improved nutrition, and superior management. Also, the benefits of each one must be weighed against its cost.

Fig. 6-24. Terramycin (an antibiotic) + vitamin B$_{12}$ made the difference! At the beginning of the experiment, the pig on the left weighed 19½ lbs., whereas the pig on the right weighed 23 lbs. They received the same ration, except terramycin + vitamin B$_{12}$ was added to the ration of the pig on the left. Nine weeks later (when photographed, above), the pig on the left weighed 76 lbs., whereas the pig on the right weighed 55 lbs. (Courtesy, Washington State University)

ANTIBIOTICS

For recommended levels of antibiotics in swine rations, see Table 6-15.

TABLE 6-15

RECOMMENDED ANTIBIOTIC LEVELS[1]

	Pig Weight		Antibiotic Level[2]	
	(lb.)	(kg)	(mg/lb. feed)	(mg/kg feed)
Baby pigs --	11	5	20	44
	22	10	20	44
Growing pigs --------------------------------------	44	20	5-10	11-22
Finishing pigs-------------------------------------	99-198	45-90	5	11
Therapeutic level----------------------------			50-100	110-220[3]
			(per lb. of supplement)	(per kg of supplement)
Supplement to be fed free choice with grain--------------------------------------			25-50	55-110

[1]From Bul. No. 2, *Nutrient Requirements of Swine*, Revised 1968, NRC Pub. 1599, with avoirdupois added by the author.
[2]Some of the newer antibiotics may be used at lower levels. One should follow Food and Drug Administration regulations on the level to use.
[3]If pigs are in very poor condition and will not eat, the antibiotic can be given in drinking water.

Experimental results to date indicate that antibiotics have the following nutritional role for swine:

1. They produce about 10 percent more rapid gains from birth to about 200 pounds, thus effecting a saving in labor and reaching an earlier market.

2. They may increase the feed efficiency of growing-finishing pigs up to 5 percent; which means that they may save approximately 20 pounds of feed per 100 pounds of gain. When used with poor-quality rations, efficiency of feed utilization may be considerably more.

3. They reduce the number of runts, thus making for more uniformity in the pig crop.

4. They lessen scouring and nonspecific enteritis. Recent studies indicate that a combination of antibiotics and an arsenical is more effective against certain cases of scours than either supplement alone.

5. They are effective under either pasture or confinement conditions, but greater response is usually obtained in the latter.

6. They produce maximum growth response when fed to young pigs under 100 pounds weight, with less response from older and heavier animals.

7. They produce 5 to 10 pounds heavier weaning weights (eight weeks) when creep-fed to suckling pigs.

8. They give less response when fed to healthy animals in a

healthy environment than when fed to *unhealthy* animals in an *unhealthy* environment.

9. They should not be taken out of the diet of young pigs to which they have been fed. When fed to a weight of 100 to 125 pounds and then withdrawn from the diet, rate of gain may be retarded.

10. Experimental results of the effect of antibiotics on carcass quality have varied. However, they may produce a fatter carcass when fed to finishing hogs over 100 pounds in weight as a result of faster gains.

11. They increase bloom.

12. There is some evidence to indicate that the feeding of antibiotics to pregnant sows may increase the birth weight, livability, and weaning weight of pigs; but more experimental work in this area is needed. It is known, however, that antibiotics are not transferred through the milk of sows in sufficient amounts to show marked stimulation in the growth of nursing pigs.

13. They seem to lessen the requirements for protein. Their effectiveness in stretching the supply of protein supplements is especially important, because proteins have always been in shorter supply and higher in price than other feeds. It is not yet clear how much of the protein-sparing effect is due to the antibiotic and how much to a ration more adequate in B_{12}, riboflavin, niacin, pantothenic acid, and other nutrients.

14. Terramycin (chlortetracycline), aureomycin (oxytetracycline), and procaine penicillin were first considered to be the antibiotics of greatest value for adding to swine rations. Now it appears that certain mixes of these antibiotics with one another or with streptomycin or bacitracin may be more effective sources of antibiotic activity for swine.

15. A majority of experiments show that the subcutaneous implantation of baby pigs with chlortetracycline, bacitracin, or penicillin pellets is not effective in increasing weaning weights or livability.

16. No detectable amounts of aureomycin have been found in the meat even when pigs were fed higher than normal levels. Moreover, cooking destroys many antibiotics.

Finally, it is recognized that antibiotics vary in their effect on swine, according to (1) the levels fed, (2) the particular kind of antibiotics, (3) the health and environment of the animal,

(4) the type of ration—producing less response on high quality rations, (5) the age of the animal, etc.

Based on this information, the progressive swine producer will wish to incorporate these products in certain practical rations. Reputable commercial feed companies are doing this. Both the farmer who mixes his own feeds, and the commercial feed company can buy these products and **thoroughly mix them,** at the levels given in Table 6-15. These levels may vary somewhat, depending on the antibiotic, the ration used, and the environmental conditions. Under some conditions, the level fed may need to be higher.

Water Needs

Weanling pigs and lactating sows have a higher water requirement than other swine. Also, the higher the temperature the greater the water consumption. Pigs normally consume an average of 2 to 2.5 pounds of water per pound of dry feed. In high temperature environment, however, water consumption may be as high as 4 to 4.5 pounds per pound of dry feed. On a live weight basis, weanlings will consume up to 2.5 gallons of water per 100 pounds of body weight, whereas finishing pigs will normally consume about 0.8 gallons of water per 100 pounds body weight. Under average conditions, the water requirements for swine are about as shown in Table 6-16.

It is preferable that swine have access to automatic waterers, with water available at all times. Otherwise they should be hand-watered at least twice daily. During winter, the drinking water should not be permitted to fall below a temperature of 35° to 40° F.

TABLE 6-16

WATER REQUIREMENTS OF SWINE

Hog Condition and Size	Water Required
	(gal./day)
Sow, gestating	4½
Sow, lactating plus litter	6
Boars, mature	4½
Growing-finishing pigs:	
Weaning to 75 lbs.	½-1½
75 to 125 lbs.	1½-2
125 lbs. to market	2-3

If swine get an abundance of such watery feeds as dairy by-products, silage, roots, or slop, there will be less need of furnishing water separately. On the other hand, when self-fed dry feeds, pigs need access to clean, fresh water at all times. Otherwise, feed consumption will be too low for satisfactory performance.

The space requirements for watering equipment are given in Table 10-9.

FEEDS FOR SWINE

Throughout the world, swine are raised on a great variety of feeds, including numerous by-products. Except when on pasture or when ground dry forages are incorporated in the ration, they eat relatively little roughage (Table 6-1).

In this country, corn and swine production have always been closely associated. Normally, more than one-half of the corn crop is fed to hogs. Yet, the agriculture of the fifty states is very diverse, and the diet of the pig is readily adapted to the feeds produced locally. A similar adaptation in feeding practices is found in other countries. Thus, in most sections of the world, swine are fed predominantly on home-grown feeds. Ireland depends largely upon potatoes and dairy by-products; the swine industry of Denmark has been built up to augment the dairy industry, with milk and whey supplementing home-grown and imported cereals (primarily barley); and in Germany the pig is fed on such crops as potatoes, sugar beets, and green forage.

Concentrates for Swine

Because of their simple monogastric stomach, swine consume more concentrates and less roughages than any other class of four-footed farm animals (see Table 6-1). This characteristic gives pigs less opportunity to consume large quantities of calcium, vitamin-rich, and better quality protein roughages. Also, swine grow more rapidly than cattle, sheep, or horses, and produce young when less mature. This combination of conditions results in swine suffering more nutritional deficiencies than other large animals. It is probably safe to assume that less than half of the swine in the United States are fed balanced rations; yet, with our present knowledge of nutrition, this need not be so.

Although most concentrate feeds are not suitable as the sole

ration for hogs, it must be realized that swine can utilize a larger variety of feeds to greater advantage than any other farm animal. In general, the grain crops—corn, barley, wheat, oats, rye, and the kafirs—constitute the major component of the swine ration. However, sweet potatoes and peanuts are used successfully and extensively in the South, soybeans in the central states, and peas in the Northwest. In those districts where they are grown, potatoes also are usually utilized in considerable quantities in feeding hogs. In addition, in most every section of the country one or more by-product feeds are fed to hogs—including the by-products of the fishing industry, the meat packing industry, the milling industry, and the dairy industry. Human food wastes, such as refuse or garbage, are also fed extensively.

It is estimated that the concentrates—including the grains, root crops, and by-product feeds—make up, on the average, 95.6 percent of the ration of hogs (see Table 6-1). Thus, normally, only limited high-quality roughages or superior pastures are included in the ration of the pig.

The protein and vitamin requirements of the monogastric pig differ very greatly from those of the ruminant, for the latter improves the quality of proteins and creates certain vitamins through bacterial synthesis.

Despite all this, it is possible to meet the nutritive needs of the pig on these concentrated feeds by keeping in mind the following factors when balancing the ration:

1. The cereal grains and their by-products are relatively good in phosphorus, but low in calcium and the other minerals.

2. Except for the carotene content of yellow corn and green peas, the grains are very poor sources of the vitamins.

3. Most cereal grains supply proteins of poor quality.

4. Protein supplements of animal origin generally supply proteins of high quality, whereas proteins of plant origin generally supply proteins of low quality.

5. Because of the inadequacies of most concentrates, it is usually necessary to rely on fortification of minerals and vitamins.

Further discussion of each of the concentrates commonly fed to swine is found in the following chapters of this book: Chapter VII, "Grains and Other High Energy Feeds for Swine"; and Chapter VIII, "Protein, Vitamin, and Milling By-Product Feeds for Swine."

HIGH LYSINE CORN

In 1963, Purdue University announced the discovery of a high lysine corn due to a mutant gene called opaque-2, which does not change the total amount of protein but does change the composition of the protein.

Opaque-2 corn contains nearly twice as much of the amino acid lysine as normal corn, thereby boosting the protein efficiency of the grain when it is consumed by humans or hogs. Thus, hog rations composed of high lysine corn, supplemented with proper vitamins and minerals, is a distinct possibility in the future.

Also, corn higher than normal in the amino acid methianine has been discovered. Since methianine is often a limiting factor in poultry rations, this development is of interest to poultry producers.

It is doubtful that high lysine or high methianine corn will give much of an assist to cattle and sheep feeders.

It is generally agreed that high lysine corn will have to yield within approximately 95 percent of today's hybrids if it is to be competitive. Plant breeders are now multiplying the quantity of high lysine seed available and selecting for higher yields. Also, animal scientists are conducting experiments to evaluate the "changed" corn.

Pastures for Swine

Although swine cannot be grown and finished economically on pasture crops alone, on many farms these crops are an important adjunct to grain rations. Green, succulent pastures are also superior to comparable quality dry roughages for swine. In addition to reducing the cost of the ration, superior pastures, especially if legumes, provide a good source of calcium, serve as an excellent source of most of the needed vitamins, are higher in protein content than the grains, and carry protein of better quality than is found in grains.

In general, temporary pastures are preferable to permanent pastures for swine, especially from the standpoint of disease and parasite control. But permanent pastures do have a very definite place in the swine program. Although no single pasture crop can be recommended as being best for any and all conditions, there are certain desirable qualities that should be considered in choosing a forage crop for swine. These qualities and other pertinent

Fig. 6-25. Pigs on alfalfa pasture, in Nebraska. Superior pastures reduce the cost of the ration, provide a good source of calcium, serve as an excellent source of most of the needed vitamins, and furnish a higher quality and quantity of proteins than the grains. (Courtesy, Agricultural Agent, Burlington Lines)

information on the subject are discussed in Chapter IX, "Pastures for Swine." Also, pasture versus confinement hog production is discussed in Chapter XIV, "Swine Management."

Dry Roughages for Swine

During the winter months or at other seasons of the year when green, succulent pastures cannot be provided, it is desirable that swine rations contain generous quantities of a high-quality ground forage, preferably alfalfa. Well-cured, green, leafy alfalfa will supply the body-building minerals, vitamins, and quality proteins that are lacking in most farm grains.

Nutritionists generally look upon alfalfa as holding a place in animal nutrition comparable to that which milk popularly holds in human nutrition. Alfalfa contains proteins of the right quality to balance the amino-acid deficiencies of grain proteins; it is a rich source of minerals, especially calcium; and, finally, it is an excellent source of all the vitamins needed by the pig. From the standpoint of vitamins alone, alfalfa is almost indispensable in confinement swine rations. If leafy and green, and not over a year old, it is high in carotene (provitamin A), a lack of which results in the poor growth and the farrowing of premature, dead, or weak pigs. Sun-cured hay is also a good source of vitamin D, the antirachitic vitamin. In the northern

latitudes in particular, the pig may have to obtain dietary sources of vitamin D, for the action of the sun's rays on the body of the animal may prove inadequate. Alfalfa is also an excellent source of the long list of B vitamins.

Because of the many virtues of well-cured, green, leafy alfalfa in the swine ration, it is generally recommended that gestating-lactating sow rations contain from 15 to 35 percent ground alfalfa, or they may be fed alfalfa hay in a rack, allowing 1 linear foot of rack space per 4 sows. Because of the more limited digestive capacity of swine and their inability to utilize fiber, the alfalfa content of the ration for growing pigs must be more restricted. Thus, the alfalfa content of the ration of growing-finishing pigs had best be held to a level of 5 to 10 percent.

In addition to its beneficial effects in supplying the needed vitamins, minerals, and proteins, the inclusion of alfalfa in swine rations generally reduces the feed cost, for alfalfa seldom costs as much per pound as the grains.

Silage for Swine

Silage is especially suitable for gestating sows and herd boars. The Purdue station[6] fed 10 to 12 pounds of silage daily plus supplement to pregnant sows, with one lot receiving grass-legume silage and another lot corn silage. They obtained satisfactory reproduction from each silage-fed lot, and effected a 28 percent saving in feed cost as a result of using silage. At the Illinois station,[7] an average daily ration of 6.6 pounds of grass-legume silage plus supplement was fed to gestating sows with good results. Silage may also be fed to growing-finishing pigs,[8] but, due to its bulk, it is not as desirable for young stock; and, too, very young pigs frequently suffer digestive disturbances when given silage.

If of good quality, and not frozen or moldy, gilts will eat 7 to 12 pounds and sows 8 to 15 pounds of silage daily; with slightly higher consumption obtained with corn silage than with grass

---

[6] Conrad, J. H., and W. M. Beeson, *Grass Silage and Corn Silage as a Feed for Brood Sows*, Mimeo. A. H. 133, Purdue Univ. Agri. Expt. Sta., 1954.

[7] Terrill, S. W., and M. C. Nesheim, *Grass-legume Silage for Brood Sows*, Mimeo. A. S. 326, Ill. Agri. Expt. Sta., 1953.

[8] Zeller, John H., "The Use of Forage in Feeding Hogs," *Grass*, the **Yearbook of Agriculture**, 1948, p. 102.

silage. Under proper conditions, the following advantages accrue from feeding silage to brood sows and herd boars:

1. It reduces feed costs.
2. It prevents animals from getting too fat.
3. It provides a close substitute for pasture, from a nutritional standpoint.
4. It supplies needed nutritional factors for winter rations which might not otherwise be available unless an exceptionally well balanced ration is fed.
5. It makes possible the use of more home-grown forages in swine rations.

Even though considerable silage may be fed to advantage, it is important that it be of good quality and that it be properly supplemented from a nutritional standpoint.

Hogging Down Crops

Pigs are sometimes allowed to do their own harvesting. Corn is the principal crop so used, the animals being turned into the field when the grain is in the dent stage. Sometimes small grain crops that have been badly lodged or otherwise damaged are harvested by hogs. Soybeans and field peas also are sometimes hogged off. In the South, such crops as peanuts, sweet potatoes, chufas, and other root and tuber crops are often harvested by hogs.

Space will not permit a full discussion of this method of utilizing the various crops. As corn is the main feed hogged down, comments will be limited to this crop; but it will be understood that the same general principles apply to the other crops, when and if they are so utilized.

ADVANTAGES OF HOGGING DOWN CORN

Some of the advantages of this practice are as follows:
1. It saves labor at a busy season of the year.
2. The maximum fertility value of the manure is conserved.
3. There is less danger of infesting swine with diseases and parasites than in confinement finishing.
4. Corn or other crops that are down or badly lodged are difficult to harvest but they may be utilized through hogging down.

Fig. 6-26. Hogging down corn. The animals are usually turned into the field when the grain is in the dent stage. This practice saves labor, conserves maximum fertility value of the manure, and lessens disease and parasite troubles. (Courtesy, USDA)

DISADVANTAGES OF HOGGING DOWN CORN

Some of the disadvantages of hogging down corn may be enumerated as follows:

1. During wet weather, a considerable amount of corn is lost by being tramped into the ground.

2. During wet weather, the tramping of animals puddles the soil and lowers its tilth. This is especially noticeable in heavy clay soils.

3. It usually requires additional fencing.

4. Early pigs cannot be used in hogging down corn, for they will be too far advanced.

5. Pigs used in hogging down corn are usually finished at a season of the year when prices are low.

6. When corn is hogged down, wheat cannot follow corn in the rotation.

SOME ADDITIONAL FACTS
ABOUT HOGGING DOWN CORN

The following points are pertinent in hogging down corn:

1. **Economy.**—Numerous experiments have been conducted

Fig. 6-27. Hogging down small grains. Sometimes small grains that have been badly lodged or otherwise damaged are harvested by hogs. (Courtesy, Miss. Agr. Exp. Sta.)

Fig. 6-28. Hogging off peanuts and sorghums. In the South, such crops as peanuts, sweet potatoes, chufas, and other root and tuber crops are often harvested by hogs. (Courtesy, USDA)

for the purpose of determining the economy of hogging down corn. Although the results have been varied, there appears to be little difference between yard-feeding and hogging down corn except when a wet season is encountered.

2. **Supplemental forage with corn.**—Experiments and practical feeding operations show that it is generally advantageous to grow some supplemental crop with the corn, even though the yield of corn is reduced slightly. Soybeans and rape are most commonly grown in the Corn Belt. A leguminous pasture adjacent to the corn will serve the same purpose.

3. **Protein supplement.**—When there is an abundance of soybeans or rape in the corn, it may not be economical to include a protein supplement when such feed is high in price. In general, however, a protein supplement should be fed at the rate of .2 to .4 pounds per head daily. The exact amount will depend on the age of the pigs and the quantity of supplemental forage available.

4. **Weight of pigs.**—Late spring pigs that are in feeder condition and weigh 80 to 125 pounds are ideal for hogging down corn. Except for gleaning the fields, breeding animals should not be turned into the field; for they will become too fat.

5. **State of maturity.**—Usually, hogs should not be turned into the corn before it is well dented. When feed is scarce or when it seems desirable for other reasons, hogs may be turned into a field of standing corn any time after the dough stage. Animals should be started on the new feed gradually in order to avoid digestive disturbances.

6. **Size of area.**—It is usually recommended that the area fenced off be no larger than can be hogged off in two to three weeks. A temporary fence can be constructed with 26-inch woven wire anchored well with solid end posts. Between the end posts, the fence may be wired to corn stalks and an occasional driven post. The carrying capacity of a given area will vary with the yield of corn, size of pigs, and available supplemental feeds.

7. **Finishing period.**—It is usually best to finish the animals by yard feeding during the last thirty days. Brood sows and young pigs can be used to glean the fields.

Garbage for Swine

Municipal garbage has long been fed to finishing hogs; but during the past three decades, the practice has declined because of a gradual lowering in the feeding value of garbage and other competition for garbage—notably its manufacture into lawn,

greenhouse, and garden fertilizer. By June, 1960, only 1.85 percent of the nation's hogs were being fed garbage.

Twenty years ago, the garbage feeder calculated that a ton of city garbage would produce 60 to 100 pounds of pork; whereas, at the present time, it is estimated that a similar quantity will not produce more than 30 pounds of pork.[9] The change in feeding value may be largely attributed to improved refrigeration and the effective use of leftovers. Institutional, hotel, and restaurant garbage is superior to household garbage.

Garbage may be utilized either as a feed for a sow and pig enterprise or for finishing feeder pigs that are obtained from other sources. Usually, the venture seems most successful when a combination of grain and garbage feeding is practiced.

It is also observed that the most successful garbage feeders use concrete feeding floors, practice rigid sanitation, and take every precaution to prevent diseases and parasites. Unless considerable grain is fed to market hogs, especially after weights are over one hundred pounds, soft pork and paunchiness will result in garbage-fed hogs.

Raw garbage has a slightly higher feeding value than cooked garbage. Cooking allows for less feed selection on the part of the pig and lowers the digestibility of some of the nutrients, especially the proteins. On the other hand, swine are more likely to become infested with trichinella, vesicular exanthema, and certain other diseases when fed on raw garbage. For this reason, all states now have laws requiring that commercial garbage be cooked; although compliance with and enforcement of the law leaves something to be desired in some areas.

The claim is frequently made that the greatest number of cases of trichinosis in humans occurs in communities where garbage is fed to hogs. It should be understood, however, that there is no danger in transmitting the disease in this way provided that pork and pork products are thoroughly cooked.

Frozen garbage should be thawed before feeding.

Preparation of Swine Feeds

Perhaps no problem is so perplexing to the amateur swine

---

[9] Some Canadian authorities consider 4 pounds of heavy garbage to be equivalent to 1 pound of concentrate *(Feeder's Guide and Formulae for Meal Mixtures*, 13th edition, published by the Quebec Provincial Feed Board, for April 1959-61, p. 46).

feeder as the proper preparation of feeds. Usually, the confusion is further accentuated by the propaganda of manufacturers and distributors of various feed preparation equipment, not to mention the pet theories of experienced feeders.

GRINDING

In general, small, hard grains—such as rye, wheat, barley, rice, emmer, spelt, and sorghum—should always be ground when hand-fed to swine. However, they may be fed whole when self-fed for the reason that pigs masticate their feeds more thoroughly when eating more leisurely. Extremely hard seeds, such as millet, should be ground even when self-fed.

Because of less bulk, hog feeds should be ground rather than rolled. In all cases, fine, floury particles should be avoided. Finely ground feed is unpalatable, and it is masticated with difficulty—"balling up" in the animal's mouth. Finely ground feeds or mill by-products are frequently fed to pigs in the form of slop.

SOAKING, COOKING (OR STEAMING), OR SLOPPING

Several years ago, it was common for swine producers to "slop hogs," and the "swill barrel" was standard hog farm equipment. Then, as management practices and equipment design changed, dry feeds were used extensively. Now, some hogmen are going back to liquid feeding, or a modification called paste feeding.

Potatoes and beans should always be cooked (boiled or steamed) when fed to swine.

PASTE FEEDING

Paste feed is a blend of complete feed with sufficient water to wet all particles, with a minimum of free water. As indicated by the name, liquid feed contains more water.

Paste feed moves through the pipes of a distribution system as a plug, with the consistency of toothpaste, and there is no settling of feed particles when the flow is stopped because the mixture is homogenous.

More research needs to be done to assess the value of paste feeds in comparison to dry feeds. However, there is indication that the use of paste feed results in slightly improved gains and feed conversion over dry feeds.

The **advantages** of paste feeding over dry or slurry feeding are:

1. Paste feeding and distribution equipment is simpler and less expensive than automatic dry feeding equipment.

2. There is no pumping of excess material, such as water or air, as is true with slurry or pneumatic systems.

3. There is no dust problem.

4. There is less feed wastage; paste feed is not splashed or blown away.

5. Little separation of feed components occurs during transportation.

6. The pump used to move feed can serve as a metering pump on a simple running time basis.

7. It provides an accurate method of medication of animals with negligible loss of potency.

The **disadvantages** of the paste system are:

1. It must be protected from freezing weather, as does any liquid system.

2. The instantaneous power requirements for paste feeding may be higher than for other mechanical systems.

3. Grains must be ground through no larger than a 3/16-inch screen for proper blending and pumping.

4. Some problems with spoilage may occur; and the system must be cleaned to avoid bacterial growth in the same manner as a Grade A dairy.

5. Within the distribution system, care must be taken to provide fittings, valves, and piping with smooth interior walls.

CUTTING OR GRINDING ROUGHAGES

When alfalfa or some other suitable legume is added to a swine ration, it is best to grind or finely chop the forage, thus permitting thorough mixing with the ration, and assuring that the animal will eat all the ingredients.

PELLETING

Pelleting consists in mechanically pressing the ground feeds into hard, dry pellets. Recently, increasing quantities of U.S. swine feeds have been prepared in this manner.

After comparing self-fed pelleted versus self-fed ground

feeds for growing-finishing pigs, the Washington Experiment Station concluded as follows:

1. Pelleting increased the value of the ration used by 10 percent.

2. Pelleting alleviated high wastage of relatively unpalatable feeds (barley and ground alfalfa).

3. Pelleting prevented the animals from selectively wasting ingredients likely to be high in certain dietary essentials.

4. Pelleting reduced the required storage space, as the bulk of the feed is reduced by compression.

5. Pelleting made for greater convenience in feeding, and saved labor.

6. Pelleting increased palatability.

7. Pelleting should be varied, with smaller pigs having smaller pellets.

In two trials of pelleted versus non-pelleted rations for growing-finishing pigs, the Idaho station found that pigs fed pelleted rations (1) consumed 0.36 to 2.73 pounds less feed daily, (2) made 0.09 to 0.28 pound more daily gain, and (3) required 45 to 160 pounds less feed for each 100 pounds gain than those pigs fed similar but non-pelleted rations.[10]

The North Dakota Agricultural Experiment Station reported that pelleting of barley rations resulted in 12 to 14 percent faster gains and a saving of 8 to 17 percent in feed required per hundred pounds of gain.[11]

It is recognized that pelleting is likely to be more profitable where feeding relatively unpalatable feeds and in windy areas. Further, there is some hazard that the vitamin value of the ration may be lowered if the feeds are subjected to high temperatures. Also, the increased value of pelleting must be appraised against the increased cost of preparing the pellets.

Feed Substitution Table for Swine

The successful swine producer is a keen student of values. He recognizes that feeds of similar nutritive properties can and should be interchanged in the ration as price relationships war-

[10]Lehrer, W. P., Jr., and T. B. Keith, "Pelleted vs. Non-Pelleted Rations for Swine," Univ. of Idaho, Expt. Sta. Bul. 295, 1953.

[11]North Dakota Agri. Expt. Sta., Bimonthly Bul. XV 162, 1953.

rant, thus making it possible at all times to obtain a balanced ration at the lowest cost.

Table 6-17, Handy Feed Substitution Table for Swine, is a summary of the comparative values of the most common U.S. and Canadian feeds. In arriving at these values, two primary factors besides chemical composition and feeding value have been considered; namely, palatability and carcass quality.

In using this feed substitution table, the following facts should be recognized:

1. That, for best results, different ages and groups of animals within classes should be fed differently.

2. That individual feeds differ widely in feeding value. Barley and oats, for example, vary widely in feeding value according to the hull content and the test weight per bushel.

3. That, based primarily on available supply and price, certain feeds— especially those of medium protein content, such as peanuts and peas (dried)—are used interchangeably as (a) grains and by-product feeds and/or (b) protein supplements.

4. That the feeding value of certain feeds is materially affected by preparation; thus, potatoes and beans should always be cooked for hogs. The values herein reported are based on proper feed preparation in each case.

For these reasons, the comparative values of feeds shown in the feed substitution table which follows are not absolute. Rather, they are reasonably accurate approximations based on average quality feeds.

Home-mixed Versus Commercial Feeds

The value of farm-grown grains—plus the cost of ingredients which need to be purchased in order to balance the ration, and the cost of grinding and mixing—as compared to the cost of commercial ready-mixed feeds laid down on the farm, should determine whether it is best to mix feeds at home or depend on ready-mixed feeds. Although there is nothing about the mixing of feeds which is beyond the capacity of the intelligent swine producer, under many conditions a commercially mixed feed supplied by a reputable dealer may be the most economical and the least irksome. Also, the commercial dealer has the distinct advantages of (1) purchase of feeds in quantity lots, making possible price advantages, (2) economical and controlled mixing, and (3) the hiring of scientifically trained personnel for use in

TABLE 6-17

HANDY FEED SUBSTITUTION TABLE FOR SWINE

Feedstuff	Relative Feeding Value (lb. for lb.) in Comparison with the Designated (underlined) Base Feed Which=100	Maximum Percentage of Base Feed (or comparable feed or feeds) Which It Can Replace for Best Results	Remarks
GRAIN, BY-PRODUCT FEEDS ROOTS AND TUBERS:[1] (Low and Medium Protein Feeds)			
Corn, No. 2	100	100	Corn is the leading U.S. swine feed, about 50% of the total production being fed to hogs. It does not pay to grind corn for growing-finishing pigs, but it should be ground for older hogs.
Barley	90-95	100	Of variable feeding value due to widespread in test wt./bu. Should be ground. In Canada, where high quality bacon is produced, barley is considered preferable to corn for finishing hogs.
Beans (Cull)	90	66 2/3	Cook thoroughly; supplement with animal protein.
Carrots (or beets, mangels, or turnips)	12-20	25	
Cassava, dried meal	85	33 1/3	
Corn meal	100	20	
Hominy feed	95	50	Hominy feed will produce soft pork if it constitutes more than 1/2 the grain ration.
Millet (Hog Millet)	85-90	50	
Molasses, beet	70-75	20	
Molasses, cane	70-75	20	
Molasses, citrus	70-75	10-20	It takes pigs 5 to 7 days to get used to the bitter taste of citrus molasses.
Oats	70-80	33 1/3-100	For growing-finishing pigs, oats is equal to corn when limited to 1/3 of the ration. In Canada, where high quality bacon is produced, oats is sometimes used to finish hogs in order to obtain a lean carcass. The feeding value of oats varies according to the test weight per bushel. Grind for swine.
Peanuts	120-125	100	Peanuts are usually fed by hogging-off.
Peas, dried	90-100	100	Normally peas should be fed to swine as a protein supplement. Two tons peas=1 ton grain+1 ton soybean meal.
Potato (Irish)	25-28	25-50	Not palatable in raw state; must be cooked.
Potato (Irish), dehydrated	100	33 1/3	
Potatoes (sweet)	20-25	33 1/3-50	Cooking also improves the feeding value of sweet potatoes.
Potatoes (sweet), dehydrated	90	33 1/3	
Rice (rough rice)	80-85	50	Rice should be ground.
Rice bran	100	33 1/3	If more than 1/3 of the grain consists of rice bran, soft pork will result.
Rice polishings	100-120	33 1/3	Limited because feed becomes rancid in storage and soft pork will be produced.
Rice screenings	95	50	
Rye	90	50	Should be limited because it is unpalatable. Grind for swine.
Sorghum, grain	90	100	All varieties have about the same feeding value. Grind when hand-fed.

Footnote on last page of table.

(Continued)

TABLE 6-17 (Continued)

Feedstuff	Relative Feeding Value (lb. for lb.) in Comparison with the Designated (underlined) Base Feed Which=100	Maximum Percentage of Base Feed (or comparable feed or feeds) Which It Can Replace for Best Results	Remarks
Sunflower seed	100	50	
Wheat	105	100	Feed whole if self-fed; grind if hand-fed.
Wheat bran	75	15-25	Bran is particularly valuable at far-rowing time. In Canada, where high quality bacon is produced, 15 to 25% wheat bran is sometimes incorporated in the finishing ration in order to obtain a lean carcass.
Wheat flour middlings	103	20	
Wheat standard middlings	85-100	25-50	Combine with animal protein and limit to 1 lb. per head daily.
Wheat red dog and wheat white shorts	115-120	25	
PROTEIN SUPPLEMENTS:			In general, animal proteins should comprise part of the total protein supplement of swine; especially in confinement and for young pigs and gestating-lactating sows; they may comprise more if they are a cheaper protein source than plant proteins. Plant proteins may comprise as much as 90% of the protein supplement, provided the ration is adequately fortified with vitamins and minerals.
Tankage (60%)	_100_	_100_	
Buttermilk, dry	90-105	100	
Buttermilk, liquid	15	100	Pound for pound, worth 1/10 as much as dried buttermilk.
Buttermilk, semisolid	33 1/3-50	100	Pound for pound, worth 1/3 as much as dried buttermilk.
Copra meal (coconut meal)	50	25	
Corn gluten meal (gluten meal)	50-75	50	
Cottonseed meal (41%)	50-75	33 1/3	Except where the new screw-processed cottonseed meal is used, high level may produce gossypol poisoning and the level of cottonseed meal in swine rations should never exceed 8 to 9% of the total ration.
Fish meal (63%)	105-110	100	
Linseed meal (35%)	50-75	25-50	
Malt sprouts	100	10	Malt sprouts contain a growth factor(s). They result in increased feed intake and gain.
Meat and bone scraps (45-50%)	95-100	100	
Meat scraps (50-55%)	100	100	
Peanut meal (41%)	75-80	50	Becomes rancid when stored too long. High levels may produce soft pork.
Peanuts	60-70	50	Peanuts are usually fed by hogging-off.
Peas, dried	50	50	
Shrimp meal	90-100	50	
Skim milk, dried	90-120	100	In limited amounts, more valuable than tankage for young pigs.
Skimmed milk, liquid	15	100	Pound for pound, worth 1/10 as much as dried skim milk.
Soybean meal (41%)	75-85	50	Soybean meal is of better quality than the other protein-rich plant protein supplements.

Footnote on last page of table.

(Continued)

TABLE 6-17 (Continued)

Feedstuff	Relative Feeding Value (lb. for lb.) in Comparison with the Designated (underlined) Base Feed Which=100	Maximum Percentage of Base Feed (or comparable feed or feeds) Which It Can Replace for Best Results	Remarks
Soybeans	70-75	50	
Whey, dried	45	100	
Whey, liquid	30	50	Worth 1/2 as much as skim milk.
PASTURES AND DRY LEGUMES:			
Pasture, good		5-20% of grain, and 20-50% of protein supplement.	Pasture and dry legumes are sources of good quality proteins, of minerals, and of vitamins. Thus, swine should have access to either pasture or ground legume.
Alfalfa meal		It can replace all of pasture, in dry-lot rations.	For confinement rations, include 5-10% alfalfa in ration of growing-finishing pigs, and 15-35% in ration of gestating-lactating sows. In Canada, where high quality bacon is produced, up to 25% alfalfa meal is sometimes included in the finishing ration in order to obtain a lean carcass.

¹Roots and tubers are of lower value than the grain and by-product feeds due to their higher moisture content.

determining the rations. Because of these advantages, commercial feeds are finding a place of increasing importance in American agriculture.

Also, it is to the everlasting credit of reputable feed dealers that they have been good teachers, often getting stockmen started in the feeding of balanced rations, a habit which is likely to remain with a producer whether or not he continues to buy commercial feeds.

Most practical swine producers find it economical to feed home-grown grains and other high energy feeds, and to purchase protein-rich supplements. Commercially mixed protein supplements may have added vitamins, antibiotics, and/or minerals. In general, commercial feed companies prepare a minimum of two different kinds of protein supplements for swine: (1) for feeding in confinement, and (2) for feeding on pasture. In addition, there is merit in having special supplements (3) for breeding, (4) for finishing swine, and (5) for animals of different ages.

HOW TO SELECT COMMERCIAL FEEDS

There is a difference in commercial feeds! That is, there is a

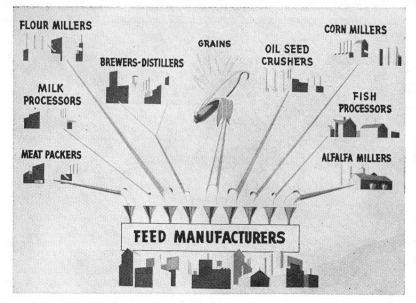

Fig. 6-29. Feed manufacturers obtain their raw materials for feeds from many sources. Over 100 different ingredients are processed into various (1) complete feeds, or (2) concentrates that are fed with home-grown grains. (Courtesy, American Feed Manufacturers Association, Inc.)

difference from the standpoint of what a hog producer can purchase with his feed dollars. The smart operator will know how to determine what constitutes the best in commercial feeds for his specific needs. He will not rely solely on the appearance or aroma of the feed, nor on the feed salesman. The most important factors to consider or look for in buying a commercial feed are:

1. **The reputation of the manufacturer.**—This should be determined by (a) conferring with other stockmen who have used the particular products, and (b) checking on whether or not the commercial feed under consideration has consistently met its guarantees. The latter can be determined by reading the bulletins or reports published by the respective state departments in charge of enforcing feed laws.

2. **The specific needs.**—Feed needs vary according to (a) the class, age, and productivity of the animals, and (b) whether the animals are fed primarily for maintenance, growth, finishing (or show-ring fitting), reproduction, or lactation. The wise operator will buy different formula feeds for different needs.

3. **The feed tag.**—Most states require that mixed feeds carry a tag that guarantees the ingredients and the chemical make-up of the feed. Feeds with more protein and fat are better, and feeds with less fiber are better.

In general, if the fiber content is less than 8 percent, the feed may be considered as top quality; if the fiber is more than 8 but less than 12 percent, the feed may be considered as medium quality; while feeds containing more than 12 percent fiber should be considered carefully. Many feeds are high in fiber simply because they contain generous quantities of alfalfa; yet they may be perfectly good feeds for the purpose intended. On the other hand, if oat hulls and similar types of high fiber ingredients are responsible for the high fiber content of the feed, the quality should be questioned. The latter type of fiber is poorly digested and does not provide the nutrients required to stimulate the digestion of the fiber in roughages.

4. **Flexible formulas.**—Feeds with flexible formulas are usually the best buy. This is because the price of feed ingredients in different source feeds varies considerably from time to time. Thus, a good feed manufacturer will shift his formulas as prices change, in order to give the stockman the most for his money. This is as it should be, for (a) there is no one best ration, and (b) if substitutions are made wisely, the price of the feed can be kept down and the feeder will continue to get equally good results.

Feeds That Cause Soft Pork

Feed fats are laid down in the body without undergoing much change. Thus, when finishing hogs are liberally fed on high-fat content feeds in which the fat is liquid at ordinary temperatures, soft pork results. This condition prevails when hogs are liberally fed such feeds as soybeans, peanuts, mast, or garbage. The fat of the cereal grains is also liquid at ordinary temperatures, but fortunately the fat content in these feeds is relatively low. When such feeds are liberally fed to swine, most of the pork fat is actually formed from the more abundant carbohydrates in these feeds.

Soft pork is undesirable from the standpoint of both the processor and the consumer. It remains flabby and oily even under refrigeration. In soft pork, there is a higher shrinkage in processing; the cuts do not stand up and are unattractive in the

show case; it is difficult to slice the bacon; and the cooking losses
are higher through loss of fat. For these reasons, hogs that are
liberally fed on those feeds known to produce soft pork are
heavily discounted on the market.

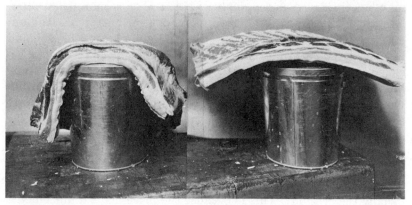

Fig. 6-30. Soft pork. Feed fats do affect body fats. The bacon belly on
the left came from a hog liberally fed on soybeans. (Courtesy, University
of Illinois)

The firmness of pork carcasses may be judged by: (1) grasping the flank below the ham, (2) lifting one end of the cut while
permitting the other end to rest on the table (a firm pork cut will
not bend readily), or (3) applying a slight pressure of the thumb
(not gouging) on a cut surface. Experimentally, either the iodine
number or the refractive index is used in determining the degree
of softness; this is a measure of the degree of unsaturation.

Unless the producer is willing to take the normal reduction
in price (about $1.00 per hundredweight), it is recommended
that feeds which normally produce soft pork be liberally fed only
to pigs under 85 pounds in weight and to the breeding herd. For
growing-finishing pigs over 85 pounds in weight, soybeans and
peanuts should not constitute more than 10 percent of the ration
if a serious soft-pork problem is to be averted.

Experimental evidence and practical observations have
shown, however, that when a ration producing hard fat is given
following a period on feeds rich in unsaturated fat, the body fat
gradually becomes harder. It has also been found that this process takes place more rapidly if the animals are first fasted for
a period before the change in ration is made. This practice is

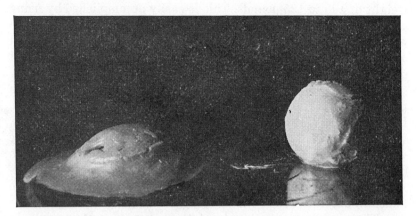

Fig. 6-31. Feed fats affect body fats. The soft lard sample (left) came from hogs fed a high soybean ration. Both samples of lard had been exposed to room temperature, 70° F., for two hours prior to photographing. (Courtesy, University of Illinois)

called hardening off. Thus, many hogs that are, for practical reasons, finished primarily on such feeds as soybeans, peanuts, or garbage, are hardened off with a ration of corn or some other suitable grain.

FEEDING GROWING-FINISHING PIGS

In the practical swine enterprise, growing-finishing generally refers to that period from weaning to market weight of about 220 pounds. Because hogs are finished at an early age, the process really consists of both growing and finishing. In a general way, there are two methods of finishing hogs for market: (1) full feeding all the time until the animals attain a market weight and (2) limited feeding. Pasture may be utilized to advantage with both methods. But, as would be expected, greater use of forage crops will accompany a system of limited rations. Neither system, full feeding or limited feeding, can be recommended as being best for any and all conditions. The plan to follow should be determined by: (1) market conditions, (2) price of feeds, (3) feeds available on the farm, (4) kind and extent of pastures available, (5) available labor, etc. Self-feeders are well adapted to a system of full-feeding, but hand-feeding is necessary in any plan for limiting the ration.

For the production of lean (bacon) carcasses, the rate of gain should be restricted to about 1½ pounds daily after a live

weight of 100 to 125 pounds. This is easily accomplished by using a lighter, bulkier finishing ration (made by inclusion of 10 to 20 percent bran, oats, alfalfa, or other suitable bulky feed). Level of protein has no direct effect on carcass excellence, though it does affect the growth of the pig.

On the average, about 400 pounds of feed are required to produce 100 pounds of gain during the growing-finishing period, but the amount varies with the inherent ability of the animals, weight (see Fig. 6-32), thrift, and the kind and amount of pasture utilized. About 360 pounds of this feed is grain and 40 pounds protein supplement. Of course, the feed consumption of the breeding herd and that of the pigs during the suckling period must be added in order to arrive at the total feed requirements.

The protein requirements of the pig are greatest early in life. For this reason, decreasing percentages of protein supplement should be incorporated in mixed rations as the finishing process progresses. If the ration is self-fed cafeteria style, the pigs generally will automatically balance these needs. In any event, however, ample protein should always be provided in the

LIGHT HOGS MAKE CHEAPER GAINS
light hogs produce
I. less lard   2. a higher proportion
of lean meat from less feed

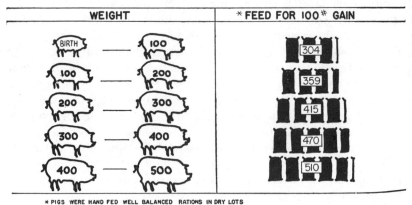

WEIGHT		* FEED FOR 100# GAIN
BIRTH — 100		304
100 — 200		359
200 — 300		415
300 — 400		470
400 — 500		510

* PIGS WERE HAND FED WELL BALANCED RATIONS IN DRY LOTS

Fig. 6-32. Young gains are cheaper gains. (Based on studies conducted at the Ohio station and reported in Ohio Bulletin 335)

Fig. 6-33. Swine feeding has gone modern—and automatic. This picture shows feed stored in outside bins and augered into a controlled environment finishing house. See Figure 6-34 for interior view of same house. (Courtesy, The Wyatt Manufacturing Company, Inc., Salina, Kansas)

Fig. 6-34. Automatic floor feed system in a controlled environment hog finishing building. See Figure 6-33 for exterior view of same building. (Courtesy, The Wyatt Manufacturing Company, Inc., Salina, Kansas)

ration, otherwise growth will be retarded. It is also important that the mineral and vitamin needs of growing-finishing pigs be met.

As previously indicated, pigs can utilize a great variety of concentrates. The chief ingredients of a growing-finishing ration, therefore, are usually, for practical reasons, those most readily available at the lowest possible price.

FEEDING PROSPECTIVE BREEDING GILTS AND BOARS

For best results, prospective breeding gilts should be fed differently from growing-finishing hogs. The ration fed during growth, from weaning to breeding age, affects the results obtained many months later in conception, reproduction, and lactation. Experimental evidence indicates that there is storage of factors during growth and that later these factors are of considerable importance. The same condition applies to prospective herd boars.

In view of this situation, it is usually important that prospective breeding animals, both gilts and boars, should be fed separate and apart from finishing hogs, beginning at 4 to 5 months of age or at 150 to 175 pounds weight. In the first place, it is neither necessary nor desirable that breeding animals become as fat as pigs that are being finished for market. Rather, size, growth, thrift, and good bone are desired. To this end, it is essential that the ration contain sufficient proteins and proteins of good quality and that there be an abundance of the essential minerals and vitamins.

Provided that good pastures are available or a generous allowance of a high quality legume is incorporated in the ration, the kind of concentrates (grain and protein supplements) fed to prospective breeding gilts or boars is relatively unimportant. If the animals are inclined to get too fat, which is likely to happen in self-feeding, (1) the ration may well contain considerable bulky feeds, such as ground oats, wheat bran, corn-and-cob meal, or ground alfalfa meal; or (2) they may be hand-fed.

FEEDING HERD BOARS

The feed requirements of the herd boar are about the same as those of a sow of equal weight. He should always be kept in

thrifty, vigorous condition and virile. To this end, feed and
exercise are important. Year-round succulent pasture is excellent
from the standpoint of providing both needed exercise and
valuable nutrients. In winter, the boar should still be allowed the
run of a lot of sufficient size so that he will get abundant exercise, and 15 to 35 percent of a high quality ground legume should
be incorporated in a well-balanced ration.

In no case should herd boars be overfat, nor should they be

Fig. 6-35. Tie stalls for sows on the farm of Stephen Viggers, Washington County, Iowa. In this system, each sow is fitted with a collar and individually fed like a stanchioned dairy cow. In such individual confinement,
a sow eats just what you want her to have—no more. (*Farm Journal*
photo—Dick Seim)

in a thin run-down condition. Except during the breeding season, about 1 pound of concentrates daily per 100 pounds live weight is sufficient for mature boars on good pasture; without pasture, the grain allowance should be about double this amount. A more liberal ration must be provided in the winter time and when the sire is in heavy service. The feed allowance should be varied with the age, development, temperament, breeding demands, and roughage consumed.

FEEDING BROOD SOWS

The gestation-lactation period is a critical one in swine nutrition. It is now known that the feed and care accorded the brood sow materially affects conception, reproduction, and lactation. The basis for successful and practical feeding of the brood sow consists of making the maximum use of pastures and of feeding a generous quantity of ground legumes during those periods when pastures are not available. Such roughages enhance the ration through increasing the quantity and improving the quality of the proteins, providing the necessary vitamins, and improving the mineral content of the ration. Pastures also provide valuable exercise for the sow.

For practical reasons, dry sows are fed considerable roughage—pasture, hay, and/or silage. Generally speaking, they are fed about 2 pounds of concentrate or its equivalent per day for each 100 pounds live weight.

Flushing Sows

The practice of conditioning or having thin sows gain in weight just prior to breeding is known as flushing. A great variety of feeds may be used satisfactorily for bringing about the condition of breeding thrift sought at this time. From a practical standpoint, it is usually best to use a home-produced grain ration together with pasture in season or a legume hay during the winter months. For young, growing animals or when non-legume pastures are being used, it is important that a protein supplement be added to the ration. In addition to providing suitable feeds for flushing, it is important that the sows be fed a ration adequate to produce gain in weight at the rate of 1 to 1½ pounds daily, beginning one to three weeks before breeding. The extra feeding of thin sows evidently stimulates the endocrine and re-

productive systems to greater activity, with the result that more eggs are produced at breeding time and litter size is increased.

The Gestation Period

The nutrients fed the pregnant sow must first take care of the usual maintenance needs. If the gilt is not fully mature, nutrients are required for maternal growth as well as for growth of the fetus. Quality and quantity of proteins, minerals, and vitamins become particularly important in the ration of young pregnant gilts, for their requirements are much greater and more exacting than those of the mature sow.

Approximately two-thirds of the growth of the fetus is made during the last month of the gestation period. It may be said, therefore, that the demands resulting from pregnancy are particularly accelerated during the latter third of the gestation period. Again, the increased needs are primarily for proteins, vitamins, and minerals.

During gestation, it is also necessary that body reserves be stored for subsequent use during lactation. With a large litter and a sow that is a heavy milker, the demands for milk production are generally greater than can be supplied by the ration fed at the time of lactation. Although desired gains will vary somewhat with the initial condition, mature sows are generally fed to gain 75 to 85 pounds during the pregnancy period, and pregnant, growing gilts should gain 100 to 125 pounds. This calls for a feed allowance of 1½ to 2 pounds per day for each 100 pounds live weight, with the upper limit fed to gilts.

There is no better place for pregnant sows than in a leguminous pasture. Luxuriant pasture of this type is particularly valuable in supplementing the grain ration with minerals, vitamins, and quality proteins. Aside from supplying the necessary nutrients at a low cost, this system provides much valuable exercise.

With reference to the quality of proteins, minerals, and vitamins in the winter or confinement ration, it is the feeling of most good swine producers that these needs can be met most easily and cheaply through adding 15 to 35 percent of a high quality ground alfalfa to the ration; or alfalfa hay may be fed in a rack. At least a part of the proteins supplied during the gestation period should be of animal origin (tankage, fish meal,

skimmed milk, etc.). It is also good and cheap protection to allow the sows free access to minerals.

Gestating sows are generally hand-fed to limit feed intake. This avoids (1) excess fatness, and (2) unnecessary feed expense. Some breeders cut down on the labor expense of hand-feeding sows by (1) feeding only once a day, or (2) allowing free access to self-feeders for only 12 hours out of each 48, or perhaps one day out of three—depending upon the condition of the sows. However, they may be self-fed if sufficient bulk—at least one-third of the ration to consist of some such suitable bulky feed as oats, alfalfa, wheat bran and/or corn-and-cob meal—is added to the ration.

Farrowing Time

It is considered good practice to feed lightly and with bulky, laxative feeds immediately before and after farrowing. Wheat bran or oats may constitute half of the limited ration, and a small amount of linseed meal may be added. From ten days to two weeks is the usual time suggested in getting the sow back on full feed after farrowing.

The sow may be watered at frequent intervals before or after farrowing, but in no event should she be allowed to gorge. It is also a good plan to take the chill off the water in the wintertime.

The Lactating Period

The nutritive requirements of a lactating sow are more rigerous than those during gestation. They are very similar to those of a milk cow, except they are more exacting relative to quality proteins and the B vitamins because of the absence of rumen synthesis in the pig. A sow will produce from $\frac{1}{2}$ to $1\frac{1}{2}$ gallons of milk daily.[12] A sow's milk is also richer than cows' milk in all nutrients, especially in fat. Thus, sows suckling litters need a liberal allowance of concentrates rich in protein, calcium, phosphorus, and vitamins.

---

[12] Hammond (*Progress in the Physiology of Farm Animals*, Vol. 1, 1954, p. 47) presented a summary of the estimation of milk yield in sows made by various workers. He reported a range of 2.75 to 13.71 pounds daily.

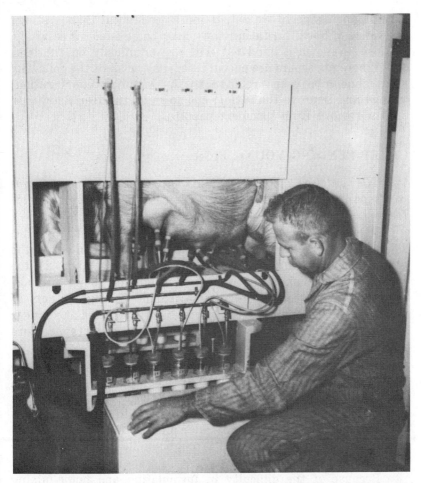

Fig. 6-36. Sows produce ½ to 1½ gallons of milk daily. Sow's milk contains a calcium-phosphorus ratio of approximately 1.3:1, 3 mg of iron per liter (1.056 qts.), and it is higher in fat than cow's milk. (Courtesy, Michigan State University)

It is essential that suckling pigs receive a generous supply of milk, for at no other stage in life will they make such economical gains. The gains made by pigs from birth to weaning are largely determined by the milk production of the sows; and this in turn is dependent upon the ration fed and the inherent ability to produce milk. The lactating sow should be provided with a liberal feed allowance—ranging from 2½ to 4 pounds daily for each 100 pounds weight. Generous feeding during lactation, with

a small shrinkage in weight, is more economical than a stingy allowance of feed. Lactating sows may be self-fed successfully, because, even when hand-fed they are practically on full-feed.

Where pig scours are encountered, any or all of the following steps should be taken relative to the lactating sow's ration: change and improve the ration, cut down on the feed allowance, and/or remove from succulent pasture.

CREEP-FEEDING YOUNG PIGS

The practice of self-feeding concentrates to young pigs in a separate enclosure away from their dams is known as creep-feeding.

It has always been said that young gains are cheap gains. This is due to (1) the higher water and lower fat content of the young animal in comparison with older animals, and (2) the higher feed consumption per unit of weight of young animals. Also, there has been an increasing demand for lighter cuts of meat, with meat animals of all species being marketed at younger ages and lighter weights. These factors have encouraged more and more creep-feeding of pigs.

The recommended levels of the major nutrients for creep-feeds are listed in Tables 6-2 and 6-3. Some swine producers use a highly palatable prestarter ration (high in protein, and well fortified with minerals, vitamins, and antibiotics) to get the pigs eating well and then switch to a regular pig starter, whereas others use a regular pig starter ration throughout the entire creep-feeding or suckling period.

Because of the difficulty in formulating and home-mixing prestarter rations, the purchase of a good commercial product generally represents a sound investment—and is the usual practice. To a lesser, but increasing extent, the same situation applies to starter rations. Whether commercially or home mixed, these rations must (1) contain high quality ingredients, (2) be well fortified with protein, minerals, vitamins, and antibiotics, and (3) be fresh and palatable. When the pigs are in confinement or on poor pasture, alfalfa meal should be included as an ingredient; but it is not needed in supplements prepared for use on good pastures. Suggested pig starter rations are given in Table 6-21, whereas Table 6-22 contains suggested creep rations. Where either scouring or lack of palatability is encountered, the starter or creep

ration should be mixed with rolled oats; up to 50 percent of the latter may be incorporated in the ration under these circumstances, or rolled oats may be fed alone for awhile.

Several procedures may be and are used in creep-feeding pigs. The grains may be self-fed in one feeder and the protein supplement (plus vitamins, antibiotics, and minerals) in another feeder; or all the ingredients may be mixed together and fed as a complete ration. Complete mixed rations are preferable for pigs up to 45 pounds in weight. It is recommended that a mineral mixture be fed free-choice in addition to the mineral supplied in the feed.

Some swine producers prefer to prepare a complete pig starter ration for pigs by mixing home-grown grains (such as cracked corn and/or ground oats) with a good commercial supplement as required. Table 6-18 shows the proportions of either cracked corn or a combination of cracked corn and ground oats (the two most commonly used U. S. grain feeds in pig starter rations) to mix with either 35 or 40 percent protein supplements in order to furnish an 18 percent complete ration; or see Table 6-26 for more alternative combinations, with and without alfalfa meal.

TABLE 6-18

PROPORTIONS OF GRAIN AND COMMERCIAL SUPPLEMENT TO USE
IN OBTAINING AN 18 PERCENT COMPLETE RATION

	Ration No. 1	Ration No. 2	Ration No. 3	Ration No. 4
Cracked yellow corn ---------	660	500	715	600
Ground oats---------------------		165		120
35% supplement----------------	340	335		
40% supplement----------------			285	280

Cracked or whole corn and rolled oats are the most popular cereal grains used in creep feeds. They are high in energy, low in fiber and, very palatable.

Young pigs prefer coarsely cracked or whole corn to finely ground grains. Also, pelleted feeds are more palatable to them than finely-ground grains and supplements.

Each thrifty pig should consume about 25 pounds of feed before reaching the age of 8 weeks, with about two-thirds of this consumption between the sixth and eighth weeks.

Skim milk, buttermilk, or condensed buttermilk may be fed in addition to the dry creep ration, either separately or along with

the other feeds in the form of a slop. Adding milk to a ration that is already properly balanced does make for a higher protein content than necessary. Thus, when skim milk or buttermilk is used, the protein feeds of the ration may be reduced by one-half without harm to the pigs.

Creep-feeding should begin before pigs are a week old. For best results, (1) provide a minimum of 1 foot of feeder space for each 5 pigs, (2) see that the edge of the feeder trough is lower than four inches above the ground floor, and (3) do not exceed a maximum of 40 pigs per creep.

Creep-feeders should be placed close to a water supply, and near the area where the sow is most of the time. In cool weather, they should be inside, in a well lighted place. During warm weather, they should be placed outside, but they should be covered to provide shade and protection from rain.

FEEDING AS AN ART

The feed requirements of hogs do not necessarily remain the same from day to day or from period to period. The age and size of the animal; the kind and degree of activity; the climatic conditions; the kind, quality, and amount of feed; the system of management; the health, condition, and temperament of the animal; and the amount of stress are all continually exerting a powerful influence in determining the nutritive needs. How well the feeder understands, anticipates, interprets, and meets these requirements usually determines the success or failure of the ration and the results obtained. Although certain principles are usually followed by all good feeders, no book of knowledge or set of instructions can substitute for experience and born livestock intuition. Skill and good judgment are essential. Indeed, there is much truth in the old adage that "the eye of the master fattens his animals."

The discussion that follows will primarily be directed at the finishing operations of hogs; the maintenance of the breeding herd has already received special attention.

Starting Hogs on Feed

In general, little difficulty is ever encountered in starting hogs on feed, because swine are less sensitive to feed changes than other classes of farm animals.

The keenness of the appetites and the consistency of the droppings of the animals are an excellent index of their capacity to take more feed. In all instances, scouring, the bane of the feeder, should be avoided.

Amount to Feed

Many farm animals throughout the United States are underfed all or some part of the year. Temporary underfeeding is most likely to occur in the winter months.

Overfeeding is also undesirable, being wasteful of feeds and creating a health hazard. Animals that suffer from mild digestive disturbances are commonly referred to as off feed. When overfeeding exists, there is usually considerable leftover feed and wastage, and there is a high incidence of scours.

When on full feed, finishing hogs will consume four to six pounds of feed, mostly concentrates, per hundred pounds of live weight; whereas cattle and sheep will consume about 3 pounds of total feed (concentrate and roughage) per 100 pounds live weight. The pig, therefore, is capable of consuming more feed in proportion to body weight than can either the cow or sheep. This is a major factor in the greater efficiency with which pigs convert feeds into meats.

LIMITED FEEDING

Among the traits which people and swine have in common is a tendency to overeat. Meat animals are selected for this ability. With people, the excuse is less obvious.

Many swine producers are using a limited feeding system of one kind or another for finishing pigs after they reach 120 to 150 pounds weight.

Limited feeding can be too severe. Most producers are using one of the following three guidelines to arrive at the amount of the limitation:

1. Feed only the amount eaten in 20 to 30 minutes.
2. Feed 70 to 90 percent of full feed.
3. Feed 1 pound of feed for each 30 pounds of body weight from 120 pounds to market weight.

Limiting the amount of feed per day will usually—

1. Improve feed efficiency.
2. Improve carcass quality.

3. Slow the growth rate or average daily gain.

4. Reduce backfat.

5. Require 10 to 30 extra days to reach market weight.

6. Necessitate that pigs be fed in small groups.

7. Require specialized feeding equipment or extra labor.

The advantages should be weighed against the disadvantages before the swine producer decides whether to full-feed or limit-feed growing-finishing pigs.

Hand-Feeding Versus Self-Feeding

Self-feeding is the most common method of feeding employed for growing-finishing hogs. The principal **advantages** derived from this method of feeding are:

1. Less labor and time are required in the feeding operations. By using self-feeders with large bins or hoppers, a large quantity of feed—enough for a week or two—may be mixed and placed before the animals at one time. Hand-feeding is a twice-a-day chore, whereas it is merely necessary to check the filled self-feeders at intervals to make certain that the feed has not clogged.

2. Slightly higher feed consumption and larger daily gains are obtained. This is especially true when hand-feeding is done by an inexperienced feeder or when irregularity occurs in time of feeding and in quantity and character of rations— conditions which sometimes prevail under ordinary farm conditions.

3. Self-fed animals are usually ready for market earlier than hand-fed animals because of their slightly more rapid gains.

4. The animals are less likely to go off feed. This is because they learn that feed is available at all times, with the result that they are inclined to eat leisurely.

5. Self-feeders are especially well adapted to grain feeding on pastures due to the distance of the pastures from the feed storage and mixing facilities.

6. With feeds of comparable palatability, pigs can be relied upon to balance their own rations when fed cafeteria style; thus, considerable time can be saved in the mixing of feeds. (Further elucidation of this point is contained in the section entitled "Pointers in Formulating Rations and Feeding Swine," points 9 and 10.)

The principal **disadvantages** of using self-feeders are the following:

1. Self-feeding is not adaptable where it is desired to utilize the maximum quantity of pasture. This is simply due to the fact that, under self-fed conditions, the animals elect to eat a large proportion of concentrates. Thus, where pastures are abundant and low in price and an early market is not important, hand-feeding may be more practical, for the reason that it permits limited feeding.

2. The gains of self-fed hogs may cost slightly more, particularly where grains are relatively higher than pasture. However, the slightly higher feed cost is usually offset by the slightly higher selling price of the earlier finished animals.

3. There is usually a slightly higher equipment cost in self-feeding.

4. Somewhat more time and expense is usually required in preparing feeds (shelling and mixing) for the self-feeder; although it is recognized that more grains can be fed whole to hogs when self-fed for they do a more thorough job of masticating when eating more leisurely.

Hand-feeding of sows and gilts during gestation and of herd boars is generally recommended as greater utilization of pasture and other desirable roughages can be attained and the condition of the animals can be controlled more easily. However, especially

Fig. 6-37. Hand-feeding during gestation prevents sows from over-eating and gaining excess weight. (Courtesy, Dr. D. E. Becker, University of Illinois)

prepared, bulky rations—comprised of approximately one-third of a suitable bulky feed—can be self-fed. The extra bulk may be obtained either by (1) adding ground hay to the grain ration, or (2) using in the ration a considerable proportion of such bulky, fibrous feeds as oats, bran, or corn-and-cob meal. With brood sows, a generous supply of ground alfalfa has the added virtues of furnishing a desirable source of vitamins, minerals, and proteins.

Lactating sows may be either self-fed or hand-fed.

For self-fed pigs intended for bacon, Canadian authorities recommend that a bulky ration (made by the inclusion of 10 to 20 percent bran, or other suitable bulky feed) be provided after 100 to 125 pounds live weight. This restriction of rate of gain results in a leaner carcass.

Frequency, Regularity, and Order of Feeding

In general, hand-fed finishing swine are fed twice daily. With animals that are being fitted for show, where maximum consumption is important, they are sometimes fed more frequently—three or four feedings daily. When self-fed, animals eat at more frequent intervals, though they consume smaller amounts each time.

Animals learn to anticipate their feed. Accordingly, they should be fed *with great regularity*, as determined by a time piece. During warm weather, they will eat better if the feeding hours are early and late, in the cool of the day.

Feeds Should Not Be Changed Abruptly

Sudden changes in diet are to be avoided, especially when changing from a less-concentrated ration to a more-concentrated one. When this rule of feeding is ignored, digestive disturbances result, and animals go "off feed." In either adding or omitting one or more ingredients, the change should be made gradually.

Selection of Feeds

In general, the successful feeder balances the ration through selecting those feeds which are most readily available at the lowest possible cost. In addition, consideration is given to supplying quality proteins, the proper minerals, and the necessary

vitamins. Attention is also given the laxative or constipating qualities of feeds and the palatability of the ration. Furthermore, the relation of the feeds to the quality of the product produced should not be overlooked; for example, in finishing hogs, excessive quantities of soybeans or peanuts produce soft pork.

Attention to Details Pays

The successful feeder pays great attention to details. In addition to maintaining the health and comfort of the animals and filling their feed troughs or feeders, consideration is also given to their likes.

It is important to avoid excessive exercise, which results in loss of energy by the animals through unnecessary muscular activity. Rough treatment, excitement, and noise usually result in nervousness and inefficient use of feed. Finishing animals should not be required to exercise any more than is deemed necessary for the maintenance of health. All males should be castrated; for they will be much quieter, and the quality of the meat will be enhanced.

FEED ALLOWANCES AND SOME SUGGESTED RATIONS[13]

Hogs can and do use many different concentrates, which makes it possible to choose as chief ingredients those most readily available at the lowest price.

Other factors being equal, a variety of feeds is preferable, although the choice of ingredients will and should vary from area to area, and even on adjoining farms. The rations in Tables 6-19 to 6-24 will serve as useful guides. As noted, these cover the following classes, ages, and sexes, with proper provision for (1) confinement, (2) pasture rations, and (3) weight divisions of pigs:

1. Gestating gilts and sows (Table 6-19).
2. Lactating gilts and sows (Table 6-20).
3. Pig starter for early weaned (two to three weeks of age) pigs, 10 to 30 pounds weight (Table 6-21).

---

[13]This section and Tables 6-19 through 6-25 were reviewed by the following well-known swine specialists: Dr. R. H. Grummer, University of Wisconsin, Madison, Wis.; Dr. R. F. Wilson, Ohio State University, Columbus, Ohio; and Professor Vaughn Speer, Iowa State University, Ames, Ia.

TABLE 6-19

HANDY GESTATING GILT AND SOW FEEDING GUIDE; FOR ALL AGES
(1) IN CONFINEMENT, AND (2) ON PASTURE[1]
(These rations are equally satisfactory for herd boars)

Ingredients (also provide minerals and vitamins as recommended elsewhere in this section)	For Sows in Confinement (14% protein)				For Sows on Good Pasture (11-13% protein)	
	Ration No. 1		Ration No. 2		Ration No. 3	
	(lb.)	(kg)	(lb.)	(kg)	(lb.)	(kg)
Ground corn, wheat, barley, oats, and/or sorghum	1,500	680.4	1,200	544.3	1,850	839.1
Alfalfa meal	300	136.1	600	272.1		
Animal protein supplement (tankage, meat meal, meat and bone scrap, fish meal, and/or dried milk)	120	54.4	100	45.4	100[2]	45.4[2]
Plant protein supplement (soybean, cottonseed, linseed, and/or peanut meal)	80	36.3	100	45.4	50[2]	22.7[2]
Total	2,000	907.2	2,000	907.2	2,000	907.2
Proximate Analysis: [using corn, alfalfa meal (sun cured), tankage (digester) with bone, and soybean meal]	(%)		(%)		(%)	
Protein, crude	14.04		14.90		12.20	
TDN	75.0		70.9		79.3	
Fiber	6.12		10.05		2.15	
Fat	3.8		3.73		4.60	
Calcium	0.91		1.06		0.57	
Phosphorus	0.63		0.63		0.60	

[1]Gestating gilts and sows are generally hand-fed to limit feed intake. This avoids (1) excess fatness and (2) unnecessary feed expense. However, they may be self-fed if more bulk is added to the ration. Bulk may be provided by (1) using considerable oats or ground ear corn, and (2) adding 25 percent or more of ground alfalfa to the ration. With mature pregnant sows, it is usually desirable to limit concentrate consumption to about 1½ pounds daily per 100 pounds live weight. With replacement pregnant gilts, concentrate consumption should be at the rate of about 2 pounds or less daily per 100 pounds live weight. Sufficient ground oats and ground alfalfa—two bulky feeds—may be added to the ration to limit feed consumption to these figures.

Ration 1, above, is suitable for self-feeding—provided at least half of the cereal grain consists of oats. Ration 2 is suitable for hand-feeding. Ration 3 is satisfactory for self-feeding on pasture, providing at least half of the grain ration is oats.

[2]On lush legume or rape pasture, the protein supplement of Ration 3 may be deleted. However, the quantities of protein supplement indicated are needed when sows are

TABLE 6-20

HANDY LACTATING GILT AND SOW FEEDING GUIDE; FOR ALL AGES (1) IN CONFINEMENT, AND (2) ON PASTURE[1]

Ingredients (also provide minerals and vitamins as recommended elsewhere in this section)	For Sows in Confinement (15% protein) Ration No. 1 (lb.)	(kg)	Ration No. 2 (lb.)	(kg)	For Sows on Good Pasture (13-14% protein) Ration No. 3 (lb.)	(kg)
Ground corn, wheat, barley, oats,[2] and/or sorghum	1,450	657.5	1,380	625.9	1,810	820.9
Alfalfa meal	300	136.1	300	136.1	90	40.8
Animal protein supplement (tankage, meat meal, meat and bone scrap, fish meal, and/or dried milk)	125	56.8				
Plant protein supplement (soybean, cottonseed, linseed, and/or peanut meal)	125	56.8	300	136.1	100	45.4
Dicalcium phosphate			20	9.1		
Total	2,000	907.2	2,000	907.2	2,000	907.2
Proximate analysis: [using corn, alfalfa meal (sun cured), tankage (digester) with bone, and soybean meal]	(%)		(%)		(%)	
Protein, crude	15.24		15.6		13.13	
TDN	74.9		74.9		79.4	
Fiber	5.85		6.2		2.20	
Fat	3.8		3.2		4.02	
Calcium	0.96		0.53		0.56	
Phosphorus	0.64		0.56		0.55	

[1]By the time the pigs are 10 days to 2 weeks of age, lactating sows may be self-fed successfully. Lactating sows will consume from 2½ to 4 pounds of concentrates daily per 100 pounds live weight, with mature sows approaching the lower side and gilts the upper side of this range. A good rule of thumb for hand-feeding lactating sows is "one pound daily per pig, plus 2 to 3 lbs."; this allows more feed for the sow suckling a large litter than for one suckling a small litter.

[2]In general, oats should not constitute more than 15% of the ration, especially for young gilts.

TABLE 6-21

PIG STARTER RATIONS FOR EARLY WEANED (2 to 3 weeks of age) PIGS, 10 TO 30 LB. (4.5 to 14 kg) WEIGHT[1]

Ration No. 1			Ration No. 2		
(Ingredient)	(lb.)	(kg)	(Ingredient)	(lb.)	(kg)
Sugar (cane or beet)	15.00	6.80	Yellow corn meal	30.65	13.93
Sugar (corn)	12.50	5.67	Soybean meal (50%)	17.50	7.94
Yellow corn (fine ground)	14.35	6.52	Dried skim milk	22.00	10.00
Dried skim milk	40.00	18.14	Dried whey	3.00	1.36
Soybean meal (solvent 44%)	7.00	3.17	Fish meal (60%)	3.00	1.36
Fish meal (70%)	5.00	2.26	Dried brewers' yeast	2.00	0.91
Lard (stabilized)	2.50	1.13	Dicalcium phosphate	0.25	0.11
Dried brewers' yeast	1.00	0.45	Fat (stabilized animal)	5.00	2.27
Trace minerals (according to Table 6-11)	0.15	0.68	Sucrose	10.00	4.54
Iodized salt	0.50	0.22	Cerelose (corn sugar)	5.00	2.27
			Salt	0.50	0.23
Vitamin-antibiotic premix (with vitamins according to Table 6-3, and antibiotics according to Table 6-15)	2.00	0.90	Trace mineral mix (according to Table 6-11)	0.10	0.05
			Vitamin-antibiotic mix (with vitamins according to Table 6-3, and antibiotics according to Table 6-15)	1.00	0.45
Total	100.00	45.94	Total	100.00	45.42
Proximate analysis:	(%)		Proximate analysis:	(%)	
Protein, crude	21.69		Protein, crude	22.09	
TDN	84.76		TDN	86.06	
Fat	3.87		Fat	6.86	
Fiber	0.78		Fiber	1.76	
Calcium	0.80		Calcium	0.61	
Phosphorus	0.65		Phosphorus	0.62	

[1]Either of these rations is satisfactory for early weaned pigs—pigs weaned at less than three weeks of age. Such feeds are generally fed as a gruel for the first two days, and then as a dry feed thereafter. Beginning with the third week, the creep ration (refers to creep ration, Table 6-22) is generally introduced as an additional feed so that during the third week the pigs have access to both the starter and the creep feeds. By the fourth week, the starter is removed and the pigs are fed the creep ration alone. When fed in this manner, each pig will consume about 5 pounds of the starter.

4. Creep feed for suckling pigs, 5 to 30 pounds weight (Table 6-22).

5. Growing-finishing pigs from 30 to 220 pounds weight (Tables 6-23 and 6-24).

Recommendations relative to feeding show animals are included in Chapter XVI of this book.

The suggested rations meet the requirements proposed by the National Research Council and provide for reasonable margins of safety.

In addition to the complete rations previously referred to, Table 6-25 gives suggested formulas for "protein-mineral-vitamin-antibiotic supplements," which may be either purchased commercially or mixed on the farm; and Table 6-26 shows how protein supplements may be combined with grain rations to obtain the desired level of protein.

In formulating the several rations given in Tables 6-19 to 6-24, cognizance was taken of the fact that two systems of swine feeding predominate; namely, (1) the use of complete rations, either commercially or home-mixed, versus (2) the grain and the supplement fed separately. Also, both hand-feeding and self-feeding methods are followed, with the latter being most common except for gestating sows.

In recent years, there has been an increasing trend toward the use of complete, mixed rations for all classes and ages of hogs, especially with creep and growing-finishing rations. The use of complete rations has been favored because they afford a more accurate means of controlling the intake of vitamins, trace minerals, and antibiotic and other feed additives. The choice between the systems, or some combination of the two, should be determined by the conditions prevailing on each individual farm, including such factors as (1) the cost of grinding and mixing, (2) the kind, amount, and palatability of available feeds, (3) facilities for handling feeds, (4) the relative cost of proteins and grains, and (5) the results obtained.

Where commercial protein supplements are bought (usually a combined protein-mineral-vitamin-antibiotic supplement) to use with farm-grown grains, they are utilized in any of the following ways:

1. Self-fed in separate self-feeders, with the ground or whole grain also being self-fed in separate self-feeders.

2. Hand-fed; the supplement and the grain each being hand-

TABLE 6-22

HANDY CREEP FEED GUIDE FOR SUCKLING PIGS 5 TO 30 POUNDS WEIGHT[1]
(17 to 20% protein)

Ingredient	Confinement Rations								Pasture Rations					
	1		2		3		4		5		6		7	
	(lb.)	(kg)	(lb.)	(kg)	(lb.)	(kg)	(lb.)	(kg)	(lb.)	(kg)	(lb.)	(kg)	(lb.)	(kg)
Cracked yellow corn	1,310	594.2	860	390.1	615	279.0	1,190	539.8	1,400	635.0	1,430	648.6	650	294.8
Ground barley					700	317.5								
Ground or rolled oats			560	254.0	200	90.7							920	417.4
Oat groats							200	90.7						
Cane or beet sugar							200	90.7						
Animal fat (stabilized)													40	18.2
Tankage or meat meal, with bone			70	31.8	125	56.7	100	45.4						
Fish meal (65%)			50	22.7			100	45.4					60	27.2
Non-fat dry milk			200	90.7	100	45.4	100	45.4			100	45.4	120	54.4
Dried buttermilk							100	45.4						
Soybean meal	550	249.5	170	77.1	200	90.7	200	90.8	550	249.5	450	204.2	180	81.7
Alfalfa meal, sun-cured	100	45.4	80	36.3	50	22.7								
Alfalfa leaf meal														
Ground limestone (or equivalent)	10	4.5							20	9.1	10	4.5	10	4.5
Steamed bone meal (or equivalent)	20	9.1							20	9.1			10	4.5
Salt (iodized salt in iodine deficient areas)	10	4.5	10	4.5	10	4.5	10	4.4	10	4.5	10	4.5	10	4.5
Vitamins (added according to Table 6-3)														
Trace minerals (added according to Table 6-11)														
Antibiotics (added according to Table 6-15)														
Total	2,000	907.2	2,000	907.2	2,000	907.2	2,000	907.3	2,000	907.2	2,000	907.2	2,000	907.2
Proximate analysis:	(%)		(%)		(%)		(%)		(%)		(%)		(%)	
Protein, crude	18.96		18.62		17.83		18.96		17.63		19.05		18.62	
TDN	76.7		80.8		75.5		79.5		77.7		78.3		86.4	
Fiber	4.36		5.17		4.63		1.99		3.05		2.93		2.60	
Fat	3.41		3.97		3.36		3.92		3.26		3.87		4.10	
Calcium	0.63		0.83		0.89		0.95		0.73		0.78		0.60	
Phosphorus	0.40		0.66		0.75		0.75		0.55		0.71		0.57	

[1]Young pigs prefer coarsely cracked or whole corn to finely ground grains. Also, pelleted feeds are more palatable to them than finely ground grains and supplements. . . . normal weaning age of 8 weeks with about two-thirds of this consumption between

TABLE 6-23

HANDY GROWING-FINISHING PIG FEEDING GUIDE;
FOR PIGS IN CONFINEMENT

Ingredients[1] (Also provide minerals and vitamins)	30 to 75 Lb. Wt. (16% protein)[2] Ration No. 1		75 to 130 Lb. Wt. (14% protein)[2] Ration No. 2		130 to 220 Lb. Wt. (13% protein)[2] Ration No. 3	
	(lb.)	(kg)	(lb.)	(kg)	(lb.)	(kg)
Yellow corn	1,490	675.8	1,580	716.7	1,670	757.4
Alfalfa meal	100	45.4	100	45.4	100	45.4
Soybean meal	260	117.9	190	86.1	130	59.0
Tankage, (digester) with bone	120	54.5	100	45.4	70	31.8
Salt	10	4.5	10	4.5	10	4.5
Steamed bone meal (or equivalent)	20	9.1	20	9.1	20	9.1
Antibiotics (see Table 6-15)						
Total	2,000	907.2	2,000	907.2	2,000	907.2
Proximate analysis:	(%)		(%)		(%)	
Protein, crude	16.42		14.79		13.15	
TDN	76.5		76.7		76.9	
Fiber	4.03		3.70		3.57	
Fat	4.12		4.16		4.15	
Calcium	1.08		0.96		0.78	
Phosphorus	0.79		0.73		0.65	

[1]Feeds of similar nutritive properties can be interchanged in the ration as price relationships warrant. Among such feeds are: (1) *the cereal grains*—corn, barley, wheat, oats, and sorghum; (2) *the animal protein supplements*—tankage, meat meal, meat and bone scrap, fish meal, and dried milk products; and (3) *the plant protein supplements*—soybean, cottonseed, linseed, and peanut meal. If wheat, barley, oats, and/or sorghum is used instead of corn as the grain in a ration, the protein supplement may be slightly reduced, because these grains have a higher protein content than corn; similar consideration should be given with shifts in protein supplements.

[2]Young pigs require a much greater proportion of protein in the ration than do those approaching market weight. For this reason, less protein supplement is indicated in the above rations as finishing progresses. Of course, as pigs advance in age and weight, they consume a larger daily ration, although the percentage of protein in the mixture is decreased.

fed in the proportions recommended (see Table 6-26).

3. Mixed with ground, farm-grown grain in appropriate amounts to make a complete ration. (See Table 6-26. The footnote for this table gives the directions for its use.)

In formulating the suggested rations herein presented, the following facts were also considered:

1. That growth up to 30 pounds in weight, gestation, and lactation constitute the most critical periods, nutritionally, in the life of the pig; that the proteins, minerals, and vitamins are especially important during these periods. Accordingly, in the rations suggested in this section, a considerable margin of safety in the most essential nutrients is provided over and above minimum requirements for these periods.

TABLE 6-24

HANDY GROWING-FINISHING PIG FEEDING GUIDE;
FOR PIGS ON GOOD PASTURE

Ingredients[1] (Also provide minerals and vitamins)	30 to 75 Lb. Wt. (14-15% protein)[2] Ration No. 1		75 to 130 Lb. Wt. (13-14% protein)[2] Ration No. 2		130-220 Lb. Wt. (12-13% protein)[2] Ration No. 3	
	(lb.)	(kg)	(lb.)	(kg)	(lb.)	(kg)
Yellow corn---------------------------------	1,680	762.0	1,755	796.1	1,780	807.3
Soybean meal-------------------------------	190	86.2	125	56.7	120	54.5
Tankage (digester) with bone-------------	100	45.4	90	40.8	70	31.8
Salt---	10	4.5	10	4.5	10	4.5
Steamed bone meal (or equivalent)-----	20	9.1	20	9.1	20	9.1
Total-------------------------------------	2,000	907.2	2,000	907.2	2,000	907.2
Proximate analysis:	(%)		(%)		(%)	
Protein, crude --------------------------	14.49		13.16		12.6	
TDN-------------------------------------	78.1		78.2		78.3	
Fiber-------------------------------------	2.40		2.26		2.20	
Fat--	4.29		4.36		3.9	
Calcium----------------------------------	0.89		0.82		0.72	
Phosphorus -----------------------------	0.73		0.70		0.64	

[1]Feeds of similar nutritive properties can be interchanged in the ration as price relationships warrant. Among such feeds are: (1) *the cereal grains*—corn, barley, wheat, oats, and sorghum; (2) *the animal protein supplements*—tankage, meat meal, meat and bone scrap, fish meal, and dried milk products; and (3) *the plant protein supplements*—soybean, cottonseed, linseed, and peanut meal. If wheat, barley, oats, and/or sorghum is used instead of corn as the grain in a ration, the protein supplement may be slightly reduced, because these grains have a higher protein content than corn; similar consideration should be given with shifts in protein supplements.

[2]Young pigs require a much greater proportion of protein in the ration than do those approaching market weight. For this reason, less protein supplement is indicated in the above rations as finishing progresses. Of course, as pigs advance in age and weight, they consume a larger daily ration, although the percentage of protein in the mixture is decreased.

2. That complete mixed rations are much preferable for pigs up to 30 pounds in weight. Because of the difficulty in formulating and home-mixing satisfactory creep or pig-starter rations, the purchase of a good commercial feed usually represents a wise investment.

Pointers in Formulating Rations and Feeding Swine

In formulating rations and in feeding swine, the following points are noteworthy:

1. Feeds of similar nutritive properties can be interchanged in the ration as price relationships warrant. Some of these feeds are: (a) *the cereal grains*—corn, barley, wheat, oats, and sorghum; (b) *the animal protein supplements*—tankage, meat meal, meat and bone scrap, fish meal, and dried milk products; and

TABLE 6-25

FORMULAS FOR PROTEIN-MINERAL-VITAMIN-ANTIBIOTIC SUPPLEMENTS FOR SWINE[1]

Ingredients	In Confinement												On Pasture											
	1		2		3		4		5		6		1		2		3		4		5		6	
	(lb.)	(kg)	(lb.)	(kg)	(lb.)	(kg)	(lb.)	(kg)	(lb.)	(kg)	(lb.)	(kg)	(lb.)	(kg)	(lb.)	(kg)	(lb.)	(kg)	(lb.)	(kg)	(lb.)	(kg)	(lb.)	(kg)
Alfalfa meal	615	279.0	780	353.8	725	328.8	415	188.2	420	190.5	450	204.2							220	99.8				
Wheat standard middlings													600	272.2	400	181.4	260	117.9			470	213.3	450	204.2
Pea meal															400	181.4								
Brewers' grains															550	249.6	600	272.2	400	181.4	500	226.8	500	226.8
Tankage (digester) with bone[2]	300	136.1	450	204.2	450	204.2							300	136.1			200	90.7						
Meat meal, with bone							200	90.7	410	186.1	450	204.2	600	272.2	600	272.2								
Fish meal (65%)[2]	100	45.3	200	90.7	100	45.4	300	136.1	200	90.7	150	68.0	400	181.4	40	18.1	150	68.0						
Soybean meal	900	408.2	500	226.8	675	306.2	800	362.9	900	408.2	900	408.2					700	317.7	1,300	589.7	960	435.4	1,000	453.6
Linseed or cottonseed meal							200	90.7																
Salt	20	9.1	40	18.1	40	18.1	20	9.1	40	18.1	40	18.1	20	9.1			40	18.1	20	9.1	40	18.1	40	18.1
Steamed bone meal or dical	35	15.9	20	9.1			35	15.9	20	9.1			30	13.6			40	18.1	30	13.6	20	9.1		
Ground limestone	20	9.1					20	9.1					40	18.1					20	9.1				
Trace minerals and vitamins (see Tables 6-3, 6-5 & 6-11)																								
Antibiotic supplement[3] (see Table 6-15)	10	4.5	10	4.5	10	4.5	10	4.5	10	4.5	10	4.5	10	4.5	10	4.5	10	4.5	10	4.5	10	4.5	10	4.5
Total	2,000	907.2	2,000	907.2	2,000	907.2	2,000	907.2	2,000	907.2	2,000	907.2	2,000	907.2	2,000	907.2	2,000	907.2	2,000	907.2	2,000	907.2	2,000	907.2
Proximate analysis:	(%)		(%)		(%)		(%)		(%)		(%)		(%)		(%)		(%)		(%)		(%)		(%)	
Protein, crude	35.29		34.76		34.93		39.05		39.78		39.39		35.11		34.89		35.28		40.49		39.70		39.56	
TDN	64.5		60.9		63.5		65.6		66.0		66.7		68.2		70.6		60.3		72.1		64.8		73.1	
Fiber	11.80		13.20		12.90		9.46		9.30		9.75		6.30		6.02		8.02		5.38		7.16		5.78	
Fat	3.05		4.25		3.94		2.85		3.88		3.98		3.01		4.85		4.47		3.47		4.86		3.85	
Calcium	3.31		3.36		3.33		3.10		3.44		3.28		2.02		3.17		2.23		3.14		3.25		2.98	
Phosphorus	1.30		1.72		1.63		1.58		1.83		1.73		1.25		1.86		1.49		1.56		1.86		1.69	

[1]Similar supplements may be either purchased commercially or mixed on the farm.
[2]Tankage, meat meal, and meat bone scraps are interchangeable.
[3]The antibiotic activity will vary with the class and age of swine.

TABLE 6-26

RATIO OF GRAIN TO PROTEIN SUPPLEMENTS NEEDED TO OBTAIN THE DESIRED LEVEL OF PROTEIN IN A RATION, WITH AND WITHOUT ALFALFA MEAL[1]

% Protein Desired	40% Supplement		35% Supplement		Corn (9.3% crude protein)		Ground Barley (11.8% crude protein)		Ground Oats (11.8% crude protein)		Ground Wheat (12.7% crude protein)		Alfalfa Meal (15.4% crude protein)	
	(lb.)	(kg)	(lb.)	(kg)	(lb.)	(kg)	(lb.)	(kg)	(lb.)	(kg)	(lb.)	(kg)	(lb.)	(kg)
18	575	261	—	—	1,325	601	—	—	—	—	—	—	100	45
	500	227	—	—	750	340	650	295	—	—	—	—	100	45
	525	238	—	—	1,000	454	—	—	375	170	—	—	100	45
	450	204	—	—	—	—	925	420	—	—	525	238	100	45
	375	170	—	—	—	—	—	—	550	249	975	442	100	45
	—	—	675	306	1,225	556	—	—	—	—	—	—	100	45
	—	—	575	261	675	306	650	295	—	—	—	—	100	45
	—	—	650	295	1,000	454	—	—	—	—	250	113	100	45
	—	—	500	227	—	—	1,000	454	—	—	400	181	100	45
	—	—	500	227	—	—	—	—	500	227	900	408	100	45
	600	272	—	—	1,400	635	—	—	—	—	—	—	—	—
	525	238	—	—	875	397	600	272	—	—	—	—	—	—
	550	249	—	—	1,000	454	—	—	450	204	—	—	—	—
	425	193	—	—	—	—	925	420	—	—	650	295	—	—
	400	181	—	—	—	—	—	—	700	318	900	408	—	—
	—	—	725	329	1,275	578	—	—	—	—	—	—	—	—
	—	—	650	295	750	340	600	272	—	—	—	—	—	—
	—	—	675	306	1,000	454	—	—	325	147	—	—	—	—
	—	—	500	227	—	—	850	386	—	—	650	295	—	—
	—	—	500	227	—	—	—	—	550	249	950	431	—	—

Footnote on last page of table.

(Continued)

TABLE 6-26 (Continued)

% Protein Desired	40% Supplement (lb.)	(kg)	35% Supplement (lb.)	(kg)	Corn (9.3% crude protein) (lb.)	(kg)	Ground Barley (11.8% crude protein) (lb.)	(kg)	Ground Oats (11.8% crude protein) (lb.)	(kg)	Ground Wheat (12.7% crude protein) (lb.)	(kg)	Alfalfa Meal (15.4% crude protein) (lb.)	(kg)
16	450	204	—	—	1,450	658	—	—	—	—	—	—	100	45
	350	159	—	—	850	386	700	318	—	—	—	—	100	45
	300	136	—	—	—	—	950	431	—	—	650	295	100	45
	400	181	—	—	1,150	522	—	—	350	159	—	—	100	45
	275	125	—	—	—	—	—	—	625	283	1,000	454	100	45
	—	—	550	249	1,350	612	—	—	—	—	—	—	100	45
	—	—	425	193	775	352	700	318	—	—	—	—	100	45
	—	—	375	170	—	—	875	397	—	—	650	295	100	45
	—	—	500	227	1,050	476	—	—	350	159	—	—	100	45
	—	—	325	147	—	—	—	—	575	261	1,000	454	100	45
	375	170	—	—	925	420	700	318	—	—	—	—	—	—
	475	215	—	—	1,525	692	—	—	—	—	—	—	—	—
	425	193	—	—	1,225	556	—	—	350	159	—	—	—	—
	250	113	—	—	1,050	476	—	—	—	—	700	318	—	—
	250	113	—	—	—	—	—	—	750	340	1,000	454	—	—
	—	—	450	204	850	386	700	318	—	—	—	—	—	—
	—	—	575	261	1,425	646	—	—	—	—	—	—	—	—
	—	—	525	238	1,125	510	—	—	350	159	—	—	—	—
	—	—	200	91	1,100	499	—	—	—	—	700	318	—	—
	—	—	175	79	—	—	—	—	725	329	1,000	499	—	—

(Continued)

Footnote on last page of table.

TABLE 6-26 (Continued)

% Protein Desired	40% Supplement		35% Supplement		Corn (9.3% crude protein)		Ground Barley (11.8% crude protein)		Ground Oats (11.8% crude protein)		Ground Wheat (12.7% crude protein)		Alfalfa Meal (15.4% crude protein)	
	(lb.)	(kg)	(lb.)	(kg)	(lb.)	(kg)	(lb.)	(kg)	(lb.)	(kg)	(lb.)	(kg)	(lb.)	(kg)
14	325	147	—	—	1,575	714	—	—	—	—	—	—	—	—
	225	102	—	—	875	397	800	363	—	—	—	—	—	—
	275	125	—	—	1,325	601	—	—	300	136	—	—	—	—
	—	—	375	170	1,525	692	—	—	—	—	—	—	—	—
	—	—	250	113	850	386	800	363	300	136	—	—	—	—
	—	—	350	159	1,250	567	—	—	—	—	—	—	—	—
	350	159	—	—	1,650	748	—	—	—	—	—	—	100	45
	250	113	—	—	950	431	800	363	400	181	—	—	100	45
	300	136	—	—	1,300	590	—	—	—	—	—	—	100	45
	—	—	425	193	1,575	714	—	—	—	—	—	—	100	45
	—	—	300	136	900	408	800	363	400	181	—	—	100	45
	—	—	330	159	1,250	567	—	—	—	—	—	—	100	45
12	200	91	—	—	1,700	771	—	—	—	—	—	—	—	—
	150	68	—	—	1,350	612	400	181	—	—	—	—	—	—
	150	68	—	—	1,450	658	—	—	300	136	—	—	—	—
	—	—	250	113	1,650	748	—	—	—	—	—	—	—	—
	—	—	175	79	1,325	601	400	181	300	136	—	—	—	—
	—	—	200	91	1,400	635	—	—	—	—	—	—	—	—
	225	102	—	—	1,775	805	—	—	—	—	—	—	100	45
	150	68	—	—	1,250	567	600	272	300	136	—	—	100	45
	200	91	—	—	1,500	680	—	—	—	—	—	—	100	45
	—	—	275	125	1,725	782	—	—	—	—	—	—	100	45
	—	—	200	91	1,300	590	500	227	300	136	—	—	100	45
	—	—	225	102	1,474	669	—	—	—	—	—	—	100	45

[1]In order to obtain an 18% protein feed, one could mix 575 lb. of 40% supplement, 1,325 lb. of corn, and 100 lb. of alfalfa meal. Likewise, a 14% supplement without alfalfa meal (for use on pasture) could be obtained by mixing 300 lb. of 35% supplement, 900 lb. of corn, and 800 lb. of barley.

(c) *the plant protein supplements*—soybean, cottonseed, linseed, and peanut meal.

2. If wheat, barley, oats, or grain sorghum is used instead of corn as the grain in a ration, the protein supplement may be slightly reduced, because these grains have a higher protein content than corn.

3. Pacific Coast grains are generally lower in protein content than grains produced elsewhere.

4. With *good* forage (ground alfalfa or pastures), the problem of the supplement is simplified from the standpoint of needed vitamins.

5. A protein supplement including both plant protein and animal protein is considered most satisfactory. However, an all-plant protein supplement of soybean meal may be satisfactory provided vitamins, minerals, and antibiotics are added.

6. When proteins of animal origin predominate, adequate mineral protection can be obtained by allowing hogs free access to a two-compartment box or self-feeder with (a) salt (iodized salt in iodine-deficient areas) in one side, and (b) a mixture of $\frac{1}{3}$ salt (salt added for purposes of palatability) and $\frac{2}{3}$ monosodium phosphate (or other phosphorus supplement) in the other side. When supplements of plant origin constitute most of the source of proteins, add a third compartment to the mineral box and place in it a mixture of $\frac{1}{3}$ salt and $\frac{2}{3}$ ground limestone or oyster shell flour.

The mineral supplement may be incorporated in the entire ration. Usually 1 to 2 percent by weight will prove adequate. If it is incorporated in the protein concentrate only, 5 to 6 pounds of mineral mixture should be added to each 94 to 95 pounds of high-protein feed.

7. Where there is insufficient sunlight or where dehydrated alfalfa meal is fed, vitamin D should be added in keeping with the requirements (Tables 6-2 to 6-5).

8. Where the ration consists chiefly of white corn, barley, wheat, oats, rye, kafir, or by-products of these grains, there may be a deficiency of vitamin A (see Tables 6-2 to 6-5 for requirements).

9. Except for gestating sows and boars of breeding age, hogs are generally self-fed. All of the ingredients may be mixed together and placed in the same self-feeder, or the grain may be placed in one self-feeder (or compartment) and the protein sup-

plements (including any ground alfalfa) in another. If the (a) cereal grains and (b) protein supplement (including ground alfalfa) are hand-fed, the grain and supplement should be fed separately, in the proportions indicated in the suggested rations.

10. An exception should be made to the cafeteria-style feeding when the grain ration consists of barley, oats, rye, or kafir. These feeds are higher in protein content than corn and, for this reason, are generally fed as a mixed ration. Otherwise, the pigs will often eat more protein supplement than is necessary to balance the ration. Likewise, when corn is fed as the grain, sometimes such protein supplements as (a) roasted soybeans, (b) soybean meal, and (c) peanut meal, are too palatable to be fed separately from the corn.

BALANCED RATIONS FOR SWINE

A balanced ration is one which provides an animal the proper proportions and amounts of all the required nutrients for a period of 24 hours.

Several suggested rations for different classes of swine are listed in Tables 6-19 to 6-24 of this chapter. Generally these rations will suffice, but it is recognized that rations should vary with conditions, and that many times they should be formulated to meet the conditions of a specific swine establishment, or to meet the practices common to an area.

Rations may be formulated by the methods which follow, but first these pointers are noteworthy:

1. In computing rations, more than simple arithmetic should be considered, for no set of figures can substitute for experience. Compounding rations is both an art and a science—the art comes from swine know-how and experience, and keen observation; the science is largely founded on chemistry, physiology, and bacteriology. Both are essential for success.

Also, a good hogman should know how to balance a ration. Then, if the occasion demands, he can do it. Perhaps of even greater importance, he will then be able more intelligently to select and buy rations with informed appraisal, to check on how well his manufacturer, dealer, or consultant is meeting his needs, and to evaluate the results.

2. Before attempting to balance a ration for swine, the following major points should be considered:

a. **Availability and cost of the different feed ingredients.**—Preferably cost of ingredients should be based on delivery to the swine plant and after processing—because delivery and processing costs are quite variable.

b. **Moisture content.**—When considering costs and balancing rations, feeds should be placed on a comparable moisture basis; usually, an air dry basis, or 10 percent moisture content, is used. This is especially important in the case of high moisture grains.

c. **Composition of the feeds under consideration.**—Feed composition tables ("book values"), or average analysis, should be considered only as guides, because of wide variations in the composition of feeds. For example, the protein content of milo is quite variable. Wherever possible, especially with large operations, it is best to take a representative sample of each major feed ingredient and have a chemical analysis made of it for the more common constituents—protein, fat, fiber, nitrogen-free extract, and moisture; and often calcium, phosphorus, and carotene. Such ingredients as oil meals and prepared supplements, which must meet specific standards, need not be analyzed so often, except as quality control measures.

Despite the recognized value of a chemical analysis, it is not the total answer. It does not provide information on the availability of nutrients to the animal; it varies from sample to sample, because feeds vary and a representative sample is not always easily obtained, and it does not tell anything about the associated effect of feedstuffs. Nor does a chemical analysis tell anything about taste, palatability, texture, undesirable physiological effects such as laxativeness, and amino acid content.

However, a chemical analysis does give a solid foundation on which to start in evaluating feeds. Also, with chemical analysis at hand, and bearing in mind that it's the composition of the total feed (the finished ration) that counts, the person formulating the ration can more intelligently determine the quantity of protein to buy, and the kind and amount of minerals and vitamins to add.

d. **Soil analysis.**—If the origin of a given feed ingredient is known, a soil analysis or knowledge of the soils of the area can be very helpful; for example, (1) the phosphorus

content of soils affects plant composition, (2) soils high in molybdenum and selenium affect the composition of the feeds produced, (3) iodine-deficient areas are important in swine nutrition, and (4) other similar soil-plant-animal relationships.

e. **The nutrient allowances.**—This should be known for the particular class of swine for which a ration is to be formulated; and, preferably, it should be based on controlled feeding experiments. Also, it must be recognized that nutrient requirements and allowances must be changed from time to time, as a result of new experimental findings.

3. In addition to providing the proper quantity of feed and to meeting the protein and energy requirements, a well balanced and satisfactory ration should be:

a. Palatable and digestible.

b. Economical. Generally speaking, this calls for the maximum use of feeds available in the area.

c. Adequate in protein content but not higher than is actually needed, for, generally speaking, medium and high protein feeds are in scarcer supply and higher in price than high energy feeds. In this connection, it is noteworthy that the newer findings in nutrition indicate that (1) much of the value formerly attributed to proteins, as such, was probably due to the amino acids, vitamins, and minerals which they furnished, and (2) lower protein content rations may be used successfully provided they are of good quality and fortified properly with the needed vitamins and minerals.

d. Well fortified with the needed vitamins.

e. Well fortified with the needed minerals, or free access to suitable minerals should be provided, but mineral imbalances should be avoided.

f. Fortified with antibiotics, or other anti-microbial agents, as justified.

g. One that will enhance, rather than impair, the quality of pork produced.

These points are pertinent to the balancing of rations, regardless of the mechanics of computation used. In the sections that follow, three different methods of ration formulation are presented: (1) the square method, (2) the trial and error method, and (3) the computer method. Despite the sometimes confusing mechanics of each system, if done properly, the end result of all

three methods is approximately the same—a ration that provides the desired allowance of nutrients, in correct proportions; economically (or least cost), but, more important, so as to achieve the greatest net returns—for it's net profit rather than cost per bag that counts. Since feed represents by far the greatest cost item in hog production (about 75 percent of the cost), the importance of balanced rations is evident.

How to Balance a Ration by the Square Method

The so-called square method (or the Pearson Square Method) is one of several methods that may be employed to balance rations. The same method is used by milk plants to determine the proportions of milk and cream, the fat percentages of which are known, to mix in order to make cream or milk of a desired percentage fat content.

The square method is simple, direct, and easy. Also, it permits quick substitution of feed ingredients in keeping with market fluctuations, without disturbing the protein content. The latter virtue is of particular value to the feed manufacturer.

In balancing rations by the square method, it is recognized that protein content alone receives major consideration. Correctly speaking, therefore, it is a method of balancing the protein requirement, with only incidental consideration given to the vitamin, mineral, and other nutritive requirements.

With the instructions given herein, the square method may be employed to balance rations by both swine producers and feed manufacturers.

In order to compute balanced rations by the square method, or by any other method, it is first necessary to have available both feeding standards and feed composition tables.

The following tables are adequate for balancing most swine rations:

1. Tables 6-2 to 6-5, and 6-11.

2. Table I-1, Appendix, Composition of Some Common Swine Feeds (this information may also be obtained from the feed tag).

In using these tables, the following points should be noted:

1. All protein recommendations are in terms of *crude protein* content, rather than digestible protein, because (a) this is what the feed manufacturer wants to know as he plans a feed formula,

and (b) this is what the stockman sees on the feed tags when he purchases feed.

2. It is recognized that most swine producers generally wish to know what crude protein content of total ration (including grains, by-product feeds, and/or protein supplements) they need to feed. Likewise, feed manufacturers have need for this information in compounding mixes.

3. It is realized that (a) stockmen may be in error in appraising the quality of their pastures and (b) pastures are generally excellent in the early spring, but become progressively poorer as the season advances unless they are irrigated.

The application of the square method will be illustrated by solving some practical problems.

Problem No. 1:

A swine producer wishes to self-feed a mixed ration to 45- to 75-pound growing-finishing pigs in confinement. Corn (No. 2 grade, 9.3% protein) is on hand, and sun-cured alfalfa meal (15.4%), digester tankage (59.8%), and soybean meal (solvent, 45.8%) are the cheapest protein feeds available. The swine producer plans to prepare a trio-mixture[14] protein supplement consisting of 5 parts of the alfalfa meal, 6 parts of tankage, and 13 parts of soybean meal. He wishes to know how much of this protein supplement (the trio-mixture) and corn to use to obtain a balanced ration.

Step by step, the answer may be obtained as follows:

(1) Place in the center of the square the percentage of crude protein needed in the mixture; in this case 16% (see Tables 6-3, for 45 to 75 pound pigs).

(2) Place at the upper left-hand corner of the square the percentage of crude protein in a trio-mixture consisting of 5 parts of sun-cured alfalfa meal (15.4%), 6 parts of tankage (59.8%), and 13 parts of soybean meal (45.8%); in this case 43%.

(3) Place in the lower left-hand corner of the square the percentage of crude protein in the corn; in this case 9.3%.

---

[14]Actually, the original trio-mixture consisted of 2 parts tankage, 1 part linseed meal, and 1 part alfalfa meal.

(4) Connect the diagonal corners of the square with lines, and subtract, diagonally across the square, the smaller figure from the larger. Place the answers in the opposite corners. This gives the following:

Alfalfa meal (sun-cured)
  5 parts (15.4) --------------------------- 77.0
Tankage (digester)
  6 parts (59.8) --------------------------- 358.8
Soybean meal (solvent)
  13 parts (45.8)-------------------------- 595.4

  24 Total   = 1,031.2
  1031.2 ÷ 24   = 43% protein

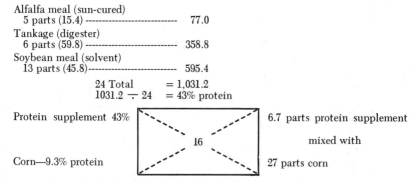

Protein supplement 43%   6.7 parts protein supplement

                                16   mixed with

Corn—9.3% protein   27 parts corn

(5) Thus, a mixture of 6.7 parts of the trio-mixture and 27 parts of corn (33.7 parts total) will provide a feed with the desired 16% crude protein content.

(6) The proportions of the trio-mixture and corn can be converted to 100 pounds of mixture as follows (or to a ton basis by using 2,000 instead of 100):

6.7 ÷ 33.7 × 100 = 20 lbs. trio-mixture
27 ÷ 33.7 × 100 = 80 lb. corn
  Total 100 lb. mix

(7) Thus in order to prepare a 16% crude protein feed from corn and the trio-mixture, the swine producer will need to mix 80 lb. of corn and 20 lb. of the trio-mixture for each 100 lb. of feed.

How to Balance a Ration by the Trial and Error Method

As stated, balancing rations by the Square Method is simple, direct, and easy, but protein alone receives major consideration. Balancing by the Trial and Error Method goes further. In it, consideration is given to meeting whatever allowances are decided upon of each of the nutrients that one cares to list and consider. Following are the steps in the Trial and Error Method:

Set down the allowances—Refer to Tables 6-2 to 6-5 but bear in mind that they list requirements, and not allowances. Requirements do not provide for margins of safety to compensate for

variations in feed composition and possible losses during storage and processing. Nor do they recognize individual animal differences and the effect of stress and environment on requirements.

The author suggests that each swine producer or feed company arrive at the nutritive allowances for a specific class of swine and set of conditions as follows:

1. **Base protein, energy, calcium, and phosphorus allowances on Table 6-3,** bearing in mind that the figures given therein are requirements, and not allowances. Considering all the factors affecting nutritive needs, come to a decision as to what margin of safety, if any, to provide over and above the protein and energy requirements given in Table 6-3; then add it to the requirements, whatever it may be—0, 10 percent, or some other level.

2. **Set down the allowances.**—Simply list them. Thus, for 75-pound pigs, the feed allowances arbitrarily decided upon are:

Crude Protein (%)	TDN (%)	Calcium (%)	Phosphorus (%)
14.5	75	.60	.50

3. **Apply the Trial and Error Method.**—Considering (a) available feeds and (b) common feeding practices, the next step is arbitrarily to set down a ration, and see how well it measures up to the desired allowances. The approximate composition of the available feeds may be arrived at from the feed composition table (Table I-1) if an actual chemical analysis is not available. Where commercial supplements are used, the guarantee on the feed tag may be used.

Let's try the following ration:

Ingredients	Per ton
	(lb.)
Corn, yellow _____	1,790
Alfalfa meal (16.8%) _____	50
Soybean meal (45.8%) _____	50
Tankage, with bone (53.4%) _____	100
Salt _____	10
TOTAL_____	2,000

Here's a listing of the desired allowance (step no. 2), followed by the composition of the proposed ration:

	Crude Protein (%)	TDN (%)	Calcium (%)	Phosphorus (%)
Desired allowances	14.5	75	0.60	0.50
Approximate analysis of proposed ration	12.2	77.4	0.65	0.57

Thus, the proposed ration meets the desired allowances in every category except for the protein; it is under the desired level of crude protein. To correct the protein deficiency, let's decrease the corn and increase the alfalfa meal and soybean meal. Thus, our trial ration is—

Ingredients	Per ton (lb.)
Corn, yellow	1,620
Alfalfa meal	100
Soybean meal	170
Tankage, with bone	100
Salt	10
TOTAL	2,000

	Crude Protein (%)	TDN (%)	Calcium (%)	Phosphorus (%)
Desired allowances	14.5	75	0.60	0.50
Approximate composition of 2nd proposed ration	14.6	76.7	0.69	0.59

This ration approximates the desired allowances and may be considered satisfactory.

How to Balance a Ration by the Computer Method[15]

Many large swine producers, and most feed companies, now use computers for ration formulation as well as for other purposes; and their use will increase.

Despite their sophistication, there is nothing magical or mysterious about balancing rations by computer. Although they can alleviate many human errors in calculations, the data which come out of a machine are no better than those which go into it; without a man, they don't know the difference between a Doberman and a Duroc. The men back of the computer—the producer and his nutritionist who prepare the data that go into it, and who evaluate and apply the results that come out of it—become more important than ever. This is so because an electronic computer doesn't know anything about (1) feed palatability, (2) feeds that produce soft pork, (3) limitations that must be imposed on certain feeds to obtain maximum utilization, (4) the goals in the feeding program—such as growing or finishing, (5) home-grown feeds for which there may not be a suitable market, (6) feed processing and storage facilities, (7) the health, environment, and stress of the hogs, and (8) the men responsible for actual feed preparation and feeding. Additionally, it must be recognized that a computer may even reflect, without challenge, the prejudices and whims of those who prepare the data for it.

Hand in hand with the use of computers in balancing rations, the term "least cost ration formulation" evolved. In some respects this designation was unfortunate, for the use of least cost rations does not necessarily assure the highest net returns—and net profit is more important than cost per ton. For example, the least cost ration may not produce the desired daily gain.

An electronic computer cannot do a thing that a good mathematician can't, but it can do it a lot faster and check all possible combinations. It alleviates the endless calculations and hours common to hand calculations. For example, it is estimated that there may be as many as 500 practical solutions when as many as six quality specifications and 10 feedstuffs are considered.

Generally speaking, electronic feed formulation (1) effects a greater saving when first applied to a ration than in subsequent

---

[15] This section was authoritatively reviewed by Mr. Wendell A. Clithero, International Business Machine Corp. (IBM), Chicago, Ill.; and Dr. T. C. Cartwright, Texas A & M University, College Station, Texas.

applications, and (2) is of most use where a wide selection of feed ingredients is available and/or prices shift rather rapidly.

STEPS IN BALANCING A RATION BY COMPUTER

The information needed and the procedure followed in formulating rations by computer are exactly the same as in the hand-method of ration formulation; namely, (1) the nutritive requirements for the particular class and kind of animal, (2) nutritive content of the feeds, and (3) ingredient costs. Sometimes this simple fact is overlooked because of the awesomeness of the computer, the high-sounding name "linear programming," and the jargon sometimes used by those who wish to impress fellow scientists. Step by step, the procedure in formulating rations by computer is:

1. **List available feed ingredients, and the cost of each.**—It is necessary that all of the available feeds be listed along with the unit cost (usually/ton) of each; preferably, ingredient cost should be based on market price plus delivery, storage, and processing cost.

2. **Record quality of feed.**—The more that is known about the quality of feed the better. This is so because of the wide variation in composition and feeding value within ingredients; for example, between two samples of alfalfa meal.

Wherever possible, an actual chemical analysis of a representative sample of each ingredient under consideration, rather than "book values," should be available and used. However, the imperfections of a chemical analysis of a feedstuff should be recognized; chiefly, (a) it does not provide information on the availability of nutrients to animals, and (b) there are variations between samples.

3. **Establish ration specifications.**—Set down the ration specifications—the nutrients and the levels of each that are to be met. This is exactly the same procedure as is followed in the hand-method. (See the Trial and Error Method, step 2, of this section.) In arriving at ration specifications, the nutritionist considers class, age, and weight of hogs, the probable market, season of year, background and stress of animals, and other similar factors.

4. **Give restrictions.**—Usually it is necessary to establish certain limitations on the use of ingredients; for example, (a) the maximum amount of alfalfa, (b) the maximum amount of

fat, (c) the proportion of one grain to another—such as 60 percent corn and 40 percent barley, (d) an upper limit on some ingredients—such as 20 percent rye, and (e) the exact amount of the premix.

It must be recognized that the more narrow the limitations imposed on the computer, the less the choice it will have in ration formulation and the higher the cost.

5. **Stipulate antibiotics and other ration ingredients.**—Generally speaking, the nutritionist makes rigid stipulations as to amounts of these ingredients; much as he does with added vitamins and minerals. All of them cost money.

6. **"Feed" the punched cards into the computer.**—When the punched cards are fed into the computer, it treats the data as one gigantic algebra problem and arrives at the ration formulation in a matter of seconds. Based on available feeds, analysis and price, the computer evolves with the mix that will meet the desired nutritive allowances at the least possible cost.

7. **Formulate as necessary.**—All rations should be reviewed at frequent intervals, and reformulated when there are shifts in (a) availability of ingredients (certain ingredients may no longer be available, but new ones may have evolved), (b) price, and/or (c) chemical composition.

8. **Validate the restrictions.**—That is, test or confirm them.

USE OF COMPUTER AS FEED BUYING AND SELLING AID

When a computer formulates a ration, it also gives a complete set of "shadow prices," which may be used as follows:

1. If a certain ingredient does not enter the formula due to its chemical analysis as related to price, the shadow price will indicate how much the market price of this ingredient must go down in order for it to enter the formula.

2. If an ingredient is home-grown and on hand, and the feeder desires to use it, despite the fact that its market value is out of line, the shadow price will indicate to him the penalty that he will pay for using it. Sometimes, it may become obvious that it is good business to sell a certain home-grown product and buy something else to replace it.

3. The shadow price provides a technique for determining the value of each ingredient based on its chemical analysis, there-

by making it possible to determine which ingredient is the best buy. As a result, it is an excellent management tool for buying and selling feed ingredients.

4. In price mapping, or the range of prices over which an ingredient will stay in the solution. By considering one ingredient at a time, this is an excellent buying guide.

5. In determining cost of restrictions; that is, the decrease in price that will occur if a restriction is released.

NUTRITIONAL DISEASES AND AILMENTS OF SWINE

More animals (and people) throughout the world suffer from hunger—from just plain lack of sufficient feed—than from the lack of one or more specific nutrients. Therefore, it is recognized that nutritional deficiencies may be brought about by either (1) too little feed, or (2) rations that are too low in one or more nutrients.

Also, forced production (such as breeding and marketing of swine at early ages) and the feeding of forages and grains which are often produced on leached and depleted soils have created many problems in swine nutrition. This condition has been further aggravated through the increased confinement of hogs, many animals being confined all or a large part of the year. Under these unnatural conditions, nutritional diseases and ailments have become increasingly common.

Although the cause, prevention, and treatment of most of these nutritional diseases and ailments are known, they continue to reduce profits in the swine industry simply because the available knowledge is not put into practice. Moreover, those widespread nutritional deficiencies which are not of sufficient proportions to produce clear-cut deficiency symptoms cause even greater economic losses because they go unnoticed and unrectified. Table 6-27 contains a summary of the important nutritional diseases and ailments affecting swine. It is recognized, however, that single nutrient deficiencies are seldom encountered under farm conditions; in most cases multiple nutrient deficiencies occur.

Disease	Species Affected	Cause	Symptoms (and age or group most affected)	Distribution and Losses Caused by
Alkali disease (See Selenium Poisoning)				
Anemia, nutritional	All warm blooded animals and man	Commonly an iron deficiency, but it may be caused by a deficiency of copper, cobalt, and/or certain vitamins (riboflavin, pyridoxine, pantothenic acid and/or folic acid).	Loss of appetite, progressive emaciation, and death. Pigs show labored breathing, and a swollen condition about the head and shoulders. Most prevalent in suckling pigs on concrete or wood floors without access to soil.	Worldwide. Losses consist of slow and inefficient gains, and deaths.
Baby Pig Shakes (See Hypoglycemia)				
Fluorine poisoning (Fluorosis)	All farm animals, poultry, and man	Ingesting excessive quantities of fluorine through either the feed or water.	Abnormal teeth (especially mottled enamel) and bones, stiffness of joints, loss of appetite, emaciation, reduction in milk flow, diarrhea, and salt hunger.	The water in parts of Arkansas, California, South Carolina, and Texas has been reported to contain excess fluorine. Occasionally throughout the U. S. high fluorine phosphates are used in mineral mixtures.
Goiter (See Iodine Deficiency)				
Hypoglycemia (Baby Pig Shakes)	Swine	Low blood sugar level accompanies the trouble, but cause of the low blood sugar is unknown. The hog cholera virus can also cause this disease.	Shivering, weakness, failure to nurse, with no evidence of scouring. If disturbed, the pigs emit a weak, crying squeal. Hair becomes erect and rough, and the heart action slow and feeble. Without treatment, death usually comes in 24 to 36 hours after the first symptoms appear. Confined to baby pigs only.	Throughout the U.S. mortality may be high.

Treatment	Control and Eradication	Prevention	Remarks
Provide dietary sources of the nutrient or nutrients lack of which is known to cause the condition.	When nutritional anemia is encountered, it can usually be brought under control by supplying dietary sources of the nutrient or nutrients lack of which is known to cause the condition.	Anemia can be prevented by: (1) injecting into the ham muscle an iron-dextran compound (containing 150 mg. of iron) at one to three days of age. Repeat at two to three weeks if necessary; (2) placing clean, hog manure-free sod in each farrowing pen several times each week; (3) giving iron pills or liquids to pigs at weekly intervals; (4) using iron fortified baby pig feeds in the creep area.	Anemia is a condition in which the blood is either deficient in quality or quantity (a deficient quality refers to a deficiency in hemoglobin and/or red cells). Levels of iron in most feeds believed to be ample, since most feeds contain 40 to 400 mg / lb.
Any damage may be permanent, but animals which have not developed severe symptoms may be helped to some extent, if the sources of excess fluorine are eliminated.	Discontinue the use of feeds, water, or mineral supplements containing excessive fluorine.	Avoid the use of feeds, water, or mineral supplement containing excessive fluorine.	Fluorine is a cumulative poison. 100 ppm (0.01) fluorine of the total dry ration is the borderline in toxicity for swine. At levels of 25-100 ppm, some mottling of the teeth may occur over periods of three to five years. In breeding animals, therefore, the permissible level is 30 ppm of the total dry ration. Not more than 65 to 100 ppm fluorine should be present in dry matter of rations when rock phosphate is fed.
Provide heat lamps for pigs. At earliest symptoms either (1) force feed at frequent intervals a mixture of 1 part of corn syrup diluted with 2 parts of water, or (2) give intraperitoneal injections of dextrose solutions. Consult veterinarian.	Apparently not contagious.	Adequate rations and good care and management of the gestating sows may lessen the incidence of disease. Be sure there is adequate milk for baby pigs during first days of life.	One of the hazards of hypoglycemia is that the milk flow of the sow will not be stimulated or may even cease, due to the inactivity of the affected pigs. In the latter case, the pigs may have to be either transferred to a foster mother or hand-fed.

(Continued

TABLE 6-27

Disease	Species Affected	Cause	Symptoms (and age or group most affected)	Distribution and Losses Caused by
Iodine Deficiency (Goiter)	All farm animals and man	A failure of the body to obtain sufficient iodine from which the thyroid gland can form thyroxin (an iodine-containing compound).	Pigs may be born hairless.	Northwestern U.S. and the Great Lakes region.
Osteomalacia	All species	Lack of vitamin D. Inadequate intake of calcium and phosphorus. Incorrect ratio of calcium and phosphorus.	Phosphorus deficiency symptoms are: depraved appetite (gnawing on bones, wood, or other objects, or eating dirt); lack of appetite, stiffness of joints, failure to breed regularly, decreased milk production, and an emaciated appearance. Calcium deficiency symptoms are: Fragile bones, reproductive failures, and lowered lactations. Mature animals most affected. Most of the acute cases occur during pregnancy and lactation.	Southwestern U.S. is classed as a phosphorus-deficient area, whereas calcium-deficient areas have been reported in parts of Florida, Louisiana, Nebraska, Virginia and West Virginia.
Parakeratosis	Swine	High calcium levels in the diet—above 0.8 percent.	Pigs have a mangy look, reduced appetite and growth rate, diarrhea, and vomiting. It affects pigs from 1 to 5 months of age.	Mortality is not high; economic loss is mainly in reduced gains and lowered feed efficiency.
Rickets	All farm animals and man	Lack of either calcium, phosphorus, or vitamin D. An incorrect ratio of the two minerals.	Enlargement of the knee and hock joints, and the animal may exhibit great pain when moving about. Irregular bulges (beaded ribs) at juncture of ribs with breastbone, and bowed legs. Swine are frequently paralyzed in the hind legs. Rickets is a disease of young animals—of calves, foals, pigs, lambs, kids, pups, and chicks.	Worldwide. It is seldom fatal.
Salt Deficiency	All farm animals and man	Lack of salt (Sodium chloride).	Depressed appetite, retarded growth, loss of weight, a rough coat, lowered production of milk, and a ravenous appetite for salt.	Worldwide, especially among grass-eating animals and the pig.

Treatment	Control and Eradication	Prevention	Remarks
)nce the iodine-deficiency symptoms appear in farm animals, no treatment is very effective.	At the first signs of iodine deficiency, an iodized salt should be fed to all farm animals.	In iodine-deficient areas, feed iodized salt to all farm animals throughout the year. Salt containing 0.007% potassium iodine is recommended.	The enlarged thyroid gland (goiter) is nature's way of attempting to make sufficient thyroxin under conditions where deficiency exists.
Increase the calcium and phosphorus content of feeds through fertilizing the soils. Select natural feeds that contain sufficient quantities of calcium and phosphorus. Feed a special mineral supplement or supplements. f the disease is far advanced, treatment will not be successful.	(See Treatment.)	Feed balanced rations, and allow animals free access to a suitable phosphorus and calcium supplement.	Calcium deficiencies are fairly common in swine because grains which are their chief feed are low in this mineral.
Add 0.4 pounds of zinc carbonate or 0.9 pounds of zinc sulfate heptahydrate/ton of feed.	It is noncontagious.	Add 0.4 pounds of zinc carbonate or 0.9 pounds of zinc sulfate heptahydrate/ton of feed where the disease is encountered.	
f the disease has not advanced too far, treatment may be successful by supplying adequate amounts of vitamin D, calcium and phosphorus, and/or adjusting the ratio of calcium to phosphorus.	(See Prevention.)	Provide (1) sufficient calcium, phosphorus, and vitamin D, and (2) a correct ratio of the two minerals.	Rickets is characterized by a failure of growing bone to ossify or harden, properly.
Salt-starved animals should be gradually accustomed to salt; slowly increasing the hand-fed allowance until the animals may be safely allowed free access to it.	(See Treatment and Prevention.)	Provide plenty of salt at all times, preferably by free-choice feeding.	Common salt is one of the most essential minerals for grass-eating animals, and one of the easiest and cheapest to provide.

(Continued)

TABLE 6-9

Disease	Species Affected	Cause	Symptoms (and age or group most affected)	Distribution and Losses Caused by
Salt poisoning (Sodium chloride)	Swine most frequently, but all farm animals.	Brine from cured meats; wet salt. Where large amounts of brine or salt have been mixed with hog slop. When excess salt is fed following starvation.	Sudden onset—1 to 2 hours after eating salt; extreme nervousness; muscle twitching and fine tremors; much weaving, wobbling, staggering, and circling; blindness; weakness; normal temperature, rapid but weak pulse, and very rapid and shallow breathing; diarrhea; death from a few hours up to 48 hours; convulsions.	Not extensive.
Selenium Poisoning (Alkali disease)	All farm animals and man	Consumption of plants grown on soils containing selenium.	Loss of hair from the mane and tail in horses, from the tail in cattle, and a general loss of hair in swine. In severe cases, the hoofs slough off, lameness occurs, food consumption decreases, and death may occur by starvation.	In certain regions of western U.S.—especially certain areas in South Dakota, Montana, Wyoming, Nebraska, Kansas, and perhaps areas in other states in the Great Plains and Rocky Mountains. Also in Canada.
Vitamin A Deficiency (Night Blindness and Xerophthalmia)	All farm animals and man	Vitamin A deficiency.	Night blindness, the first symptom of vitamin A deficiency, is characterized by faulty vision, especially noticeable when the afflicted animal is forced to move about in twilight in strange surroundings. Xerophthalmia develops in the advanced stages of vitamin A deficiency. The eyes become severely affected, and blindness may follow.	Worldwide.

Treatment	Control and Eradication	Prevention	Remarks
Provide large quantities of fresh water to affected animals. Those that can and do drink seldom need additional treatment. Those unable to drink should be given water via stomach tube, by the veterinarian. The vet may also give (I.V. or intraperitoneally) calcium gluconate to severely affected animals.	(See Prevention and Treatment.)	Avoid feeding excess salt. If hogs are salt-starved, gradually accustom them to salt.	Actually, salt poisoning is relatively rare.
Although arsenic has been shown to counteract the effects of selenium toxicity, there appears to be no practical method of treating other than removal of animals from affected areas.	(Control measures based on Prevention.)	Abandon areas where soils contain selenium, because crops produced on such soils constitute a menace to both animals and man.	Chronic cases of selenium poisoning occur when animals consume feeds containing 8.5 ppm of selenium over an extended period, acute cases occur on 500 to 1,000 ppm. The toxic level of selenium is in the range of 2.27 to 4.54 mg/lb. of feed.
Treatment consists of correcting the dietary deficiencies.	(See Prevention and Treatment.)	Provide good sources of carotene (vitamin A) through green, leafy hays; silage; lush, green pastures; yellow corn or green and yellow peas; whole milk; or fish oils; or add stabilized vitamin A to the ration.	High levels of nitrates in the silage or hay may tie up the conversion of carotene into vitamin A in the intestinal wall.

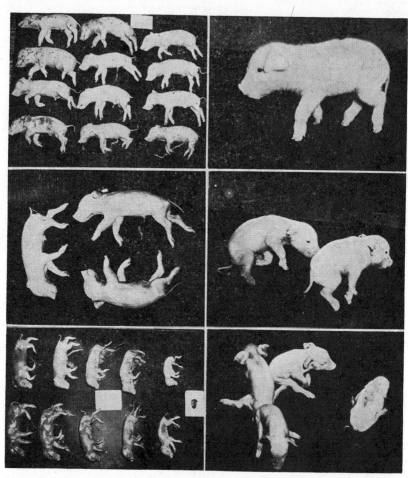

Fig. 6-38. Three pictures on the left are from litters of riboflavin-deficient sows. *Upper left:* litter from riboflavin-deficient sow 551—note enlarged front legs and generalized edema in some pigs. All pigs were born hairless. *Center left:* three pigs from riboflavin-deficient sow 338—note enlargement of legs in two pigs, compared with normal pig. No pigs were hairless. *Lower left:* litter from riboflavin-deficient sow 569. This litter was in the process of resorption. All pigs were hairless. The pictures on the right are of pigs representing leg weaknesses obtained from sows on rations where choline and thiamine were omitted. (Courtesy, Washington State University)

Fig. 6-39. Selenium poisoning (alkali disease). An "alkalied" pig. Notice the general rundown condition, thinness of hair, and diseased feet. (Courtesy, South Dakota Agricultural Experiment Station, Bulletin 311)

QUESTIONS FOR STUDY AND DISCUSSION

1. Why is knowledge of swine feeding so important?

2. Compare the nutritive needs of swine with those of ruminants.

3. The current nutrient requirements for swine, as recommended by the National Research Council, make provision for the following innovations:
   a. Lower protein requirements than formerly.
   b. A difference between hogs full-fed corn and those full-fed small grains.
   How do you account for, or justify, these changes?

4. Explain the difference between (a) nutrient requirements, and (b) recommended allowance? Which should one follow in practical rations, and why?

5. Why is protein most frequently the limiting factor in the ration of swine, both from the standpoint of quantity and

quality? Why should one be concerned about the amino acid content of rations?

6. What peculiarities of swine husbandry are conducive to swine suffering from mineral deficiencies?

7. Compare the price of one or more commercial minerals with the price of a home-mixed product, and relate their respective analyses to the needs of the class of livestock for which they are intended.

8. Should a swine producer (a) incorporate the minerals in the ration, (b) self-feed minerals, or (c) use a combination of these two systems?

9. For swine, list the vitamins most apt to be deficient; then (a) list some of the deficiency symptoms, and (b) give practical sources of each vitamin for use on your farm.

10. What recent (within the past two decades) nutritional discovery has had the greatest impact on the swine industry? Justify your answer.

11. When would you use (a) antibiotics and/or (b) other antimicrobial agents in the swine rations? When wouldn't you?

12. On your home farm (or a farm with which you are familiar) would you (a) utilize pastures for swine, (b) feed silage to swine, and (c) hog-off certain crops? If so, explain how and why.

13. Is it fair to incriminate the feeding of raw garbage for the majority of trichinosis in humans?

14. What factors should be considered in the selection of feeds, and why?

15. Under what conditions should commercial feeds be used instead of home-mixed rations?

16. How and why would you "flush" sows?

17. Should we always avoid producing soft pork?

18. Select a specific class of swine and prepare a balanced ration, using those feeds that are available at the lowest cost.

19. Under what circumstances would you recommend (a) the use of complete rations, (b) that the grain and the supplement be fed separately, or (c) a combination of the two systems?

20. List the most common nutritional diseases and ailments of

swine; then give the (a) cause, (b) symptoms, (c) treatment, and (d) prevention for each.

SELECTED REFERENCES

Title of Publication	Author(s)	Publisher
Animal Nutrition	L. A. Maynard J. K. Loosli	McGraw-Hill Book Co., New York, N. Y., 1962.
Applied Animal Nutrition	E. W. Crampton L. E. Harris	W. H. Freeman & Co., San Francisco, Calif., 1969.
Balancing Swine Rations	D. E. Becker, et al.	Ext. Cir. 866, Revised 1966, University of Illinois, Urbana, Illinois.
Better Feeding of Livestock	Farmers' Bul. 2052	U. S. Department of Agriculture, Washington, D. C.
Composition of Cereal Grains and Forages	Publication 585	National Academy of Sciences, National Research Council, Washington, D. C.
Composition of Concentrate By- Product Feeding Stuffs	Publication 449	National Academy of Sciences, National Research Council, Washington, D. C.
Feed Formulation Handbook	T. W. Perry	The Interstate Printers & Publishers, Inc., Danville, Ill., 1966.
Feed Mixers' Handbook	R. M. Sherwood	The Interstate Printers & Publishers, Inc., Danville, Ill., 1951.
Feeders' Guide and Formulae for Meal Mixtures	Quebec Provin- cial Feed Board	Department of Agriculture, Quebec, Canada.
Feeding Practices	Educational Service	National Cottonseed Products Assn., 618 Wilson Bldg., Dallas, Tex.
Feeds and Feeding, Abridged	F. B. Morrison	Morrison Publishing Co., Ithaca, N. Y., 1958.
Feeds and Feeding 22nd edition	F. B. Morrison	Morrison Publishing Co., Ithaca, N. Y., 1956.
Feeds of the World	B. H. Schneider	Agri. Expt. Sta., West Virginia University, Morgantown, W. Va., 1947.
Fundamentals of Nutrition	E. W. Crampton L. E. Lloyd	W. H. Freeman and Company, San Francisco, Calif., 1959.
Handbook of Feedstuffs, The	Rudolph Seiden	Springer Publishing Co., New York, N. Y., 1957.
Nutrient Require- ments of Swine	Revised 1968 Publication 1599	National Academy of Sciences, National Research Council, Washington, D. C.
Nutrition of Pigs and Poultry	Edited by J. T. Morgan D. Lewis	Butterworths, London, 1962.

Title of Publication	Author(s)	Publisher
Nutritional Deficiencies in Livestock	R. T. Allman T. S. Hamilton	Food and Agriculture Organization Studies No. 5, Rome, Italy.
Nutritive Requirements of Farm Livestock, The; No. 3, Pigs	Sir Ronald Baskett, *et al.*	Agricultural Research Council, London, England, 1967.
Proteins and Amino Acids in Animal Nutrition	H. J. Almquist	U. S. Industrial Chemicals Co., 99 Park Ave., New York, N. Y.
Salt in Animal Nutrition		Salt Institute, 33 North LaSalle Street, Chicago, Ill., 1957.
Stockman's Handbook, The	M. E. Ensminger	The Interstate Printers & Publishers, Inc., Danville, Ill., 1970.
Swine Feeding and Nutrition	T. J. Cunha	Interscience Publishers, Inc., New York, N. Y., 1957.

In addition to the above selected references, valuable publications on feeding and feeds for swine can be obtained from:
1. Division of Publications
   Office of Information
   U. S. Department of Agriculture
   Washington, D. C. 20250
2. Your state agricultural college.
3. Feed manufacturers and pharmaceutical houses.

Chapter VII

GRAINS AND OTHER HIGH ENERGY FEEDS FOR SWINE[1]

Contents   **Page**

The largest amount of pork is produced in those areas where the most grain is grown. As a result, swine producers generally have plenty of home-grown grain, but they purchase the protein, mineral, and vitamin concentrates needed to balance the ration.

---

[1]Where feed definitions are used in this chapter, they are either taken from or similar to those used by the American Feed Control Officials.

The selection of swine feeds requires more careful attention than the selection of cattle or sheep feeds for the following reasons:

1. More of the production cost of swine is constituted by feeds than with other classes of farm animals. Feed costs account for approximately 75 percent of the total cost of producing pork. Thus, the proper selection of feeds makes the difference between profit and loss on many a pig crop.

2. Swine suffer from nutritional deficiencies more frequently than do cattle or sheep because:

    a.   They are fed chiefly on concentrates—feeds lacking in good quality proteins, in minerals, and in vitamins. It is estimated that grains, root crops, and by-product feeds make up 95.6 percent of the ration of hogs, with growing-finishing pigs holding to the upper limit.

    b.   They grow more rapidly.

    c.   They reproduce at a younger age.

    d.   They have less protein and vitamin synthesis in their monogastric stomachs.

3. Many feeds utilized by swine produce soft pork, thus lowering the value of the end product.

These factors have stimulated much scientific research on the feeding value of the products utilized by omnivorous swine, which consume a larger variety of feeds than any other farm animal.

Corn is the leading U. S. hog feed, but in certain areas the small grains—wheat, barley, oats, rye, and the sorghums—are grown and fed extensively. In still other areas, the root and tuber crops—peanuts, Irish potatoes, sweet potatoes, chufas, cassavas, and Jerusalem artichokes—are major components of the swine ration. By-products of the packing and fishing industries, and of the industries processing corn, wheat, rice, cottonseed, soybeans, flaxseed, and peanuts are used in hog feeding. Additional and valuable by-product feeds for swine are obtained from the dairy industry—including skimmed milk, buttermilk, and whey. Generally, these swine feeds are supplemented with various kinds of forage and pasture crops.

The partial composition of some of the more commonly used grains and high energy feeds is given in Appendix Table I-1. Although this and other similar information may serve as a valu-

able guide, it must be used with judgment. Climate, soil, and variety in plant material or species in animal or marine products, as well as storage method, all affect the composition of several feed constituents.

Two factors besides chemical composition are important in evaluating a swine feed—palatability and carcass quality. The most infallible way in which to appraise these two factors is through actual swine feeding trials. But knowing feeds is not the only requisite to successful swine production. The modern and successful swine producer also is a keen student of values. He changes the composition of the ration in keeping with comparative feed prices, and adjusts the number of hogs raised in keeping with feed-market hog ratios.

AREAS OF SWINE FEEDING

The general principles involved in good swine breeding, feeding, and management apply equally well to all sections of the United States. But due chiefly to differences in available locally grown feed, there are some rather characteristic feeding practices common to the following areas: (1) the Corn Belt and North Central states, (2) the South, (3) the Atlantic Coast, and (4) the West. Figure 7-1 graphically defines these four major hog-producing regions.

The Corn Belt and North Central States

Normally, the twelve-state area comprising the Corn Belt (Illinois, Iowa, Kansas, Nebraska, Missouri, Indiana, and Ohio) and the North Central states produces about two-thirds of the U.S. corn crop, and supports a high proportion of the U.S. swine population; on January 1, 1967, 79.1 percent of the hogs and pigs on farms were in this area.[2] About one-half the corn crop is fed to hogs.

Although corn is the chief cereal grain used in feeding hogs in this area, wheat, oats, barley, and rye are used quite extensively—sometimes as a partial substitute for corn.

The common protein supplements used by these swine producers include by-products of the dairy and meat packing in-

---

[2] Also see Table 2-2, Chapter II, for swine production by geographical areas.

Fig. 7-1. The four areas of swine feeding: (1) The Corn Belt and North Central states, (2) the South, (3) the Atlantic Coast, and (4) the West. Some rather characteristic feeding practices are common to each. (Drawing by R. F. Johnson)

dustries (skimmed milk, buttermilk, whey, tankage, and meat scraps), and soybean, cottonseed, linseed, and gluten meals.

In this area, pastures—chiefly bluegrass, alfalfa, the clovers, and various temporary pastures—are used extensively as a further source of proteins, minerals, and vitamins. Also some Corn Belt farmers use swine regularly in hogging down corn and/or soybeans, and in following steers in the feedlot.

The South

In number of hogs, the South—an eight-state area (see Fig. 7-1)—ranks next in importance to the Corn Belt, having about 9.6 percent of the U.S. hog population on January 1, 1967. As a result of improved swine feeding and management practices in recent years and the trend toward further agricultural diversification, increased hog numbers and improved quality of market hogs in the South are inevitable.

The available swine feeds vary between localities. The chief grains consist of corn, soybeans, velvet beans, and the sorghums. In many sections, peanuts and sweet potatoes are fed extensively,

either using the animals to glean the fields after the crop is harvested or turning them in to harvest the entire crop.

In Arkansas, Louisiana, and Texas, by-products of the rice industry—including rice bran, rice polish, and brewers' rice—are fed.

The common, locally-produced and used, protein supplements include tankage, shrimp meal, milk by-products, cottonseed and peanut meals, and ground alfalfa.

Pastures occupy a position of unique importance in the swine production of the South, chiefly because of the advantage of year-round grazing. Among the common swine pastures of the area are alfalfa, the clovers, lespedeza, Sudan grass, kudzu, vetch, Bermuda grass, rape, soybeans, cowpeas, oats, rye, and wheat.

The Atlantic Coast

On January 1, 1967, 9.4 percent of the total hog population was found in the seventeen states comprising the Atlantic Coast region. Throughout much of the area, swine are fed for home use. Near the large cities, many hogs are grown and finished on municipal garbage.

In the South Atlantic states, the principal swine feeds and pastures are identical to those used in many sections of the South.

In the North Atlantic states, the chief grain crops produced and fed are corn, barley, oats, and rye. The common protein supplements include skimmed milk, tankage, fish meal, and middlings.

Pasture crops of alfalfa, the clovers, lespedeza, soybeans, cowpeas, rape, Sudan grass, winter rye, and oats are commonly used in the Atlantic Coast states.

The West

Less than 2 (on January 1, 1967, it was 1.9) percent of the total hog population is found in the eleven western states. The bulk of the feeds—chiefly native range grasses—are better adapted to beef cattle and sheep production. However, the small grain crops of the area and many of the feeds produced in the irrigated sections are ideal for feeding swine. The common grains fed hogs in this area include barley, wheat, corn, rye, oats, and

hog millet. The grain sorghums—chiefly Kafir and milo—and rice bran and rice polish, by-products of the rice-milling industry, are used to some extent. The common protein supplements used in the area are fish meal, tankage, skimmed milk, wheat middlings, alfalfa, linseed meal, cottonseed meal, and soybean meal. In addition, low-grade fruits and vegetables are sometimes fed to hogs; and in some areas of the West such root and tuber crops as artichokes, sweet potatoes, beets, and Irish potatoes are fed in combination with the grain feeds.

Alfalfa, the clovers, Sudan grass, brome grass, rye, and peas are the common swine pasture crops of the West.

GRAINS AND OTHER HIGH ENERGY FEEDS

In general, corn, barley, wheat, oats, rye, peanuts, and the grain sorghums constitute the major component of the swine ration. Other feeds are of importance in certain localities.

It is important that the characteristics of each available feed be thoroughly understood, thus making it possible to formulate economical rations which take full advantage of their nutritive properties and compensate for their deficiencies. A brief discussion of each of the more important grain and other high energy feeds utilized by swine will follow.

Corn (Maize)

Corn, first grown in fish-fertilized hills by the Inca Indians, has long been the most important U. S. cereal grain and swine feed. The annual yield, averaging over 4 billion bushels,[3] is equal to that of any other three cereals combined. About 50 percent of this production is fed to hogs. For this reason, the feeding value of corn is usually accepted as the standard with which other cereals are compared.

Corn is palatable, nutritious, and rich in the energy-producing carbohydrates and fats, but it has certain very definite limitations. It lacks quality (being especially low in the amino acids, lysine and tryptophan) and quantity of proteins, and it is deficient in minerals, particularly calcium (see Appendix Table I-1). Thus, hogs fed on corn alone gain slowly and require a larger amount of feed per unit of gain.

---

[3]In 1966, the U.S. produced 4,103,323,000 bushels of corn on 65,784,000 acres.

Fig. 7-2. Corn—as high as an elephant's eye and climbing clear up to the sky—has long been the most important U. S. cereal grain and swine feed. (Courtesy, J. C. Allen and Son, West Lafayette, Ind.)

The protein deficiency of corn may be corrected easily by the addition of a protein supplement.

White corn is low in carotene (the precursor of vitamin A), the growth-promoting substance. However, when pigs have access to a good pasture, when the ration is supplemented adequately with alfalfa meal, or when vitamin A is added, white and yellow corn appear to be equal in feeding value. It is noteworthy that the carotene content of yellow corn decreases with storage; about 25 percent of its original vitamin A value may be lost after one year of storage and 50 percent after two years.

Corn may be fed on the cob or shelled. Within the weight limits followed in ordinary commercial pork production, 200 to 225 pounds, it usually does not pay to grind or soak corn unless it is desired to combine it in definite proportions with other feeds. Then it is easier to make a more uniform mixture by grinding the corn.

Contrary to the opinion prevailing in some quarters, experimental studies have not revealed any difference between hybrid and open-pollinated yellow dent corns in feeding value for growing-finishing hogs. Waxy corn (which is sometimes grown for industrial use because of its special type of starch) is equal in feeding value to yellow dent corn, whereas flint corn is 97 percent as valuable as yellow dent for hogs. Despite its hardness, flint corn need not be ground, provided it is self-fed.

From a market standpoint, the swine producer should be familiar with the following federal grades of corn:

No. 1, which must not exceed 14.0 percent moisture.
No. 2, which must not exceed 15.5 percent moisture.
No. 3, which must not exceed 17.5 percent moisture.
No. 4, which must not exceed 20.0 percent moisture.
No. 5, which must not exceed 23.0 percent moisture.
Sample grade, which is in excess of 23.0 percent moisture.

Although moisture content is the chief criterion in determining federal grades of corn, the percentage of unsound kernels and amount of foreign materials are also factors. From a swine feeding standpoint, the value of the several grades of corn is about equal, providing they are placed on a comparable dry matter basis. The same situation applies to soft corn (corn frosted before maturity). Of course, handling and storage problems are

increased with higher moisture content. Corn with more moisture than No. 2 will not keep well in storage.

When rating corn—the chief swine feed—as 100 percent, Table 6-17, Handy Feed Substitution Table for Swine, shows how some other grain and high energy feeds, properly fed, compare with it, pound for pound.

Wheat

Down through the ages, wheat has been made into the precious bread of mankind. It was utilized for this purpose by the aboriginal Swiss lake dwellers; by the ancient Egyptians, Assyrians, Greeks, and Romans; and by the Hebrews, who, according to the Book of Revelations, exchanged "a measure of wheat for a penny." Even today, most U. S. wheat is utilized as a bread grain.

The total annual U. S. wheat tonnage is second only to corn. However, because it is produced mainly for the manufacture of flour and other human foods, it is generally too high in price to feed to hogs. When the price is favorable or when the grain has been damaged by insects, frost, fire, or disease, it may be more profitable to market it through hogs than for human consumption.

Compared with corn, wheat is higher in protein and carbohydrates, lower in fat, slightly higher in total digestible nutrients, and more palatable. Wheat, like white corn, is deficient in carotene (see Appendix Table I-1). Pound for pound, it is up to 5 percent more valuable than corn in producing gains on hogs, thus having the unique distinction of being the only cereal grain that excels corn as a swine feed (see Table 6-17).

Since the kernels are small and hard, wheat should be coarsely ground for most economical utilization, unless swine are self-fed. Self-fed hogs eat more leisurely and masticate the grain more thoroughly. Wheat produces good quality pork.

Oats

In total annual U. S. tonnage, oats rank third among the cereals; but, in importance for stock feeding, they stand next to corn.

Like the other cereal grains, they should be reinforced in protein, vitamin A, and calcium when fed to hogs (see Appendix

Fig. 7-3. Oats, a favorite feed for brood sows and boars. (Courtesy, J. C. Allen and Son, West Lafayette, Ind.)

Table I-1). Oats are considered a good feed for growing pigs and for brood sows, but they are too high in fiber and too bulky to constitute a major portion of the ration of young pigs. For growing-finishing pigs, good quality oats, weighing 32 pounds per bushel, are worth as much as shelled corn, pound for pound, when limited to less than one-third of the ration. In larger quantities, oats retard the rate of gain, becoming about 80 percent as valuable as corn. For mature breeding animals the oats content of the ration may well be higher than one-third.

Grinding increases by 25 to 30 percent the feeding value of oats for swine. Oatmeal or rolled oats, such as are used for human consumption, are excellent feeds in fitting young pigs for the show. But they are usually expensive.

Leftover seed oats that have been treated with mercuric compounds should not be fed to swine.

Hulled oats are particularly valuable in rations for very young pigs; 100 pounds of them being equal to 140 pounds of corn. However, it takes 155 to 165 pounds of whole oats to produce 100 pounds of hulled oats.

Barley

Barley, the world's most ancient and most widely grown cereal, ranks fourth in importance among U. S. grain crops. It is grown extensively in sections too cool for corn to thrive, such as in the northern part of the United States. In Canada and northern Europe, it is the most common grain for swine. It is an excellent feed, producing firm pork of high quality.

Compared with corn, barley contains somewhat more protein and fiber (due to the hulls) and somewhat less carbohydrates and fats (see Appendix Table I-1). Like oats, the feeding value of barley is quite variable, due to the wide spread in test weight per bushel. When properly supplemented, ground barley is worth about 90 to 95 percent as much as shelled corn for hogs. Grinding increases its feeding value by about 15 percent. Barley is not well adapted to self-feeding, free choice, because pigs usually eat more of the accompanying protein supplement than is required to balance the ration. This is because barley is less palatable and higher in protein content than corn. For this reason, it is best to feed the barley and supplement together as a mixed ration.

Barley that is moderately infested with scab (*Gibberella*

saubinetti) may be fed to growing-finishing pigs, provided it is limited to 10 percent of the ration. In no case should scab-infested barley be fed to gestating-lactating sows or young pigs.

Rye

Rye thrives on poor sandy soils. In such areas, it is some-

Ergot in a head
of rye

Fig. 7-4. A head of rye infested with ergot (a common fungus disease). (Drawing by R. F. Johnson)

times marketed through hogs, although it generally sells at a premium for bread-making or brewing.

Rye is similar to wheat in chemical composition (see Appendix Table I-1), but it is less palatable to pigs. For the latter reason, it should be fed in combination with more relished feeds and limited to no more than one-half of the swine ration. When properly supplemented, ground rye has a feeding value approximately 90 percent that of corn. Because of the small, hard kernel, rye should be ground for hog feed.

Rye that is mildly infested with ergot (a common fungus disease in rye) may be fed to growing-finishing hogs, providing it does not constitute more than 10 percent of the total ration. Since ergot may cause abortion, rye infested with it should never be fed to pregnant sows. Likewise, ergot should not be permitted in the ration of lactating sows or suckling pigs.

Grain Sorghums

The grain sorghums—which include a number of varieties of earless plants, bearing heads of seeds—are assuming an increasingly important role in American agriculture. New and higher-yielding varieties have been developed and become popular. As a result, more and more grain sorghums are being fed to hogs.

Kafirs and milos are among the more important sorghums grown for grain. Other less widely produced types include sorgo, feterita, durra, hegari, kaoliang, and shallu. These grains are generally grown in regions where climatic and soil conditions are unfavorable for corn. A noteworthy exception, however, is reported in the Columbia Basin of Washington—an area adapted to both corn and the sorghums—where amazing yields of the latter have been reported on irrigated land.

Like white corn, the grain sorghums are low in carotene (vitamin A value). Also, they are deficient in other vitamins, and in proteins and minerals (see Appendix Table I-1). Feeding trials show that the grain sorghums are worth about 90 percent as much as shelled corn for growing-finishing pigs or of about the same feeding value as barley.

For swine, the sorghums should be threshed. Grinding is not necessary when self-feeding (for when eating more leisurely, the pigs chew the grain more thoroughly), but such preparation is

Fig. 7-5. A Texas kafir crop. Kafir is usually threshed for swine, but grinding is not necessary when self-feeding. Sometimes kafir is harvested by hogging off. (Courtesy, USDA, Soil Conservation Service)

recommended when the sorghums are hand-fed. Sorghum-fed hogs yield firm carcasses of good quality.

Soybeans

Soybeans, the precious beans from the Orient, have advanced from a minor to a major U. S. grain crop in the past two decades. For the most part, soybeans are processed, with the oil used for human food and the by-products therefrom used for livestock feeds. However, a widespread interest in their use as a home-grown feed for swine has been created.

Soybeans contain a much higher percentage of protein and fat than the cereal grains (they average about 38 percent protein and 18 percent fat). The beans are not palatable to pigs, and their proteins, minerals, and vitamins do not effectively supplement the deficiences of the cereal grains. Moreover, if they constitute more than 10 percent of the ration of pigs over 100 pounds weight, soft pork will result. Because of these several

Fig. 7-6. Soybeans, the precious beans from the Orient; now a major U. S. grain crop. (Courtesy, J. C. Allen and Son, West Lafayette, Ind.)

limitations, if home-grown soybeans can be exchanged on a favorable basis for other grains or for soybean meal, it is preferable to do so.

Fig. 7-7. Soybeans produce soft pork. The loin at the left is from a hog that was fed liberally on soybeans, whereas the loin at the right is from a hog that was fed corn, soybean meal, and alfalfa meal. Both loins had been stored in a cooler at 32° to 34° F. prior to photographing. (Courtesy, Professor Sleeter Bull, University of Illinois)

Roasting or otherwise cooking soybeans improves the palatability, but it does not prevent the softening effect on the carcass. Also, roasting makes the beans so palatable to pigs that, when self-fed, free-choice, they will eat much greater amounts than needed to balance the ration. Therefore, roasted soybeans must either be hand-fed or mixed with the other ingredients of self-fed rations. Grinding reduces the palatability of the feed and exposes the oil to the air, which in warm weather causes it to become rancid and unpalatable. Accordingly, it is best that the beans be fed whole.

Peanuts

Peanuts are an important cash and feed crop of the South. Normally, about two-thirds of the peanut acreage is grown for human consumption as peanuts, peanut butter, or peanut oil. The remaining one-third is harvested by hogging off (turning pigs into the field to root out the nuts). Peanuts are frequently planted with corn when the crop is to be hogged off. Even where the peanuts are harvested for sale through human channels, it is common practice to allow hogs to glean the fields.

With the hulls on, peanuts contain about 25 percent protein and 36 percent fat. They are deficient in carotene, vitamin D, and calcium, and only fair in phosphorus.

Pigs in confinement will make satisfactory gains on a ration with harvested peanuts as the only concentrate, plus salt and a calcium supplement such as ground limestone or oyster shell flour. Even so, a high quality alfalfa hay or meal should be provided in addition, thus alleviating any vitamin deficiency.

Pigs should have free access to salt and a calcium supplement when hogging down peanuts. Generally, Spanish peanuts are grown for hogging down early in the fall, whereas runner peanuts are grown for winter use. Most practical swine producers use the brood sows and the young pigs for gleaning the fields, saving new fields for finishing hogs.

Unfortunately, the feeding of large quantities of peanuts will produce soft pork, unless they are restricted to pigs weighing under 85 pounds. Under most conditions, such a limitation is impractical. It seems more logical, therefore, that the swine producers of the South should attempt to extol the reputed "nutty flavor" of peanut-fed pork, rather than to discontinue the utiliza-

Fig. 7-8. Peanuts and corn in Georgia. This is a common planting in the South when both crops are to be hogged off. (Courtesy, USDA, Soil Conservation Service)

tion of such a widely-grown and otherwise highly satisfactory swine feed.

Rice

Rice is one of the most important cereal grains of the world and provides most of the food for half the human population of the earth. It forms a major part of the diet of Oriental peoples, with whose chopsticks every American school boy associates rice. In this country, it is grown extensively for human food in Louisiana, Arkansas, Texas, and California. When low priced or offgrade, it is frequently fed to swine. Also, a considerable part of the by-products of rice processing is profitably utilized as swine feed.

The whole rice fed to swine is known as ground rough rice (or ground paddy rice). It is finely ground, threshed rice (or rough rice) from which the hull has not been removed. From the standpoint of chemical composition and feeding value for swine,

ground rough rice compares favorably with oats. For growing-finishing pigs, it is worth 80 to 85 percent as much as corn when it is finely ground and limited to less than one-half of the grains in the ration. Ground rough rice produces firm pork of good quality.

Buckwheat

Although not a cereal, buckwheat has the same general nutritive characteristics as the cereal grains. It is used chiefly for flour manufacture for making pancakes, a breakfast delicacy. However, when low in price or offgrade, buckwheat is often utilized for stock feeding. Because it is high in fiber—containing about 10 percent—and somewhat unpalatable, buckwheat should not constitute more than one-third of the swine ration. It should be ground for hogs. Some pigs, especially white ones, suffer from photosensitization (sensitiveness to light) when fed buckwheat.

Millet (Hog Millet or Broom Corn Millet)

Millet has been raised since prehistoric times in the Old World as an important bread grain crop. In this country, hog millet, often called broom corn millet, is sometimes grown for livestock feeding purposes in the northern part of the Great Plains, where the growing season is too short for the grain sorghums. The yields usually range from 10 to 30 bushels per acre. Ground millet is worth 85 to 90 percent as much as shelled corn for hogs.

Emmer and Spelt

Emmer and spelt resemble barley somewhat in appearance and feeding value for hogs, for the hulls are not usually removed from the kernels in threshing. Three-fourths of the acreage of these grains (mostly emmer) are produced in North and South Dakota.

When ground and limited to not more than one-third of the ration, they are equal to barley in feeding value for hogs.

Molasses

Three kinds of molasses are fed to swine—cane molasses,

beet molasses, and citrus molasses. The first two are by-products of sugar manufacture; the cane molasses being derived from sugar cane and the beet molasses from sugar beets. As the name implies, citrus molasses is a by-product of the citrus industry.

As early as 1900, sugar planters in Louisiana fed cane molasses in long, open troughs to mules, cows, and hogs. The animals did their own mixing—alternating between a mouthful of hay, corn, oats, and molasses; and washing the molasses down with a drink of muddy water from a nearby bayou. Feeding was a sticky, messy business, and there were swarms of flies. Even so, molasses was fed simply because it had to be disposed of, and the animals liked it. It couldn't be sold for the price of the barrel container, and there was still the matter of freight charges. Gradually, the feeding value of the product was appreciated, and, by 1914, the demand exceeded the domestic supply. Shipments were brought in from Cuba.

CANE MOLASSES (OR BLACKSTRAP)

A large quantity of this carbohydrate feed is produced in the southern states, and an additional tonnage is imported. Molasses averages about 26 percent water and 54 percent total digestible nutrients; the latter figure is two-thirds that of corn. It is very low in phosphorus (see Appendix Table I-1), thus indicating the need for feeding this mineral supplement when molasses constitutes much of the ration.

Molasses may cause scours in pigs unless they are started on it gradually and then limited in quantities fed. Results of swine feeding trials have varied widely. It seems safe to assume that, when limited to 20 percent of the grain ration, its feeding value for swine will be 70 to 75 percent that of corn. This is the same ratio as the digestible nutrients in the two feeds.

BEET MOLASSES

Beet molasses, a by-product of beet sugar factories, has a laxative effect, thus necessitating that pigs be started on it gradually and then fed limited amounts (5 to 10 pounds daily). It may constitute up to 40 percent of the ration for growing-finishing pigs weighing over 100 pounds.

Beet molasses had best not be fed to pigs under 100 pounds or to gestating sows. In fact, it is generally recommended that it

be fed to farm animals other than swine. When properly used, beet molasses is equal to cane molasses as a swine feed, which means that it is 70 to 75 percent as valuable as corn.

CITRUS MOLASSES

Citrus molasses is unpalatable to hogs, due to its bitter taste. Since cattle do not object to the taste, most citrus molasses is fed to them. When mixed with more palatable feeds, citrus molasses can be fed to swine at about the same levels as cane molasses; and the two products have about the same feeding value.

Velvet Beans

Velvet beans are grown chiefly for forage, but occasionally the beans are harvested for livestock feed. When hulled and ground, it is known as "velvet bean meal." When the beans and pod are ground together, it is known as "ground velvet bean and pod." Regardless of the type of preparation, velvet beans should not constitute more than one-fourth of the ration for any class of swine; otherwise, toxicity (due to dihydroxyphenylalanine, which is closely related to adrenalin)—with accompanying severe diarrhea and vomiting—will result. Cooking decreases the toxicity and increases the palatability and digestibility, but it does not generally make them entirely satisfactory.

In the Gulf Coast region, velvet beans are sometimes grown with corn or with corn and peanuts for hogging down.

Beans (Cull Beans)

Throughout the United States, several varieties of beans— including navy, Lima, kidney, pinto, and tepary beans—are raised for human food. Occasionally, low prices result in some of these beans being marketed through livestock channels. Also, cull beans—consisting of the discolored, shrunken, and cracked seeds, together with some foreign materials sorted out from the first-quality dry beans—are frequently cooked and fed to swine.

Chemically, beans of all varieties closely resemble peas, but their feeding value is much lower. For swine, beans should be cooked thoroughly, limited to two-thirds of the grain ration (on a dry weight basis), and supplemented with a protein feed of animal origin. When prepared and fed to swine in this manner, beans are 90 percent as valuable as corn.

Root and Tuber Crops

Several root and tuber crops are fed to hogs, including sweet potatoes, white or Irish potatoes, chufas, cassava, and Jerusalem artichoke. Roots are palatable, succulent, and laxative, but they are low in protein, calcium, and vitamin D, and except for carrots and sweet potatoes, they have little or no carotene (vitamin A value).

SWEET POTATOES

Sweet potatoes, a palatable swine feed, are frequently fed to hogs in the South, usually by allowing the pigs to glean the fields after digging. They are high in carbohydrates in proportion to their protein and mineral content. Best results are usually obtained when pigs grazing sweet potatoes are given one-third to one-half the usual grain allowance plus a protein supplement of animal or marine origin (tankage, fish meal, or milk by-products), and a suitable mineral supplement. Sweet potatoes are too bulky for young pigs. It requires 400 to 500 pounds of sweet potatoes to equal 100 pounds of cereal grain when fed to hogs, the higher values being obtained in confinement feeding. Cooking improves the feeding value of sweet potatoes. They produce firm pork of good quality, although market animals fed on sweet potatoes are paunchy and have a low dressing percentage.

Dehydrated sweet potatoes have approximately 90 percent the feeding value of corn when used at levels of one-third to one-half in a well balanced ration.

POTATOES (IRISH POTATOES)

Potatoes are often called Irish potatoes because their introduction to Ireland saved the people from the terrible famines that had previously devastated the country. They are sometimes used as hog feed when they have little value on the market, especially if grain prices are high. Since potatoes are not palatable in the raw state, they must be steamed or boiled (preferably in salt water, with any cooking water discarded) to increase palatability. When properly cooked, and when not replacing more than 50 percent of the grain ration, 350 to 400 pounds of potatoes will be equivalent in feeding value to 100 pounds of the common cereal grains. Potatoes should not be fed to sows dur-

ing the latter part of gestation or immediately after farrowing.

When limited to one-third of the ration of growing-finishing pigs, dehydrated Irish potatoes (known as potato meal or potato flakes) are about equal to corn, pound for pound. Of course, the cost of dehydrating is too great to consider the process practical, but surplus dehydrated potatoes are sometimes available at a nominal price.

CHUFAS

Chufas, a southern tuber crop, are frequently planted from April to June for hogging down. The chufas sedge, frequently a weed in damp fields on southern farms, will remain over winter in the ground without killing. Chufas should be supplemented properly with proteins and minerals. They will produce 300 to 600 pounds of pork per acre, after making allowance for the supplemental feeds consumed. Chufas produce soft pork.

CASSAVA

This is a fleshy root crop that grows in Florida and along the Gulf Coast, yielding 5 to 6 tons per acre. The roots, containing 25 of 30 percent starch, are used in the production of the tapioca of commerce and as a swine feed.

When not constituting over one-third of the dry matter in the ration, cassavas are a satisfactory feed for hogs. Dried cassava meal is worth about 85 percent as much as corn for growing-finishing hogs.

JERUSALEM ARTICHOKE

Jerusalem artichoke, a hardy perennial vegetable, produces tubers resembling the potato in composition, except that the chief carbohydrate is inulin instead of starch. They yield 6 to 15 tons of tubers per acre. The tubers live over the winter in the ground, and, even when hogged off or dug in the fall, usually enough tubers will remain to make the next crop. When hogging off artichoke, pigs should be fed grain and supplement, because they will make but little gain on the tubers alone.

OTHER ROOT CROPS

Such root crops as beets, mangels, carrots, and turnips are

never produced in this country specifically for hog feed. However, when they are not salable for human food, they are sometimes fed to hogs. Because of their high water content (usually 80 to 90 percent), about 9 pounds of roots are required to equal the feeding value of 1 pound of grain. Best results are secured when the roots are cut in small pieces, fed raw, and limited to a replacement of not more than one-fourth of the grain ration.

Citrus Fruits

Citrus fruits—drop and offgrade oranges, tangerines, grapefruit, and lemons—are sometimes used as hog feed in those areas where they are produced. They should be fed along with some grain and a protein supplement.

CITRUS MEAL; DRIED CITRUS PULP

Citrus meal consists of the finer particles of dried citrus, whereas citrus pulp is the bulkier portions. Both are by-products of citrus-canning factories which make citrus fruit juices, canned

Fig. 7-9. Pigs eating cull tangerines in Florida. (Courtesy, Dr. T. J. Cunha, Head, Department of Animal Science and Nutrition, University of Florida)

fruit, and other products. They consist of the dried and ground peel, residue of the inside portions, and occasional cull fruits of the citrus family with or without extraction of part of the oil of the peel.

These products somewhat resemble dried beet pulp in chemical composition, but they are less palatable. They contain about 6 percent protein, 2.5 to 5 percent fat, 12 to 20 percent fiber, and 50 to 65 percent nitrogen-free extract. Citrus meal and citrus pulp are best suited as cattle feeds, but they may be satisfactorily used for growing-finishing pigs if limited to 5 percent of the ration. Higher levels result in smaller rate and efficiency of gains, digestive disturbances, and lower dressing percentage and carcass grade.

Animal Fats

The feeding of animal fats was prompted in an effort to find a profitable outlet for surplus packing house fats. For the most part fats were formerly used for soap making, but they are not used extensively in detergents. Thus, with the rise in the use of detergents in recent years, they became a drug on the market.

Common belief to the contrary, animals can tolerate a rather high fat content in the ration. As evidence of this, it is to be noted that sucklings normally handle a relatively large amount of fat, for milk contains 25 to 40 percent of this nutrient on a dry-matter basis. Also, except for the soft pork problem, no apparent difficulty is encountered in feeding hogs on a rather high fat diet, such as results when large quantities of peanuts and soybeans are fed.

As livestock feeds, fats function much like carbohydrates in that they serve as a source of heat and energy, and for the formation of fat. Because of the larger proportion of carbon and hydrogen, however, fats liberate more heat than carbohydrates when digested, furnishing approximately 2.25 times as much heat or energy per pound on oxidation as do the carbohydrates. A smaller quantity of fat is required, therefore, to serve the same function. In addition to having a higher energy value, fats serve as carriers of the fat-soluble vitamins, lend palatability to the diet, and provide a source of essential unsaturated fatty acids (there is evidence that humans, rats, and dogs require certain of the fatty acids).

Although more experimental work is needed, it appears that up to 6 percent animal fat can be added successfully—with increased rate of gain and feed efficiency—to the rations of farm animals and poultry, provided the fat is first stabilized to prevent rancidity.[4] Rancid fat in feed will destroy vitamins E and A quite rapidly, thereby impairing feeding results. Also, in compounding such rations, consideration must be given to the fact that fats do not provide proteins, vitamins, or minerals.

It is estimated that we are currently feeding animal fats at the rate of over 300 million pounds annually.[5] Thus, stabilized animal fat has become accepted as a high quality ingredient of today's feed bag.

With favorable prices—that is, if price relationships are such that fats can be used to furnish energy more cheaply than carbohydrates—it is predicted that the feeding of animal fats will increase, because, in addition to feed efficiency and possible other animal benefits, there are several advantages to adding fats to rations from the standpoint of feed mixing. Among the latter are: (1) control of dustiness, (2) decreased wear on mixing machinery, (3) improved appearance and feel of the ration, and (4) greater ease in pelleting.

QUESTIONS FOR STUDY AND DISCUSSION

1. Feed prices vary widely. For profitable production, therefore, feeds with similar nutritive properties should be interchanged as price relationships warrant; and, in buying feeds, stockmen should check prices against values received. To the latter end, herewith is presented a simple, easy way to calculate the best buy in energy feeds, based on the cost per pound of total digestible nutrients (TDN):

   If corn is priced at $2.50 per 100 pounds and has a TDN of 80 percent, divide $2.50 by 80 and the result is 3.1¢ per pound of TDN. If molasses with 60 per cent TDN sells for $3.75 per 100 pounds, divide $3.75 by 60, and the price is 6.2¢ per pound of TDN. Thus, corn would be the better buy —by 3.1¢ per pound of TDN.

---

[4] In order to prevent rancidity and to increase the utilization and stability of vitamin A and carotene, the use of an approved antioxidant is recommended.

[5] Three hundred twenty-eight million tons in 1964; according to *Supplement for 1964 to Grain and Feed Statistics*, USDA, p. 46.

Of course, it is recognized that many other factors affect the actual feeding value of each feed, such as (a) palatability, (b) grade of feed, (c) preparation of feed, (d) ingredients with which each feed is combined, and (e) quantities of each feed fed.

Secure current prices of available energy feeds for swine. Then, by referring to Appendix Table I-1 and books listed as references at the end of this chapter, determine which is the best buy from the standpoint of cost per pound of TDN.

2. As a group, the cereal grains are high in energy. However, they possess certain nutritive deficiencies which may prove to be quite limiting if they are not properly used. Refer to Appendix Table I-1 and the books listed as references at the end of this chapter for analyses, and obtain prices of available high energy swine feeds locally. Then fill out the following table:

AVAILABLE HIGH ENERGY SWINE FEEDS

Feed	Retail Price Per Cwt.	Total Protein Per 100 Lbs.	Digestible Protein Per 100 Lbs.	TDN Per 100 Lbs.	Cost Per 100 Lbs. Digestible Protein	Cost Per 100 Lbs. TDN	Carotene Mg. Per Lb.	Calcium Content (%)	Phosphorus Content (%)

3. Under what circumstances might a swine producer be justified in producing soft pork?

SELECTED REFERENCES

Title of Publication	Author(s)	Publisher
Applied Animal Nutrition	E. W. Crampton L. E. Harris	W. H. Freeman & Co., San Francisco, Calif., 1969.

Title of Publication	Author(s)	Publisher
Composition of Cereal Grains and Forages	Publication 585	National Academy of Sciences, National Research Council, Washington, D. C.
Composition of Concentrate By-Product Feeding Stuffs	Publication 449	National Academy of Sciences, National Research Council, Washington, D. C.
Feeds and Feeding, Abridged	F. B. Morrison	Morrison Publishing Co., Ithaca, N. Y., 1958.
Feeds and Feeding, 22nd edition	F. B. Morrison	Morrison Publishing Co., Ithaca, N. Y., 1956.
Feed Formulations Handbook	T. W. Perry	The Interstate Printers & Publishers, Inc., Danville, Ill., 1966.
Feeds of the World	B. H. Schneider	Agri. Exp. Sta., West Virginia University Morgantown, W. Va., 1947.
Nutrient Requirements for Swine	Publication 1599	National Academy of Sciences, National Research Council, Washington, D. C., 1968.
Pork Production	W. W. Smith	The Macmillan Company, New York, N. Y., 1952.
Swine Feeding and Nutrition	T. J. Cunha	Interscience Publishers, Inc., New York, N. Y., 1957.
Swine Production	W. E. Carroll J. L. Krider F. N. Andrews	McGraw-Hill Book Co., New York, N. Y., 1962.
United States-Canadian Tables of Feed Composition	Publication 1684	National Academy of Sciences, National Research Council, Washington, D. C.

CHAPTER VIII

PROTEIN, VITAMIN, AND MILLING BY-PRODUCT FEEDS FOR SWINE[1]

Contents   **Page**

Prior to 1890, no one was concerned about adding proteins to livestock rations, and vitamins were unknown. The flour mills in Minneapolis dumped wheat bran into the Mississippi River, because nobody wanted to buy it. Cottonseed meal was used as a fertilizer, if used at all. Most of the linseed meal was shipped to Europe. Soybeans were little known outside the Orient, and tankage had not been processed.

Before 1890, swine were either handled as self-sustaining razorbacks or fed whatever home-grown grains—chiefly corn— and farm wastes as were available. They were marketed at 10 to 16 months of age. Sows were farrowed once a year. But, what was time to a hog!

Beginning about 1900, scientists discovered that the kind or quality of protein in livestock feeds was of tremendous importance, thus ushering in the golden era in nutrition. Soon the race was on for protein-rich feeds. Many of the by-products that once polluted the streams of the nation were in unprecedented demand, first as protein supplements, and later because of the recognized added vitamin value of many of them.

---

[1]Where feed definitions are used in this chapter, they are either taken from or similar to those used by the Association of American Feed Control Officials.

At the present time, the protein supplements are regularly in shorter supply and higher priced than the cereal grains and other high energy feeds used in swine feeding. Normally, the U.S. produces annually about 13.5 million tons of oilseed proteins, about 3.4 million tons of animal proteins, and 2.3 million tons of grain protein feeds, for a total of approximately 19 million tons of protein supplements, exclusive of urea (Fig. 8-1). But it is estimated that an additional 2 to 5 million tons of these products

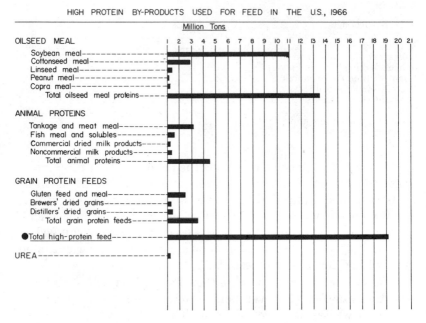

Fig. 8-1. Tonnage of different protein supplements used for feed in the U.S., 1966. Data from *Feed Situation*, Nov. 1966, p. 21, pub. by USDA.

could be used advantageously if all animals were supplied an adequate amount of protein.

Normally, about 30 percent of all U.S. concentrates is fed to swine.[2] More concentrates are fed to swine than to any other class of livestock.

In general, the cereal grains—which average from 8 to 11 percent protein content—will meet about one-half of the total

[2] *Feed Consumed by Various Classes of Livestock*, Statistical Bul. No. 379, p. 2, USDA, 1966.

protein requirement of swine. Not only are the cereal grains
deficient in quantity of proteins, but their proteins are of poor
quality. Also, except for yellow corn, they are low in vitamin A,
and they are low in vitamin D and several of the B vitamins. To

Fig. 8-2. Prior to 1890 many swine were fed chiefly corn. They were
marketed at 10 to 16 months of age. Sows farrowed once a year. But, what
was time to a hog! (Courtesy, American Feed Manufacturers Association,
Chicago, Ill.)

rectify these deficiencies, certain protein- and vitamin-rich feeds
should be added to the ration, with consideration given to the
following:

    1. The comparative cost of each, based primarily upon pro-
tein and vitamin content.

    2. The quality of the proteins, recognizing

        a.   that, unlike ruminants (cattle and sheep), there is
only limited bacterial action in the digestive tract of
the monogastric pig. This means that he cannot
manufacture high quality proteins from low quality
proteins and inorganic nitrogen. Therefore, the

feeder should select and incorporate the proper amino acids in the ration.

b. that, in general, proteins of plant origin (such as linseed, cottonseed, and peanut meals) are of poor quality; whereas proteins of animal or marine origin (such as the by-products of meat, milk, and fish) are high quality.

c. that the quality of the proteins in the ration is likely to be higher if a variety of feeds is combined.

3. The temptation not to feed sufficient proteins to balance the ration, because, in general, they are more expensive than those feeds high in carbohydrates or fats.

For practical reasons, most grain feeds are produced on the farm supporting the swine enterprise, but the protein- and vitamin-rich supplements are generally purchased. In the present vitamin and antibiotic era, more and more swine producers are depending upon commercial feed manufacturers, with their staffs of nutrition specialists, (1) for ready-mixed protein and vitamin supplements which will properly balance out home-grown grains, and (2) for complete rations.

The chemical composition of a part of these protein- and vitamin-rich supplements is reported in Table I-1 of the Appendix. Also, the relative feeding value, pound for pound, of the common protein supplements in comparison with tankage is given in Table 6-17, Handy Feed Substitution Table for Swine.

MILK BY-PRODUCTS

Skimmed milk, buttermilk, and whey have long been used on or in close proximity to the farms where they are produced. However, in their liquid form it is impossible to ship them long distances or to store them and it is difficult to maintain sanitary feeding conditions in using them.

Along about 1910, processes were developed for drying buttermilk. Soon thereafter, special plants were built for dehydrating buttermilk, and the process was extended to skimmed milk and whey. Beginning about 1915, dried milk by-products were incorporated in commercial poultry feeds. Subsequently they have been used for swine feeding. But even today poultry consume a larger quantity of dried milk by-products than swine.

But milk by-products furnish a relatively small percentage

of the total high-protein feeds consumed by livestock. In 1966, the several dairy products—in liquid, dry, and condensed forms— constituted only 3.8 percent of the high-protein feeds used by livestock.[3]

The superior nutritive values of milk by-products are due to their high quality proteins, vitamins, a good mineral balance, and the beneficial effect of the milk sugar, lactose. In addition, these products are palatable and highly digestible. They are an ideal feed for young pigs and for balancing out the deficiencies of the cereal grains. The chief limitation to their wider use is price, together with the perishability and bulkiness of the liquid products. Liquid products coming from cows that have not been tested and found free from tuberculosis should be pasteurized.

Although whole milk is an excellent feed—worth about twice as much as skimmed milk—it is usually too expensive to feed to swine. For this reason, only the milk by-product feeds will be discussed. In general, liquid milk products contain 10 percent dry matter; semisolid milk products, 30 percent dry matter; and dried milk products, 90 percent dry matter.

The mode of action is not understood, but there is experimental evidence, substantiated by practical observation, to indicate that milk and its by-products are helpful in holding in check some of the internal parasites of swine. Milk-fed pigs make more rapid gains and have fewer parasites in the digestive tract.

Skimmed Milk

Because of the removal of the fat, skimmed milk supplies but little vitamin A value. However, in comparison with whole milk, it is higher in content of protein, milk sugar, and minerals. Like all milk products, skimmed milk is low in vitamin D and iron.

Skimmed milk is the best single protein supplement for swine. It is especially valuable for young pigs prior to and immediately after weaning. The addition of either pasture or a choice legume hay will supplement skimmed milk with the needed vitamins A and D.

Skimmed milk should be fed consistently sweet or sour, because abrupt changes are apt to produce digestive disturbances. Where a choice is possible, fresh skimmed milk is recommended.

---

[3] *Feed Situation*, USDA, Nov. 1966, p. 21.

The amount of skimmed milk to feed will vary according to (1) the available supply, (2) the relative price of feeds, (3) the kind of grain ration fed, and (4) whether or not pasture is available.

Under confinement conditions and with corn constituting all or most of the grain ration, a daily allowance of 1 to 1½ gallons of skimmed milk per pig will be about right to balance the ration. With the same grain ration and good pasture, the skimmed milk allowance may be cut in half. With barley or wheat (feeds of higher protein content) replacing the corn, about two-thirds these amounts of skimmed milk will suffice. Since the protein requirement of the swine ration decreases with the age of the animal while total daily feed consumption increases, a constant daily intake of skimmed milk on this basis will about balance the swine ration throughout the life of the pig.

The feeding value of skimmed milk varies with the age of the pigs, the type of ration, the price of other feeds, and the amount of milk fed. Naturally, it has a higher value per pound when fed in limited amounts than when an excess is used. On the other hand, when the supply of milk is abundant and cheap, a larger proportion may be fed profitably—especially when grain is scarce and high in price. Roughly, it can be figured that (1) 15 pounds of skimmed milk will replace 1 pound of tankage or meat meal, or (2) 6 pounds of skimmed milk will replace 1 pound of complete feed.

Buttermilk

Buttermilk and skimmed milk have approximately the same composition and feeding value for swine, providing buttermilk has not been diluted by the addition of churn washings. Accordingly, the discussion of skimmed milk is also applicable to buttermilk; and it may be considered that (1) 15 pounds of buttermilk will replace 1 pound of tankage or meat meal, or (2) 6 pounds of buttermilk will replace 1 pound of complete feed.

Condensed Buttermilk

Condensed buttermilk is made by evaporating buttermilk to about one-third of its original weight. It contains 27 percent minimum total solids, 0.055 percent minimum milk fat for each

percent of total solids, and 0.14 percent maximum ash for each percent of total solids.

One pound of condensed buttermilk is worth about 3 pounds of liquid buttermilk. But it requires about 3 pounds of condensed buttermilk to equal 1 pound of dried milk. Another basis of evaluating condensed buttermilk is that, pound for pound, it is worth approximately one-half as much as tankage.

Like the other milk by-products, condensed buttermilk is (1) very palatable to pigs, (2) more valuable for young pigs than for older animals, and (3) more valuable for confinement feeding than for pigs on pasture. Perhaps the greatest value of condensed buttermilk is in the capacity of an appetizer. Showmen make extensive use of it in their fitting rations.

Dried Skimmed Milk and Dried Buttermilk

As the names indicate, these products are dehydrated skim milk and buttermilk, respectively. They contain less than 8 percent moisture, and average 32 to 35 percent protein. One pound of dried skimmed milk or dried buttermilk has about the same composition and feeding value as 10 pounds of their liquid forms. Although dried skimmed milk and dried buttermilk are excellent swine feeds, they are generally too high priced to be economical for this purpose except for limited use in pig starter rations.

Because of the palatability, pigs will consume excessive amounts of dried skimmed milk and dried buttermilk when self-fed free-choice.

Prior to World War II, dried skimmed milk was the most widely used dried milk product included in feeds. During and since the war, however, much of it has been marketed as a human food.

Whey

Whey is a by-product of cheese making. Practically all of the casein and most of the fat go into the cheese, leaving the whey which is high in lactose (milk sugar), but low in protein (0.6 to 0.9 percent) and fat (0.1 to 0.3 percent). However, its protein is of high quality. In general, whey has a feeding value equal to about one-half that of skimmed milk or buttermilk; thus, (1) 30 pounds of whey will replace 1 pound of tankage, or (2) 12 pounds of whey will replace 1 pound of complete feed. Pigs

should be gradually accustomed to whey, after which it may be fed free choice. Because of its low protein content, pigs weighing under 100 pounds should receive a protein-rich supplement in addition to grain and whey. In order to prevent the spread of disease, whey should be pasteurized at the factory and fed under sanitary conditions.

Condensed Whey

Condensed whey is the product resulting from the removal of a considerable portion of water of either cheese whey or casein whey. According to the definition of the Association of American Feed Control Officials, the minimum percent total whey solids must be prominently declared on the label.

Based on their respective nutrient contents, 1 pound of condensed whey should be worth about 9 pounds of liquid whey for hogs.

Dried Whey (Milk Sugar Feed)

Dried whey is derived from drying whey from cheese manufacture. It is high in lactose (milk sugar), containing at least 65 percent, and rich in riboflavin, pantothenic acid, and some of the important unidentified factors. One pound of dried whey contains about the same nutrients as 13 to 14 pounds of liquid whey.

Dried Whey-Product

When a portion of the lactose (milk sugar) which normally occurs in whey is removed, the resulting dried residue is called dried whey-product. According to the Association of American Feed Control Officials, the minimum percent of lactose must be prominently declared on the label of the dried whey-product. Dried whey-product is a rich source of the water-soluble vitamins. When price relationships warrant, dried whey-product may replace alfalfa meal in confinement rations for swine on a comparable protein content basis.

Cheese Rind (Cheese Meal)

This is a by-product from the manufacture of processed cheese, consisting of the cheese trimmings from which most of the fat has been removed. It contains around 60 percent protein

and 9 percent fat. It is slightly more valuable than tankage as a swine feed.

MEAT PACKING BY-PRODUCTS

Although the meat or flesh of animals is the primary object of slaughtering, modern meat packing plants process numerous and valuable by-products, including protein-rich livestock feeds.

In the early days of the meat packing industry, the only salvaged by-products were hides, wool, tallow, and tongue. The remainder of the offal was usually carted away and dumped into the river or burned or buried. In some instances, packers even paid for having the offal taken away. Later, during the 1870's and 1880's, some of these by-products were recovered, dried, and utilized as fertilizers.

In the early 1890's, some of the selected meat residues from lard-rendering—known as cracklings—were sold locally for chicken feed. Finally, about 1900, poultry feeders on the Pacific Coast, principally at Petaluma, California, started using dried tankage in poultry rations. Almost simultaneously, this new feed was utilized in hog feeding, with experiment stations leading the way. Thus was born a new era in the utilization of packing house by-products, and a new era in livestock feeding.

Today, tankage and meat meal provide 11 percent of the total supply of high protein feeds available for livestock feeding.

Tankage and Meat Meal

Tankage and meat meal, synonymous with hog feeding, are made from the trimmings that originate on the killing floor, inedible parts and organs, cleaned entrails, fetuses, residues from the production of fats, and certain condemned carcasses and parts of carcasses.

The end products, and the methods of processing each, are:

1. **Tankage (or; digester tankage, meat meal tankage, feeding tankage)**, produced by the older wet-rendering method, in which all of the material is cooked by steam under pressure in large closed tanks; hence the derivation of the name tankage. After cooking, the fat is skimmed off, the soupy liquid drained off, and the remaining residue pressed to remove as much of the fat and water as possible. The soupy liquid is then evaporated down

until it becomes gluey, at which state it is called *stick*. The stick is added to the pressed residue, following which the mixture is dried and ground.

According to the Association of American Feed Control Officials, the raw materials from which tankage is made should not contain hair, hoof, horn, manure, stomach contents, and hide trimmings except in such traces as might occur unavoidably in good factory practice.

The level of protein of tankage (generally 60 percent) is often standardized during manufacture by the addition of enough blood to raise the total protein to the desired level.

In addition to tanking under live steam (as previously described), tankage may also be made by the dry-rendering method (a description of which follows), or by mixing products containing both wet-rendered and dry-rendered materials.

2. **Meat meal (or meat scrap),** produced by the newer and more efficient dry-rendering method, in which all of the material is cooked in its own grease by dry heat in open steam-jacketed drums until the moisture has evaporated. Then as much of the fat as possible is removed by draining off and the solid residue is passed through a screw press. Next the dry residue is granulated or ground into a meal. This product is lighter colored and does not have so strong an odor as wet-rendered tankage.

According to the Association of American Feed Control Officials, the raw materials from which meat meal is made should not contain hair, hoof, horn, hide trimmings, blood meal, manure, and stomach contents, except in such traces as might occur unavoidably in good factory practice.

The level of protein of meat meal (generally 50 to 55 percent) was originally established because the normal proportions of raw materials available for rendering resulted in a product which, after being pressed and ground, contained approximately 50 percent protein. The protein content of meat meal is adjusted up or down by raising or lowering the quantity of bone and fat in the raw material.

Tankage and meat meal are widely used as protein supplements for swine feeding. Their proteins are of excellent quality, effectively correcting the deficiencies in the proteins of the cereal grains. Tankage is also rich in minerals (especially calcium and phosphorus), and is a good source of riboflavin, niacin,

and vitamin B_{12}. However, it is lacking in vitamins A and D and pantothenic acid.

The protein contents of meat scraps is somewhat lower than that of digester tankage; yet, the two products are about equal in feeding value, probably due to the greater digestibility and high nutritive value of the protein in the dry-rendered product, since it is subjected to less heat.

Since corn and tankage or meat meal are nearly equal in palatability, pigs will consume about the right proportion of each to balance the ration when they are fed free-choice from a self feeder, with the two feeds in separate compartments; no matter whether they are in dry lot or on pasture. With less palatable and higher protein grains (particularly barley, rye, and oats), the consumption of tankage is frequently increased to the extent that self-feeding is uneconomical. This condition can be corrected by either (1) mixing the protein supplement with the ground cereal grain, (2) hand-feeding the tankage, or (3) mixing the tankage with some such feeds as oats or alfalfa meal.

Despite the fact that protein-rich packing house by-product feeds are adapted to free-choice, self-feeding with corn, a more economical ration for pigs can usually be compounded by combining the meat by-products with protein supplements of plant origin (soybean meal, linseed meal, cottonseed meal, or peanut meal). For confinement feeding, alfalfa meal should be incorporated in the ration, thus providing a source of certain needed vitamins.

Protein content alone is not an infallible criterion of the feeding value of tankage or meat meal, for they vary considerably according to the kind of raw material from which they are produced. Further, there is strong suspicion in many quarters that these products are not as nutritious as they used to be, chiefly because the modern meat packing plant has developed more remunerative outlets for some materials that formerly went into tankage or meat meal. Today, the heart, liver, brains, kidneys, tongue, cheek meat, tail, feet, sweetbreads, and tripe—former components of tankage or meat meal—are sold over the counter as *variety meats* or *fancy meats*. With this change, there has been a very natural tendency to incorporate in tankage a higher proportion of gristle, connective tissue, bone, stick, and blood meal—all materials of lower nutritive value than meat and glands. It would appear, therefore, that it is timely that some

re-evaluation be made of the feeding value of present-day tankage. Also, it is important that the practical swine producer (1) purchase tankage or other meat meal from a reputable source, and (2) mix tankage with other protein supplements, especially for confinement feeding.

Meat and Bone Meal Tankage, and Meat and Bone Meal

When, because of added bone, tankage or meat meal contain more than 4.4 percent phosphorus (P), the word "bone" must be inserted in the name and they must be designated, according to the method of processing, as either (1) meat and bone meal tankage, or (2) meat and bone meal. Thus, when such high phosphorus products are prepared by the older wet-rendering method, they are known as *meat and bone meal tankage*. Likewise, when products in excess of 4.4 percent phosphorus are prepared by the newer dry-rendering method, they are designated as *meat and bone meal*.

Meat and bone meal tankage and meat and bone meal, or other similar bone-containing products, contain less protein than tankage or meat meal, usually 45 to 50 percent. Except for noting this difference, the swine feeding recommendations given relative to tankage and meat meal are equally applicable to meat and bone meal tankage and meat and bone meal.

Rendering Plant Tankage

In recent years, many small rendering plants have been placed in operation throughout the country. They collect scrap meat and bones from butcher shops and carcasses from the farms or ranches in close proximity to the plant. Hides, and sometimes bones, are salvaged and the other assorted materials are processed into soap grease, fertilizer, and tankage. The latter product is sometimes sold as swine feed. There is no danger of spreading infection through feeding rendering plant tankage to swine, for the high processing temperature thoroughly sterilizes it.

The composition and feeding value of rendering plant tankage differ widely according to the type and quality of raw material used, with decomposition prior to processing lowering the value of the end product.

In determining whether or not to use rendering plant tank-

age, consideration should be given to (1) the feed-price relationships based on protein content, and (2) the reputation of the rendering plant for consistently producing a satisfactory product.

Animal Liver Meal, and Animal Liver and Glandular Meal

These products are produced in limited quantities by meat packing plants; most of our supply comes from South America and Australia. *Animal liver meal* is made entirely by drying and grinding livers; whereas *animal liver and glandular meal* is made by drying and grinding liver and other glandular tissue, but at least 50 percent of the dry weight of the product must be derived from liver. These products contain proteins of high quality and are rich sources of both the fat-soluble and water-soluble vitamins.

For pigs under 100 pounds weight in confinement, the addition to the ration of 1 to 5 percent liver meal will stimulate growth and increase feed efficiency. Even so, it may not be an economical practice, because liver meal is usually high priced.

Blood Meal

Although the Germans had long incorporated blood in livestock rations, in this country there was strong prejudice against the practice until quite recently. Further, manufacturing difficulties were encountered, due chiefly to inadequate drying methods. It is not surprising, therefore, to learn that, along about 1900, the use of dried blood as a feed ingredient was tried but found wanting. Later, the process was perfected.

Blood meal is ground-dried blood. When prepared by a special process and reduced to a fine powder, the end product is called *blood flour*. It contains 80 to 82 percent protein, more than any other packing house products. However, due to the high temperature of processing, the protein is less digestible and of lower quality than that in high-grade tankage or meat meal. Also, blood meal and blood flour differ from tankage and meat meal in that they are low in calcium and phosphorus. For swine, tankage or meat meal is usually superior and cheaper than blood meal or blood flour. For this reason, most of the blood meal and blood flour is incorporated in commercial calf meals, for which purpose they are better adapted.

MARINE BY-PRODUCTS

In the beginning, marine wastes were dumped into the sea. Later, some of them were dried at high temperatures—usually in an open flame dryer—and used in fertilizers. About 1910, it was discovered that waste materials from fish canning plants and inedible fish were a desirable protein source for livestock feeding. Again experiment stations led the way in determining the feeding value of these new products which are now incorporated in swine and poultry rations from coast to coast.

Fish Meal

Fish meal—a by-product of the fisheries industry—consists of dried, ground whole fish or fish cuttings—either or both—with or without the extraction of part of the oil. If it contains more than 3 percent salt, the salt content must be a part of the brand name. In no case shall the salt content exceed 7 percent.

Fig. 8-3. A typical menhaden fishing boat, the David K. Philip, owned by the Reedville Oil and Guano Company, Reedville, Virginia. Fishing is big business, of which fish meal is one of the by-products. (Courtesy, National Fisheries Institute, Washington, D. C.)

The feeding value of fish meal varies somewhat, according to:

1. **The method of drying.**—It may be either vacuum, steam, or flame dried. The older flame drying method exposes the product to a higher temperature. This makes the proteins less digestible and destroys some of the vitamins.

2. **The type of raw material used.**—It may be made from the offal produced in fish packing or canning factories, or from the whole fish with or without extraction of part of the oil.

Fish meal made from offal containing a large proportion of heads is less desirable because of the lower quality and digestibility of the proteins. Although few feeding comparisons have been made between the different kinds of fish meals, it is apparent that all of them are satisfactory when properly processed raw materials of good quality and moderate fat content are used. A

Fig. 8-4. A close-up view of menhaden taken aboard the fishing vessel Margaret, owned by the Reedville Oil and Guano Company of Reedville, Virginia. Menhaden herring is a very fat fish not suited for human food, caught primarily for their body oil. The meal is the dried residue after most of the oil has been extracted. (Courtesy, National Fisheries Institute, Inc., Washington, D. C.)

high fat content may impart a fishy taste to eggs, meat, and milk.[4] Also, such meal is apt to become rancid in storage.

It is of interest to the swine producer to know the sources of the commonly used fish meals. These are:

(1) **Menhaden fish meal.**—This is the most common kind of fish meal used in the eastern states. It is made from menhaden herring (a very fat fish not suited for human food) caught primarily for their body oil. The meal is the dried residue after most of the oil has been extracted.

(2) **Sardine meal or pilchard meal.**—This is made from sardine canning waste and from the whole fish, principally on the West Coast.

(3) **Herring meal.**—This is a high grade product produced in the Pacific Northwest and Alaska.

(4) **Salmon meal.**—This is a by-product of the salmon canning industry in the Pacific Northwest and in Alaska.

(5) **White fish meal.**—This is a by-product from fisheries making cod and haddock products for human food. Its proteins are of very high quality.

Fish meal should be purchased from a reputable company on the basis of protein content. They vary in protein content from 57 to 77 percent, depending on the kind of fish from which they are made. In addition, it should be recognized that the proteins are of excellent quality, and that fish meal is a good source of calcium and phosphorus.

When of comparable quality, fish meal is even superior to tankage or meat meal as a protein supplement for swine. When fed as the only protein supplement to grain for growing-finishing pigs in confinement, fish meal is decidedly superior to tankage or meat meal. It produces more rapid and more efficient gains. However, for confinement rations, instead of feeding fish meal alone it is recommended that it be incorporated in a trio-type supplemental mixture. This would include a ground legume (thus

---

[4]The Indiana Station (Vestal, *et al., Jr. An. Sci.,* Vol. 4, No. 1, 1945) found that the addition to the ration of 0.5 and 1.5 percent fish oil produced a fishy flavor in pork, which was more pronounced in the roasts and bacon than in the chops.

assuring a plentiful supply of vitamin A, vitamin D, and the B-complex vitamins) and a protein supplement of plant origin (such as soybean, linseed, cottonseed, or peanut meal). When fed in this manner, fish meal is worth 5 to 10 percent more than tankage or meat meal.

The difference between fish meal and tankage or meat meal is not so marked for pigs on pasture as for pigs in confinement. When fed as the only protein supplement to corn for pigs on pasture, fish meal is worth approximately 10 percent more, pound for pound, than tankage or meat meal. Because of the generally higher cost of fish meal, it is commonly recommended that it be mixed with one or more protein-rich feeds of plant origin in providing supplements for pigs on pasture.

Fish Residue Meal

This is the dried residue from the manufacture of glue from non-oily fish. The provisions relative to salt content are the same as those for fish meal.

Shrimp Meal (Shrimp Bran)

Shrimp meal is the ground, dried waste of the shrimp industry, which may consist of the head, hull (or shell), and/or whole shrimp. The provisions relative to salt content are the same as those for fish meal. It is either steam dried or sun dried, with the former method being preferable. Shrimp meal is made in the South, along the Gulf of Mexico.

Shrimp meal contains about 47 percent protein. It is about equal to tankage or meat meal for growing-finishing hogs, whether fed alone or in combination with other protein supplements. For best results, it is recommended (1) that shrimp meal be incorporated in a trio-type mixture for hogs in confinement, and (2) that shrimp meal be mixed with equal parts by weight of one or more plant protein supplements for pigs on pasture.

Condensed Fish Solubles

This is a semisolid by-product obtained by evaporating the liquid remaining from the steam rendering of fish, chiefly sardines, menhaden, and redfish. Condensed fish solubles, containing approximately 30 percent protein, are a rich source of the B

vitamins and unknown factors. Where hogs are kept under confined conditions and little or no animal proteins fed, the addition of 2 to 3 percent or more of fish solubles will markedly improve the ration.

Unfortunately, fish solubles cannot be stored successfully in dried form but must be left in a sticky, semisolid form. For this reason, their use is largely limited to commercially mixed rations or supplements for swine in confinement.

Semisolid Fish Product

This product is made by the acid hydrolysis of undecomposed fish and/or fish trimmings, from which the oil may or may not have been removed, followed by evaporation to a semisolid consistency. It should have a minimum of 40 percent solids. Like condensed fish solubles, this product is largely limited to 2 to 3 percent of commercially mixed rations or supplements for swine in confinement.

OILSEED BY-PRODUCTS AND PEAS

Several rich oil-bearing seeds are produced in the United States as vegetable oils for human food (oleomargarine, shortenings, and salad oil), for use in paints, etc. In the processing of these seeds, protein-rich products of value in swine feedings are obtained. Among such high protein feeds are soybean meal, cottonseed meal, linseed meal, peanut meal, and coconut meal. In addition, a small but valuable quantity of peas is used as a protein supplement for swine in the North and Northwest.

Soybean meal

Soybean meal, processed from the precious oil-bearing seed from the Orient, is now the most widely used protein supplement in the United States. Processing of soybeans, and the production of soybean oil and meal, began in a small way in the early twenties, but the real impetus came in 1928 when the American Milling Company agreed to purchase on contract all soybeans produced from 50,000 acres in Illinois at a guaranteed minimum of $1.37 per bushel. Following this, soybean acreage continued to expand, and with it the production of soybean meal. Soybean meal passed cottonseed meal tonnage during World War

II when soybean acreage was increased greatly to provide needed oil for use in human foods and for industrial purposes. Currently, soybean meal makes up two-thirds of the total annual protein concentrates produced in the United States (Fig. 8-1). Also, soybean meal is the only protein concentrate available in substantially increasing supplies.

Soybean meal is the ground residue (soybean oil cake or soybean oil chips) remaining after the removal of most of the oil from soybeans. The oil is extracted by either of three processes: (1) the expeller process, (2) the hydraulic process, or (3) the solvent process. Although a name descriptive of the extraction process must be used in the brand name, well-cooked soybean meal produced by each of the extraction processes is of approximately the same feeding value. Regardless of the method of extraction employed, reputable manufacturers now use the proper heat treatment so that the protein quality is good.

Soybean meal normally contains 41, 44, or 50 percent protein, according to the amount of hull removed; and the proteins are of better quality than the other protein-rich supplements of plant origin. It is low in calcium, phosphorus, carotene, and vitamin D. Unlike the whole beans from which it is derived, soybean meal will not produce soft pork when fed in normal amounts required to balance the ration.

Since soybean meal is extremely palatable to pigs, when self-fed, free-choice, as the supplement to grain, they will often eat much more of it than is required to balance the ration. This is uneconomical because of the higher cost of the supplement in comparison with cereal grains and other high energy feeds. This wasteful practice may be alleviated in any of the following ways:

1. By hand-feeding the soybean meal once daily in troughs, providing the daily allowance.

2. By self-feeding the soybean meal in some such mixture as (a) 2 parts ground oats and 1 part of soybean meal, or (b) 1 part of ground legume and 1 part of soybean meal.

3. By self-feeding soybean meal as a part of a supplement mixture, such as 1 to 2 parts of animal or marine products and 1 part of soybean meal.

4. By mixing the ground grain and soybean meal together and self-feeding as a complete ration.

Young pigs under 75 pounds in weight and gestating-lactat-

ing sows kept in confinement should not be fed soybean meal as the only protein supplement, even though it is an excellent plant protein. Instead, it is recommended that during these critical periods in the life of the pig the soybean meal be incorporated in a trio-type mixture, along with a ground legume and a protein-rich animal supplement.

Soybean meal is satisfactory as the only protein supplement to grain for well-grown confinement-fed pigs weighing over 75 pounds, providing a high quality ground legume is incorporated in the ration and adequate sources of calcium and phosphorus are provided.

For swine of all ages—including young pigs and gestating-lactating sows—on good pasture, soybean meal gives excellent results when used as the only protein supplement, if a mineral supplement is provided to supply additional calcium and phosphorus. Growing-finishing pigs on pasture will make slightly more rapid, but no more efficient, gains when an animal protein is incorporated in the supplement. Whether or not the latter practice is followed should be determined by the comparative prices of the protein supplements, based on their respective protein contents.

Linseed Meal

While the feeding value of linseed meal was recognized prior to 1900, most of the output was shipped to Europe. As late as 1917, 331,000 tons out of the 500,000 tons produced in this country were sold abroad.

Linseed meal is a by-product of flax, a fiber plant which antedates recorded history. In this country, most of the flax is produced as a cash crop for oil from the seed and the resulting by-product, linseed meal. Practically none of the U.S. flax crop is grown for fiber, for it is more economical to import it from those countries where cheaper labor is available.

Most of the nation's flax is produced in North Dakota, South Dakota, Minnesota, Montana, Arizona, and California. Normally, an additional quantity of seed is imported and processed in our plants.

The oil is extracted from the seed by either of two processes: (1) the mechanical process (or so-called old process), or (2) the solvent process (or so-called new process). If solvent

extracted, it must be so designated. Stockmen prefer the commonly used mechanical process, for the remaining meal is more palatable.

Linseed meal is the finely ground residue (known as cake, chips, or flakes) remaining after the oil extraction. It averages about 35 percent protein content, about half as much as tankage. For swine, the proteins of linseed meal do not effectively make good the deficiencies of the cereal grains; linseed meal being low in the amino acids, lysine and tryptophan. Also, linseed meal is lacking in carotene and vitamin D, and is only fair in calcium and the B vitamins. It is laxative and produces a glossy coat on animals to which it is fed. Because of its deficiencies, linseed meal should not be fed to swine as the sole protein supplement.

For swine in confinement, it is recommended that linseed meal be incorporated in a trio-type mixture (for example, 25 pounds of linseed meal, 50 pounds of animal or marine products, and 25 pounds of ground legume).

Where good pasture is available for swine, linseed meal may be mixed with a protein-rich animal or marine product, with the linseed meal limited to 50 percent of the protein supplement.

Because of its laxative nature, linseed meal in limited quantities is a valuable addition to the ration of brood sows (about ¼ pound daily for mature sows) at farrowing time or for animals that are being forced for the show. Also, it imparts a desirable "bloom" to the hair of show animals.

Cottonseed Meal

According to historical records, oil was first successfully extracted from cottonseed in a New Orleans plant in 1885. However, due to strong prejudice, most of the meal continued to be sold as fertilizer at not too remunerative prices until sometime after 1900. Stockmen who had ventured to feed the product attributed blindness and abortion to its use. Eventually, the experiment stations came to the rescue of the manufacturers and demonstrated that cottonseed meal would give excellent results if fed in properly balanced rations.

Today, the U.S. cotton crop ranks third in value, being exceeded only by corn and wheat. Among the oilseed meals, cottonseed meal ranks second in tonnage to soybean meal and cake. The processing steps in making cottonseed meal are as follows: (1)

cleaning the seeds; (2) dehulling the seeds; (3) crushing the kernels; (4) extracting the oil by either the (a) mechanical (or screw pressed), (b) solvent, or (c) partially mechanically extracted and then solvent extracted process; and (5) grinding the remaining residue or cake, thus forming cottonseed meal.

The protein content of cottonseed meal can vary from about 22 percent in meal made from undecorticated seed to 60 percent in flour made from seed from which the hulls have been removed completely. Thus, by screening out the residual hulls, which are low in protein and high in fiber, the processor is able to make a cottonseed meal of the protein content desired—usually 41, 44, or 50 percent.

For the monogastric pig, cottonseed meal is low in lysine and trytophan and deficient in vitamin D, carotene (vitamin A value), and calcium. Also, it contains a toxic substance known as gossypol, varying in amounts with the seed and the processing. But, it is rich in phosphorus.

It is recommended that the cottonseed meal content of practical swine rations (especially rations for growing swine)

Fig. 8-5. A victim of gossypol poisoning, resulting from feeding too much cottonseed meal high in gossypol. This pig died soon after the picture was taken. (Courtesy, Prof. E. L. Stephenson, University of Arkansas)

be limited to one-half of the protein supplement of the ration. At this level, it is unlikely that the total ration will contain more than 0.01 percent free gossypol. However, if the level of free gossypol is higher than 0.01 percent, then iron as ferrous sulfate ($FeSO_4$) should be added in a 1:1 weight ratio up to a maximum of 500 ppm of added iron in the total ration. When used in this manner, cottonseed meal is an economical and satisfactory protein supplement for swine.

Today, glandless cottonseed, free of gossypol, is being improved. Someday, meal made from it may replace conventional cottonseed meal in swine rations and alleviate (1) any restrictions as to levels of meal, and (2) the need to add iron.

Peanut Meal and Peanut Meal and Hulls

Peanut meal, a by-product of the peanut industry, is ground peanut cake, the product which remains after the extraction of part of the oil of peanuts by pressure or solvents. It is a palatable, high quality vegetable protein supplement used extensively in livestock and poultry feeds. Peanut meal ranges from 41 to 50 percent protein and from 4.5 to 8 percent fat. It is low in methionine, lysine, and tryptophan; and low in calcium, carotene, and vitamin D.

Since peanut meal tends to become rancid when held too long—especially in warm, moist climates—it should not be stored longer than 6 weeks in the summer or 2 to 3 months in the winter.

If a calcium supplement is provided—such as ground limestone or oyster shell flour—peanut meal is satisfactory as the only protein supplement for pigs or brood sows on good pasture or for well-grown pigs in confinement. For young pigs and gestating-lactating sows in confinement, peanut meal—like other proteins of vegetable origin—should not constitute more than one-half the protein supplement, the other one-half being composed of proteins of animal or marine origin.

Peanut meal is so palatable to swine that they will eat more of it than is necessary to balance their ration when self-fed, free-choice (cafeteria style). For this reason, unless peanut meal costs no more per pound than the grain with which it is fed (in which case the producer can afford to use it as an energy feed as well as a protein supplement), when self-feeding, it should be mixed with the rest of the ingredients of the ration. Further,

when constituting one-fourth to one-third of the ration, peanut meal often produces soft pork.

Peanut meal and hulls is ground peanut meal with added hulls, or the ground by-product remaining after extraction of part of the oil from whole or unshelled peanuts. According to the Association of American Feed Control Officials, if solvent extracted, it must be so designated. Since about one-fourth of peanut meal and hulls consists of peanut hulls, it is high in fiber, averaging about 22.5 percent.

Coconut Meal (Copra Meal)

This is the by-product from the production of oil from the dried meats of coconuts. The oil is generally extracted by either (1) the mechanical process, or (2) the expeller process. Coconut meal averages about 21 percent protein content. Since the proteins are of not too high quality, it is generally recommended that coconut meal not constitute more than one-fourth of the supplement of swine rations.

Sunflower Seed Meal

Sunflower seed meal contains 41 or 45 percent protein, although it is quite variable, depending on whether it is prepared from hulled or unhulled seed. It should not be used as the only protein supplement for swine, because it is low in lysine. Sunflower seed meal should not constitute more than one-third of the protein supplement of growing-finishing pigs, and it should be combined with such supplements as meat scrap or fish meal, which are rich in lysine.

Peas (Cull Peas)

Dry peas, 80 to 90 percent of which are produced in Idaho and Washington, have been studied in extensive swine trials conducted at the Washington Agricultural Experiment Station. Cull peas—consisting of the small, shriveled, cracked and otherwise damaged seeds not suited for split peas for human food—when ground and fed on an equal protein content basis and supplemented with either pasture or ground alfalfa, proved as satisfactory a supplement for growing-finishing and gestating-lactating

swine as either meat meal or soybean meal. Although it is normally recommended that peas be fed to swine as a protein supplement, it is noteworthy that in the Washington experiments growing-finishing pigs on Sudan grass pasture were successfully fed a grain ration composed of 98.5 percent cull peas (with the peas serving as both a protein supplement and a grain substitute).

Cull peas average about 24 percent digestible protein—more than twice the protein content of the common cereal grains. The green varieties equal yellow corn in carotene content. Based on the protein content of the peas and the feeding trials to which reference is made, it may be concluded that 2 tons of cull peas are equivalent in feeding value to 1 ton of cereal grain plus 1 ton of soybean meal. Thus, as a rule of thumb, if barley costs $60.00 a ton and soybean meal costs $100.00 a ton, a swine producer can afford to pay $80.00 a ton for peas. It appears, therefore, that as a protein supplement peas mean to the swine producer of the Pacific Northwest what soybeans mean to the Corn Belt and peanuts mean to the South.

WHEAT MILLING BY-PRODUCTS

Prior to 1890, the flour milling by-products of Minneapolis were dumped into the Mississippi River. Beginning about 1890, these cheap and plentiful by-products, along with prairie hay, were fed to sheep. Such feeding operations proved very lucrative. Huge yards were built near the milling centers of Minneapolis and Chicago, and thousands of sheep, mostly mature animals, passed through these feeding plants. But gradually the competition for feeder sheep increased, with the result that prices rose. Simultaneously, the by-products of the mills were found useful in feeding other classes of livestock, thus increasing in price. All of these factors brought about the steady decline of the feed yards centered near the large flour mills, beginning about 1900, and the wider use of wheat milling by-products for other classes of animals. Today, most of these flour milling by-product feeds are utilized in swine rations.

The terms used to designate the common wheat by-products resulting from flour milling differ according to (1) the section of the country, and (2) whether they are obtained from winter or spring wheat. The by-products feeds resulting from the milling of spring wheat are commonly known as bran, standard mid-

dlings, flour middlings, and wheat red dog. The by-products resulting from the milling of winter wheat are known as bran, brown shorts, gray shorts, and white middlings.

In the average wheat milling operations, 72 to 75 percent of the weight of the wheat kernel is converted into flour, with the remaining 25 to 28 percent going into by-product feeds.

Although the wheat milling products are higher in protein content than the cereal grains (and this fact is taken advantage of in formulating rations), in actual swine feeding practice they function more as grain replacements than as protein supplements (see Table 6-17, Handy Feed Substitution Table for Swine).

Wheat Bran

Wheat bran is the coarse outer covering of the wheat kernel. It contains a fair amount of protein (averaging about 16 percent), a good amount of phosphorus, and is laxative in action. Because of its bulk, wheat bran is not used extensively in rations for growing-finishing pigs. It does have a very definite place in the rations of pregnant and suckling sows. It is a good plan to include wheat bran in the ration to the amount of one-third by weight immediately before and after farrowing.

Wheat Middlings (or; Standard Middlings, Middlings)

Wheat middlings are a by-product from spring wheat. They consist mostly of fine particles of bran and germ, with very little of the red dog flour. According to the definition of the Association of American Feed Control Officials, this feed must not contain more than 9.5 percent fiber.

In general, this feed is characterized by fair amounts of proteins (about 17 percent) which are somewhat lacking in quality. It is high in phosphorus, low in calcium, and deficient in both carotene and vitamin D. Because of these deficiencies, middlings are best used in combination with protein supplements of animal origin, and then limited to about 1 pound per head daily. When fed to hogs in this manner, they are worth approximately as much as corn, pound for pound. In larger amounts, middlings are worth only about 85 percent as much as corn.

Wheat Shorts

Wheat shorts consist of fine particles of wheat bran, wheat

germ, wheat flour, and the offal from the "tail of the mill." The Association of American Feed Control Officials states that wheat shorts shall contain not more than 7.0 percent crude fiber.

Wheat Red Dog

Wheat red dog (red dog flour, or wheat red dog flour), which is a by-product from milling spring wheat, consists chiefly of the aleurone layer together with small quantities of flour and fine bran particles. It contains less than 4 percent crude fiber and over 17 percent protein.

Wheat Mill Run

Wheat mill run consists of the coarse wheat bran, fine particles of wheat bran, wheat shorts, wheat germ, wheat flour, and the offal from the "tail of the mill."

According to the Association of American Feed Control Officials, this product must contain not more than 9.5 percent crude fiber. Because of its bulkiness, it is recommended that wheat mill run be fed to the older hogs.

CORN MILLING BY-PRODUCTS

Corn by-products produced from the manufacture of corn starch and corn syrup were the first protein-rich feeds to be utilized as livestock feeds. According to legend, the famous blizzard of 1888 provided the needed impetus. After the great thaw which followed this unprecedented March snowstorm, Buffalo's Hamburg Canal—dumping place for early-day corn processing wastes—spilled over its banks, carrying its load of foul-smelling by-products into the city streets and the nearby barnyards. The whimsical story goes on to say that the cows ate freely of the sour corn wastes, much to the concern of the owners. Soon these cows were producing amazing quantities of milk, far more than they had been giving on the feeds provided before the flood. Buffalo's corn-processors got wind of this startling happenstance and proceeded to circulate the story. Soon the despised and unwanted corn refuse skyrocketed into one of the most popular livestock feeds. Eventually, satisfactory methods of drying the product were developed, thus making for greater economy in

shipment and ease in storage. Today, corn by-products are popular ingredients of livestock rations from coast to coast.

In the modern manufacture of starch, sugar, syrup, and corn oil for human food, the following common by-product feeds are obtained: (1) corn gluten feed, (2) corn gluten meal, and (3) corn germ meal.

Corn Gluten Feed (Gluten Feed)

Corn gluten feed is the corn by-product remaining after the extraction of most of the starch and germ in the wet milling manufacture of corn starch or syrup, with or without fermented corn extractives or corn germ meal. This feed contains approximately 25 percent protein and 7.5 percent fiber. Because of its bulkiness, unpalatability, and poor quality proteins, it is recommended that corn gluten feed be incorporated in the ration of ruminants rather than fed to swine.

Corn Gluten Meal (Gluten Meal)

Corn gluten meal is similar to corn gluten feed without the bran. It averages about 43 percent protein and 3.0 percent fiber.

Because the proteins are of low quality, corn gluten meal should never be fed as the sole protein supplement to swine. When price relationships are favorable, it may be satisfactorily incorporated in confinement rations as the plant protein of a trio-mixture. For pasture feeding, it may constitute 50 percent of the protein supplement—provided the other half is of animal or marine origin. When used in this manner, corn gluten feed is of about equal value to any of the common protein-rich plant supplements.

Corn Germ Meal (Wet Milled)

This is a by-product of the wet milling of corn starch, corn syrup, and other corn products. The corn germs obtained in these processing operations are dried, crushed, and the oil extracted. Then the remaining residue or cake is ground, producing corn germ meal.

Corn germ meal contains about 22 percent protein and 10 percent fiber. When used in combination with higher quality proteins, corn germ meal is a satisfactory feed for swine. As a protein feed for pigs on pasture, it should not constitute more than

half of the supplement, with the other half consisting of protein-rich animal or marine products. For swine in confinement, it may be used as the protein-rich plant component of a trio-mixture.

When price relationships are favorable, corn germ meal can be used as a partial grain substitute in the ration, but it should not constitute more than 20 percent of the total feed. When so limited, corn germ meal is equal in value to corn, pound for pound.

Corn Germ Meal (Dry Milled)

This is a by-product of the dry milling of corn for corn meal, corn grits, hominy feed, and other corn products.

For best results in swine feeding, it is recommended that corn germ meal (dry milled) be utilized in the same manner as recommended for corn germ meal (wet milled).

Hominy Feed

Hominy feed, a by-product of corn milling, is a mixture of corn bran, corn germ, and a part of the starchy portion of either white or yellow corn kernels or mixtures thereof, as produced in the manufacture of pearl hominy, hominy grits, or table meal (ordinary corn meal). This feed shall not contain less than 5 percent crude fat.

Hominy feed is a satisfactory substitute for corn in swine feeding, but it is somewhat higher in fiber and less palatable than the grain from which it is derived. Yellow hominy feed supplies carotene (vitamin A), while white hominy feed lacks this factor. From the standpoint of gains and feed efficiency, properly supplemented hominy feed is worth approximately 95 percent as much as corn, but it will produce soft pork if it constitutes more than half the grain ration.

RICE MILLING BY-PRODUCTS

The common by-products resulting from processing rice are: brewers rice, rice bran, rice polishing or rice polish, and rice meal. In swine feeding, these products are used as grain replacements or energy feeds.

Chipped Rice (or; Broken Rice, Brewers Rice)

Chipped rice consists of the small broken kernels of rice

resulting from the milling operations. It is used chiefly in the brewing industry. Chipped rice is similar to corn in composition and feeding value. For best results in swine feeding, it should be finely ground, mixed with more palatable feeds, and included in a properly balanced ration. The carcasses of hogs fed on chipped rice are hard and firm.

Rice Bran

Rice bran is the pericarp, or bran layer, obtained in milling rice for human food, together with such quantity of hull fragments as is unavoidable in the regular milling operations. It contains about 12.4 percent protein, 13.6 percent fat, and 11.6 percent fiber. When limited to one-third of the swine ration, rice bran is equal in value to corn. Higher proportions have a lower feeding value and produce soft pork.

Rice Polishings (Rice Polish)

Rice polishings are the finely powdered by-product obtained in polishing the rice kernels after the hulls and bran have been removed. They average about 12.8 percent protein, 13.4 percent fat, and 2.7 percent fiber, and are high in thiamine. Because of the high fat content, rice polishings become rancid in storage and produce soft pork unless fed in amounts restricted to less than one-third of the ration. When incorporated in a properly balanced ration, they are equal or superior in feeding value to corn for all classes of swine, including young pigs and gestating-lactating sows.

Ground Brown Rice

Ground brown rice is the product obtained in grinding the rice kernels after the hull has been removed. It is nearly equal to corn as a swine feed and produces hard pork.

VITAMIN SUPPLEMENTS

Swine are more apt to suffer from vitamin deficiencies than any other class of farm animals. This is especially true during the winter months or under confinement conditions. Further, these requirements are especially critical with young pigs and gestating-lactating sows.

The maximum year-round use of either green pastures or well-cured green, leafy hay not over one year old, along with rations that are otherwise balanced, will eliminate most of the vitamin deficiencies of swine under practical farm conditions.

Numerous vitamin supplements are on the market. The Association of American Feed Control Officials lists the following: cod-liver oil, cod-liver oil with added vitamins A and D, vitamin A oil, vitamin D_2 supplement, vitamin D oil, vitamin A and D oil, D-activated animal sterol, D-activated plant sterol, dried—fermentation solubles, vitamin B_{12} supplement, vitamin E supplement, riboflavin supplement, and vitamin A supplement.

Legume Hays

The addition of a choice legume hay not over a year old (whole, chopped, or ground) to a swine ration is particularly beneficial during the winter months or during times of confinement feeding. Such roughage is fairly rich in proteins of good quality; it is high in calcium, and it contains an abundant supply of vitamins. It possesses all the essential elements of a pasture, except its succulence. When combined with other protein supplements, legumes balance out the deficiencies of the cereal grains in a most admirable manner.

Because of bulk, a legume hay should not be fed as the sole protein supplement to finishing pigs, but it may be combined successfully with other more concentrated proteins. Young growing and finishing pigs usually make the most rapid and economical gains when their rations do not contain too much fiber. However, pregnant brood sows and herd boars may handle a considerable quantity of bulky feeds.

Alfalfa Meal

By 1900, feed men were including alfalfa meal in mixtures. Some extolled the virtues of this ground product as one that would "cut down the wear and tear on the jaw muscles and teeth of domestic animals, maybe 70 to 80 percent." It is doubtful if any scientific evidence was ever uncovered to substantiate this statement, but, through the years, experiments have revealed that alfalfa meal has nutritional values far exceeding the wildest claims first made for it. It has come to hold a place in animal nutrition comparable to that which milk popularly holds in hu-

man nutrition. Today, more than half of all the tame hay produced in the United States is alfalfa.

Alfalfa meal is the product obtained from the grinding of the entire alfalfa hay. It contains proteins of the right quality to balance out the amino-acid deficiencies of the cereal grains; it is a rich source of minerals, especially calcium; and, finally and most important. it is an excellent source of vitamins, both known and unknown, needed by the pig. If leafy and green and not over a year old, alfalfa is high in carotene (provitamin A), a lack of which results in poor growth of young pigs and the farrowing of premature, dead, or weak pigs. Sun-cured hay is also a good source of vitamin D, the anti-rachitic vitamin. Alfalfa is an excellent source of the long list of B vitamins.

Because of the many virtues of well-cured, green, leafy alfalfa under confinement conditions, it is generally recommended that the ration of gestating-lactating sows contain from 15 to 35 percent ground alfalfa and that young pig rations contain from 5 to 10 percent ground alfalfa. In addition to its beneficial effects in supplying the needed vitamins, minerals, and quality proteins, the inclusion of a ground legume in confinement swine rations generally reduces the feed cost, for it seldom costs as much per pound as the other ingredients of the ration.

Although legume hays may be fed from a rack, especially to sows, more assurance of consumption of proper quantities is obtained through grinding and incorporating it in the ration. Where there is no means of grinding home-grown legume hays of high quality, it is recommended that the leaves and chaff from the haymow be made available to swine.

In recent years, the trend has been toward the production of a larger tonnage of dehydrated than of sun-cured alfalfa meal. Almost two-thirds of the alfalfa products are now dehydrated, and the ratio is still increasing. Artificial dehydration results (1) in the loss of fewer leaves, and (2) in less destruction of vitamins. On the average, the dehydrated product is higher in protein, in carotene, and in the water soluble vitamins, and lower in fiber than the sun-cured product. However, due to the fact that it is not exposed to sunlight in the curing process, the vitamin D content of the artificially dehydrated meal is only one-fourth to one-third as high as in the sun-cured meal.

Since the carotene (provitamin A value) of alfalfa products is one of the reasons for incorporating them in confinement

rations, the swine producer should take cognizance of the normal losses in carotene accruing through oxidation in storage. Because this destruction is accelerated by high temperatures and light, it is recommended that alfalfa meal and other such feeds be stored in a cool, dark place. Also, it is noteworthy that the loss in green color of dry forages is less rapid than the loss of carotene; hence, the degree of green coloration is not an accurate criterion of the carotene content of stored forages, especially after the first year.

Alfalfa Leaf Meal

Alfalfa leaf meal is the ground product consisting chiefly of alfalfa leaves and a minimum of stems. In comparison with alfalfa hay or meal, it is higher in protein and vitamin content, and lower in fiber. Although a smaller quantity of this product is needed for swine rations than of alfalfa meal, price relationships usually do not favor its use.

Other Ground Forages

Although alfalfa is more extensively used for confinement swine rations than any other forage, any of the following dried forages may be successfully fed: ladino clover, red clover, sweet clover, lespedeza, soybeans, cowpeas, field peas, kudzus, Sudan grass, and grass-legume mixtures. Because many of these forages are less palatable to swine than alfalfa, they should be ground and incorporated in the ration—preferably in a trio-type mixture.

Distillers Products

This includes a number of by-products obtained from the manufacture of alcohol and distilled liquors from corn, rye, grain sorghum, wheat, molasses, and potatoes. Although the products are similar, the name of the product from which each by-product was made is always included. For example, where corn is used, the by-product is correctly known as *corn distillers dried solubles.*

Distillers products contain from 25 to 30 percent protein, but the protein is not of good quality, being deficient in lysine and tryptophan. They are of particular value for swine as a vita-

min supplement in confinement rations, because of their high content of the B-complex vitamins. Where little (less than 5 percent) or no alfalfa meal is included in the confinement ration, the addition of from 6 to 12 percent distillers products will be beneficial. Cost relationships should be considered, for extra alfalfa generally produces as good results as adding distillers products, and at lower cost.

Yeast

Yeast is a microscopic, one-celled plant of the same family as the mushroom. There are hundreds of different kinds of yeasts, just as there are many species of grasses. However, based on their particular functions or contributions to the ration as vitamin products, yeast and yeast products may be classified roughly into the following two groups:

1. **Yeast products used chiefly as a source of B vitamins and protein.**—This group includes brewers dried yeast, torula dried yeast, grain distillers dried yeast, and molasses distillers dried yeast.

2. **Irradiated dried yeast.**—This is yeast that has been exposed to ultraviolet light, and which may be used as a source of vitamin D for four-footed animals.

Yeast is high in protein, averaging about 44.9 percent. From the standpoint of quality, it is among the best of the plant proteins, but not as good as the animal proteins. It is deficient in methionine. Whether or not yeast is used as a protein supplement in animal rations should be determined solely by its price relationship to other protein supplements.

Yeast is high in the B vitamins. Also it may contain an unidentified factor or factors. Usually yeast is used at levels of 2 to 5 percent of the ration in supplying B vitamins.

Yeast contains considerable ergosterol, which, when exposed to ultraviolet light, produces vitamin D. After having been subjected to ultraviolet light, it is known as irradiated yeast. Irradiated yeast is usually considered a practical source of vitamin D for swine. When the conditions are such that hogs may not get sufficient vitamin D, about 0.1 pound of irradiated yeast may be added to each 2 tons of feed.

THE TRIO-MIXTURE

Many protein supplements, particularly those of vegetable origin, are lacking in certain of the essential amino acids or building stones. Further, most protein feeds are deficient in certain vitamins and minerals, and perhaps in unknown factors. Therefore, pigs in confinement that are fed a ration consisting only of cereal grain and any of the common protein supplements are apt to suffer deficiency trouble, with unthrifty and runty pigs resulting. By bringing together proteins from different sources, there is a likelihood that the deficiencies (in amino acids, in vitamins, and/or in minerals) of one will be off-set by surpluses from another. More important, vitamin deficiencies will likely be alleviated. As a result, mixed protein supplements have usually proved more efficient than single supplements.

One of the earliest and most widely used protein mixtures was the "trio-" or "trinity-" mixture developed at the Wisconsin Experiment Station. Originally, this mixture consisted of two parts tankage, one part linseed meal, and one part alfalfa meal. This mixture provides adequate proteins (about 40 percent protein of excellent quality), and it is rich in minerals and vitamins. It is simple to mix, palatable, and adapted to all classes of swine.

For practical reasons, certain substitutions in the trio-mixture may sometimes be advisable. Using judgment, these can be made so as not to affect materially the feeding value of the mixture. For example, any protein-rich animal or marine product can be substituted for tankage; any protein-rich plant product (such as soybean meal, peanut meal, or cottonseed meal) can replace the linseed meal, and any choice legume (such as clover or soybean hay) can replace the alfalfa. When hogs are on good pasture, the alfalfa meal should be omitted from the mixture. On the other hand, when hogs are in confinement it may be desirable to increase the proportion of ground legume in the trio-mixture, especially for gestating-lactating sows and when the ration contains little or no protein supplement of animal or marine origin.

Aside from being nutritionally balanced, protein mixtures need not be made up of too many feeds (because of added mixing expense). And they should be palatable enough to allow of free choice, self-feeding with grain. The trio-mixture meets these requirements admirably.

With corn as the cereal grain, the trio-mixture may be self-fed, free-choice—using separate compartments for the corn and the protein supplement. With grains which are less palatable and richer in protein (particularly barley, oats, and rye), pigs may eat more of the supplement than is necessary for most economical results. Under such conditions it is usually advisable to mix the proper proportion of supplement with the grain and then self-feed the entire mixture.

QUESTIONS FOR STUDY AND DISCUSSION

1. Feed prices vary widely. For profitable production, therefore, feeds with similar nutritive properties should be interchanged as price relationships warrant; and, in buying feeds, stockmen should check prices against values received. To the latter end, herewith is presented a simple, easy way to calculate the best buy in protein feeds:

   If 44 percent protein soybean meal is selling at $3.65 per 100 pounds, whereas 35 percent linseed meal is selling for $3.50 per 100 pounds, which is the better buy? Divide $3.65 by 44 to get 8.3¢ per pound of protein for the soybean meal. Then, divide $3.50 by 35 and get 10¢ per pound for the linseed meal. Thus, at these prices soybean meal is the better buy—by 1.7¢ per pound of protein.

   Of course, it is recognized that many other factors affect the actual feeding value of each feed, such as (a) species of animals, (b) palatability, (c) grade of feed, (d) preparation of feed, (e) ingredients with which each feed is combined, and (f) quantities of each feed fed.

   Secure current prices of available protein supplements for swine. Then, by referring to Table I-1 of the Appendix and books listed as references at the end of this chapter, determine which is the best buy from the standpoint of cost per pound of protein.

2. Under what circumstances might you recommend soybean meal as the only supplement for swine?

3. Discuss the use of each of the leading vitamin supplements for swine.

SELECTED REFERENCES

Title of Publication	Author(s)	Publisher
Applied Animal Nutrition	E. W. Crampton L. E. Harris	W. H. Freeman & Co., San Francisco, Calif., 1969.
Composition of Cereal Grains and Forages	Publication 585	National Academy of Sciences, National Research Council, Washington, D. C.
Composition of Concentrate By-Product Feeding Stuffs	Publication 449	National Academy of Sciences, National Research Council, Washington, D. C.
Feeds and Feeding, Abridged	F. B. Morrison	Morrison Publishing Co., Ithaca, N. Y., 1958.
Feeds and Feeding, 22nd edition	F. B. Morrison	Morrison Publishing Co., Ithaca, N. Y., 1956.
Feed Formulations Handbook	T. W. Perry	The Interstate Printers & Publishers, Inc., Danville, Ill., 1966.
Feeds of the World	B. H. Schneider	Agri. Exp. Sta., West Virginia University, Morgantown, W. Va., 1947.
Nutrient Requirements for Swine	Publication 1599	National Academy of Sciences, National Research Council, Washington, D. C., 1968.
Pork Production	W. W. Smith	The Macmillan Company, New York, N. Y., 1952.
Swine Feeding and Nutrition	T. J. Cunha	Interscience Publishers, Inc., New York, N. Y., 1957.
Swine Production	W. E. Carroll J. L. Krider F. N. Andrews	McGraw-Hill Book Co., New York, N. Y., 1962.

PASTURES FOR SWINE

Recently, there has been a pronounced trend away from pasture rearing of swine, to confinement production—especially among large-scale, highly specialized operators. The truth is that, in the past, many times pastures concealed the inadequacies of poor rations and hogs performed rather poorly without them.

Today, only 4.4 percent of U.S. swine feed is derived from pasture and dry forage—a small proportion, indeed. Yet, often hogs will yield good returns from an acre of good pasture. Of course, unlike cattle and sheep, the monogastric pig cannot be grown and finished satisfactorily on forages alone. But these crops are an excellent adjunct to a grain ration. Further, swine can handle more pasture and other roughages than was originally suspected; after all, the European wild boar gleaned the fields provided by nature, and the Arkansas razorback was a self-sustaining vegetarian.

Without doubt, many successful swine producers will make use of pastures for a long time to come; some may combine pasture and confinement rearing. In season, most producers will continue to utilize pastures for breeding animals. In any event, pastures for swine are not obsolete; rather there now exists two alternatives for the management of swine, instead of just one— and the able manager will choose wisely between them.

Although hundreds of species of forages are grown and fed to swine in different areas, the underlying principles in their utilization are the same. Except for variation in the length of the growing season, there is not as much difference in the manage-

Fig. 9-1. Pastures are excellent for brood sows. (Courtesy, Dr. D. E. Becker, University of Illinois)

ment of swine on pastures and in the management of pastures as some people would have us believe.

ADVANTAGES OF PASTURES

Many practical swine producers feel that pasture production does have certain real advantages over confinement production. It should be acknowledged, however, that in much of the earlier work in which comparisons were made between confinement and pasture rations, inadequate confinement rations were used. As a result, actually such trials were comparisons between the advantages of adequate pasture rations over inadequate confinement rations. Despite present nutritional knowledge, more confinement rations continue to be inadequate than is the case with pasture rations.

In general, the following advantages may be cited in favor of pasture production over confinement production of swine:

1. **Saves in feed.**—Pastures make for a saving in feed costs in both grain and protein supplements. With properly balanced rations used in each case, the feed saving effected through the utilization of swine pastures is about as follows:

    a. Good pastures will reduce (1) the grain required in producing 100 pounds of pork by 15 to 20 percent and (2) the protein supplement required in producing 100 pounds of pork by 20 to 50 percent.

    b. An acre of good pasture will result in a saving of 500 to 1,000 pounds of grain and 300 to 500 pounds of protein supplement.

    c. With mature brood sows, good pastures may lower feed costs by 50 percent. In fact, sows may get the major portion of their feed from good pastures up to 6 to 8 weeks before farrowing. The condition of sows is the best guide as to the amount of concentrate feeding necessary.

    d. Good pastures furnish a convenient and economical way to compensate for the protein, mineral, and vitamin deficiencies of grain and other high energy feeds. This does not infer that protein, mineral, and vitamin supplements need not be added to the ration. Rather, the problem is simplified, and it may be solved at lower cost. For example, good pastures make it possible to use a higher proportion of lower quality and cheaper protein feeds of plant origin in the supplement.

    e. Good pastures make for a slight saving in minerals —about 3 pounds per acre.

With inadequate confinement rations, the saving in feed by utilizing pastures for swine will be even greater than indicated.

2. **Lessens nutritional deficiencies.**—Pastures lessen nutritional deficiencies in swine, chiefly because of (a) their high quality proteins, (b) their vitamins (an abundance of carotene and the water-soluble vitamins, plus the vitamin D value of the sunlight to which animals on pasture are exposed), (c) their unknown factors (most, if not all, of which they contain), and (d) their minerals (especially calcium). These nutrients are not present in adequate amounts in all confinement rations consisting of grains, oil meals, and mill feeds. Of course, with present

knowledge of nutrition and available supplements, many confinement rations are as well balanced as most pasture rations.

3. **Lessens communicable diseases.**—Hogs on pasture come in contact with each other less than hogs in confinement, with the result that fewer communicable disease problems are encountered than where hogs are in close confinement.

4. **Does not require as much capital for buildings and equipment.**—Lower cost buildings (including movable houses) and equipment can be used in a pasture system than in confinement, with the result that it requires less capital investment on a per hog basis.

5. **Makes for greater flexibility.**—Pasture operations are more flexible than confinement programs—an important consideration where renters are involved or where other uncertainties exist about a long-range program.

6. **Does not require as high levels of skill and management.** —Pasture rearing does not require as high levels of skill and management as are necessary to make confinement production work. Also, it requires more competent labor to operate a fully-automated, highly-mechanized, confinement complex than a pasture operation.

7. **Makes for approved soil conservation practices on rolling land.**—Where there is rolling land and/or need for organic matter, a pasture system may be preferred to confinement. Certainly, pastures conserve the maximum fertility value of the manure and lessen erosion. When animals are on pasture, 80 percent of the plant nutrients may be returned to the soil.

8. **Favors limited feeding.**—Pastures permit limited feeding. This may be important when the producer is gambling on a higher market at a later date or when feed is high or scarce and he desires to carry the hogs along until the new crop is available.

9. **Improves reproduction.**—Pastures provide a desirable way of life for breeding animals, chiefly because of improved nutrition and valuable exercise. Thus, they result in more satisfactory litters being farrowed and in a more abundant milk flow. Also, boars on pasture are more vigorous and surer breeders.

DISADVANTAGES OF PASTURES

A number of disadvantages of pasturing hogs have caused,

and will continue to cause, a shift away from their use to confinement hog production. Among the disadvantages sometimes attributed to pasture systems are:

1. **It may require more labor.**—Running hogs on pasture does not lend itself to automation and labor-saving devices to the extent of confinement production, primarily in feeding and watering.

2. **It may prevent more remunerative uses of land.**—On many hog farms, operators can make more money from growing corn, soybeans and other crops than they can from pastures.

3. **It does not facilitate manure handling.**—Although less manure has to be handled in a pasture system than in confinement, it is more difficult to automate and handle manure where hogs are scattered over a large area.

4. **It mitigates against enlarging hog production without enlarging the farm.**—With high priced land, this fact must be weighed when it is desired to increase the size of the hog operation.

DESIRABLE CHARACTERISTICS OF A GOOD PASTURE

Although it is recognized that no one forage excels all others in all the desired qualities, the following desirable characteristics may serve as criteria in the choice of pasture crops for swine:

1. Adapted to local soil and climatic conditions. Although this is a prime requisite, practical swine producers cannot afford to disregard the grazing qualities.

2. Palatable and succulent.

3. Ability to endure tramping and grazing.

4. Easy to grow, and grown at a nominal cost.

5. Provide tender and succulent growth for a short period or consistent growth over a long period.

6. Highly nutritious; rich in proteins, vitamins, and minerals, and low in fiber.

7. High carrying capacity.

8. Fit satisfactorily into the crop rotation.

9. Uncontaminated with diseases or parasites.

Over most of the United States, one or more adapted legumes possess most of these qualities. Fortunately, they can be selected

without fear of bloat, for swine—unlike cattle and sheep—are not susceptible to this ailment.

MANAGEMENT OF SWINE AND PASTURES

The principles of good swine management on pastures are the same, regardless of the kind of pasture or its location. Further, good management of both the pastured animals and the pastures go hand in hand; they are inseparable. They both require attention in order to get the highest returns. In brief, good producers, good pastures, and good hogs go together.

In general, consciously or unconsciously, the practical operator gives attention to the following swine pasture management factors:

1. **Self-feeding vs. hand-feeding.**—Unless there are reasons for limiting the ration, swine on pasture are almost universally self-fed. Just because swine are self-fed, the producer cannot neglect his swine enterprise.

2. **Full-feeding vs. limited-feeding.**—When hogs are finished on pasture either of the following systems may be employed: (a) full-feeding or (b) limited-feeding. The particular system decided upon will, for the most part, depend upon the relative price of grain and pasture, and the time at which it is desired to market. Full-fed pigs usually reach an earlier and better market, and bring returns more quickly. On the other hand, limited-feeding usually requires less feed. In any event, it must be remembered that pastures, fine as they may be, are roughages and not concentrates.

With lactating sows, liberal feeding is recommended in order to enable the sow to produce the necessary milk for nursing pigs. Also, pigs under 75 pounds are normally full-fed even where it is planned to limit the ration later.

3. **Quantity of protein.**—In arriving at the quantity of protein supplement to feed swine on pasture, consideration should be given to the following:

   a. Less protein supplement is required where limited grain feeding is practiced than with full-feeding, for less protein is required to balance the ration. In general, pigs full fed on a good legume pasture require about 50 percent as much protein supplement as

when full-fed in confinement. Pigs limited-fed on good pasture will eat more forage and require only 30 to 40 percent as much protein supplement as confinement fed pigs.

b. Less protein supplement is required for older hogs than for young pigs, because mature animals consume more pasture—finally reaching the stage where pastures supply ample proteins to balance their needs. Where an early market is not too important, the protein supplement may be deleted on good pastures after (1) full-fed pigs reach 125 pounds or (2) limited-fed pigs reach 75 pounds.

c. Less protein supplement is required with pastures that are higher in protein content and more palatable.

d. Less protein supplement will result in slower gains and a later market. Regardless of the weight of the hogs—whether weaner pigs or 150-pound shoates— any lowering of the protein supplement below that required to balance the ration will result in less rapid gains, with younger pigs being relatively more affected. Thus, where an earlier market is apt to mean higher prices, it may, in the end, be more economical to put more money into the purchase of high priced protein supplements.

e. Less protein supplement will require more pasture acreage, because of higher forage consumption per animal.

f. Less protein supplement will result in more rooting, as the pig attempts to meet his requirements from the soil.

4. **Providing young succulent pastures.**—As pasture crops mature, they become less palatable and less desirable because of higher fiber content and lower amounts of proteins, minerals, and vitamins. Clipping at intervals during the growing season is the best method of keeping swine pastures young and succulent. Mowing is also effective in both weed and parasite control (the latter because of exposing the feces to drying).

5. **Fencing.**—Hogs on pastures should be fenced properly, with consideration given to kind of fence and size of area. With smaller areas and higher concentration of hogs, it is recom-

mended that the woven wire used meet the following specifications: 32- to 36-inch height, 6-inch mesh, number 9 top and bottom wires, and number 11 staves. With larger areas (10 acres or more) and less concentration of swine, a 26-inch woven wire is satisfactory, with the other specifications remaining the same as for the higher fence. With all hog fences, one strand of barbed wire—either 2 or 4 point—should be stretched tightly between the woven wire and the ground. Of course, it goes without saying that hog fences—like any farm fence—should be stretched properly and stapled to durable posts that are properly set and spaced, and have suitable corner posts that are well braced.

6. **Shelter.**—Swine on pastures should be provided with proper shelter, including both houses and shades. For flexibility in rotating pastures, portable equipment is preferable. Suitable movable houses and shades are illustrated in Chapter X.

7. **Clean, fresh water.**—Swine should have access to clean, fresh water at all times. Under a system of pasture rotation, it is often difficult and expensive to pipe water to the area. But usually the added expense will be justified. Where possible, automatic waterers should be provided. Hand-watering on pasture is inconvenient, labor-consuming, and otherwise unsatisfactory.

8. **Ringing.**—When rooting is encountered—a somewhat normal habit with any pig, but a condition which is accentuated with deficient or limited rations—the animals should be rung. Any one of several types of rings may be used with success if properly inserted in the snout.

9. **Minerals.**—To protect them from wind and moisture, pasture-fed minerals should be placed in a self-feeder or in a protected mineral box.

The cereal grains and their by-products, and most all protein-rich supplements, are high in phosphorus, whereas legume and rape pastures are a fair source of calcium. With such a combination of feeds, salt (iodized salt in iodine-deficient areas) is likely to be the only mineral deficiency. However, it is good protection to make dicalcium phosphate or bone meal available (or a mixture of two-thirds dicalcium phosphate or bone meal and one-third salt). Then, the mineral will be consumed only if needed.

10. **Early spring and late fall grazing.**—Early spring and late fall grazing are desirable for swine, but undesirable for pas-

tures. In the fall, the plants need protection to build up root reserves. In recognition of this situation, a compromise is usually necessary—pasturing early and late, but not enough to do too great harm to the pastures. Where plenty of pasture areas are available, good swine and good pasture management in this regard are usually achieved through the rotation of pastures.

11. **Overgrazing.**—Continuous overgrazing is to be avoided. For this reason, it is recommended that, except for annuals, the forage be left to grow up so that one to two crops of hay may be harvested each season in addition to the pasture. As a rule of thumb, the grazing should be regulated so as to allow the top growth to maintain a height of 3 to 6 inches. To accomplish this, the swine producer should always have more than just enough pasture.

An acre of good pasture plus full-feeding of grain and supplement should, without overgrazing, provide enough forage for fifteen to twenty growing-finishing pigs from weaning to the end of the pasture season, or for six to eight mature bred sows, or four to six sows with litters. When limited-feeding is practiced, pastures will carry only one-half to two-thirds as many hogs per acre as when full-feeding.

12. **Combination grazing with other classes of animals.**— More than one class of animals can be grazed on most pastures— the practice of so-called combination grazing—with benefit to both the animals and the pastures. Although the carrying capacity (or animal units per acre) is slightly higher when combination grazing is practiced, there is a tendency to overstock, through trying to add what would be a normal number of animals per acre of each class when pastured separately.

Swine and cattle or sheep can be advantageously grazed on the same area. But avoid overgrazing. And do not include cows near calving because of the hazard of hogs inflicting injury on the vulva of cows or harming newborn calves. The swine-cattle combination is particularly desirable because (a) cattle will eat the coarser vegetation, leaving young succulent growth for swine; and (b) most diseases and parasites afflict only one or the other class of animals.

13. **Scattering droppings and handling manure.**—Proper scattering of the droppings on pasture is desirable for two reasons: (a) it conserves the maximum fertility value of the ma-

nure; and (b) it lessens the disease and parasite hazard, through exposing the droppings to the action of the sun and the air. The droppings may be scattered easily by harrowing the area at intervals, especially in the early spring and late fall.

For best parasite and disease control, swine manure should never be hauled from swine barns or lots and scattered on pastures utilized by this particular class of livestock.

14. **Rotating pastures.**—Modern swine producers realize the importance of rotating pastures in order to control parasites and lessen the disease hazard. Pigs should never be allowed to follow pigs on a particular pasture without plowing the field in the interim. In the more heavily parasitized areas, it is recommended that swine be kept off permanent pastures for 2 or 3 years. Also, in rotating pastures, avoid cross-drainage from one field to another.

15. **Year-round grazing.**—Because of the many advantages of pastures (as listed in an earlier section in this chapter), good swine management involves as nearly year-round grazing as is possible. From this standpoint, the southern states have a very real advantage over other areas. Through planting different crops at different seasons, progressive southern swine producers are achieving year-round grazing. This fact, together with modern and more effective parasite and disease control measures, is the primary reason for the recent great expansion of all livestock production in the South.

Some Corn Belt swine producers are obtaining a 12-months hog pasture by using two crops only, ladino clover and rye. In the North, where year-round grazing cannot be secured, it is merely recommended that swine producers attain as long a grazing season as is possible, especially through arranging for early spring and late fall pastures.

16. **Permanent vs. temporary pastures.**—It is advisable to use temporary rather than permanent pastures in small lots or where a high concentration of hogs are kept during most of the pasture season. Also, temporary pastures are better suited to a system requiring frequent plowing—once or twice each year—from the standpoint of parasite and disease control. One or more such pastures are usually included in the plan in order to secure the longest possible grazing season.

17. **Puddling.**—Pastures should be protected during periods of heavy rainfall or when irrigating by removing swine until the soil has dried sufficiently to prevent puddling.

TYPE OF PASTURE

General recommendations, by areas (see Fig. 7-1 for four areas), for planting and grazing the more common pasture crops for swine are given in the following tables:

Table 9-1, The Corn Belt and North Central States.

Table 9-2, The South.

Table 9-3, The Atlantic Coast.

Table 9-4, The West.

For further and more specific information on swine pasture crops for a particular farm, consult the local county extension agent or vocational agriculture instructor, or write to the state agricultural college.

No one plant embodies all the desirable characteristics of a good swine pasture (see earlier selection on this subject). None of them will grow the year-round, or during extremely cold or dry weather. Further, each of them has a period of peak growth which must be conserved for periods of low growth. Consequently, the progressive swine producer will find it desirable (1) to grow more than one species, (2) to plan for each month of the year, and (3) to secure either year-round grazing or as early spring and late fall grazing as is possible in the particular area. In general, a combination of permanent and temporary pastures will best achieve these ends.

In the South, year-round grazing is a reality on many a successful swine farm. By careful planning, other areas can approach this desired goal. Figure 9-2, based on Table 9-1, illustrates in graphic form the growth period of each of the common swine pasture plants of the Corn Belt and North Central states. As noted, by selecting the proper combination of crops, swine pastures for each month of the year are assured. A similar graph for the South, the Atlantic Coast, and the West can be developed from the respective tables (Tables 9-2, 9-3, and 9-4).

Where it fits into the operations, such crops as corn, soybeans, small grains, peanuts, sweet potatoes, and sorghums may be harvested by hogging off. The chief advantages of the system are that it saves labor costs of harvesting the crop, increases soil

TABLE 9-1

GENERAL RECOMMENDATIONS FOR PLANTING AND GRAZING PASTURE CROPS FOR SWINE IN THE CORN BELT AND NORTH CENTRAL STATES[1]

Crop	Variety	When to Plant	Seeding Rate/Acre, Lbs.	Method of Planting	Time Elapsing After Planting, Before Pasturing, Months	Time of Use (or grazing season) Start	Time of Use (or grazing season) End	No. Full-fed Growing-Finishing Pigs[2] /Acre	Adaptation and Other Comments
Alfalfa (the most important and most widely distributed U.S. forage crop)	Ladak Ranger Buffalo Vernal Narragansett Atlantic Culver	Spring or late summer	12-15	Broadcast or drill	4-5	When 6-8" high	Late fall, but allow 6-8" of growth to remain	20-25	Where soils are sufficiently fertile and not acid. Cannot tolerate poorly drained soils. It provides palatable, nutritious forage over a long grazing season, from early spring until late fall. Alfalfa-grass mixtures are frequently used for swine pastures.
Alsike clover		Early spring or late summer	6-10	Drill or broadcast	4	When 6-8" high	Late fall, but allow 3-5" of growth to remain	10-12	Equal in feeding value to red clover, but shorter season of use and lower yielding. Not equal to red clover, alfalfa, or ladino as a hog pasture. Will grow on wet soils, but if soil is acid it should be limed. For swine pasture, alsike clover is almost always mixed with one or more grasses or with other legumes
Birdsfoot trefoil	Cascade Empire (for North) Viking Granger	Spring; late summer in southern part only	6	Drill or broadcast	Spring of second year	When 6-8" high	Late fall, but allow 4-6" of growth to remain with 1st year birdsfoot trefoil	12-15	Well adapted to soils of lower and poorer drainage than alfalfa. Long-lived plant. Highly nutritious, second only to ladino in ease of management. Slow to become established. Will live with bluegrass better than any other legume.
Bluegrass (With the possible exception of timothy, bluegrass is the most widely known grass in America.)	Kentucky bluegrass	Late summer or fall	Volunteer stands 2-4	Volunteer. Frequently, 2-4 lbs. seeded to insure rapid establishment		April 1	Late fall after frost	5-10	Bluegrass is inferior to alfalfa, the clovers, and rape for swine pasture, producing smaller gains and requiring more concentrates. Bluegrass is a permanent pasture adapted to the cool, humid areas of the northern states. It generally provides grazing earlier *(Continued)*

Footnotes on last page of table.

(Continued)

TABLE 9-1 (Continued)

Crop	Variety	When to Plant	Seeding Rate/Acre, Lbs.	Method of Planting	Time Elapsing After Planting, Before Pasturing, Months	Time of Use (or grazing season)		No. Full-fed Growing-Finishing Pigs /Acre[2]	Adaption and Other Comments
						Start	End		
Bluegrass (Continued)									in the spring and later in the fall than the legumes. It becomes dormant in the hot summer months, July and August. It is improved when combined with some legume, such as white clover, ladino clover, or birdsfoot trefoil. **For reasons of parasite control, young pigs should not be placed on bluegrass pasture unless it has not had hogs on it for 2-3 years.**
Bromegrass (or preferably bromegrass-legume mixtures)	Achenbach Lincoln Southland	Spring or late summer	Mixture[3] 5-7 lbs. bromegrass, 6-8 lbs. alfalfa	Drill or broadcast	4-5	April 1	Nov. 1	15-20	Bromegrass, a palatable perennial pasture crop, is sometimes used as a swine pasture. It will endure heavy grazing and tramping. It is not so valuable a swine pasture as alfalfa, where the latter is adapted. Bromegrass-alfalfa mixtures are equal to straight alfalfa for swine pastures.
Ladino (a large type of white clover first found growing in Italy)		Spring or late summer	1-2	Broadcast or drill	Spring of 2nd year, but frequently may be lightly grazed fall of 1st year	When 4-6" high	Late fall, but allow 3-5" of growth to remain	20-25	Where adapted, ladino clover is superior to alfalfa as a swine pasture. Will last 3-5 yrs. in pasture. Ladino-grass mixtures are frequently used for swine pastures. Winter-hardy varieties now being developed will extend its use even more in the northernmost states.
Oats	Adapted varieties	Early spring	65-130	Broadcast or drill	1½-2	Spring, 6-8 weeks after planting	Early summer (4-6 weeks after starting grazing)	10-15	Oats are a good pasture while they last, but pasture period is short.
Rape	Dwarf Essex	March to June	4-10	Rows or broadcast	1½-2	Spring, 6-8 weeks after planting (when 4-6" high)	Late fall, because not killed by mild frost	20-25	Although not a legume, rape is nearly equal to alfalfa as a swine pasture. It is palatable to pigs. *(Continued)*

Footnotes on last page of table.

(Continued)

TABLE 9-1 (Continued)

Crop	Variety	When to Plant	Seeding Rate/Acre, Lbs.	Method of Planting	Time Elapsing After Planting, Before Pasturing, Months	Time of Use (or grazing season) Start	End	No. Full-fed Growing-Finishing Pigs /Acre[2]	Adaptation and Other Comments
Rape (Continued)									It can be grown easily and at low cost. In the northern areas, rape is frequently seeded with one of the cereals (commonly oats) and field peas. If grazed when wet, rape sometimes causes blistering or sunscalding, especially with white hogs or hogs with white markings or spots. Rape is subject to destruction by plant lice or aphids.
Red Clover (Even with the increasing popularity of certain other legumes, red clover still remains one of the great legumes of the world.)	Kenland Dollard Lakeland Local common	Spring (commonly seeded on winter grain in the spring)	8-10	Broadcast or drill	4	When 6-8" high	Late fall, but allow 4-6" of growth to remain with first yr. red clover.	10-15	Requires well-drained, fairly rich soil that has plenty of lime. Where adapted, ranks next to ladino and alfalfa as a pasture crop for swine. Later spring growth and lower yield than alfalfa. Red clover-grass mixtures are excellent for swine pastures.
Rye	Balbo Abruzzi Rosen (northern section) Adapted varieties (northern section)	Fall, from Aug. 1 to Dec. 1	85-170	Broadcast or drill	1-2	Late fall	Until covered by snow, and again in early spring	12-14	Late summer or early fall seeded rye is best used as a winter and early spring swine pasture for (1) growing-finishing fall pigs, (2) fall bred sows, (3) early farrowed spring pigs, or (4) lactating sows. For desirable winter pasture, rye should be seeded in the late summer, thus allowing for ample growth prior to cold weather. Rye is seldom used for winter pasture in the northern part of the area.
Soybeans (Records of the culture of soybeans—the ancient (Continued)	Adapted varieties	May to July	60-120	Rows or drill	1½-2	When plants are 6-8" high	Until crop is consumed	12-15	For swine pastures, soybeans are less valuable than alfalfa, the clovers, or rape. (Continued)

Footnotes on last page of table.

(Continued)

TABLE 9-1 (Continued)

Crop	Variety	When to Plant	Seeding Rate/Acre, Lbs.	Method of Planting	Time Elapsing After Planting, Before Pasturing, Months	Time of Use (or grazing season)		No. Full-fed Growing-Finishing Pigs/Acre[2]	Adaptation and Other Comments
						Start	End		
Soybeans (Continued) bean of the Orient—in China go back more than 4,700 yrs. Today it is a major U.S. crop.)									They should either be grown in rows or drilled with adequate spacing to allow hogs to move through them with a minimum of trampling damage. They require warm weather for rapid growth.
Sudangrass (Sudangrass was discovered and introduced into U.S. from Africa in 1909.)	Sweet Tift Piper Greenleaf	May to July (about 2 weeks after corn planting time is best)	20-30	Broadcast or drill	1½-2	July 15 (6" high)	Late fall, until frost	15-20	Sudangrass is a rank-growing, warm-weather annual plant, palatable to swine. Where the growth is normal and not checked by drought or frost, there is little or no danger of prussic acid poisoning. Anyway, swine usually are not affected.
Sweetclover (a roadside weed 40 yrs. ago, but now a prominent U.S. legume, used chiefly for pasture and soil improvement)	Biennial White (Spanish and Evergreen) Biennial Yellow (Madrid)	Early spring	10-15	Broadcast or drill	3-4	When 4-6" high	Oct. 1, with first year sweetclover	15-20	Where adapted, ladino, alfalfa, red clover, and rape are preferred to sweetclover as swine pastures, because of their greater palatability and longer grazing season. With biennial sweetclover, the first year's growth is much superior to the second year's growth for swine pasture. May be fitted easily into established cropping systems. Sweetclover-grass mixtures are frequently used for swine pastures. Clipping at intervals may be necessary in order to alleviate coarse woody stems.
Winter wheat	Adapted varieties	Spring or fall (Fly-free varieties may be seeded in Aug.)	90	Broadcast or drill	1-2	Late fall or spring	June 1	10-12	Some northern Corn Belt swine producers spring seed Peruvian alfalfa with winter wheat. Ordinarily it furnishes reasonably good grazing after the spring sown winter wheat is gone. Peruvian alfalfa does not live through the winter where temperatures *(Continued)*

Footnotes on last page of table.

(Continued)

TABLE 9-1 (Continued)

Crop	Variety	When to Plant	Seeding Rate/Acre, Lbs.	Method of Planting	Time Elapsing After Planting, Before Pasturing, Months	Time of Use (or grazing season) Start	Time of Use (or grazing season) End	No. Full-fed Growing-Finishing Pigs /Acre[2]	Adaptation and Other Comments
Winter Wheat (Continued)									drop much below 10 degrees above zero. Wheat is seldom used for winter pasture in the northern part of the area.
CROPS FOR HOGGING-DOWN Corn	Adapted hybrids	Spring	8-16	Rows	3-5	When well dented	60 days after turning hogs into the field	An acre of 50 bu. corn will provide about 30 days feed for 15-17 pigs weighing 75-100 lbs. or for 8-12 pigs weighing 100-200 lbs.	The practice of hogging-down corn decreased with the advent of the mechanical corn picker. Soybeans or rape are sometimes planted with corn for hogging-down, or a pasture is provided adjacent to the corn field. Unless the price of corn is very low in relation to the price of protein supplements, it will pay to (1) self-feed a supplement where corn alone is available, or (2) hand-feed ¼ to 1/3 lb. of supplement per head daily to pigs having access to a supplemental crop grown in or adjacent to the corn.
Soybeans	Adapted varieties	May to July	60-120	Rows or drill	4¼-5	When the beans are developed	60 days after turning hogs into the field	An acre of 25 bu. soybeans will produce 300-450 lbs. of pork	Swine will make excellent gains in hogging-down soybeans, but soft pork will be produced. Because of the soft pork problem and other limitations, soybeans are usually harvested and sold as cash crop.

[1]The author gratefully acknowledges the helpful suggestions of the following authorities who reviewed the General Recommendations for Planting and Grazing Pasture Crops for Swine in the Corn Belt and North Central States: Dr. A. R. Schmid, Division of Agronomy, University of Minnesota, St. Paul, Minn.; and Dr. H. W. Jones, Department of Animal Husbandry, Purdue University, Lafayette, Ind.
[2]Carrying capacity will vary according to supplemental feeding of swine, thickness of the stand, soil type, soil fertility, rainfall, temperature, etc.
[3]Bromegrass may be sown in mixtures with alfalfa, sweetclover, red clover, or ladino; singly or in combination.

TABLE 9-2

GENERAL RECOMMENDATIONS FOR PLANTING AND GRAZING PASTURE CROPS FOR SWINE IN THE SOUTH[1]

Crop[2]	Variety	When to Plant	Seeding Rate/Acre, Lbs.	Method of Planting	Time Elapsing After Planting Before Pasturing, Months	Time of Use (or grazing season)		No. Full-fed Growing-Finishing Pigs[3] /Acre	Adaptation and Other Comments
						Start	End		
Alfalfa (the most important and most widely distributed U.S. forage crop)	Buffalo Williamsburg Atlantic Narragansett Cody Dupuits	Spring or fall	20	Broadcast or drill	4-6	When 6-8" high	Late fall, but allow 6-8" of growth to remain	15-20	Where soils are sufficiently sweet. Cannot tolerate poorly drained soils. It provides palatable, nutritious forage over a long grazing season, from early spring until late fall. Alfalfa-grass mixtures are frequently used for swine pastures. Rotational grazing will prevent rapid depletion of the stand.
Bermudagrass	Coastal Midland Greenfield	Early spring	1-2 lbs., or roots	Coastal Bermuda, which is seedless, is propagated by transplanting roots, which are set out 2 ft. apart	2nd year	June 1, or 2nd year	Nov. 1	10-12	Bermudagrass provides a short grazing season for swine, starting late in the spring. Bermudagrass, lespedeza, white clover, and/or ladino are often seeded together for swine pasture.
Cowpeas	Whippoorwill Iron New Era Chinese Red	May to July	60-180	Rows or drill	1½-2	When 6-8" high	Until crop is consumed	12-15	Where adapted, alfalfa, the clovers, rape, and soybeans are superior to cowpeas as a swine pasture. Cowpeas will succeed under a greater diversity of conditions than soybeans or velvet beans. Sometimes cowpeas are grown with corn or sorghum for hogging-down.
Crimson clover	Dixie Auburn Chief	Fall	20	Broadcast or drill	2-4	When 4-6" high	May-June	20	May be seeded with adapted small grain or ryegrass. Winter annual; a very excellent producer especially with small grain.

Footnotes on last page of table.

(Continued)

TABLE 9-2 (Continued)

Crop[2]	Variety	When to Plant	Seeding Rate/Acre, Lbs.	Method of Planting	Time Elapsing After Planting Before Pasturing, Months	Time of Use (or grazing season) Start	Time of Use (or grazing season) End	No. Full-fed Growing-Finishing Pigs /Acre[3]	Adaptation and Other Comments
Kudzu		December to April	400-600 roots/acre	New fields of Kudzu are established from root runners, cuttings, or from seedling plants	May be lightly grazed 2nd year, but preferable to delay grazing until 3rd year	After once established, begin pasturing in May or June	Frost or even later	20-25	Kudzu is an excellent plant for erosion control on hillsides and gullies, but it is decreasing as a swine pasture. Avoid overgrazing Kudzu.
Ladino or Louisiana Giant white clover (a large type of white clover first found in Italy)	Ladino Louisiana white	Spring or fall	2-3	Broadcast or drill	3-6	When 4-6" high	Summer to fall, but allow 3-5" of growth to remain	20-25	Where adapted, ladino clover is superior to alfalfa as a swine pasture. Will last 3 to 5 years in pasture. Ladino-grass mixtures are frequently used for swine pastures.
Lespedeza	Kobe Korean	Early spring	Kobe: 40 Korean: 25	Broadcast or drill	2-3	When 4-6" high	Early fall to frost (Oct.)		An annual which reseeds itself. Will grow on poor acid soils. Less palatable to swine than alfalfa or ladino. Not ready for early spring but grows in summer.
Oats	Adapted varieties	Spring or fall	90	Broadcast or drill	2-3	When 6-8" high	Spring (Feb.)	10-15	Spring oats are a good pasture while they last, but pasture period is short. Winter oats provide pasture from Nov. to May.
Rape	Dwarf Essex	Spring or fall	4-10	Drill or broadcast	1½-2	Summer, fall, or early spring— when 6-8" high	Until crop is consumed	20-25	Although not a legume, rape is nearly equal to alfalfa as a swine pasture. It is palatable to pigs. It can be grown easily. In the South, rape is sometimes planted in September or October for use as a late winter and early spring swine pasture (Jan. to May). If grazed when wet, rape some- (Continued)

(Continued)

TABLE 9-2 (Continued)

Crop[2]	Variety	When to Plant	Seeding Rate/Acre, Lbs.	Method of Planting	Time Elapsing After Planting Before Pasturing, Months	Time of Use (or grazing season) Start	Time of Use (or grazing season) End	No. Full-fed Growing-Finishing Pigs /Acre[3]	Adaptation and Other Comments
Rape (Continued)									times causes blistering or sunscalding, especially with white hogs or hogs with white markings or spots. Rape is subject to destruction by plant lice or aphids.
Red Clover (Even with the increasing popularity of certain other legumes, red clover still remains one of the great legumes of the world.)	Kenland Louisiana S-1	Fall or spring (commonly seeded on winter grain)	6-10	Broadcast or drill	3-6	When 6-8" high	Late fall and winter, but allow 4-6" of growth to remain with 1st year red clover	10-15	Requires well-drained, fairly rich soil that has medium amounts of lime. Where adapted, ranks next to ladino and alfalfa as a pasture crop for swine. Later spring growth and lower yield than alfalfa. Red clover-grass mixtures are excellent for swine pastures.
Rye	Balbo Elbon	Late summer or fall	90	Broadcast or drill	2-3	When 6-8" high	Spring	15-20	Late summer or early fall seeded rye is best used as a winter and early spring swine pasture, for (1) growing-finishing fall pigs, (2) fall bred sows, or (3) early-farrowed spring pigs. For desirable winter pasture, rye should be seeded in late summer, thus allowing for ample growth prior to cold weather.
Soybeans (Records of the culture of soybeans—the ancient bean of the Orient —in China go back more than 4,700 years. Today it is a major U.S. crop.)	Adapted varieties	May to June	60-120	Rows or drill	1½-2	When plants are 12-24" high (summer)	Until crop is consumed	12-15	For swine pastures, soybeans are less valuable than alfalfa, the clovers, or rape. They should either be grown in rows or drilled with adequate spacing to allow hogs to move through them with a minimum of tramping damage. They require warm weather for rapid growth.

Footnotes on last page of table.

(Continued)

TABLE 9-2 (Continued)

Crop[2]	Variety	When to Plant	Seeding Rate/Acre, Lbs.	Method of Planting	Time Elapsing After Planting Before Pasturing, Months	Time of Use (or grazing season)		No. Full-fed Growing-Finishing Pigs /Acre[3]	Adaptation and Other Comments
						Start	End		
Sudangrass (Sudangrass was discovered and introduced into U.S. from Africa in 1909.)	Sweet Piper Lahoma Green leaf	March to July (about 2 weeks after corn planting time is best)	30-45	Broadcast or drill	1-1½	April-July (12-15" high)	Late fall until frost	15-20	Sudangrass is a warm weather annual plant, palatable to swine. Sudangrass-cowpea or Sudangrass-soybean mixtures are frequently used for swine pastures.
Vetch (best known as an important winter cover crop in the southeastern states)	Hairy	Mostly fall sown (Sept and Oct.)	20-30	Broadcast or drill	3-5	January to March	April to May	12-15	Vetch supplies late winter and early spring swine pasture. For pasture, it is usually seeded with a small grain crop.
Winter wheat	Adapted varieties	Fall	90-120	Broadcast or drill	2-3	When 6-8" high	Spring	10-12	Wheat is more palatable to hogs than rye, but it provides less forage per acre. Rye will make earlier pasture than wheat, but wheat will be available later in the spring. Winter wheat can be grazed lightly by hogs in the fall and early spring without lowering the yield of grain.
CROPS FOR HOGGING-DOWN									
Chufas		April to June		Rows		Fall (over winter grazing)	Spring		Chufas should be supplemented properly with proteins and minerals. They produce soft pork. Currently, few chufas are grown for swine.
Corn	Adapted hybrids	Spring	8-16	Rows	3-6	When well dented	60 days after turning hogs into field	An acre of 50 bu. corn will provide about 30 days feed for 15-17 pigs *(Continued)*	The practice of hogging-down decreased with the advent of the mechanical corn picker. Cowpeas, velvet beans, or soybeans are sometimes grown with corn *(Continued)*

Footnotes on last page of table.

(Continued)

TABLE 9-2 (Continued)

Crop[2]	Variety	When to Plant	Seeding Rate/Acre, Lbs.	Method of Planting	Time Elapsing After Planting Before Pasturing, Months	Time of Use (or grazing season) Start	Time of Use (or grazing season) End	No. Full-fed Growing-Finishing Pigs /Acre[3]	Adaptation and Other Comments
Corn (Continued)								weighing 75 to 100 lbs., or for 8-12 pigs weighing 100-200 pounds	for hogging-down, or corn and peanuts planted in alternate rows; but the yield of corn and pounds of pork produced per acre are lowered. Sometimes pasture is provided adjacent to the cornfield. Unless the price of corn is very low in relation to the price of protein supplement, it will pay to (1) self-feed a supplement where corn alone is available, or (2) hand-feed 1/4 to 1/3 pound of supplement per head daily to pigs having access to a supplemental crop grown in or adjacent to the corn.
Peanuts	Spanish (for fall hogging-off) Runner (for winter hogging-off)	Late spring	30-50	Rows		Fall or winter depending upon the variety of peanuts	Late fall or early spring, depending on the variety of peanuts	An acre of 25 to 30 bu. peanuts will produce 300 to 350 lbs. of pork	Peanuts are frequently planted with corn when the crop is to be hogged-off. Provide free access to salt and a calcium supplement. Peanuts will produce soft pork.
Sorghum	Adapted varieties	Spring	6″ rows; 20-24, broadcast	Rows or broadcast	5-5½	When grain is developed	60 days after turning hogs into field	An acre of 30 bu. sorghum will produce 300-400 lbs. of pork.	The grain sorghums are generally grown in areas where climatic and soil conditions are less favorable to corn. Since feeding trials show that the threshed grain sorghums are worth about 90 percent as much as shelled corn, it is reasonable to assume that, where the acre yields are comparable, the hogging-down value of the two crops is of about the same relationship. Cowpeas, velvet beans, or soybeans are sometimes grown with grain sorghum for hogging-down, or grain sorghum and peanuts are planted in alternate rows; but the *(Continued)*

(Continued)

Footnotes on last page of table.

TABLE 9-2 (Continued)

Crop[2]	Variety	When to Plant	Seeding Rate/Acre, Lbs.	Method of Planting	Time Elapsing After Planting Before Pasturing, Months	Time of Use (or grazing season)		No. Full-fed Growing-Finishing Pigs/Acre[3]	Adaptation and Other Comments
						Start	End		
Sorghum (*Continued*)									yield of sorghum and pounds of pork produced per acre are lowered. Sometimes pasture is provided adjacent to the grain sorghum field. Unless the price of grain sorghum is very low in relation to the price of protein supplement, it will pay to (1) self-feed a supplement where sorghum alone is available or (2) hand-feed 1/4 to 1/3 lb. of protein feed to pigs having access to a supplemental crop in or adjacent to the grain sorghum.
Soybeans	Adapted varieties	Late spring	60-90	Rows or drill	5-5½	When the beans are developed	60 days after turning hogs into field	An acre of 25 bu soybeans will produce 300-450 lbs. pork	Swine will make excellent gains in hogging-down soybeans, but soft pork will be produced. Because of the soft pork problem and other limitations, soybeans are usually harvested and sold as a cash crop.
Sweet potatoes				Rows		Late fall	Early spring	An acre of 180 bu. sweet potatoes will provide about 30 days grazing for 7-10 pigs weighing 100 to 200 lbs.	Sweet potatoes can be grown on soil that is sandy and too thin for good corn production. Best results are usually obtained when pigs grazing sweet potatoes are given one-third to one-half of a grain ration in addition to a protein supplement of animal or marine origin and a mineral mixture. Generally it is most profitable to sell sweet potatoes as a cash crop, using swine to glean the fields or consume the culls.
Velvet beans	Florida Georgia Alabama	Spring after danger of frost	4-12 when planted with corn	Rows with corn are most popular	4-6	Late fall, when beans are mature (Nov.)	Early spring (February)	An acre of 20 to 25 bu. velvet beans will produce 250- (*Continued*)	Velvet beans are a warm weather plant. They are usually planted with a supporting plant such as corn, (*Continued*)

TABLE 9-2 (Continued)

Crop[2]	Variety	When to Plant	Seeding Rate/Acre, Lbs.	Method of Planting	Time Elapsing After Planting Before Pasturing, Months	Time of Use (or grazing season)		No. Full-fed Growing-Finishing Pigs /Acre[3]	Adaptation and Other Comments
						Start	End		
Velvet beans (Continued)								300 lbs. pork	pearl millet, Japanese sugarcane or sorghum. Swine do not do well on velvet beans alone.

[1]The author gratefully acknowledges the helpful suggestions of the following authorities who reviewed the General Recommendations for Planting and Grazing Pasture Crops for Swine in the South: Dr. Ethan C. Holt, Department of Agronomy, Agricultural and Mechanical College of Texas, College Station, Tex.; and Dr. Charles S. Hobbs and Dr. Harold Smith, Department of Animal Husbandry and Veterinary Science, University of Tennessee, Knoxville, Tenn.

[2]Other pasture crops—generally seeded in mixtures—sometimes used for swine pastures in the South, are: pearl or cattal millet, Johnsongrass (not seeded, but where present), sweetclover, Alfa or Kentucky 31 fescue, and Dallisgrass.

[3]Carrying capacity will vary according to supplemental feeding of swine, thickness of the stand, soil type, soil fertility, rainfall, temperature, etc.

TABLE 9-3
GENERAL RECOMMENDATIONS FOR PLANTING AND GRAZING PASTURE CROPS FOR SWINE IN THE ATLANTIC COAST STATES[1]

Crop[2]	Variety	When to Plant	Seeding Rate/Acre, Lbs.	Method of Planting	Time Elapsing After Planting Before Pasturing, Months	Time of Use (or grazing season)		No. Full-fed Growing-Finishing Pigs /Acre[3]	Adaptation and Other Comments
						Start	End		
Alfalfa (the most important and most widely distributed U.S. forage crop)	Atlantic Narragansett Buffalo Dupuits Vernal Williamsburg Southern common (in Cottonbelt) Hairy Peruvian (in Cottonbelt)	Spring or fall	15-25	Broadcast or drill	4-6	When 8-12'' high	Late summer or fall, but allow 6-8'' of growth to remain	15-20	Where soils are sufficiently sweet. Cannot tolerate poorly drained soils. It provides palatable, nutritious forage over a long grazing season from early spring until late fall. Alfalfa-grass mixtures are frequently used for swine pastures. Responds to boron in addition to phosphorus and potassium on some soils.
Bermudagrass (for South Atlantic states)	Coastal or Suwannee Bermuda, and other strains	Early spring	5-10 lbs. or sprigs	Coastal Bermuda which is seedless is propagated by transplanting stolons, which are set out about 2' apart	2-4	When 6-8'' high	Nov. 15	10-12	Bermudagrass provides a short grazing season for swine, starting late in the spring. Bermudagrass, lespedeza, white clover, and/or ladino are often seeded together for swine pasture.
Cowpeas	Whippoorwill Iron New Era	May to July	60-180	Rows or drills	1½-2	When plants are 4-6'' high	Until crop is consumed	12-15	Where adapted, alfalfa, the clovers, rape, and soybeans are superior to cowpeas as a swine pasture. Cowpeas will succeed under a greater diversity of conditions than soybeans or velvet beans. Sometimes cowpeas are grown with corn or sorghum for hogging-down.

Footnotes on last page of table.

(Continued)

TABLE 9-3 (Continued)

Crop[2]	Variety	When to Plant	Seeding Rate/Acre, Lbs.	Method of Planting	Time Elapsing After Planting Before Pasturing, Months	Time of Use (or grazing season) Start	Time of Use (or grazing season) End	No. Full-fed Growing-Finishing Pigs/Acre[3]	Adaptation and Other Comments
Crimson clover (for South Atlantic states)	Dixie Auburn	Fall	12-20	Broadcast or drill	2-3	Jan.	May	10-15	A winter annual, which makes very good growth during winter months. Associates well with cereal grains, and as such is one of the highest producing pasture crops during the winter season.
Kudzu	Adapted strains	Dec. to April	400-600 roots per acre	New fields of Kudzu are established from root runners, from cuttings, or from seedling plants	May be lightly grazed 2nd year, but preferable to delay grazing until 3rd year	After once established, begin pasturing in May or June	Frost or even later	20-25	Kudzu is an excellent plant for erosion control on hillside and gullies; but it is decreasing as a swine pasture. Avoid overgrazing Kudzu.
Ladino or Louisiana Giant white clover (for South; a larger type of white clover first found growing in Italy)		Spring or fall	2-6	Broadcast or drill	3-5	When 6" high	Late fall, but allow 3-5" of growth to remain. Season long in South	20-25	Fall seed in Fla., Ga., S.C., and N.C. Where adapted, ladino clover is superior to alfalfa as a swine pasture. Will last 3 to 5 years in pasture. Ladino-grass mixtures are frequently used for swine pastures, although ladino alone is preferable. Also, a ladino-alfalfa mixture is preferred to ladino above in certain areas.
Lespedeza (for Mid- and South-Atlantic States)	Climax Kobe Korean Sericea	Early spring	20-30 unhulled seed	Drill or broadcast	2-3	Late spring or summer	Early fall	10-12	An annual which reseeds itself. Will grow on poor acid soils. Less palatable to swine than alfalfa or ladino. Not ready for early spring grazing, but excellent in summertime.
Millet	Starr Cahi	Apr. to July	15-20	Drill or broadcast	1-1½	18"	Until frost	25-30	In North Carolina, millet is preferred to Sudangrass.

Footnotes on last page of table.

(Continued)

TABLE 9-3 (Continued)

Crop[2]	Variety	When to Plant	Seeding Rate/Acre, Lbs.	Method of Planting	Time Elapsing After Planting Before Pasturing, Months	Time of Use (or grazing season) Start	Time of Use (or grazing season) End	No. Full-fed Growing-Finishing Pigs /Acre[3]	Adaptation and Other Comments
Oats	Adapted varieties	Spring, late summer, or fall	48-120	Broadcast or drill	2-3	Fall (including winter grazing)	Spring	10-15	Oats are a good pasture while they last, but pasture period is short. In the Deep South, oats make an excellent winter pasture for swine.
Orchardgrass (for North Atlantic)	Adapted strain	Spring or fall	6-12	Broadcast or drill	4-5	When 6-8" high	Late fall	10-15	Usually seeded in a mixture with a legume. More useful as a pasture in such a mixture. Adapted to medium fertile to fertile soil.
Rape	Dwarf Essex	March to June in North; fall and winter in South	4-10	Rows or broadcast	1½-2	Spring, 6-8 weeks after planting (when 6-10" high)	Late fall, because not killed by mild frost	20-25	Although not a legume, rape is nearly equal to alfalfa as a swine pasture. It is palatable to pigs. It can be grown easily and at low cost. In the northern areas, rape is frequently seeded with one of the cereals (commonly oats) and field peas. If grazed when wet, rape sometimes causes blistering or sunscalding, especially with white hog or hogs with white markings or spots. Rape is subject to destruction by plant lice or aphids.
Red clover (Even with the increasing popularity of certain other legumes, red clover still remains one of the great legumes of the world.)	Kenland Pennscott Dollard Louisiana red Nolin red Chesapeake Lakeland	Spring (in North), or fall (in South); commonly seeded on winter grain	10-15	Broadcast or drill	2-3	When 6-8" high	Late fall, but allow 4-6" of growth to remain with first yr. red clover. Winter months in South	10-15	Requires well-drained fairly rich soil that has medium amount of lime. Where adapted, ranks next to ladino and alfalfa as a pasture crop for swine. Later spring growth and lower yield than alfalfa. Red clover-grass mixtures are excellent for swine pastures.

Footnotes on last page of table.

(Continued)

TABLE 9-3 (Continued)

Crop[2]	Variety	When to Plant	Seeding Rate/Acre, Lbs.	Method of Planting	Time Elapsing After Planting Before Pasturing, Months	Time of Use (or grazing season)		No. Full-fed Growing-Finishing Pigs/Acre[3]	Adaptation and Other Comments
						Start	End		
Rye	Rosen (in North) Balbo (in South) Abruzzi (in South) Gator (in South)	Fall	90-120	Broadcast or drill	1½-2	Fall (including winter grazing)	Spring (including winter grazing)	15-20	Late summer seeded rye is best used as a winter and early spring swine pasture, for (1) growing-finishing fall pigs, (2) fall bred sows, or (3) early-farrowed spring pigs. For desirable winter pasture, rye should be seeded in the late summer or fall, thus allowing for ample growth prior to cold weather.
Soybeans (Records of the culture of soybeans—the ancient bean of the Orient—in China go back more than 4,700 years. Today, it is a major U.S. crop.)	Biloxi Locally adapted varieties	April to July	60-120	Rows or drill	1½-2	When plants are 6-8" high	Until crop is consumed	12-15	For swine pastures, soybeans are less valuable than alfalfa, the clovers, or rape. They should either be grown in rows or drilled with adequate spacing to allow hogs to move through them with a minimum of tramping damage. They require warm weather for rapid growth.
Sudangrass (Sudangrass was first discovered and introduced into the U.S. from Africa in 1909.)	Sweet Tift Piper	April to July	15-20	Broadcast or drill	1-1½	May-July (18-24" high)	Late fall, until frost	25-30	Sudangrass is a rank-growing warm weather annual plant, palatable to swine. Where the growth is normal and not checked by drought or frost, there is little or no danger of prussic acid poisoning. Anyway, swine are not usually affected. Millet is replacing Sudan in some areas.
CROPS FOR HOGGING-DOWN Corn	Adapted hybrids	Spring	8-16	Rows	3-5	When well dented	60 days after turning hogs into the field	An acre of 50 bu. corn will provide about 30 days feed for 15-17 pigs weighing 75-100 lbs. or for *(Continued)*	The practice of hogging-down corn decreased somewhat with the advent of the mechanical corn picker, but it is still a common practice in the Atlantic Coast States. Cowpeas, velvet beans, or soybeans are sometimes grown with corn *(Continued)*

Footnotes on last page of table.

(Continued)

TABLE 9-3 (Continued)

Crop[2]	Variety	When to Plant	Seeding Rate/Acre, Lbs.	Method of Planting	Time Elapsing After Planting Before Pasturing, Months	Time of Use (or grazing season)		No. Full-fed Growing-Finishing Pigs /Acre[3]	Adaptation and Other Comments
						Start	End		
Corn (Continued)								8-12 pigs weighing 100-200 lbs.	for hogging-down, or corn and peanuts are planted in alternate rows; but the yield of corn and pounds of pork produced per acre are lowered. Unless the price of corn is very low in relation to the price of protein supplement, it will pay to (1) self-feed a supplement where corn alone is available, or (2) hand-feed 1/4 to 1/3 lb. of supplement per head daily to pigs having access to a supplemental crop grown in or adjacent to the corn.
Chufas		April to June	25-30	Rows 2' apart; 12" in rows	5	Fall (over winter grazing)	Spring	An acre of Chufas will produce about 330 lbs. of pork.	Currently, few Chufas are grown for swine. Chufas should be supplemented properly with proteins and minerals. They produce soft pork. Satisfactory for delayed grazing.
Peanuts	Spanish (for summer and fall hogging-off) Runner (for fall and winter hogging-off)	Late spring	35-50	Rows	3½-4½	Fall or winter depending upon the variety of peanuts	Late fall or early spring depending on the variety of peanuts	An acre of 25 to 30 bu. peanuts will produce 300 to 350 lbs. of pork	Peanuts are frequently planted with corn when the crop is to be hogged-off. Provide free access to salt and a calcium supplement. Peanuts will produce soft pork. Graze when nuts are mature.
Sorghum	Adapted varieties	Late spring	8 in rows; 25-35 broadcast	Rows or broadcast	3-4½	When mature	60 days after turning hogs into field	An acre of 30 bu. sorghum will produce 300 to 400 lbs. of pork.	The grain sorghums are generally grown in areas where climatic and soil conditions are less favorable to corn. Since feeding trials show that the threshed grain sorghums are worth about 90 percent as much

(Continued)

Footnotes on last page of table.

(Continued)

TABLE 9-3.(Continued)

Crop[2]	Variety	When to Plant	Seeding Rate/Acre, Lbs.	Method of Planting	Time Elapsing After Planting Before Pasturing, Months	Time of Use (or grazing season) Start	Time of Use (or grazing season) End	No. Full-fed Growing-Finishing Pigs /Acre[3]	Adaptation and Other Comments
Sorghum (Continued)									as shelled corn, it is reasonable to assume that, where the acre yields are comparable, the hogging-down value of the two crops is about the same relationship. Cowpeas, velvet beans, or soybeans are sometimes grown with grain sorghum for hogging-down, or grain sorghum and peanuts are planted in alternate rows; but the yield of sorghum and pounds of pork produced per acre are lowered. Sometimes pasture is provided adjacent to the grain sorghum field. Unless the price of grain sorghum is very low in relation to the price of protein supplement, it will pay to (1) self-feed a supplement where sorghum alone is available or (2) hand-feed 1/4 to 1/3 lb. of supplement per head daily to pigs having access to a supplemental crop grown in or adjacent to the grain sorghum.
Soybeans	Adapted varieties	Late spring to early summer	60-120	Rows or drill	4½-5	When beans are developed	60 days after turning hogs into field	An acre of 25 bu. soybeans will produce 300-450 lbs. pork	Swine will make excellent gains in hogging-down soybeans, but soft pork will be produced. Because the soft pork problem and other limitations, soybeans are usually harvested and sold as a cash crop.
Sweet potatoes				Rows		Late fall	Early spring	An acre of 180 bu. sweet potatoes will provide about 30 days grazing for 7 to 10 pigs weighing (*Continued*)	Sweet potatoes can be grown on soil that is sandy and too thin for good corn production. Best results are usually obtained when pigs grazing sweet potatoes are given 1/3 to 1/2 of a grain ration in addition to a protein (*Continued*)

Footnotes on last page of table.

(Continued)

TABLE 9-3 (Continued)

Crop[2]	Variety	When to Plant	Seeding Rate/Acre, Lbs.	Method of Planting	Time Elapsing After Planting Before Pasturing, Months	Time of Use (or grazing season)		No. Full-fed Growing-Finishing Pigs /Acre[3]	Adaptation and Other Comments
						Start	End		
Sweet potatoes (Continued)								100 to 200 lbs. and produce about 450 lbs. of pork.	supplement of animal or marine origin and a mineral mixture. Generally it is most profitable to sell sweet potatoes as a cash crop, using swine to glean the fields or consume the culls.
Velvet beans (Southern states only)	Florida Georgia Alabama (or other adapted variety)	Spring after danger of frost	4-12 when planted with corn	Rows with corn are most popular	6	Late fall, when beans are mature (Nov.)	Early spring (Feb.)	An acre of 20-25 bu. velvet beans will produce 250-300 lbs. of pork	Velvet beans are a warm weather plant. They are usually planted with a supporting plant, such as corn, pearl millet, Japanese sugarcane or sorghum. Swine do not do well on velvet beans alone.

[1]The author gratefully acknowledges the helpful suggestions of the following authorities who reviewed the General Recommendations for Planting and Grazing Pasture Crops for Swine in the Atlantic Coast States: Dr. E. R. Barrick, Department of Animal Industry, and Dr. W. W. Woodhouse, Department of Soils, University of North Carolina, Raleigh, N.C.; Dr. T. J. Cunha, Department of Animal Husbandry and Nutrition, and Dr. G. B. Killinger, Department of Agronomy, University of Florida, Gainesville, Fla.; Professor W. Allen Cowan, Department of Animal Husbandry, University of Connecticut, Storrs, Conn.; and Mr. Ralph Donaldson, Extension Agronomist, University of Massachusetts, Amherst, Mass.

[2]Other pasture crops—generally seeded in mixtures—sometimes used for swine pastures in the Southern Atlantic Coast States are: pearl or cattail millet, Johnsongrass (not seeded, but where present), Alta or Kentucky 31 fescue, and Dallisgrass.

[3]Carrying capacity will vary according to supplemental feeding of swine, thickness of the stand, soil type, soil fertility, rainfall, temperature, etc.

TABLE 9-4

GENERAL RECOMMENDATIONS FOR PLANTING AND GRAZING
PASTURE CROPS FOR SWINE IN THE WEST[1]

Crop	Variety	When to Plant	Seeding Rate/Acre, Lbs.	Method of Planting	Time Elapsing After Planting Before Pasturing, Months	Time of Use (or grazing season)		No. Full-fed Growing-Finishing Pigs /Acre[2]	Adaptation and Other Comments
						Start	End		
Alfalfa (the most important and most widely distributed U.S. forage crop)	Ladak Vernal Ranger Buffalo (Ore. and South) Grimm (Mont. and northern states) Southern Commons, Moapa or Caliverde (for New Mex., Ariz., and Cal.)	Spring or fall	6-20	Broadcast or drill	4-5	When 6-8" high	Late fall, but allow 6-8" of growth to remain	15-20	Where soils are sufficiently sweet. Cannot tolerate poorly drained soils. It provides palatable, nutritious forage over a long grazing season, from early spring until late fall. Alfalfa-grass mixtures are frequently used for swine pastures.
Birdsfoot trefoil	Cascade Empire Italian	Spring and fall	6	Drill or broadcast	Spring of 2nd year	When 6-8" high	Late fall, but allow 4-6" of growth to remain with 1st year bird's-foot trefoil	15-18	Well adapted to soils of lower pH and poorer drainage than alfalfa. Long-lived plant, 15 to 20 years. Highly nutritious; second only to ladino in ease of management. Slow to become established. Will live with bluegrass better than any other legume.
Bromegrass (or preferably bromegrass-legume mixtures)	Mancher Lincoln Southland	Spring or late summer	Mixture[3] 8 lbs. bromegrass, 4-6 lbs. alfalfa	Drill or broadcast	4-5	When 6-8" high	Late fall, but allow 6-8" of growth to remain	15-20	Bromegrass, a palatable perennial pasture crop, is sometimes used as a swine pasture. It will endure heavy grazing and tramping. It is not as valuable a swine pasture as alfalfa, where the latter is adapted. Bromegrass-alfalfa mixtures are equal to straight alfalfa for swine pastures.

Footnotes on last page of table.

(Continued)

TABLE 9-4 (Continued)

Crop	Variety	When to Plant	Seeding Rate/Acre, Lbs.	Method of Planting	Time Elapsing After Planting Before Pasturing, Months	Time of Use (or grazing season)		No. Full-fed Growing-Finishing Pigs/Acre[2]	Adaptation and Other Comments
						Start	End		
Ladino (a large type of white clover first found growing in Italy)	White Canadian Alaska Austrian Winter peas	Spring	2-4	Broadcast or drill	Spring of 2nd year, but frequently may be lightly grazed fall of 1st year	When 6-8" high	Late fall, but allow 3-5" of growth to remain	20-25	Where adapted, ladino clover is superior to alfalfa as a swine pasture. Will last 3-5 years in pasture. Ladino-grass mixtures are frequently used for swine pastures.
Peas		Spring	120	Drill	1-1½	April 20-May 10	Aug.	12-14	For annual crop program in the northern states. Provide an excellent pasture over a short period. Varieties equal in feed value.
Red clover (Even with the increasing popularity of certain other legumes, red clover still remains one of the great legumes of the world.)	Kenland[1] Pennscott	Spring or fall (commonly seeded on winter grain in the spring)	5-10	Broadcast or drill	4	When 6-8" high	Late fall, but allow 4-6" of growth to remain with 1st year red clover	10-15	Requires well-drained fairly rich soil that has medium amounts of lime. Where adapted, ranks next to ladino and alfalfa as a pasture crop for swine. Later spring growth and lower yield than alfalfa. Red clover-grass mixtures are excellent for swine pastures.
Rye	Abruzzi Balbo Rosen (northern section) Merced (southern section)	Late summer or fall	85-170	Broadcast or drill	1½-2	March 15	July 1	12-14	Fall seeded rye is best used as a winter and early spring swine pasture for (1) growing-finishing fall pigs, (2) fall bred sows, or (3) early-farrowed spring pigs. For desirable winter pasture, rye should be seeded in the late summer, thus allowing for ample growth prior to cold weather.
Sudangrass (Sudangrass was discovered and introduced into U.S. from Africa in 1909.)	Sweet Piper	May to July (about 2 weeks after corn planting time is best)	20-30	Broadcast or drill	1-1½	May-July (15" high)	Late fall, until frost	15-20	Sudangrass is a rank-growing, warm-weather annual plant, palatable to swine. Where the growth is normal and not checked by drought or frost, there is little or no danger of prussic acid poisoning. Anyway, swine are not usually affected.

Footnotes on last page of table.

(Continued)

TABLE 9-4 (Continued)

Crop	Variety	When to Plant	Seeding Rate/Acre, Lbs.	Method of Planting	Time Elapsing After Planting Before Pasturing, Months	Time of Use (or grazing season) Start	Time of Use (or grazing season) End	No. Full-fed Growing-Finishing Pigs/Acre[2]	Adaptation and Other Comments
Sweetclover (a roadside weed 40 yrs. ago, but now a prominent U.S. legume, used chiefly for pasture and soil improvement)	White sweetclover Yellow sweetclover Hubam (annual)	Early spring	10-15	Broadcast or drill	3-4	When 6-8" high	Sept. with 1st year sweetclover	15-20	Where adapted, ladino, alfalfa, red clover, and rape are preferred to sweetclover as swine pastures, because of their greater palatability and longer grazing season. With biennial sweetclover, the first year's growth is much superior to the second year's growth for swine pasture. May be fitted easily into established cropping systems. Sweetclover-grass mixtures are frequently used for swine pastures. Clipping at intervals may be necessary in order to alleviate coarse woody stems.
CROPS FOR HOGGING-DOWN Peas, ripe field	Any adapted variety	Early spring	120	Drill	3½	Turn in anytime after pods begin to form	When crop is consumed	About 400 lbs. of pork per acre	Adapted to the Northwest. For best results, provide minerals and a limited amount of grain in addition to the peas.

[1]The author gratefully acknowledges the helpful suggestions of the following authorities who reviewed the General Recommendations for Planting and Grazing Pasture Crops for Swine in the West: Mr. Wade C. Wells, Extension Swine Specialist, University of Idaho, Moscow, Ida.; and Dr. H. Heitman, Jr., Animal Husbandry Department, and Dr. M. L. Peterson, Agronomy Department, University of California, Davis, California.

[2]Carrying capacity will vary according to supplemental feeding of swine, thickness of the stand, soil type, soil fertility, rainfall, temperature, etc.

[3]Bromegrass may be sown in mixtures with alfalfa, sweetclover, red clover, or ladino, singly or in combination. Other adapted grasses can be used with such legumes.

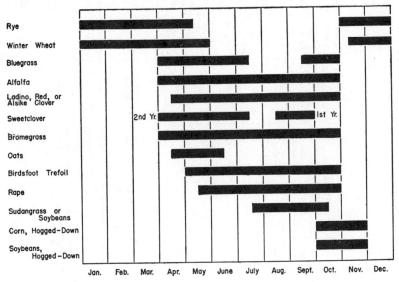

Fig. 9-2. As shown, by selecting the proper combination of crops, year-round grazing can be achieved. For example, 12 months hog pasture may be obtained by using two crops only, rye and ladino clover. (Drawing by R. F. Johnson)

fertility, aids in swine sanitation, lowers cost of pork production, and furnishes a profitable way of salvaging lodged or damaged crops. The practice of hogging-down corn is discussed in Chapter VI. The practice of hogging-off crops is far more prevalent in the southern and southeastern states than any other area. This is due chiefly to (1) the desirable fall and winter hogging-off conditions afforded by the warmer climate, and (2) the abundance of adapted root crops (peanuts, sweet potatoes, chufas, etc.) which are successfully and profitably harvested by swine.

Fig. 9-3. Poland China sows and litters on red clover pasture. (Courtesy, Dr. John F. Lasley, University of Missouri)

Fig. 9-4. A Poland China sow and litter on bluegrass pasture, one of the most widely known grasses in America. (Courtesy, J. C. Allen and Son, West Lafayette, Ind.)

Fig. 9-5. Brood sows on oats, a common overwinter swine pasture in the South. (Courtesy, USDA)

Fig. 9-6. Hampshire pigs grazing kudzu, a valuable pasture crop in the South. (Courtesy, USDA)

Fig. 9-7. Berkshire pigs grazing a rape-oats mixture, a common swine pasture crop in the Atlantic Coast states. (Courtesy, J. C. Allen and Son, West Lafayette, Ind.)

Fig. 9-8. Brood sows on ladino pasture, an excellent legume in the Atlantic Coast states. (Courtesy, J. C. Allen and Son, West Lafayette, Ind.)

Fig. 9-9. Hogs on red clover-grass, a common swine pasture throughout the West. (Courtesy, J. C. Allen and Son, West Lafayette, Ind.)

Fig. 9-10. Sows on alfalfa pasture, the most important and most widely distributed swine pasture in the West. (Courtesy, Dr. H. Heitman, Jr., University of California)

QUESTIONS FOR STUDY AND DISCUSSION

1. List and discuss the advantages and disadvantages of producing hogs on pasture. How do you account for the current trend to confinement rearing of swine by large, highly specialized swine producers?

2. Compute the monetary return that might reasonably be expected from an acre of pasture grazed by hogs versus the return from alternate cropping programs.

3. What are the primary differences between good management of hogs on pasture versus good management of hogs in confinement?

4. Select a specific farm (either your home farm or ranch or one with which your are familiar). Then tell what pastures you would use for swine, and justify your decision. Prepare a chart showing how you could advantageously extend the grazing season.

SELECTED REFERENCES

Title of Publication	Author(s)	Publisher
Crop Production	Richard J. Delorit Henry L. Ahlgren	Prentice-Hall, Inc., Englewood Cliffs, N. J., 1967.
Forages	H. D. Hughes M. E. Heath D. S. Metcalfe	The Iowa University Press, Ames, Ia., 1951.
Forage and Pasture Crops	W. A. Wheeler	D. Van Nostrand Company, New York, N. Y., 1950.
Grass, Yearbook of Agriculture 1948	USDA	Superintendent of Documents, Washington, D. C.
Pasture Book, The	W. R. Thompson	W. R. Thompson, State College, Miss., 1950.
Pork Production	W. W. Smith	The Macmillan Company, New York, N. Y., 1952.
Practical Grassland Management	B. W. Allred	The Interstate Printers & Publishers, Inc., Danville, Ill., 1952.
Swine Feeding and Nutrition	T. J. Cunha	Interscience Publishers, Inc., New York, N. Y., 1957.
Swine Production	W. E. Carroll J. L. Krider F. N. Andrews	McGraw-Hill Book Co., New York, N. Y., 1962.

CHAPTER X

BUILDINGS AND EQUIPMENT FOR SWINE[1]

Contents **Page**

Hog houses and equipment have changed with the shift to
more confinement production, particularly on the larger commer-

_____

[1] The author gratefully acknowledges the helpful suggestions of the
following persons who reviewed this chapter: Prof. Arthur J. Muehling,
Assistant Professor, Department of Agricultural Engineering, University
of Illinois, Urbana, Ill.; Dr. Richard F. Wilson, Professor in Charge of
Swine, The Ohio State University, Columbus, Ohio; and Prof. Jesse T. Bell,
Chairman, Department of Animal Husbandry, Fresno State College, Fresno,
California.

cial establishments. The savings in labor and the improved environment for both hogs and operator are the two major reasons back of this shift. Mechanized equipment and slotted floors are largely responsible for the reduction in labor. This transition was revealed by a survey of Illinois hog producers, reported in 1966, which showed the following:[2]

1. That 35 percent of the producers were feeding in confinement—all or in part, with 13 percent of those using confinement having totally enclosed buildings. Moreover, confinement production and bigness went together; 63 percent of the producers raising over 500 hogs per year reported using confinement as compared with 25 percent in the group producing fewer than 100 hogs per year.

2. That for farrowing houses 46 percent were using central houses only, 24 percent were using both central and portable houses, while 30 percent were using portable houses only.

3. That partially or completely slotted floors were found in 5 percent of the confinement feeding structures and 6 percent of the central farrowing houses. By size of operation, the slats were more common on farms reporting more than 500 head.

A consensus, obtained by the author, of swine authorities on four pertinent points pertaining to swine buildings and equipment follows:

1. **Controlled environment.**—Although more research is needed on the economics of controlled environment, there is no question that such facilities do result in greater rate and efficiency of gains. Also, the biggest returns from controlled environment accrue (a) from eliminating extremes in temperature—when it's below zero or above 85 degrees outside, and (b) to younger animals—baby pigs.

2. **Type of feed facilities.**—A self-feeding regime, with feed moved automatically, is recommended.

3. **Manure handling facilities.**—Pit storage and hauling liquid manure to the fields appears to be the most satisfactory method of handling manure of confinement operations.

4. **Investment in buildings and equipment.**—Here again

---

[2] Moats, Robert H., Burton R. Miller, and George Wangen, *Hog Production Practices*, Ill. Agricultural Statistics, Ill. Cooperative Crop Reporting Service, Ill. Department of Agriculture and U. S. Department of Agriculture, Bul. 66-7, Sept. 1, 1966.

more research is needed as to how much money on a per head per year basis can be invested in buildings and equipment—basically, it gets down to a decision on how much capital can be substituted for labor. Also, when deciding on total investment, consideration needs to be given to (a) how long the person intends to raise hogs, and (b) building depreciation.

The functions and requisites of swine buildings and equipment are similar to those for any other class of livestock with increased emphasis on (1) temperature control—because hogs are so sensitive to extremes of heat and cold, and (2) ventilation, sanitation, automation, and manure disposal—because swine are confined more than other four-footed farm animals.

Naturally, no standard set of buildings and equipment can be expected to be well adapted to such diverse conditions and systems of swine production as exist in the United States. For example, where the winters are long and severe and snow storms are frequent, warmer buildings must be constructed than are necessary in the South, where the temperature seldom gets below freezing and snow storms rarely occur. In presenting the discussions and illustrations that follow, it is intended, therefore, that they be considered as guides only. Detailed plans and specifications for buildings and equipment usually can be obtained through a local architect, county agricultural agent, vocational agriculture instructor, lumber dealer, or through writing the college of agriculture of the state.

SPECIALIZED SWINE BUILDINGS FOR SPECIALIZED SYSTEMS

The starting point in designing hog buildings is the selection of a system, with a choice between (1) the pasture system, (2) the combined pasture and confinement system, and (3) complete confinement. Then, after deciding on the system, plans and specifications for specialized buildings adapted to the system chosen should be developed.

Portable Houses for Pasture Systems

The pasture system and portable houses go hand in hand.

Portable houses were originally designed to accommodate one sow and her litter, as they were designed for individual sow

houses. In recent years, however, the size of the movable house has been greatly increased. Consequently, double-unit portable houses are common, and some portable houses will accommodate as many as six sows.

The **advantages** of the portable house over the permanent or central-type house are:

    1. **Greater flexibility.**

Fig. 10-1. Portable hog houses and rotation of pastures are prime requisites in following the McLean County System of Swine Sanitation. The McLean County System involves the following four simple steps: (1) cleaning and disinfecting the farrowing quarters, (2) washing the sow before moving into farrowing quarters, (3) hauling the sow and litter to clean pasture, and (4) keeping the pigs on clean pasture until they are at least four months old. (Courtesy, Washington State University)

    2. **Better adaptation for the small farmer or tenant.**
    3. **Provides greater quiet and privacy.**
    4. **More isolation and segregation.**
    5. **Ease of construction**
    6. **Lower initial cost.**
    7. **Less fire risk.**
    8. **Adaptation to tenant farming.**
    9. **Provides more exercise.**

There are, however, certain real **disadvantages** to the portable type of house. These are:

    1. **Less supervision at farrowing time.**

2. More labor and equipment required.

3. Could be more costly in the long run.

4. Difficulty in keeping warm.

KINDS OF PORTABLE HOUSES

The design of the individual hog house varies with local conditions and individual preference, and they may be built or purchased. Generally, portable houses may be classified as follows, according to roof styles and kinds of sides:

1. **Roof styles.**—From the standpoint of roof styles, portable houses are most generally of the following types: (a) A-type, (b) shed, or (c) gable roof. Modifications of each of these styles are rather common, however. Sometimes portable houses other than the A-type are referred to as "box-type" houses.

2. **Fixed or hinged sides.**—The sides may either be fixed or

Fig. 10-2. The portable double-unit WSU Sunshine Hog House. Note folding doors in front. (Courtesy, Washington State University)

hinged. Hinged sides provide additional shade and ventilation for hot weather but cause more drafts during cold weather. Hinged sides also add to the cost and reduce the service life of the house.

Types of Unit Houses

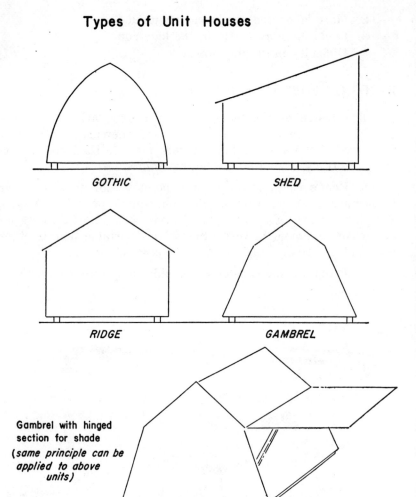

Fig. 10-3. Kinds of portable hog houses, showing four roof styles: (1) gothic, (2) shed, (3) ridge, and (4) gambrel; and showing hinged sides for shade. (Drawings by R. F. Johnson)

In the South, the portable house may be enclosed on only three sides.

Portable Multi-use Houses for Pasture-Confinement Systems

Where pasture and confinement systems are combined, it is almost inevitable that portable hog houses will be used. Ad-

ditionally, on many such establishments either or both (1) the portable multi-use house, or (2) the permanent multi-use house will be needed.

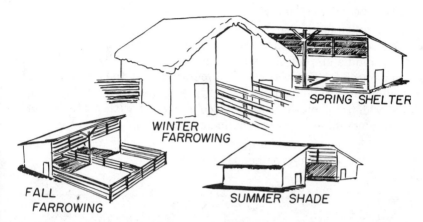

WINTER
FARROWING

SPRING SHELTER

FALL
FARROWING

SUMMER SHADE

Fig. 10-4. Portable multi-use house, showing the flexibility of this type of structure. (Drawing by Steve Allured)

The portable multi-use house is, as the name implies, an attempt to combine within a large portable-type house—usually a four- or six-unit (but larger units are used)—the virtues of both the permanent or central and the individual house, while at the same time deleting the chief disadvantages of each. The combination house is usually a two-section type of house permitting movability. The advocates of the portable multi-use house claim that this building, in comparison with the conventional permanent or central house, is (1) almost as well adapted to farrowing during cold weather, (2) cooler in summer, and (3) more sanitary in that one may not have to use disease-contaminated lots adjacent to the building. In comparison with the smaller portable-type house, it is claimed that the portable multi-use house is warmer for winter farrowing in northern climates and cooler in summer.

Permanent Multi-use House (or Central House) for Pasture-Confinement Systems

A permanent multi-use house is usually a fairly sizable unit, consisting of several pens and of rather durable construction. It

is, as indicated by the name, designed to serve several purposes—farrowing, growing, finishing. and/or housing gestating sows and herd boars. Generally speaking, permanent multi-use houses are used along with portable houses, in a combination pasture-confinement system.

Multi-use houses mark the transition from portable houses and a straight pasture system to total confinement—they were the middle step of the way, as it were. But multi-use houses are not obsolete. For the smaller operator, and the hogman who is following a two-litter-per-year system, the multi-use house has a very definite place, usually in combination with portable houses and a combined pasture-confinement system.

The special **advantages** of the permanent multi-use house over the portable-type house are:

Fig. 10-5. A durable central hog house. (Courtesy, Portland Cement Association)

1. **Greater convenience and efficiency.**
2. **Closer attention at farrowing time.**
3. **More uniform temperature.**
4. **More adequate storage.**
5. **Greater permanency.**
6. **More easily cleaned and disinfected.**
7. **Superior ventilation.**

8. **Less equipment required.**
9. **More sunlight.**

With all their virtues, however, permanent multi-use houses have the following **disadvantages:**

1. **Higher initial cost.**
2. **Lot sanitation more difficult.** (Of course, lots are not used in many cases.)

KINDS OF PERMANENT MULTI-USE HOUSES

Several kinds of permanent multi-use houses are in use. Without going into construction details, they may be classified as follows:

1. **Single-row vs. double-row houses.**—In general, the single-row type of permanent multi-use house is best adapted where a south exposure is desired for all pens and where a fewer number of hogs (10 or less sows) are kept.

Where 10 or more sows are kept, the double-row permanent multi-use house is standard construction. Houses of this design are usually located with the long axis north-south, so that the pens on each side may receive direct sunlight during a part of the day. However, the latter point is not so important where space heaters and electricity are used.

2. **Types of roofs.**—Shed, gable, and gambrel roofs are commonly used on permanent multi-use houses. Because of the difficulties in maintaining warmth for the animals during the winter months, monitor and half-monitor roofs are no longer advocated in swine barn construction.

Fig. 10-6 illustrates single-row and double-row permanent multi-use houses with approved types of roofs.

Confinement System Houses

Large and highly specialized hog producers have developed specialized confinement buildings for specialized purposes. The number of different kinds of hog houses varies according to (1) the size of enterprise, (2) the frequency of farrowing, and (3) the ideas of the operator. Also, there is hardly any limit to the number of different styles, sizes, building materials, and colors. Yet, certain principles are observed in farrowing houses, in nur-

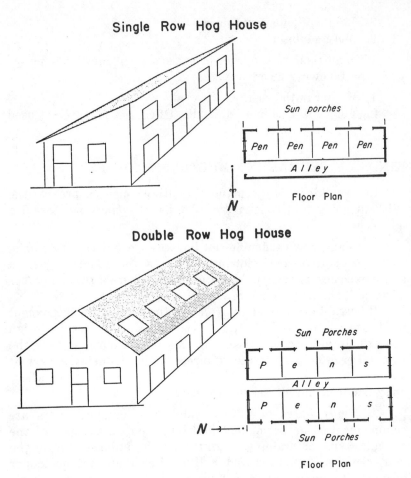

Fig. 10-6. Two kinds of permanent multi-use houses; (upper picture) single-row hog house, and (lower picture) double-row hog house. Today, many operators are lessening or eliminating windows in hog houses in order to reduce construction costs and heat exchange between the building and the outside. (Drawing by R. F. Johnson)

series, in growing houses, in finishing houses, and in gestating houses. Some producers combine two or more of these units into one building; for example, it is not uncommon to find the growing-finishing operations in one building. Also, the farrowing-nursery operations are often combined.

Where specialized buildings are used, with the hogs moved progressively from one building to another—for example, farrowing→nursery→growing→finishing—it is imperative that the

buildings be carefully integrated as to size, so as not to have too much space in one and too little in another.

The building and equipment requisites for each type of specialized building follow.

FARROWING HOUSES

Farrowing houses, as used in specialized confinement operations, are for the care and protection of sows and baby pigs during farrowing and until the pigs are about four to five weeks old.

The design and construction of the farrowing house should be such as to provide optimum environmental control, minimum pig losses, maximum labor efficiency, and satisfactory manure handling. To this end, the following features are being incorporated in modern farrowing houses:

1. **Floors.**—Slotted floor farrowing houses are becoming more common. Studies conducted by the Agricultural Economics Department of the University of Illinois show that slotted floors

Fig. 10-7. Modern farrowing house—Cedar Point Farms, Eaton, Maryland. (Courtesy, Harold Boucher, Executive Secretary, Hampshire Swine Registry)

Fig. 10-8. Interior of modern farrowing house. (Courtesy, Harold Boucher, Executive Secretary, Hampshire Swine Registry)

save more labor in farrowing than in any other phase of confinement production.

Concrete, steel, or wood slats may be used. A 3-inch slat with ⅜-inch spacing appears to be most popular for farrowing houses.

2. **Farrowing crates (or stalls).**—A variety of designs and sizes of farrowing crates or stalls are available. Those with a pit under the entire crate are popular. The important thing is that the farrowing crate include a brooder area about 24 inches wide for the baby pigs.

Also, some producers are using a combination of portable crates in pens.

Alleys should be provided for easy access of animals to and from pens or crates, and of the operator to the brooder area.

Where slats are used, they should be covered for a few days after farrowing.

3. **Temperature.**—The brooder temperature for newborn pigs should be maintained at 80° to 90° F.

Winter environment is more critical inside a slotted floor farrowing house than in a house with a solid floor. Air temperatures should be warmer, and drafts are more critical.

Many commercial producers use space heat to maintain up to 80° F. at farrowing time.

NURSERY, GROWING, AND FINISHING HOUSES

In larger confinement operations with multiple farrowing, three separate buildings—nursery, growing, and finishing—may be used in housing pigs from about four to five weeks of age to marketing. If properly integrated, this makes it possible to effect some savings in total building space, for the reason that nursery-age pigs require less space per pig than hogs approaching market weight.

Fig. 10-9. Nursery unit. These are generally designed for pigs from 20 pounds to 100 pounds. (Courtesy, Harold Boucher, Executive Secretary, Hampshire Swine Registry)

On the smaller confinement establishments, two, or even all three, of these types of units may be combined; for example, there may be a nursery and a combined growing-finishing house.

The following features are being incorporated in nurseries, growing houses, finishing houses, and combinations of them:

Fig. 10-10. Interior of a modern hog finishing house, with automatic feeders. (Photo by J. C. Allen and Son, West Lafayette, Ind.)

1. **Slotted floors.**[3]—Both partially and totally slotted floors are being used.

Partially slotted floors are generally 6 to 8 feet wide, with about one-third of the floor slotted. Lengths range from 12 feet long with 4 feet slotted to 30 feet long with 10 feet slotted.

Totally slotted floors are becoming more popular in nursery and finishing units. The elimination of floor cleaning and the shift back to self-feeding are largely responsible for this change.

A new type of open-front, partially-slotted finishing house appears promising for use in moderate climates. It has a well-insulated roof, heat in the floor, and a slotted floor next to the open front.

Most producers favor a 4- or 5-inch slat with a 1-inch slot. Pigs over two weeks of age have no trouble with a 1-inch spacing.

---

[3] For more detail on slotted floors, see the section entitled "Slotted Floors."

2. **Temperature.**—The following temperature schedule is considered nearly ideal for pigs from weaning to marketing:

Pig Weight (lb.)	Temperature (degrees F.)
10-50	70-75
50-220	60-65

GESTATING HOUSES

Until recently, even those producers who used total confinement for all other phases of the swine operation, favored outdoor exercise, preferably on pasture, for pregnant sows. Now, keeping gestating sows in total confinement is increasing in popularity because of the following **advantages:**

1. **Less labor.**—The labor requirements are reduced in confinement, primarily in handling, cleaning, and feeding.

2. **Higher land use.**—Pastures may be used for crop production, thereby (a) saving fencing, and (b) making for higher return from the land.

3. **Facilitates individual feeding.**—Tying (tethering) individual sows in stalls has been common practice in Europe for many years. Now the practice of keeping gestating sows in total confinement and individually feeding is increasing in the United States. Among its advantages are:

   a. It allows limited feeding of each sow.

   b. It discourages bossism and fighting among sows.

   c. It makes it possible to control dosages for drug or hormone feeding.

   d. It provides facilities (stalls) for artificial breeding and other sow care.

Three types of individual feeding arrangements are being tried; namely—

   a. **Loose feeding stalls.**—Loose feeding stalls are generally about 20 inches wide and 8 feet long. Usually, the back end is open, although a gate may be used to shut the sows in.

   b. **Tie stalls.**—In this arrangement, sows are tied in their individual stalls with a strap. A tie-ring for the tether is centered in the floor under each sow's neck, about 8 inches behind the feed trough.

Tie stalls should be about 24 inches wide, from 3 feet to 7 feet long, and about 30 inches high. When in the stalls, the sows should be able to see each other. This applies to both loose and tie stalls.

c. **Individual pens or crates.**—This refers to small, individual, enclosed pens, in which one sow is kept during the gestation period.

Not all confinement handled gestating sows are individually fed. Many of them are, and will likely continue to be, group fed—either in a separate feeding area, or in their regular pen.

On some confinement swine establishments, gestating sows are kept in open-fronted houses; in others, completely enclosed houses are used. A brief discussion of each follows:

1. **Open-fronted houses for gestating sows.**—Some producers provide about 15 square feet per gestating sow in open-fronted houses (cold housing), which they divide into pen areas that will hold 10, 20, or 30 sows. The sows require bedding, and manure is handled as solids. Feeders or feed stalls are placed outside the shelter on a concrete floor.

2. **Enclosed houses for gestating sows.**—Other producers are building completely enclosed (warm) buildings for gestating sows, which allow year-round climate moderation. Such buildings should be well insulated and have vapor barriers installed in all walls and ceilings. They should be equipped with fans with a total capacity of 30 to 40 cfm per sow. The inside temperature should be kept above 50° F., which can usually be achieved by running the fans. During the summer, large ventilator doors in the walls should be opened. Such buildings are divided into pens holding 10 to 30 sows, as in open housing; and the sows are either group or individually fed.

Generally, slotted floors are used; each sow is allowed about 15 square feet of building area; no bedding is used; and manure is handled as a liquid.

The major disadvantage to confinement housing of gestating sows is the high initial investment in buildings and equipment.

REQUISITES OF CONFINEMENT SWINE HOUSING

There are certain general requisites of all animal buildings, regardless of the class of livestock, that should always be con-

sidered; among them, reasonable construction and maintenance costs, reduced labor, and utility value. In the case of swine in confinement, however, increased emphasis needs to be placed on the following features of buildings.

TEMPERATURE AND HUMIDITY

Hogs are poorly equipped to cope with either heat or cold. They possess very few sweat glands for cooling off in hot weather; and they have little hair for protection against cold. During cold weather, the necessary added warmth should be

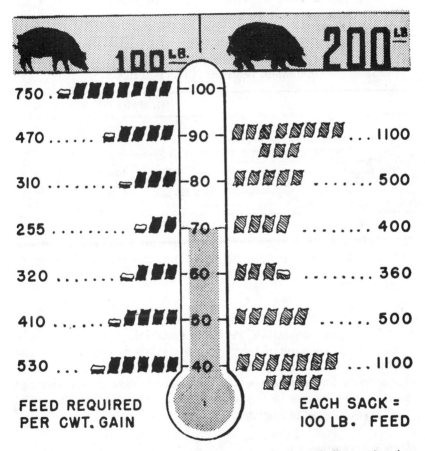

Fig. 10-11. Effect of temperature on production efficiency of swine. (Courtesy, T. E. Bond, Agricultural Engineer, Agricultural Engineering Research Division, Agricultural Research Service, USDA)

provided through properly constructed buildings and artificial means (heated buildings, brooders, etc.) ; and summer coolness should be enhanced by shades, wallows, and sprinklers.

Rate of gain and feed efficiency are lowered when swine must endure temperatures appreciably below or above the comfort zone. Figure 10-11 shows the feed consumption of growing-finishing pigs housed in a controlled temperature room and indicates the effect temperature may have on production. From the standpoint of promoting maximum efficiency, therefore, it is desirable to provide animal housing, shades, wallows, etc., which eliminate extreme changes in environment temperature.

The most desirable temperatures for different classes and ages of hogs are given in Table 10-1.

TABLE 10-1

DESIRABLE TEMPERATURES FOR HOGS

	Wt. of Pigs		Temperature	
	(lb.)	(kg)	(degree F.)	(C.)
1. Farrowing house—sows---------------------------			60-70	15-20
Brooder area -----------------------------------	baby pigs		80-90	27-32
2. Nursery—sows----------------------------------			60-65	15-17
Pig quarters -----------------------------------	10-50	4-23	70-75	20-24
3. Growing house ---------------------------------	50-125	23-57	65-70	17-20
4. Finishing house--------------------------------	120-220	55-100	60-65	15-17
5. Gestating sow house ---------------------------	—	—	50-60	11-15

Humidity influences are tied closely to temperature effects. The relative humidity should be within the range of 70 to 80 percent.

INSULATION

The term "insulation" refers to materials which have a high resistance to the flow of heat. Such materials are commonly used in the walls and ceiling of hog houses. Proper insulation makes for a more uniform temperature—cooler houses in the summer and warmer houses in the winter—and makes for a substantial fuel saving in heated houses.

VAPOR BARRIER

There is much moisture in hog houses; it comes from

waterers, wet bedding, the respiration of the animals, and from the feces and urine. When the amount of water vapor in the house is greater than in the outside air, the vapor will tend to move from inside to outside. Since warm air holds more water vapor than cold air, the movement of vapor is most pronounced during the winter months. The effective way to combat this problem in a hog house is to use a vapor barrier (4-mil plastic film, aluminum foil, etc.) with the insulation. It should be placed on the warm side or inside of the house.

HEAT

In the northern part of the United States, houses should be heated. A space heater with output of 2,500 BTU's per hour for each sow and litter is recommended. Hence, a 20-sow farrowing house needs a heater with an output of 50,000 BTU's (2,500 BTU's x 20 sows = 50,000 BTU's). The installation should be of such size as to provide the desirable temperatures indicated earlier in this chapter.

Table 10-2 shows the amount of heat produced by hogs of different weights. Even with insulation, about 60 percent of this body heat is lost by ventilation to remove moisture; without insulation the heat loss is more.

TABLE 10-2

HEAT PRODUCTION OF SWINE[1]

Size of Hog		BTU/Hr. Produced by Animal[2]	BTU/Hr. Available for Heating[3]
1 day old		33	13
lb.	kg		
10	5	200	80
50	23	375	150
100	45	520	208
150	68	675	270
200	91	800	320
300	136; fat hog	1,025	410
300	136; gestating sow	870	348

[1]From *Hog Houses*, USDA Misc. Pub. No. 744, Jan., 1958, p. 3.
[2]Mitchell, H. H. and M. A. R. Kelley. Energy requirements of swine and estimates of heat production and gaseous exchange for use in planning ventilation of hog houses. *Jour. Agri. Res.* 56, 1938, pp. 811-829.
[3]Heat loss by ventilation sufficient to remove moisture respired by hog assumed to be 60 percent.

VENTILATION

Ventilation refers to the changing of air—the replacement

of foul air with fresh air. Hog houses should be well ventilated, but care must be taken to avoid direct drafts and coldness. Good swine house ventilation saves feed and helps make for maximum production.

Four factors are essential for good ventilation: (1) fresh air moving into the hog house (inlets), (2) insulation to keep the house temperatures warm, (3) supplemental heat in the winter in cold areas, and (4) removal of moist air (outlets). The importance of the latter point becomes evident when it is realized that, through breathing, each sow and litter adds about a gallon of water per day and fifty 125-pound pigs give off about a gallon of moisture per hour.

In most hog houses, easily controlled electric fans do the best job of putting air where it is needed.

Fans are rated in cubic feet per minute (cfm) of air they move. By selecting and using two or three fans, each of a different size, the needed variable rate, or flexibility, of ventilation can be achieved.

Provision should be made for one or more of the following, should there be a power or equipment failure in a closed building:

1. A battery-operated alarm which sounds in the home of the caretaker if power goes off.

2. A standby generator to supply power.

3. Solenoid or other electrically closed doors which open if power goes off.

4. Manually opened doors and windows.

5. A place to move the hogs outside if the building cannot be opened sufficiently.

The amount of ventilation air required depends upon the (1) inside-of-house temperature desired, (2) outside air temperature, (3) relative humidity, (4) number and size of animals in the building, and (5) amount of insulation. Since size of hog is a factor, and since the comfort zone of baby pigs and finishing hogs differs, it is obvious that at least two ventilation tables are needed; one for the farrowing house, and the other for the finishing house.

1. **Amount of air needed for farrowing house.**—The winter temperature inside a farrowing house should be kept at 50° F. or above.

The maximum amount of air needed per sow and litter in the winter is 50 cfm. Hence, this figure can be used to calculate

fan capacity for the winter operation. However, at 70° F. and above, the ventilation rate should be increased to about 100 cfm per sow and litter.

Table 10-3 shows the amount of ventilation air needed at different temperatures in a well insulated farrowing house.

TABLE 10-3

VENTILATION AIR NEEDED IN A FARROWING HOUSE[1]

Outside Temperature		Approx. Air Needed/ Sow and Litter
(degrees F.)	(C.)	(cfm)
-20	-29	12
-10	-23	13
0	-18	14
10	-12	16
20	- 7	18
30	- 1	22
40	4	36
50	10	50 (winter design)
50-70	10-21	50
above 70	21	100 (summer design)

[1]From: *Ventilate Your Farrowing House*, Iowa State University, AE-992, Jan. 1965, p. 4.

2. **Amount of air needed for growing-finishing house.**—The best temperature for efficient feed conversion in growing-finishing houses is about 60° F., with a relative humidity below 80 percent.

Table 10-4 shows the ventilation rate needed in a well-insulated growing-finishing house. Thus, if it is desired to have a winter ventilation system for 100 head of 125-pound hogs, a total fan capacity of 2,500 cubic feet per minute (25 cfm/pig x 100 pigs = 2,500 cfm) is needed when the outside air is about 50° F. But as the outside temperature drops, less air is needed, as shown in Table 10-5.

TABLE 10-4

VENTILATION CAPACITY NEEDED FOR WELL-INSULATED BUILDING[1]

Weight of Pig		Winter Ventilation	Summer Ventilation
(lb.)	(kg)	(cfm/pig)	(cfm/pig)
50	23	15	50
125	57	25	75
200	91	35	100

[1]From *Ventilate Your Swine Finishing House*, Iowa State University, AE-993, Feb. 1965, p. 3.

TABLE 10-5

APPROXIMATE VENTILATION NEEDS FOR 125-POUND HOGS[1]
(Temperature inside at 50° F. in cold weather, higher in mild weather.)

Outside Temperature		cfm per Hog
(°F.)	(°C.)	
-10	-23	7
0	-18	7.5
10	-12	8
20	- 7	9
30	- 1	12
40	4	20
50	10	25
50-70	10-21	30
above 70	21	75

[1]From *Ventilate Your Swine Finishing House*, Iowa State University, AE—993, Feb. 1965, p. 3.

Approximately three times more air is required during the summer than for maximum ventilation during the winter. Therefore, many producers prefer to provide openings in the sidewalls so that natural ventilation furnishes the majority of summer ventilation. Even where the latter is done, circulating fans above the pens and a thermostatically controlled sprinkler system should be installed in hog houses in warm areas.

A complete ventilation system has four parts: (1) a fan, or fans, to move fresh air through the house, (2) enough inlets to let plenty of fresh air in, (3) enough outlets to let stale, moisture-laden air out, and (4) adequate controls to make the system operate when needed. All these parts are necessary for success.

Either an exhaust-type or a forced intake (or pressurized) ventilation system may be used.

The water-holding capacity of air increases with rising temperature (Fig. 10-12).

AUTOMATED FEED AND WATER

Confinement buildings lend themselves to automating, because of their compactness. It goes without saying, therefore, that the feed and water facilities of confinement houses should be automated.

Slotted Floors

Slotted floors for hogs are not new; they have been used

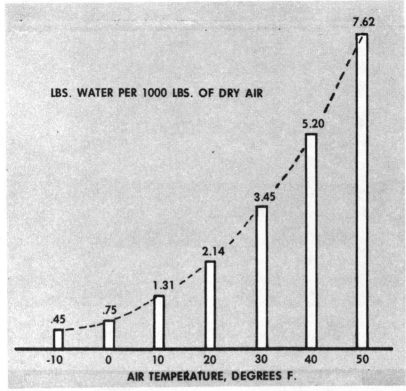

LBS. WATER PER 1000 LBS. OF DRY AIR

AIR TEMPERATURE, DEGREES F.

Fig. 10-12. Influence of air temperature on its water holding capacity. (From Iowa State University, AE-993, Feb. 1965, p. 2.)

in Europe for over 200 years. Slotted floor buildings should be warm and well ventilated.

The main **advantages** of using slotted floors are:

1. **Less space is needed.**—Normally, slightly less space is needed for slotted than for solid floors. However, the space requirements for pigs kept on each of the two kinds of floors are about the same provided (a) solid floors are scraped daily and/or (b) one is not too concerned over the soiled appearance of hogs that are rather crowded on solid floors (such pigs on solid floors will be dirty, but they will perform well).

2. **Bedding is eliminated.**—Bedding is expensive; that is, when all costs are computed—initial purchase price, storage space, handling, spreading it in the pens, and removal of the straw with the manure.

Fig. 10-13. Totally slotted floor, occupied by two sows and their litters. (Courtesy, Farmaster Products, Inc., Shenandoah, Iowa)

3. **Manure handling is reduced.**—Conventional solid floors require frequent removal of manure; daily scraping is best. With a slotted floor, manure may be handled every month, or every six months, depending on the type and size of the pit under the floor.

The chief **disadvantages** of slotted floors are: (1) higher initial cost, (2) less flexibility in the use of the building, (3) any spilled feed may be lost through the slots, (4) pigs raised on slotted floors resist being driven over a solid floor, and (5) environmental conditions become more critical.

SLOTTED FLOOR CONSTRUCTION

The main features that control the successful operation of a slotted floor system are:

1. **The storage pit under the slots.**—A concrete-lined pit is located under slot floors. Depth of the pit varies with the method of manure disposal. If the manure is to be drained to a lagoon, the pit usually ranges from 1½ to 2 feet deep. If six months storage is desired, the pit should be 5 to 6 feet deep. The floor

of the pit should slope slightly (about 1 inch per 25 feet) to the clean-out location.

2. **Slats.**—Slats are usually made from wood, concrete, or steel. Wood slats are less costly than concrete or steel, but also less durable. Concrete slats are most durable and most widely used.

Slat width and spacing (slot width) are governed by size of hogs and cleaning efficiency. Narrow slots are usually more effective in farrowing and nursery units; too wide spacing of narrow slats can cause injury to the feet and legs of finishing hogs. On the other hand, wide slats and narrow openings result in floors that are not completely self-cleaning. For growing-finishing pigs, most producers seem to favor ¾-inch slots up to 140 pounds weight, and 1-inch slots from 140 pounds to market weight; and for sows they favor 1¼-inch spacing. The recommended slat-slot relationship is given in Table 10-6.

TABLE 10-6

SLAT-SLOT RELATIONSHIP

Slat Width		Slot Width	
(in.)	(cm)	(in)	(cm)
2.5	6.3	5/8	1.5
3	7.6	3/4	1.9
4	10.2	1	2.5
5	12.7	1	2.5
6	15.2	1-1/4	3.2

Slats stay cleaner if they are run at right angles to the pigs' major traffic pattern.

PARTIALLY SLOTTED FLOORS

Generally speaking, a combination solid and slotted floor offers most of the advantages of completely slotted floors and fewer of the disadvantages. With such construction, the ratio of slotted to solid floor should be about 3:1 or 4:1; the objective being to limit the space on the solid concrete floor so that there is just enough room for the pigs to lie down.

The following plans and practices are pertinent to the success of a partially slotted floor arrangement:

1. Place the feeder in one end of the pen, and the waterer in the other on slats.

Fig. 10-14. Partially slotted floor, showing automatic waterers in the slatted area. (Courtesy, The Wyatt Manufacturing Company, Inc., Salina, Kansas)

2. Use a continuous feeder along one wall; this arrangement will alleviate dunging along the wall.

3. Avoid long pens; the distance from the feeder to the slats shouldn't be more than 12 feet. A hog will seldom move more than 12 feet before defecating.

4. Slope the solid floor into the pit—½ to ¾ inch per foot.

5. Keep pens full of pigs.

Manure Management

The handling of manure is probably the single, most important problem confronting commercial hogmen today. It must be removed for sanitary reasons, and there is a limit to how much of it can be left to accumulate in pits or other storage areas. Higher labor costs and lower price commercial fertilizers have made manure relatively less valuable as a fertilizer. Also, to the urbanite and city dweller alike, manure odor is taboo. Manure is too costly to burn, too bulky to bury or put in a dump,

and, with large operations, there is too much of it to put in lagoons.

The use of slotted floors, either partial or total, along with pit storage and hauling to the fields appears to be the most satisfactory method of handling manure in confinement buildings.

SWINE EQUIPMENT

The successful hog producer must have adequate equipment with which to provide feed, water, shelter, and care for the animals. Suitable equipment saves labor and prevents the loss of many baby pigs—and even the loss of older animals. These are items which should not be overlooked.

Certain features are desirable in hog-lot equipment. Equipment should be convenient and economical; and, as hogs are subject to numerous diseases and parasites, it should be constructed for easy cleaning and disinfection. Equipment should be useful, durable, and yet economical.

There are many types and designs of the various pieces of hog-lot equipment, and some producers will introduce their own ideas to fit the material available to local conditions. It is expected that certain adaptations should be made in designs to meet individual conditions.

Breeding Crate

A breeding crate is often very necessary in breeding a young gilt to a mature, heavy boar; or in breeding a large, mature sow to a young boar. Satisfactory breeding crates may either be purchased commercially or built in the farm workshop (see Fig. 5-21 in Chapter V).

Creep

Various types of creeps are used. The enclosed area should be of sufficient size to accommodate the number of pigs intended along with the feeders. There should be enough openings in the fence, or panels, through which the little pigs can pass. The openings should be wide enough for the pigs, but narrow enough to keep older hogs out; preferably, they should be adjustable, so that they can be widened as the pigs become older. It is important

Fig. 10-15. Creep-feeding is the practice of feeding concentrates to young pigs in a separate enclosure away from their dams. (Drawing by R. F. Johnson)

that the openings be sufficiently high that the pigs do not have to lower their backs when passing through; otherwise there is a tendency to produce objectionable low backs. Detailed plans for building a creep are not necessary.

Heat Lamps and Brooders

Newborn pigs are quite comfortable at temperatures of 80° to 90° F. (27° to 32° C.), shiver when standing alone at 70° F. (21°C.), and are quite cold at 60°F. (16°C.). Recent estimates indicate that swine producers can save an average of 1½ pigs per litter by using supplementary heat to keep baby pigs warm.

Brooders of various designs are used. Where sows are farrowed in conventional pens, a triangular-shaped brooder is usually secured in one corner of the pen.

Heat may be supplied by infrared-heat lamps or electric hovers in cold climates. Heat lamps should be of hard pyrex glass (red filter type) that resists breakage when splashed with water. Use heavy porcelain sockets, a metal hood, and suspend the lamp by a chain. **Never suspend the heat lamp by the elec-**

trical cord. A 125-watt lamp should be 24 inches (2.5 cm) above the floor of the brooder area.

Any type of heating device can cause a fire, so heaters should be installed carefully.

Farrowing Crates (Stalls) or Pens

Adequate facilities for farrowing are highly important because one-third or more of all death losses before weaning result from over-laying or crushing. Mechanical devices such as guard rails and farrowing crates are valuable aids in reducing these losses.

Fig. 10-16. Farrowing crate (stall) with (1) wood slotted floor and (2) a separate baby pig compartment warmed by supplementary heat. (Courtesy, North States Wood Products, Inc., Minneapolis, Minn.)

A variety of farrowing crates or stalls of different designs and sizes are available. Some are equipped with self-feeders and waterers. The important thing is that they include a brooder or creep area about 24 inches wide for the baby pigs. Where crates are equipped with waterers, the waterers should be designed and located so that the pen area will not get wet.

Some producers keep sows in crates continuously from far-

rowing to weaning, but generally the sow and litter are moved to other quarters about two weeks after farrowing. By this time, normal pigs are quite active and crushing by the sow is not likely.

Loading Chute

Loading chutes are desirable on most farms. Chutes make possible loading hogs without injury and with the least amount of effort. Loading chutes may either be fixed or portable. Although slightly more expensive to build, a stairstep loading chute is preferable to the ramp-and-cleat type; hogs find the steps easier to ascend, and will go up more willingly and with less chance of injury. Ramp-type chutes are still the most prevalent, due to their slightly lower initial cost.

Fig. 10-17. Portable stairstep loading chute. Stairsteps are safer and are preferred by hogs. (Courtesy, V. J. Morford, Department of Agricultural Engineering, Iowa State University)

The chute should be fairly narrow so animals cannot turn around. Care should be taken so that no cleats, nails, or other projections injure the hog. A portable chute is convenient, because hogs can be loaded from any lot or pasture. The chute should be durably constructed.

Self-feeder

The virtues of "hand-feeding versus self-feeding" are discussed under a similar heading in Chapter VI; thus repetition is unnecessary.

The design of the self-feeder is extremely important. An adequate self-feeder should be constructed so that:

1. It will be sturdy and durable.

Fig. 10-18. Self-feeders in outside pens of a partially open-fronted growing-finishing house. (Courtesy, Harold Boucher, Hampshire Swine Registry)

2. The feed will not clog; to this end, the feeder should have means for agitating the feed to keep it from bridging and adjustable throats for controlling the rate of flow.

3. Waste will be reduced to a minimum.

4. The feed will be protected from wind, rain, birds, and rodents.

5. It is large enough to hold several days' feed.

Many satisfactory designs of self-feeders are available, including both commercial and homemade equipment. A separate, small self-feeder is the best means through which to provide the necessary minerals for swine, for they result in less waste than an open box.

When stationed out-of-doors, self-feeders should always be placed on concrete or plank platforms; otherwise, mudholes soon appear around the base in wet weather, and this causes much waste of feed. Also, they should be so designed and located that they can be filled with a self-unloading wagon, an auger, or a blower.

Shade

Hogs require shade during the hot months of the year. Studies show that they gain little or no weight at temperatures above 90° F.; at 85° F., it takes 1,200 pounds of feed to produce 100 pounds of gain; whereas at 60° F., 400 pounds of feed will produce 100 pounds of gain.

Fig. 10-19. A portable shade for hogs. (Courtesy, Washington State University)

In many cases, houses may double for shade purposes. But it is often desirable to provide additional protection from the sun. The portable shade (Fig. 10-19), when well constructed, will last many years. On most farms this portable shade is the only shelter hogs need during the summer months.

Shipping Crate

Shipping crates are often used for transporting breeding stock. Crates must be durably constructed to prevent animals breaking out during shipment. Crates should be sufficiently light so shipping charges will be held at a minimum. A good crate is an advertisement for the breeder.

Troughs

The hog trough, a universally-used piece of feedlot equipment, is often carelessly constructed. A good trough should be easy to clean and should be constructed so that hogs cannot lie in it or otherwise contaminate the feed. The trough illustrated in Fig. 10-20 meets these requirements. The removable rack across the top provides for easy cleaning and prevents hogs from lying in the trough. The long ends make tipping of this trough extremely difficult. The little pig trough is similar in construction and is useful for small creep-fed pigs.

Fig. 10-20. A good trough that is easy to clean and constructed so that hogs cannot lie in it. (Courtesy, Washington State University)

Vaccinating and Castrating Rack

A vaccinating and castrating rack makes for convenience in treating young pigs. This is a simple rack, made like a common

sawbuck with a V-shaped trough added. A rope or strap is attached at one or both ends of the trough to hold the pigs securely in place.

Wallows; Sprinklers

Hogs have very few sweat glands; thus they cannot cool themselves by perspiration. In the South, therefore, mature breeding animals and finishing hogs need a wallow during the hot, summer months. Instead of permitting an unsanitary mud wallow, successful swine producers install hog wallows. This equipment, which may be either movable or fixed, will keep the animals cool and clean and make for faster and more economical gains. The wallow should be in close proximity to shade, but in no case should shade be built directly over the wallow. Such an arrangement will cause all the hogs to lie in the water all day. The size of wallow to build will depend upon the number and size of animals. Up to 50 growing-finishing pigs can be accommodated per 100 sq. ft. of wallow provided shade or shelter is nearby.

Where sprinklers are used for cooling, (1) provide 1 nozzle per 25 to 30 hogs, (2) station the nozzles 4 to 6 feet from the floor or ground and about 8 feet apart, (3) spray 1 gallon per hour per sq. in. at 20 to 40 pounds of pressure, (4) shut-off by thermostat at 75° F., and (5) provide a fine inline filter. Sprinklers should be limited to concrete lots or sandy soils where mud holes do not develop.

Waterer

Hogs need a constant supply of clean, fresh water in order to be comfortable and to utilize their feed to the best advantage. A pressure water system is the most desirable type for the hog enterprise. To insure an adequate water supply, automatic, non-back-siphoning, easily cleaned waterers are recommended; and, in cold areas, they should have automatic heating units to prevent freezing (if heating units are electrically controlled, they should be properly installed and grounded to prevent electrocution).

For running water to pastures and other fields, plastic pipe is recommended, because it can be quickly rolled out in long lengths either on top of the ground or in a trench. By locating the waterer in a line fence, two pastures can be supplied from one unit.

Many modifications of water troughs exist. Some consist of attachments to a water tank or storage barrel, and the more expensive ones provide for a heating device for winter use. Hogs are prone to form mudholes around waterers; so a substantial platform under the waterer is desirable.

LAGOONS FOR MANURE DISPOSAL

A lagoon is a body of water or pond into which liquid manure is discharged, where it is digested by bacterial action. Three types of bacteria are involved: (1) aerobic—which require free oxygen, (2) anaerobic—which do not require free oxygen, and (3) faculative—which can grow with or without free oxygen.

Most of the fertility value of the manure is wasted, but the savings in equipment and labor may offset the loss. The use of a lagoon embraces a new concept in handling manure; simply to get the excrement out of the building or off the floor and out of the way, but not to conserve its fertility value.

Although lagoons have been used for city sewage and factory wastes for years, their use for swine manure disposal is relatively new.

Interest in lagoons envolved hand-in-hand with the increase in confinement rearing of hogs, because disposal of manure is probably the biggest single job connected with this system of production. Under some circumstances, lagoons may be the solution to the problem.

Based on observations to date, the following points seem pertinent to the construction and operation of a lagoon:

1. **Location.**—The hog operation, including the lagoon, should be on the side of the farmhouse away from the direction of the prevailing winds, and preferably at least 500 feet from any dwelling. There will be some odors on still, humid days in the summer and for a period in the spring while the lagoon re-establishes itself after it has been frozen over in the winter. However, most swine operators who have lagoons report that there is less odor from them than from the buildings or floors which they serve. Also, because the waste material is submerged below the water level, there is little or no fly problem.

The most convenient arrangement is to locate the lagoon adjacent to the feeding floor, so that manure can be scraped or washed directly into it. Where this is not feasible, or where the

Fig. 10-21. Lagoon adjacent to a hog feeding barn on the Bob Tackett farm, Warrensburg, Mo. (Courtesy, Marion W. Clark, Extension Agricultural Engineer, University of Missouri)

lagoon is to serve several buildings, let the liquid manure accumulate in a gutter or pit, then empty periodically. This will lessen clogging or freezing of the lines. Where manure is taken from a building (or pit) to a lagoon, it can be piped through a 6- to 8-inch (the larger size is preferable) sewer tile, or an open concrete runway may be used instead of a tile. The fall on the tile should be at about 2 feet per 100 feet; and the outlet should discharge in the center of the lagoon, about 24 inches above the liquid surface of the lagoon.

Lagoons should not be built on (a) sandy soils, (b) soils less than 50 feet deep over limestone, or (c) porous soils within 150 feet of a well.

2. **Construction specifications.**—Currently, agricultural engineers seem to be fairly well agreed relative to the following construction specifications:

a. **Size and shape.**—Today, lagoon size is usually based on water volume. For swine, 2 cubic feet of volume should be allowed for each pound of animal. Hence, if a hog producer wishes to build a lagoon that will handle the wastes from 100 market hogs averaging 200 pounds weight, the computa-

tion is—2 cu. ft. x 100 hogs x 200 lbs. = 40,000 cu ft. minimum volume of water needed. When lagoons for manure disposal first came in, it was recommended that a minimum of 15 square feet of water surface area per hog be provided. But this is not enough.

In general, the more the manure is diluted, the better; and a lagoon that is larger than the minimum will allow for later expansion of the hog enterprise. Whenever possible, a lagoon should be nearly round or square.

b. **Depth.**—Build the lagoon at least 6 feet deep; this will allow for a minimum liquid depth of 3 feet and a maximum of 5 feet.

c. **Other construction details.**—Make the bottom as level and impervious as possible. Construct well compacted embankments and dikes of impervious soil according to standard practice for pond construction. The embankments should have side slopes of 3 feet horizontally to 1 foot vertically; and the top of the embankment should be 8 feet wide to permit easy maintenance. Divert storm water and surface run-off away from the lagoon. Seed the embankments above the water level, put a dog-tight and child-proof fence around the lagoon, and post a sign properly indicating its contents.

3. **Water in lagoon.**—Lagoons should be kept filled with water. Where the soil is impervious, water from washing the feeding floor plus rain water falling on the feeding floor and into the lagoon is usually sufficient.

4. **Water pressure for cleaning.**—The buildings and/or floors served should be cleaned with water under pressure; a minimum pressure of 75 pounds per square inch and 500 gallons of water an hour are necessary.

5. **Bacteria need not be introduced.**—It is not necessary to introduce bacteria; simply put the liquid waste in the pool and the bacterial action will follow.

6. **Winter use.**—If the lagoon freezes over, the waste material may be deposited on top of the ice, where it will also become frozen—thus avoiding any odor problem. When the ice melts, the material on top of it drops below the surface of the water, and algae become re-established in 2 to 4 weeks. Because of limited storage space on top of the ice, the lagoon may need to

be partially drained; or, during very cold weather, it may be preferable to handle the excrement as a solid, either storing it in a pit or hauling it directly to the field.

7. **Lagoon management.**—These points are pertinent to managing a lagoon: (a) a new lagoon should be filled with water (surface or run-off, or well water), (b) manure should be added to the lagoon gradually, (c) a lagoon functions best if manure is added daily, and (d) the manure should not contain bedding.

8. **Cleanout of lagoon.**—Swine wastes cause sludge accumulation in a lagoon at a rate of about 12 cubic feet per year per animal. When necessary (when the accumulated sludge fills the lagoon to a depth of 3 feet), cleaning may be done either (a) by use of a liquid pump, or (b) by draining the lagoon and removing the solids with a scraper after they have dried.

FACILITIES AND EQUIPMENT FOR HANDLING LIQUID MANURE

Handling swine wastes as liquid requires some special equipment and facilities, including—

1. **Storage container.**—A watertight storage container to which water can be added will be needed. The size of container will depend on the way the swine operation is managed, the length of time between emptyings, and the kind, number, and size of hogs. Large storages have maximum labor advantage.

Approximate daily liquid manure production figures for swine are given in Table 10-7.

These further points are pertinent in arriving at the size of storage container:

TABLE 10-7

APPROXIMATE DAILY LIQUID MANURE PRODUCTION[1]

Per 10 Head of Hogs of av. wt. of:		Cu. Ft./Day Solids & Liquids	Percent Water	Gallons (liters)/ Day	
(lb.)	(kg)	(cu. ft.)	(%)	(gal.)	(l)
50	23	⅔	75	5	19
100	45	1⅓	75	10	38
150	68	2¼	75	17	64
200	91	2¾	75	20½	78
250	114	3½	75	26	98

[1]From: *Handling Liquid Manure,* 1966 Midwest Plan Service, Ames, Iowa, p. 2.

a. There are approximately 34 cubic feet in a ton of manure.

b. Cleaning swine facilities with high-pressure water may double the volume of wastes.

c. Roof or lot drainage will have an unpredictable effect if allowed to run into the storage.

d. Extra water may have to be added if the manure is to be pumped; anywhere from $\frac{1}{5}$ to $\frac{3}{5}$ of the storage volume may be needed for extra water. For irrigation, there should be about 95 percent water and 5 percent manure; for field spreading the extra water should be held to a minimum.

The needed storage capacity for a given swine unit can be computed as follows: storage capacity = no. of animals $\times$ daily manure production (Table 10-7) $\times$ desired storage time (days) + extra water.

It is also important that indoor storage containers be well ventilated, that all storage containers (indoor and outdoor) be insulated against freezing, that water be added to the storage container before filling it with manure (add 3 to 4 inches of water under slotted floors, and 6 to 12 inches of water where manure is scraped into the storage area), that frozen manure never be added to a storage container, that all openings be closed when not in use, and that there be a fly control program (including baits and sprays).

2. **Equipment or facility to move excrement to storage.—** For this purpose, a scraper, gutters, slotted floors, or drains may be used.

3. **Equipment that will stir manure and remove it from storage.—**This includes pumps, agitators, augers, etc.

4. **Equipment or facilities that will dispose of liquid manure.** —This may involve a tank truck or wagon, irrigated fields, available land, a lagoon, etc.

FENCES FOR HOGS

Good fences (1) maintain farm boundaries, (2) make livestock operations possible, (3) reduce losses to both animals and crops, (4) increase land values, (5) promote better relationships between neighbors, (6) lessen accidents from animals getting on roads, and (7) add to the attractiveness and distinctiveness of the premises.

The discussion which follows will be limited primarily to wire fencing, although it is recognized that such materials as rails, poles, boards, stone, and hedge have a place and are used under certain circumstances. Also, where there is a heavy concentration of animals, such as on feeding floors, there is need for a more rigid type of fencing material than wire. Moreover, certain fencing materials have more artistic appeal than others;

Fig. 10-22. Fence for hogs. (Drawing by Steve Allured)

and this is an especially important consideration on the purebred establishment.

The kind of wire to purchase should be determined primarily by the class of animals to be confined. Table 10-8 is a suggested guide.

The following additional points are pertinent in the selection of wire:

1. **Styles of woven wire.**—The standard styles of woven wire fences are designated by numbers as 958, *1155*, 849, *1047*, 741, *939*, *832* and *726* (the figures in italics are most common).

TABLE 10-8

HANDY WOVEN WIRE FENCE CHART

Kind of Stock	Recommended Woven Wire Height	Recommended Weight of Stay Wire	Recommended Mesh or Spacing Between Stays	Number Recommended Strands of Barbed Wire to Add to Woven Wire	Comments
	(inches)	(gauge)	(inches)		
Swine ---------------- 26, 32, or 39	9 or 11	6	1 strand on bottom.	Barbed wire on bottom prevents rooting.	
Mixed livestock ---- 26 or	9 or 11	6 --------	{ 3 strands on top; 1 strand on bottom.	
32	9 or 11	6 --------	{ 2 strands on top; 1 strand on bottom.	

The first one or two digits represent the number of line (horizontal) wires; the last two the height in inches; i.e., 832 has 8 horizontal wires and is 32 inches in height. Each style can be obtained in either (a) 12-inch spacing of stays (or mesh), or (b) 6-inch spacing of stays.

2. **Mesh.**—Generally, a close-spaced fence with stay or vertical wires 6 inches apart (6 in. mesh) will give better service than a wide-spaced (12-in. mesh) fence. However, some fence manufacturers believe that a 12-inch spacing with a No. 9 wire is superior to a 6-inch spacing with No. 11 filler wire (about the same amount of material is involved in each case).

3. **Weight of wire.**—A fence made of heavier weight wires will usually last longer and prove cheaper than one made of light wires. Heavier or larger size wire is designated by a smaller gauge number. Thus, No. 9 gauge wire is heavier and larger than No. 11 gauge. Woven wire fencing comes in Nos. 9, 11, 12½, and 14½ gauges—which refers to the gauge of the wires other than the top and bottom line wires. Barbed wire is usually 12½ gauge.

Heavier or larger wire than normal should be used in those areas subject to (a) salty air from the ocean, (b) smoke from close proximity industries which may give off chemical fumes into the atmosphere, (c) rapid temperature changes, or (d) overflow or flood. Also, heavier or larger wire than normal should be used in fencing (a) small areas, (b) where a dense concentration of animals is involved, and (c) where animals have already learned to get out.

4. **Styles of barbed wire.**—Styles of barbed wire differ in the shape and number of the points of the barb, and the spac-

ing of the barbs on the line wires. The two-point barbs are commonly spaced 4 inches apart while four-point barbs are generally spaced 5 inches apart. Since any style is satisfactory, selection is a matter of personal preference.

5. **Standard size rolls or spools.**—Woven wire comes in 20 and 40 rod rolls; barbed wire in 80 rod spools.

6. **Wire coating.**—The kind and amount of coating on wire definitely affects its lasting qualities.

Three kinds of material are commonly used for fence posts: wood, metal, and concrete. The selection of the particular kind of posts should be determined by (1) the availability and cost of each, (2) the length of service desired (posts should last as long as the fencing material attached to it, or the maintenance cost may be too high), (3) the kind and amount of livestock to be confined, and (4) the cost of installation.

Electric Fences

Where a temporary enclosure is desired or where existing fences need bolstering from roguish or breachy animals, it may be desirable to install an electric fence, which can be done at minimum cost.

The following points are pertinent in the construction of an electric fence:

1. **Safety.**—If an electric fence is to be installed and used, (a) necessary safety precautions against accidents to both persons and animals should be taken, and (b) the hog producer should first check into the regulations of his own state relative to the installation and use of electric fences. *Remember that an electric fence can be dangerous.* Fence controllers should be purchased from a reliable manufacturer; homemade controllers may be dangerous.

2. **Wire height.**—As a rule of thumb, the correct wire height for an electric fence is about three-fourths the height of the animal; with two wires provided for swine. Following are average fence heights above the ground for swine:

Swine: two wires—one wire 6 to 8 inches and the other 14 to 16 inches.

Mixed livestock: three wires—8, 12, and 32 inches.

3. **Posts.**—Either wood or steel posts may be used for

Fig. 10-23. Recommended height for electric fence for hogs. (Drawing by R. F. Johnson)

electric fencing. Corner posts should be as firmly set and well braced as required for any non-electric fence so as to stand the pull necessary to stretch the wire tight. Line posts (a) need only be heavy enough to support the wire and withstand the elements, and (b) may be spaced 25 to 40 feet apart for hogs.

4. **Wire.**—In those states where barbed wire is legal, new four-point hog wire is preferred. Barbed wire is recommended, because the barbs will penetrate the hair of animals and touch the skin, but smooth wire can be used satisfactorily. Rusty wire should never be used, because rust is an insulator.

5. **Insulators.**—Wire should be fastened to the posts by insulators and should not come into direct contact with posts, weeds, or the ground. Inexpensive solid glass or porcelain insulators should be used, rather than old rubber or necks of bottles.

6. **Grounding.**—One lead from the controller should be grounded to a pipe driven into the moist earth. *An electric fence should never be grounded to a water pipe, because it could carry lightning directly to connecting buildings.* A lightning arrestor should be installed on the ground wire.

SPACE REQUIREMENTS OF BUILDINGS AND EQUIPMENT FOR SWINE

Table 10-9 contains average figures, based on the author's experiences and observations of successful swine enterprises, of the space requirements for buildings and equipment for swine.

Age and Size of Animal	Swine Buildings					Shades		Pasture or Feeding Floor	
	Inside Sleeping Space or Shelter per Animal[1]	Height of Ceiling[2]	Height of Pen Partition	Hog Door Height	Hog Door Width	Shade per Animal	Shade Height	Good Pasture	Paved F ing Floc Additio Sleeping $ When Cor Per Ani
	(sq. ft.)	(ft.)	(in.)	(in.)	(in.)	(sq. ft.)	(ft.)	(animals/acre)	(sq. f
Sows, before farrowing:									
Gilts----------------	15-17	7-8	36	36	24	17	4-6	10-12	15-2(
Mature sows ----	18-20	,,	,,	,,	,,	20	,,	8-10	,,
Sows with pigs:									
Gilts----------------	48	,,	,,	,,	,,	50	,,	6-8	48
Mature sows ----	64	,,	,,	,,	,,	60	,,	6-8	64
Herd Boars -------------	15-20	,,	48	,,	,,	15-20		¼ acre/boar	15-2(
Growing-finishing swine:									
(1) weaning[5] to 75 lbs. -------------	5-6[6,7]	,,	30	,,	,,	6	,,	20 on full feed; 10-15 limited feed	6-8[8]
(2) 75 lbs. to 125 lbs. -------------	6-7[6,7]	,,	33	,,	,,	7	,,	,,	7-9[8]
(3) 125 lbs. to market-------------	8-10[6,7]	,,	36	,,	,,	10	,,	,,	8-1(

[1]Normally, less space is needed for slotted floors than for solid floors. However, the space requirements pigs kept on each of the two kinds of floors are about the same provided (1) solid floors are scraped daily an (2) one is not too concerned over the soiled appearance of hogs that are rather crowded on solid floors (such on solid floors will be dirty, but they will perform well).
[2]Ceiling heights in excess of 7 to 8 feet make for cold hog houses in the northern half of the United States.
[3]For example, a 6 ft. feeder open on both sides has 12 linear ft. of feeding space.
[4]With creep provided for pigs in addition.

It is noteworthy that with slotted floors only half as much floor space per hog is needed as when using conventional solid floors.

Storage Space Requirements for Feed and Bedding

Table 10-10 gives the space requirements for feed and bedding. This information may be helpful to the individual operator who desires to compute the building space requirements for storage. Also, it provides a convenient means of estimating the amount of feed and bedding in storage. A sow may require a little over a ton of feed each year, or a space allowance of about 60 cubic feet for a year's supply of feed. It will require ½ ton of feed

D EQUIPMENT FOR SWINE

					Watering Equipment (see Table 6-16 for water requirements)		
Feeding Equipment							
Self-feeder Space (Animals/ Linear Ft. or per Hole)		% of Total Self-feeder Space Given to Protein Supplement		Feed Trough Space/ Animal for Hand-feeding	Water Trough Space Hand-feeding	Automatic Watering Cups (two openings considered 2 cups)	Comments
Drylot	Pasture	Drylot	Pasture				
. animals/ ɩnear ft.)³	(no. animals/ linear ft.)³	(% total feeder space)	(% total feeder space)	(linear ft./ animal)	(linear ft./ animal)		
2	3	15	10-15	1½	1½	1 cup/12 gilts	When alfalfa hay is
3	4	,,	,,	2	2	1 cup/10 sows	fed in rack, allow 4 sows/linear ft.
1⁴	1⁴	,,	,,	1½⁴	2	1 cup/4 sows	For the pig creep,
1⁴	1⁴	,,	,,	1½⁴	2	1 cup/4 sows	provide a minimum of 1 ft. of
1	1	,,	,,	2	2	1 cup/2 boars	feeder space/5 pigs, see that the edge of the feeder trough does not exceed 4 in. above the ground floor,
4	4-5	25%	20-25%	¾	¾	1 cup for each 20 pigs	and do not allow more than 40 pigs per creep.
3	3-4	20%	15-20%	1	1	,, ,, ,,	When salt or mineral is fed free-choice, provide 1
3	3-4	15%	10-15%	1¼	1¼	,, ,, ,,	linear ft. of mineral box space/100 pigs.

⁵For early weaning (under 5 to 6 weeks) space requirements, see Table 14-1, under section entitled "Early
ning of Pigs," in Chapter XIV, "Swine Management."
⁶Over and above the sleeping space given herein, pigs that are confined from weaning to market should be
¬ided the feeding floor space recommended in the column headed "Paved Feeding Floor in Addition to Sleeping
ᴄe, When Confined, Per Animal."
⁷The larger area in the summer time.
⁸The larger area when fed from troughs; the smaller area is adequate where self-feeders are used.

to raise a pig from birth to market; or 25 cubic feet. Feeder pigs
will use about 400 pounds of feed for each 100 pounds gain, requiring storage space of 10 cubic feet per 100 pounds gain. Bedding requirements will be from ¼ to ½ ton per pig.

TABLE 10-10

STORAGE SPACE REQUIREMENTS FOR FEED AND BEDDING

Kind of Feed or Bedding		Pounds per Cubic Feet (approx.)	Cubic Feet per Ton (approx.)	Pounds per Bushel of Grain	Cubic Feet per Bushel
Straw and Shavings	Straw, baled ----------	10	200		
	Straw, loose -----------	2-3	600-1,000		
	Shavings, baled------	20	100		
Silage	Corn or sorghum si-lage in tower silos---	40	50		
	Corn or sorghum si-lage in trench silos--	35	57		
Mill Feed	Bran---------------------	13	154		
	Middlings--------------	25	80		
	Linseed or soybean meal --------------------	35	57		
Grain	Corn, shelled----------	45	45	56	1.25
	Corn, ear ---------------	28	72	70	2.50
	Oats----------------------	26	77	32	1.25
	Barley ------------------	39	51	48	1.25
	Wheat ------------------	48	42	60	1.25
	Rye ---------------------	45	44	56	1.25
	Grain sorghum -------	45	44	56	1.25

QUESTIONS FOR STUDY AND DISCUSSION

1. Why is there so much interest in swine buildings and equipment at this time?

2. Make a critical study of your own swine buildings and equipment, or those on a hog farm with which you are familiar, and determine their (a) desirable and (b) undesirable features.

3. What are the determining factors in choosing between (a) a pasture system, (b) a combined pasture and confinement system, and (c) total confinement?

4. Why are hogs more sensitive to extremes in temperatures— either hot or cold—than other farm animals? What is the most desirable temperature for each class of hogs? What can be done to modify (a) winter and (b) summer temperatures?

5. One of the first, and frequently one of the most difficult, problems confronting the swine producer who wishes to construct a building or item of equipment is that of arriving at

the proper size or dimensions. In planning to construct new buildings and equipment for swine, what factors and measurements for buildings and equipment should be considered?

6. List and discuss the factors determining the type and size of swine buildings.

7. Discuss the important and specific construction details that should be incorporated in farrowing houses.

8. In your area, will the savings effected in equipment and labor by the use of a lagoon offset the wastage of the fertility value of the manure?

SELECTED REFERENCES

Title of Publication	Author(s)	Publisher
Approved Practices in Swine Production	G. C. Cook E. M. Juergenson	The Interstate Printers & Publishers, Inc., Danville, Ill., 1962.
Effects of Floor Space Allowance and Number per Group on Performance of Growing-Finishing Swine	G. D. Gehlback, et al.	*Journal of Animal Science,* Vol. 25, No. 2, May, 1966.
Farm Buildings	John C. Wooley	McGraw-Hill Book Company, Inc., New York, N. Y., 1946.
Farm Service Buildings	Harold E. Gray	McGraw-Hill Book Company, Inc., New York, N. Y., 1955.
Farm Structures	H. J. Barre L. L. Sammet	John Wiley & Sons, Inc., New York, N. Y., 1950.
Hog Houses	T. E. Bond G. M. Peterson	Misc. Pub. 744, USDA, Washington, D. C., January, 1958.
Hog Shelters and Equipment for Southern States	Agri. Handbook No. 115	USDA, Washington, D. C., February, 1957.
Lagoon Manure Disposal		Midwest Plan Service, Iowa State University, Ames, Ia., 1966.
Management of Farm Animal Wastes	Symposium Proceedings	American Society of Agricultural Engineers, St. Joseph, Mich., 1966.
Meat Hog, The	C. H. Hinman	Claude H. Hinman, Grand Junction, Colo., 1955.
Pork Production	W. W. Smith	The Macmillan Company, New York, N. Y., 1952.
Raising Swine	G. P. Deyoe J. L. Krider	McGraw-Hill Book Co., New York, N. Y., 1952.

Title of Publication	Author(s)	Publisher
Southern Hog Raising	C. C. Scarborough	The Interstate Printers & Publishers, Inc., Danville, Ill., 1958.
Stockman's Handbook, The	M. E. Ensminger	The Interstate Printers & Publishers, Inc., Danville, Ill., 1970.
Swine Equipment Plans and Housing	Midwest Plan Service	Midwest Plan Service, Iowa State University, Ames, Ia., 1964.
Swine Production	Staff	Farmers' Bul. 2166, USDA, U. S. Gov't. Printing Office, Washington, D. C., 1966.
Swine Production	C. E. Bundy R. V. Diggins	Prentice-Hall, Inc., Englewood Cliffs, N. J., 1956.
Swine Production	W. E. Carroll J. L. Krider F. N. Andrews	McGraw-Hill Book Co., New York, N. Y., 1962.
Ventilation for Swine	D. R. Daum F. W. Andrews	Circ. 862, University of Illinois, Urbana, Ill., 1964.

CHAPTER XI

SWINE HEALTH, DISEASE PREVENTION, AND PARASITE CONTROL[1]

by

Dr. Robert F. Behlow, DVM, Professor and Extension
Veterinarian, North Carolina State University,
Raleigh, North Carolina,

and

Dr. M. E. Ensminger, Ph.D., Distinguished Professor,
Wisconsin State University; and Collaborator, U.S.
Department of Agriculture.

Contents   Page

----

[1] The material presented in this chapter is based on factual information
believed to be accurate, but it is not guaranteed. Where the instructions and
precautions given herein are in disagreement with those of competent local
authorities or reputable manufacturers, always follow the latter two.

Contents   Page

In the discussion that follows, an attempt is made to give a combination of practical and scientific information relative to the most important diseases affecting swine. It is intended that this should enhance the services of the veterinarian; and the producer can do a better job in controlling diseases when he has enlightened information at his disposal. Effective animal health programs call for full cooperation between the producer and the veterinarian.

The estimated average annual swine losses, including baby pig losses, caused by diseases and parasites total $370 million, with a breakdown as follows: infectious and noninfectious diseases, $300,850,000; internal parasites, $65,739,000; and external parasites, $3,000,000.[2]

Swine men should also be well informed relative to the relationship of swine diseases and parasites to other classes of animals and to human health, because many of them are transmissible between species. It is noteworthy, for example, that

---

[2]*Losses in Agriculture*, Agriculture Handbook No. 291, ARS, USDA, 1965, pp. 74, 79, and 82. Figures are estimated average annual losses for the period 1951-1960.

over ninety different types of infectious and parasitic diseases can be spread from animals to human beings.[3] Accordingly, other classes of animals and humans necessarily will be mentioned in the discussion which follows relative to swine diseases and parasites.

Some of the common swine diseases and parasites will be discussed in this chapter.

NORMAL TEMPERATURE, PULSE RATE, AND BREATHING RATE OF SWINE

Table 11-1 gives the normal temperature, pulse rate, and breathing rate of swine. In general, any marked and persistent deviations from these normals may be looked upon as a sign of animal ill health.

TABLE 11-1

NORMAL TEMPERATURE, PULSE RATE, AND BREATHING RATE OF SWINE

Normal Rectal Temperature		Normal Pulse Rate	Normal Breathing Rate
Average	Range		
(degrees F.)	(degrees F.)	(rate/min.)	(rate/min.)
102.6	102-103.6	60-80	8-18

Every stockman should provide himself with an animal thermometer, which is heavier and more rugged than the ordinary human thermometer. The temperature is measured by inserting the thermometer full length in the rectum, where it should be left a minimum of 3 minutes. Prior to inserting the thermometer, a long string should be tied to the end.

In general, infectious diseases are ushered in with a rise in body temperature, but it must be remembered that body temperature is affected by barn or outside temperature, exercise, excitement, age, feed, etc. It is lower in cold weather, in older animals, and at night.

---

[3] Table 67 of the fourth edition of *Diseases Transmitted from Animals to Man*, by Dr. Thomas G. Hull, published by Charles C. Thomas, Springfield, Ill., lists 92 diseases which animals transmit to man.

The pulse rate indicates the rapidity of the heart action. The pulse of swine is taken on the inside of the thigh where the femoral artery comes in close proximity to the skin. It should be pointed out that the younger, the smaller, and the more nervous the animal, the higher the pulse rate. Also, the pulse rate increases with exercise, excitement, digestion, and high outside temperature.

The breathing rate can be determined by placing the hand on the flank, by observing the rise and fall of the flanks, or, in the winter, by watching the breath condensate in coming from the nostrils. Rapid breathing due to recent exercise, excitement, hot weather or poorly ventilated buildings should not be confused with disease. Respiration is accelerated in pain and in febrile conditions.

A PROGRAM OF SWINE HEALTH, DISEASE PREVENTION, AND PARASITE CONTROL[4]

Successful swine production necessitates the application of health-conserving, disease-prevention, and parasite-control measures to the breeding, feeding, and management of the herd. By nature, the pig possesses clean habits, if only he is given an opportunity. In altogether too many cases, however, the pig is placed in crowded conditions, old hog lots, and filthy quarters. Such conditions favor the attack by the common diseases and parasites of swine.

The following program of swine health, disease prevention, and parasite control is presented with the hope that the swine producer will use it (1) as a yardstick with which to compare his existing program, and (2) as a guidepost so that he and his local veterinarian, and other advisors, may develop a similar and specific program for his own enterprise.

I. General Swine Health Program

The basic goal of swine sanitation is that there be healthy animals raised in clean, dry quarters that are well-ventilated, with plenty of clean water (water fountains should be drained

---

[4] The authors are very grateful to Dr. Maynard L. Spear, DVM, Extension Veterinarian, Iowa State University, Ames, Iowa, who reviewed this section and made many helpful suggestions.

and cleaned frequently). At its best, this involves observance of the following rules:

1. Plan the entire physical plant layout for efficient, rapid, and adequate cleaning, and locate it so as to allow natural drainage away from buildings and feeding floors.

2. Separate farrowing and nursery area at least 100 feet from other buildings, with all traffic away from area.

3. Provide isolation quarters at least 300 feet from other swine buildings; and so that drainage will be away from, rather than toward, any swine lots, pastures, or buildings.

4. Remove soiled bedding and body discharges frequently— daily if necessary.

5. Provide for adequate disposal of manure. Do not spread hog manure on hog pastures.

6. Clean and disinfect all buildings and equipment immediately after each period of use.

7. Allow buildings to remain idle three days to three weeks before bringing in a new group of hogs, according to specific needs and depending on how well cleaning and disinfecting are carried out.

8. Provide special footwear and coveralls for use in farrowing and nursery area and disinfectant footbath at entrance.

9. Dispose of dead animals (a) through licensed, properly equipped rendering trucks, (b) by deep burial—at least 6 feet with carcass covered with lime before dirt is replaced, or (c) by complete burning.

10. Dispose of comtaminated bedding by (a) burial or burning; (b) complete soaking of entire mass with 3 percent solution of U.S.P. cresol compound, with chloride of lime—30 percent available chlorine, or with formaldehyde; or (c) spreading on cropland.

II. The Breeding Herd

1. Maintain a closed herd insofar as is possible. Do not allow breeding stock to come into contact, either directly or indirectly, with hogs from other herds. Start with breeding stock that is apparently free of infectious diseases. Do not allow poultry to mingle with breeding stock.

2. Buy breeding stock from as few herds as possible (one is best). Insist on evidence of freedom from disease in the herds from which you buy stock. Such evidence may include general disease certification programs, brucellosis validation, or specific pathogen-free certification, as well as observation of the herd by the buyer or his veterinarian. As a further safeguard, keep newly purchased breeding stock isolated for at least six weeks. During this period, observe them for symptoms of disease, and blood test for brucellosis and leptospirosis.

3. Validate the herd for brucellosis by (a) blood testing all animals 6 months of age or over, and (b) obtaining two consecutive negative tests 30 to 90 days apart. Then, recertify the herd annually thereafter, by passing a single negative test on the entire herd. If brucellosis is found, select and follow the appropriate eradication plan (1, 2, or 3) as given in this chapter under "Brucellosis (Cause, Prevention, and Treatment)."

4. Blood test all animals for leptospirosis at the time of purchase; then isolate them for 30 days and retest prior to adding to the herd. Revaccinate all sows annually in areas where the disease is known to be present. Consult with your veterinarian.

5. Consult with your veterinarian relative to your hog cholera prevention program for the breeding herd, as shipping rules and preventive vaccination recommendations relative to this disease are being revised frequently. Never vaccinate sows during pregnancy; serum alone may be used if necessary.

6. Vaccinate females and boars for erysipelas if recommended by the veterinarian. Sows can also be vaccinated during pregnancy, to within a month to three weeks before farrowing. This increases the antibody level of the sow's milk so that the pigs probably will not need to be vaccinated during the first few weeks of life; in fact, vaccination of pigs should be delayed since a high antibody level in the sow's milk may prevent development of satisfactory immunity by the pigs. The advice of a veterinarian should be sought on erysipelas control programs in herds where the disease has been a problem.

7. Consult a veterinarian before attempting to develop immunity to transmissible gastroenteritis (TGE) by exposing sows to the virus.

8. Control external parasites on sows and boars. Malathion or toxaphene will give effective control of hog mange and lice if applied according to the manufacturer's directions. But do not

use these products on pigs before they are weaned, and do not use toxaphene on animals during the last 28 days before slaughter. Since low-grade, unnoticed mange may be present on sows in the summer, it is good insurance routinely to treat every sow in the fall or winter during the last six weeks before farrowing. Lindane, used according to directions, will also control both lice and mange, and many hogmen use it; but toxicity problems have been reported.

If hogs are lousy and no mange is present, apply 5 percent ronnel (Korlan) evenly to the bedding at the rate of 0.5 lbs./100 sq. ft.

9. Treat sows for ascarids (large roundworms) with dichlorvos or piperazine 10 days to 4 weeks before farrowing. In the South, where strongyloides are a problem, gilts and sows should be wormed 10 days before breeding. Where ascarids are the only problem, piperazine is effective and cheaper than dichlorvos.

10. House sows in well-ventilated, draft-free buildings. Bedding should be dry at all times.

11. Group sows according to age and weight, with no more than 20 to 25 sows to a group.

12. Arrange housing and feeding facilities to insure maximum exercise. However, do not force sows or boars to travel great distances over rough, frozen ground or on ice.

13. Provide adequate shade for the breeding herd during summer months. Access to a wallow or a sprinkler may increase the number of live pigs farrowed, but hogs should be kept out of filth such as old wallows that are used year after year.

14. Isolate and treat sows showing signs of flu or pneumonia. Do not breed sows that are suffering from flu or pneumonia; be certain they have recovered before breeding.

15. Wash sows with warm water and soap and rinse with a mild antiseptic solution before moving them into the farrowing area. When washing the sow, particular care should be taken to remove the small plug of dirt from the end of each teat. Also, sows may be sprayed for mange and lice at this time.

16. If sows have been rather generously fed during gestation, reduce the allowance and use a laxative feed after they are placed in farrowing stalls. The amount necessary to satisfy them will vary, but should not be more than approximately 30 to 50 percent of normal daily intake during the latter part of gestation.

Where sows have been fed 4 pounds per head per day until 30 days before farrowing, then 4 to 6 pounds daily from this time until they are placed in farrowing stalls, no reduction in allowance is necessary until farrowing. Give little or no feed on day of farrowing, then feed 4 pounds the first day after farrowing.

17. Inject sows with antibiotics before and after farrowing to prevent uterine infections following farrowing, provided the veterinarian so recommends.

18. Do not allow other hog producers and visitors in pens or on pastures with the breeding herd without first changing their outer clothing and washing footwear in a disinfectant solution; and do not allow equipment and dogs from other farms and delivery vehicles to enter pens or pastures with sows. Post buildings and lots with signs requesting compliance with these rules.

III. Farrowing to Weaning

From birth to weaning is the most critical period in the life of a pig. About one out of four pigs dies before weaning, with a large percentage of these losses occurring during the first week after farrowing. The following program will materially lessen baby pig losses.

1. Provide farrowing quarters that are warm, dry, and free of drafts, as it will help prevent scours and other baby pig diseases. Scrape, clean, and disinfect the farrowing house between farrowing periods. Having the farrowing house idle for three weeks between farrowing periods helps to check the buildup of infectious organisms. Farrowing stalls, guard rails, or other structural design should be used to save pigs from being laid on by the sows. Use a small amount of bedding such as coarsely ground corncobs, chopped straw, or wood shavings. Keep bedding clean and dry.

2. Be on hand when sows farrow, or at least check on them every few hours. Remove the newborn pigs from the surrounding membrane and clean the mucus from their noses and mouths. Placing the pigs under a brooder or heat lamp may save some of them from being laid on or chilled.

3. Help weak or chilled pigs to nurse, as pigs should receive colostrum milk soon after birth.

4. Provide heat lamps or other supplemental heat for baby pigs when temperature drops below 55° to 60° F. Use a heat lamp

over the protected area for the pigs. Suspend the heat lamp from 24 to 28 inches above the bedding and follow other rules for safe use of heat lamps.

5. Even up litters and provide for orphan pigs by switching among sows farrowing within 48 hours of each other. But first the pigs should be allowed to nurse, and runt pigs should be destroyed, before extra pigs in a litter are transferred to another sow. Attempts to transfer pigs to a sow that has farrowed more than three or four days beforehand are seldom successful, since teats that are not nursed dry up. Masking the body odor of the pigs by spraying the litter and the transferred pigs with a disinfectant may be helpful in changing older pigs.

6. Sever navel cord $\frac{1}{2}$ to 1 inch long. This can be done by grasping between the thumb and finger of each hand and pulling until it parts. The cord can be cut, but this may result in excessive bleeding. Disinfect navel with 7 percent tincture of iodine solution to protect against infections that enter through the navel.

7. Clip "needle teeth" soon after birth to prevent cuts on the sow's udder or injury to pigs' noses when they fight. Cut the tip off the tooth with a pair of sharp sidecutter pliers. Be careful not to crush the teeth, injure the gum, or leave jagged edges or you may do more harm than good.

8. Prevent nutritional anemia (blood deficiency) in pigs kept on wood or concrete floors for two weeks or more after farrowing. This can be accomplished by—

   a. Injecting in the flank armpit or in the loose skin of the neck an iron-dextran compound (containing 150 mg of iron) at one to three days of age. Repeat at two to three weeks if necessary. Be sure needles and syringes are boiled for 25 to 30 minutes to avoid abscess formation.

   b. Placing clean, hog-manure-free, sod in each farrowing pen several times a week.

   c. Giving iron pills or liquid to pigs at weekly intervals.

   d. Using iron fortified baby pig feeds in the creep area.

9. Castrate male pigs early—three days to two weeks of age. This reduces shock and the possibility of infection. Care should be taken to make the incisions low enough to drain properly. Sterilize instruments used in castration before use by boiling for 15 minutes. Keep them clean by placing the instrument in a disinfectant solution before and after each pig is castrated.

On farms where tetanus (lockjaw) is a problem, keep pigs confined to clean quarters until healed.

10. Provide clean, fresh drinking water.

11. Where disease conditions warrant, feed antibiotics in the creep feed and until the pigs reach 75 to 100 pounds.

12. Consult with your veterinarian relative to your hog cholera prevention program of suckling pigs, as shipping rules and preventive vaccination recommendations relative to this disease are being revised frequently. Pigs vaccinated under five weeks of age while nursing an immune sow may not develop good immunity from vaccination.

13. Vaccinate pigs for erysipelas if this disease is in the herd, or if it is prevalent in your community. Vaccinating pigs for erysipelas at eight weeks or older gives better immunity than vaccinating at a younger age. Vaccinate sows to protect baby pigs while nursing. A water vaccine, currently available through veterinarians, appears to be effective when used properly; but be sure to follow directions.

14. Use dichlorvos (Atgard V) or piperazine to deworm pigs when they are five to eight weeks old. They are not as effective when used on younger pigs. The treatment should be repeated in seven to eight weeks under most farm conditions. Worming the sow one to two weeks before putting her in the farrowing house will help protect the pigs from roundworms.

15. Protect suckling pigs from lice and mange by treating the sows and boars as recommended under "The Breeding Herd," point no. 8. Do not spray pigs before they are six weeks old. Treating the bedding with ronnel (Korlan) at the rate of ½ lb. per 100 square feet will eliminate lice, but it has not been shown to be effective against mange.

IV. Weaning to Market

1. Provide dry, well-bedded, draft-free sleeping quarters that are well ventilated. Pigs put in buildings that are cold and drafty are susceptible to diseases such as pneumonia, and they usually make poor daily gains. Extra bedding will help reduce the stress of cold weather. In hot weather, adequate shade is necessary. A mist spray system or wallow helps reduce the stress of hot weather, but hogs should be kept out of stagnant pools or old wallows that are used year after year.

2. Separate pigs into groups according to size, rather than age. Keep groups as uniform as possible with regard to size. Generally, it is not advisable to have more than 40 feeder pigs in a group.

3. Feed well-balanced rations, properly fortified. Keep clean drinking water available at all times. Provide one fountain for each 30 head and no more than four pigs per feeder hole.

4. Control internal parasites, especially ascarids (round-worms), through sanitation, pasture rotation, and use of drugs. The McLean County system of rotating pastures and sanitation remains the best method of preventing infestation by worms of pigs on pasture. For pigs in confinement, thorough and frequent cleaning of buildings and floors is the best control program.

Worm routinely if autopsy or fecal examinations reveal adult worms or worm eggs, using dichlorvos or piperazine every 50 days. All preparations used as wormers should be administered according to the directions of the manufacturer or the veterinarian.

5. Follow a louse and mange control program routinely. A spray or dip is best, and malathion or toxaphene, used according to manufacturer's directions, are best for control of both lice and mange. Lindane may be used according to directions, but toxicity problems have been reported.

Small groups of animals should be sprayed at one time, and complete coverage of the body is necessary to control the parasites. Re-treatment in 10 to 14 days is recommended. If weather does not permit the use of a spray or dip, dusting powders can be used. To be treated properly, pigs must be confined. If temperatures are extreme, simply hold the pigs in confinement until they are dry.

6. Isolate sick hogs immediately, and notify the veterinarian.

V. Purchased Feeder Pigs

Normally, death losses from the time of delivery of feeder pigs to your farm until market time should not exceed 2 percent. About half these losses occur during the first week after arrival.

Feeder pigs that are in good condition and purchased from a reliable source, then handled as described, will have the best chance of getting off to a good start with minimum death losses:

1. Abide by the legal health regulations of your state. These

laws are for your protection. Vaccinations and other health certificates should be furnished by the seller and demanded by the buyer.

2. Avoid unnecessary handling, watch the pigs closely during this critical period, and work with your veterinarian to maintain optimum herd health.

3. Keep newly arrived feeder pigs isolated from other hogs for at least three weeks.

4. Avoid contact between feeder pigs and breeding stock, because feeder pigs can sometimes be carriers of diseases which can be spread to other hogs on the farm. Wear different outer clothing and boots when working with two sets of pigs to avoid spreading disease.

5. Provide warm, dry, draft-free, disinfected, well-bedded quarters.

6. Allow ample space for feeding, watering, and sleeping; provide one feeder space at the feeder for each five pigs, one waterer for each 30 pigs, and 4 to 6 square feet of sleeping space per pig.

7. Feed a low protein (10 percent or less) ration for the first three to four days.

8. Use high antibiotic level for the first three days, preferably in the drinking water.

9. Dust bedding for control of lice and mange before pigs arrive. Do not spray pigs sooner than five days after arrival or when weather is unfavorable.

10. Do not worm or castrate pigs for at least 10 days after arrival.

11. Keep pigs of different sizes separated; otherwise, the bigger ones will crowd the smaller ones away from feed and water.

12. When signs of trouble appear, call your veterinarian.

Disease-free Pigs

Two widespread and costly swine diseases—atrophic rhinitis and mycoplasma pneumonia (PPLO)—are chiefly responsible for the development of disease-free pig programs.

The following two types of disease-free pig programs are being followed by some:

1. **The SPF (Specific Pathogen Free) Pig Method.**—The pertinent facts about this method, which was originated by Dr. George Young of the Hormel Institute, are:

a. **Definition of an SPF pig.**—An SPF pig is a pig free from specific pathogens. A pathogen is any disease-causing virus, microorganism, or other substance. The specific diseases and parasites eliminated by the SPF program are: virus pig pneumonia (VPP), atrophic rhinitis (AR), lice, mange, and vibronic dysentery (bloody scours), and other unknown intestinal diseases.

b. **Definition of a primary SPF pig.**—A primary SPF pig is one that was removed from its mother just prior to birth by a surgical process (Caesarean section) and raised in laboratory isolation, never having a chance to contract one of the diseases which its mother might be carrying or spreading.

c. **Definition of a secondary SPF pig.**—A secondary SPF pig is one that was farrowed and raised normally by either a primary SPF mother or another secondary SPF mother. Secondary SPF pigs are referred to as first, second, and third generation, depending on how far they are removed from the primary or laboratory pig.

d. **Definition of a closed herd.**—A closed herd is one which admits only SPF stock for new additions. Primary stock can be admitted direct from the laboratory. Any secondary or naturally farrowed stock should be only from certified (accredited) herds to be sure that no pathogen is being carried in. Closing the herd also pertains to human traffic. Allow no one to enter buildings or pens without wearing boots and coveralls furnished by the owner. Feed deliveries should be made "over the fence."

e. **Length of time that a herd will remain disease-free from the specific diseases which were eliminated.**—With care, a clean herd may remain free of such specific diseases indefinitely. The only way a herd can become infected is by bringing a disease back on the farm. This can be done by introducing non-SPF swine to the farm or by the careless use of feeders, equipment, boots, shoes, or clothing that has been used around non-SPF hogs.

f. **How to make sure that new stock brought into a herd is really SPF.**—This can be done by buying only from certified (accredited) primary or secondary herds or direct from the laboratory. The National SPF Accrediting Agency has been formed to govern the accreditation of SPF herds. A portion of each three-months farrowing must undergo post mortem inspection at packing house to determine that virus pneumonia and rhinitis are not present. A percentage of pigs must be submitted from each crop unless a producer is following a continuous farrowing program in which case these requirements apply. The herd must be brucellosis free. A veterinarian must inspect the herd every 90 days. Every animal in the herd must be posted to determine the cause of death. A complete health record of the herd must be available for inspection. In addition to health standards, certification (accreditation) will require meeting certain growth and performance standards.

g. **Diseases that are not eliminated by the SPF program.**—Hog cholera, leptospirosis, and erysipelas are not eliminated by the SPF program. Neither are internal parasites (roundworms) eliminated by such a program.

h. **The dollars and cents value of an SPF program.**—A comparison of first and second generation SPF herds versus non-SPF herds showed that total production per litter was increased 32.7 percent, or 42 lbs. of pork, for the SPF herds. This is equivalent to two 200-lb. pigs every farrowing. The profit from these two pigs would average $20 to $25. A large operator farrowing 20 sows every two months could average $2,400 extra profit per year on this basis. It has been conservatively figured that a herd with virus pneumonia requires 200 lbs. of extra feed to market each pig. The feed conversion on a clean hog would be around 3 (300 lbs. of feed to produce 100 lbs. of pork). Virus pig pneumonia and atrophic rhinitis can raise this feed conversion to 4, 5, or even 6. A thousand head of hogs requiring 200 lbs. of extra feed for each hog (feed conversion of 4) would mean an increased feed cost of $6,000 based on a cost of $3.00 per cwt.

2. **The isolation method.**—The province of Ontario, Canada, has designed an isolation program for cleaning up atrophic

rhinitis and mycoplasma pneumonia (PPLO). Enrolled herds are inspected by provincial department veterinarians every six weeks the first year, and four times yearly thereafter. The pertinent provisions of the isolation method are:

a. Select gilts or sows showing no visible signs of atrophic rhinitis or mycoplasma pneumonia, and isolate one animal to the pen.

b. Slaughter one-third of all pigs raised to market weight, and at least two pigs per litter; with inspection of the heads and lungs by a veterinarian from the Ontario Veterinary College.

Certification is granted to herds showing no evidence of either disease after two litters from each sow or gilt chosen for the test have passed the post-mortem examination. Replacement breeding stock can be taken only from the second litter.

The Certified Herd Policy also stipulates that the breeder must keep records of births, deaths, and sales of all pigs born on the premises; mark individually all pigs before they are six weeks old; submit for examination by the veterinarian of the Ontario Veterinary Laboratory the head and lungs of all pigs that die after six weeks of age; permit a veterinary inspector to look at the pigs as often as deemed necessary; permit the inspection of at least one-third of the total number of pigs raised to market weight; slaughter or have slaughtered any pigs requested by the veterinary inspector for a diagnostic examination; carry out such sanitary programs as prescribed by the inspector; guard against the introduction of disease into the herd by visitors; restrict purchase of additions of animals from herds of similar health status; and refrain from returning to the premises any pigs that are removed for show and sale purposes.

Both of these methods are drastic and costly. However, at the present time, they are the only means whereby atrophic rhinitis and mycoplasma pneumonia (PPLO) can be controlled effectively and subsequently eradicated. Also, disease-free pigs offer the most hope in the continuing battle against infectious scours in young pigs.

DISEASES OF SWINE

Adequate sanitation is the first and most important re-

quirement that must be fulfilled if the swine enterprise is to be disease free. Filthy quarters, feeding floors, and watering places favor the entrance of disease-producing germs into the body of the animal. In addition to maintaining a program of sanitation, the good herdsman is ever alert in observing any deviation from the normal in the functions of the animal—such as loss of appetite, lameness, digestive disturbances, etc.

A competent veterinarian should be called with the appearance of serious trouble, but often intelligent help may be given before a veterinarian can be reached. Moreover, the appearance of serious disorders can be recognized and control measures instituted before the spread of the disease has made much progress. The herdsman who is sufficiently familiar with the nature and causes of the common diseases is in a position to employ sound preventive measures.

This chapter is limited to non-nutritional diseases and ailments; the nutritional diseases and ailments of swine are covered in Chapter VI.

Anthrax (or Splenic Fever, Charbon)

Anthrax, also referred to as splenic fever or charbon, is an acute infectious disease affecting all warm-blooded animals and man; but cattle are most susceptible. It usually occurs as scattered outbreaks or cases, but hundreds of animals may be involved. Certain sections are known as anthrax districts because of the repeated appearance of the disease. Grazing animals are particularly subject to anthrax, especially when pasturing closely following a drought or on land that has been recently flooded. In the United States, human beings get the disease mostly from handling diseased or dead animals on the farm or hides, hair, and wool in factories.

Historically, anthrax is of great importance. It is one of the first scourges to be described in ancient and Biblical literature; it marks the beginning of modern bacteriology, being described by Koch in 1876; and it is the first disease in which immunization was effected by means of an attenuated culture, Pasteur having immunized animals against anthrax in 1881.

Anthrax causes estimated average annual swine losses of $51,000.[5]

---

[5]*Losses in Agriculture*, Agriculture Handbook No. 291, ARS, USDA, 1965, p. 74.

SYMPTOMS AND SIGNS[6]

The mortality is usually quite high. It runs a very short course and is characterized by a blood poisoning (septicemia). In swine, the disease is usually evidenced by swelling of the throat, which leads to death from suffocation and blood poisoning. It is accompanied by high temperature, loss of appetite, muscular weakness, depression, and the passage of blood-stained feces.

CAUSE, PREVENTION, AND TREATMENT

The disease is identified by a microscopic examination of the blood in which will be found the typical large, rod-shaped organ-

Fig. 11-1. Hog with anthrax. Note the swelling of the throat. This was rapidly followed by blood poisoning and death. (Courtesy, Dept. of Veterinary Pathology and Hygiene, College of Veterinary Medicine, University of Illinois)

---

[6] Currently, many veterinarians prefer the word "signs" rather than "symptoms," but throughout this chapter the author accedes to the more commonly accepted terminology among swine producers and includes the word "symptoms."

isms causing anthrax, *Bacillus anthracis.* The bacillus that causes anthrax can survive for years in a spore stage, resisting all destructive agents. As a result, it may remain in the soil for extremely long periods.

This disease is one that can largely be prevented by immunization. In the so-called anthrax regions, vaccination should be performed well in advance of the time when the disease normally makes its appearance. At least nine types of biologics (serums, bacterins, and vaccines) are now available for use in anthrax vaccination, and the choice of the one to be used should be left to the local veterinarian or state livestock sanitary officials. In infested areas, vaccination should be repeated each year. Herds that are infected should be quarantined, and all milk and other products should be withheld from the market until the danger of disease transmission is past. The farmer or rancher should never open the carcass of a dead animal suspected of having died from anthrax; instead, the veterinarian should be summoned at the first sign of an outbreak.

When the presence of anthrax is suspected or proved, all carcasses and contaminated material should be completely burned or deeply buried, preferably on the spot. This precaution is important because the disease can be spread by dogs, coyotes, buzzards, and other flesh eaters and by flies and other insects.

When an outbreak of anthrax is discovered, all sick animals should be isolated promptly and treated (penicillin or the tetracyclines are most commonly used). All exposed healthy animals should be vaccinated; pastures should be rotated; the premises should be quarantined; and a rigid program of sanitation should be initiated. These control measures should be carried out under the supervision of a veterinarian.

The treatment of affected animals is not too satisfactory. Penicillin or the tetracyclines are effective if given early.

Atrophic Rhinitis (or Infectious Atrophic Rhinitis)

Atrophic rhinitis is quite widespread in the United States, and it has been reported in other countries. Apparently, it affects swine only; for it does not seem to be related to atrophic rhinitis in man. The annual losses from atrophic rhinitis are estimated at $40,085,000.[7]

_____
[7]*Losses in Agriculture*, Agriculture Handbook No. 291, ARS, USDA, 1965, p. 74.

SYMPTOMS AND SIGNS

Persistent sneezing, which becomes more pronounced as the pigs grow older, is the first symptom. At 4 to 8 weeks of age, the snout begins to show wrinkles, and it may bulge and thicken. At 8 to 16 weeks of age, the snout and face may twist to one side. Nose bleeding is often seen. Affected pigs become rough all over, and make slow and inefficient gains. Actual death may be due to pneumonia. Young pigs under 60 to 80 pounds weight are most susceptible. No simple test is available to check for carrier swine.

CAUSE, PREVENTION, AND TREATMENT

The etiology of the disease has not been completely elucidated. However, it appears to be caused by *Bordetella bronchiseptica* and other bacteria. Also, a calcium-phosphorus imbalance or a calcium deficiency in growing pigs have been shown to produce similar, if not identical, lesions. Actually, atrophic rhinitis is a disease complex, rather than a single disease.

Preventive measures consist in (1) selecting breeding stock from herds known to be clean, and isolating new animals for a period of 30 days; (2) using clean farrowing quarters; (3) if feeder pigs are purchased, selecting animals above 60 to 80 pounds in weight, as they are less susceptible; and (4) separating different age groups.

When the disease strikes, initiate one of the following control plans:

1. Put affected pigs on a creep ration containing 100 grams of sulfa-methazine per ton of feed (Aureo SP-250 has F.D.A. clearance). Use this drug in the feed until pigs reach 75 pounds body weight. This will eliminate *Bordetella* infection, which is the major cause of the disease. Sodium sulfathiazole at the level of 0.5 to 0.66 gm/gallon of drinking water is also effective.

2. Isolate bred females in separate lots and never allow contact with any other swine except their offspring until they are culled. Keep individual litters separate until a month after removal of the sow at weaning time. Then select and isolate new breeding stock from those litters which show no evidence of symptoms.

3. Allow the pigs to nurse the sow one or a few times (to obtain colostrum), and then remove and raise them as orphaned pigs; but never allow them to get near the head of their dam.

Consult a veterinarian relative to treatment. Sulfa drugs in the feed or water will destroy *Bordetella* organisms. Hog cholera antiserum may help in the early stages of the virus disease.

4. Obtain Specific Pathogen Free breeding stock.

Brucellosis

Brucellosis is an insidious (hidden) disease in which the lesions frequently are not evident. Although the medical term "brucellosis" is used in a collective way to designate the disease caused by the three different but closely related *Brucella* organisms, the species names further differentiate the germs as (1) *Brucella abortus*, (2) *Br. suis*, and (3) *Br. melitensis*.

Brucella abortus is known as Bang's disease (after Professor Bang, noted Danish research worker, who, in 1896, first discovered the organism responsible for bovine brucellosis), or contagious abortion in cattle; *Br. suis* causes Traum's disease or infectious abortion in swine; and *Br. melitensis* causes Malta fever, or abortion, in goats. The disease is known as Malta fever, Mediterranean fever, undulant fever, or brucellosis in man. The causative organism is often associated with fistulous withers and poll-evil of horses.

Swine brucellosis control and eradication is important for two reasons: (1) the danger of human infection, and (2) the economic loss. It is estimated that brucellosis causes annual swine losses of $9,876,000.[8]

The blood (agglutination) test is a safe, reliable, and practical method for the diagnosis of brucellosis in all farm animals. Either the tube test method or the rapid plate method is satisfactory when conducted by an experienced technician. There is nothing mysterious about the blood test. It is simply based on the following phenomenon: The bloodstream of an infected animal contains an antibody, known as agglutinin. When the blood serum containing this substance is brought in contact with a suspension

---

[8] *Losses in Agriculture*, Agriculture Handbook No. 291, ARS, USDA, 1965, p. 74.

of brucella organisms (called an antigen), it causes the organisms to adhere to one another and form clumps.

This action, known as agglutination, constitutes a simple test for diagnosing brucellosis in the living animal. The blood test of swine is unquestionably the most readily available diagnostic method for this species.

SYMPTOMS AND SIGNS

Unfortunately, the symptoms of brucellosis are often rather indefinite. It should be borne in mind that not all animals that abort are affected with brucellosis and that not all animals affected with brucellosis will necessarily abort. On the other hand, every case of abortion should be regarded with suspicion until proved noninfectious.

In swine, abortion and sterility are not as common as in cattle; infection may cause swollen joints and lameness, and swelling or atrophy of the testes, epididymus, and prostate in the male.

CAUSE, PREVENTION, AND TREATMENT

The disease is caused by bacteria called *Brucella suis* in

Fig. 11-2. Aborted swine fetuses, the result of brucellosis. While the act of abortion is the most readily observed symptom of this disease in sows, it should be borne in mind that not all sows that abort are affected with brucellosis and that not all sows affected with brucellosis will necessarily abort. (Courtesy, Dept. of Veterinary Pathology and Hygiene, College of Veterinary Medicine, University of Illinois)

swine, *Br. abortus* in cattle, and *Br. melitensis* in goats. The suis and melitensis types are seen in cattle, but the incidence is rare.

Man is susceptible to all three types of brucellosis. The swine organism causes a more severe disease in human beings than the cattle organism, although not so severe as that induced by the goat type. Fortunately, far fewer people are exposed to the latter simply because of the limited number of goats and the rarity of the disease in goats in the United States. Stockmen are aware of the possibility that human beings may contract undulant fever from handling affected animals, especially at the time of parturition; from slaughtering operations or handling raw meats from affected animals; or from consuming raw milk or other raw by-products from goats or cows, and eating uncooked meats infected with brucellosis organisms. The simple precautions of pasteurizing milk and cooking meat, however, make these foods safe for human consumption.

The brucella organism is relatively resistant to drying but is killed by the common disinfectants and by pasteurization. The organism is found in immense numbers in the various tissues of the aborted young and in the discharges and membranes from the aborted animal. It is harbored indefinitely in the udder and may also be found in the sex glands, spleen, liver, kidneys, bloodstream, joints, and lymph nodes.

Brucellosis appears to be commonly acquired through the mouth in feed and water contaminated with the bacteria, or by licking infected animals, contaminated feeders, or other objects to which the bacteria may adhere. There is also evidence that boars frequently transmit the disease through the act of service.

Freedom from disease should be the goal of all control programs. Strict sanitation; the recognition and removal of infected animals through testing programs; isolation at the time of parturition; and the control of animals, feed, and water brought into the premises is the key to the successful control and eradication of brucellosis.

Sound management practices, which include either buying replacement animals that are free of the disease or raising all females, are a necessary adjunct in prevention. Drainage from infected areas should be diverted or fenced off, and visitors (man and animal) should be kept away from animal barns and feed-

lots. Animals taken to livestock shows and fairs should be isolated on their return and tested thirty days later.

To date, vaccination procedures in swine—by the use of Strain 19 (*Brucella abortus*), heat-killed strains of *Br. suis*, or modified live strains of *Br. suis*—have not been successful in brucellosis control programs. Instead, for recommended uniform methods and rules for establishing and maintaining brucellosis-free herds of swine, and areas, see the following publication: *Brucellosis Eradication, recommended uniform methods and rules*, U. S. Department of Agriculture, ARS-91-10-3, Feb. 1963 and Revised, Part V, Section I and Section II thereof. The recommendations therein, which carry the approval of both the USDA and the United States Livestock Sanitary Association, for individual herds of swine are:

A. **Negative herds.**—Validation on the basis of two consecutive negative tests on the entire breeding herd (all breeding animals 6 months of age or over) 30 to 90 days apart.

B. **Infected herds.**—

Plan I.—For use in a commercial herd:

Market the entire herd for slaughter; clean and disinfect houses and equipment; restock premises with animals from Validated Brucellosis-free Herds, placing them on clean ground for at least 60 days; pass two consecutive negative tests 30 to 90 days apart, at which time herd is eligible for validation.

Plan II.—For use in a purebred herd:

Separate pigs from sows at 42 days of age or younger, and isolate; market infected herd for slaughter as soon as practical; test replacement gilts 30 days before breeding, save only those that are negative and breed them to negative boars; retest gilts after farrowing and before moving them from individual farrowing pens, segregate any reactors and retain only pigs from negative sows for breeding purposes; and repeat this procedure until two consecutive negative tests not less than 90 days apart are obtained, at which time the herd is eligible for validation.

Plan III.—Which may be used in herds where only a few reactors are found and no clinical symptoms of brucellosis have been noted:

Market reactors for slaughter; retest herd at 30 day

intervals, removing reactors for slaughter, until entire herd is negative; two negative tests, not less than 90 days apart, qualifying the herd for validation; and if herd is not readily freed of infection, abandon this plan in favor of Plan I or II.

No known medicinal agent is effective in the treatment of brucellosis in any class of farm animals. Therefore, the farmer and rancher should not waste valuable time and money on so-called "cures" that are advocated by fraudulent operators.

Cholera, Hog

This is a highly contagious disease affecting only swine. It is perhaps the most serious disease of swine in North America. Despite widespread use of preventive measures, losses from hog cholera cost $2,945,000 each year.[9]

SYMPTOMS AND SIGNS

The symptoms appear after an incubation period of about a week. The disease is marked by a sudden onset, fever, loss of appetite, and weakness—although some pigs may die without showing any symptoms. Affected animals separate themselves from the herd, show a wobbly, scissor-like gait; and although refusing feed, they may drink much water. The underside of the pig may show a purplish red coloring (also seen in erysipelas and in other acute febrile diseases). Sometimes there is chilling, causing the animals affected to bury themselves in the bedding or to pile up. There is constipation alternating with diarrhea, and coughing is often evident. There may be a discharge from the eyes. Often the disease is associated with pneumonia and/or enteritis. Since this disease is often confused with erysipelas, diagnosis should include a post-mortem examination of one or more of the sick pigs that have recently died, a bacteriological check for the erysipelas bacteria, and perhaps a blood test for white cell count. Microscopic sections of the brain and the Fluorescent Antibody Test have provided the pathologist with the tools with which to diagnose this disease. Positive proof of hog cholera can also be obtained by injecting a cholera-susceptible

---

[9]*Losses in Agriculture*, Agriculture Handbook No. 291, ARS, USDA, 1965, p. 74.

Fig. 11-3. Hogs sick with hog cholera. Note the extreme depression and weakness. (Courtesy, USDA)

pig and cholera-immune pig with blood or filtered suspension of macerated tissues from the suspected animal. If the susceptible pig dies and the control remains well, the disease is confirmed.

CAUSE, PREVENTION, AND TREATMENT

For many years the disease was thought to be due to an organism resembling the typhoid bacillus. Eventually, a virus was incriminated.

The USDA first introduced the simultaneous serum-virus hog cholera vaccination in 1908. This type of immunization had the following effects:

1. It checked the widespread hog cholera epidemics of the old days, when so many hogs died that there was a stench in the air from burning the carcasses.

2. It kept the live, "hot" hog cholera virus (which it contained) spread all over the country.

3. It provided fairly good control; just good enough that American swine producers lived with the disease, rather than wiping it out as has been done in Canada where the use of the live hog cholera virus is forbidden.

In 1951, the USDA granted the first special licenses for the

commercial sale of Modified Live Virus (MLV) preparations of either rabbit, swine, or tissue culture origin. These preparations consist of modified (attenuated) live virus capable of producing long-lasting immunity. But, unfortunately, they were found capable of spreading the infection to susceptible animals. As a result, the USDA banned all interstate shipments of modified hog cholera vaccines after March 1, 1969.

Inactivated vaccine (R114) does not appear to produce cholera. However, the immunity conferred is not strong. States in the "control" phase of eradication (phases 1 and 2 of the four-phase National Hog Cholera Eradication Program that follows) are permitted to use inactivated vaccine until they reach the "stamping out" phase.

In 1961, a National Hog Cholera Eradication Program was enacted (known as Senate Bill 1908). It provides for a federal-state cooperative program to stamp out hog cholera through the following four phases:

1. Educating and legislating.

2. Lowering the incidence rate by increasing vaccination with inactivated vaccine, eliminating use of virulent virus, cooking garbage fed to swine, and accomplishing better control of pig movements.

3. Eliminating hog cholera virus, including all known sources of infection, after the incidence has dropped to a low level.

4. Identifying and eliminating all possible sources of virus introduction.

The objective of the program is to establish a hog cholera-free swine population.

By January 1, 1969, 40 states and Puerto Rico had reached the "stamping out" phase (phases 3 and 4 of the National Hog Cholera Eradication Program).

Circling Disease (or Listerellosis, Encephalitis, Listeriosis)

Circling disease, also called listerellosis or listeriosis, is an infectious disease affecting mainly sheep, goats, and cattle; but it has been reported in swine, foals, and other animals and man. It occurs most often in winter and spring, with a mortality approaching 100 percent.

SYMPTOMS AND SIGNS

This disease principally affects the nervous system. Depression, staggering, circling, and strange awkward movements are noted. Larger pigs may show stilted movements in the front legs and may drag the hind legs. The course of the disease is very short, with paralysis and death the usual termination. Positive diagnosis can be made only by isolation and identification of the specific etiological agent.

CAUSE, PREVENTION, AND TREATMENT

Circling disease results from the invasion of the central nervous system by bacteria called *Listeria monocytogenes*. The method of transmission is unknown, and there are no practical methods of treatment. Various sulfa derivatives, alone and in conjunction with antibiotics, have shown beneficial results if given early.

Dysentery, Swine (or Hemorrhagic Enteritis, Bloody Diarrhea, Bloody Scours, Bloody Dysentery, Bloody Flux, Black Scours, Colitis)

Swine dysentery, an acute infectious disease, has been reported from coast to coast, but it is most common in the Corn Belt, where the swine population is densest. Outbreaks of the disease are usually associated with animals that pass through central markets or public auctions.

SYMPTOMS AND SIGNS

The most characteristic symptom of swine dysentery is a profuse bloody diarrhea. Sometimes the feces are black instead of bloody and contain shreds of tissue. Most affected animals go off feed, and there is a moderate rise in temperature. Some pigs die suddenly after a couple days of illness, whereas others linger on for two weeks or longer. On autopsy or post-mortem, the large intestine is found to be inflamed and bloody.

CAUSE, PREVENTION, AND TREATMENT

Swine dysentery appears to be caused by a microorganism, *Vibrio coli.*

Prevention consists in avoiding public stockyards and auction rings, in isolating newly acquired animals, and in relying on sanitation. In case of an outbreak, sick animals should be removed from the healthy ones and a rigid program of sanitation initiated.

Some animals that have gone through an outbreak of swine dysentery remain carriers, although they may appear to be healthy. When such carriers are introduced into a herd, the signs may not appear in the contact animals until the end of several weeks or months.

Some of the antibiotics, arsenicals, and nitrofurans administered by the veterinarian, may reduce death losses due to swine dysentery. Because infected swine eat very little, if at all, medication through the drinking water is essential. Also, good management and nursing will help.

Edema Disease (or Enterotoxemia, Gut Edema, Gastric Edema, Edema of the Bowel)

This is an acute, usually fatal disease of young pigs (6 to 16 weeks of age). It appears to be increasing in this country.

SYMPTOMS AND SIGNS

The disease usually strikes the most thrifty, rapid-growing pigs. It is commonly ushered in by high temperature and swollen eyelids. Constipation, inability to eat, and a staggering gait may be observed. Affected pigs may display nervous symptoms, such as fits or convulsions. As the disease progresses, the hog becomes completely paralyzed. Death usually follows in from a few hours to 2 to 3 days. The term "gut edema" is derived from the common post-mortem findings of a jelly-like swelling (edema) of the stomach and portions of the intestines.

CAUSE, PREVENTION, AND TREATMENT

The cause of gut edema is not known, but it is believed to be due to the action of toxins associated with hemolytic coliform organisms.

There is no justification, based on present knowledge of this disease, to warrant consideration of quarantine measures.

The administration of 60 gm of magnesium sulfate as a drench is the most common form of treatment, although no treat-

ment is entirely satisfactory. Withholding feed for a short period of time or reduction in the amount of feed will help.

Enteritis (or Swine Enteritis)

This is a general term which includes several enteritic diseases, all of which produce an inflammation of the intestines and are associated primarily with *Salmonella cholerae-suis* (*suipestifer*). Also, internal parasites, or a deficiency of some B-complex vitamins, may cause enteritis.

SYMPTOMS AND SIGNS

It is no longer considered adequate to diagnose the condition as enteritis; it is now necessary to separate and identify the agents which may damage the intestinal tracts of swine.

The symptoms of each of the enteritic diseases are:

Acute salmonellosis.—This is an acute enteritis and septicemia, which usually proves fatal.

Infectious enteritis.—This is an acute enteritis and gastritis, due to *S. cholerae-suis*. Some cases may progress rapidly and terminate in death; others tend to become chronic, with the affected pigs becoming stunted and unthrifty.

Necrotic enteritis.—This is due either to (1) a B-vitamin deficiency and *S. cholerae-suis*, (2) a similar condition—fibrino necrotic enteritis—caused by *S. cholerae-suis* and *Spherophorus necrophorus* (more common now), (3) unsanitary conditions, etc. In necrotic enteritis, there is an inflammation (enteritis) of the large intestine in particular which leads to the development of areas of "necrotic" or dead tissue in the linings of the intestines; hence, the name necrotic enteritis or "necro," as it is often called.

CAUSE, PREVENTION, AND TREATMENT

The cause of each of the three enteritic conditions is given, along with the symptoms, in the previous section.

Prevention rests on good sanitation and management practices. All incoming swine should be quarantined for three weeks prior to introduction into the herd. All sick animals should be immediately separated and the well animals moved to clean quarters if practicable.

Fig. 11-4. (Top) Shows pigs with the typical overt symptoms of enter-itis. Pigs were approximately 80 days of age and averaged 20 pounds in weight. (Bottom) Shows the same pigs 35 days later, after treatment with B vitamins and gaining an average of 1.19 pounds daily. (Courtesy, Dr. R. H. Nelson, Head, Department of Animal Husbandry, Michigan State University)

The veterinarian should be consulted in the event of an out-break. Appropriate sulfa drugs, nitrofurans, B vitamins, and/or antibiotics may be indicated.

Erysipelas, Swine

This is an acute or chronic infectious disease of swine, but

it has also been reported in sheep, rabbits, and turkeys. When it attacks man, it is called erysipeloid, which should not be confused with human erysipelas which is caused by a streptococcal bacteria. Erysipelas causes losses in swine production estimated at $5,490,000 annually.[10]

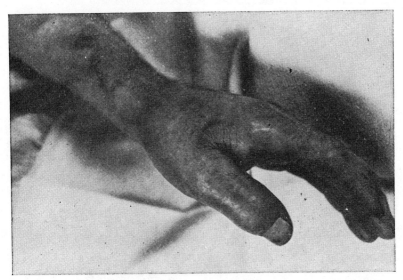

Fig. 11-5. Erysipeloid or swine erysipelas infection in man. This is a troublesome and disabling wound infection. (Courtesy, Dept. of Veterinary Pathology and Hygiene, College of Veterinary Medicine, University of Illinois)

SYMPTOMS AND SIGNS

The disease occurs in three forms. The symptoms of the acute septicemic form resemble those seen in hog cholera. The affected animals show a high fever, and frequently have edema of the nose, ears, and limbs. Edema of the nose usually causes affected animals to breathe with a snoring sound. Also, there may be purplish patches under the belly similar to those described for hog cholera. Death may result, chronicity develop, or complete recovery occur.

The diamond-skin form is a subacute form lasting from one

---

[10]*Losses in Agriculture*, Agriculture Handbook No. 291, ARS, USDA, 1965, p. 74.

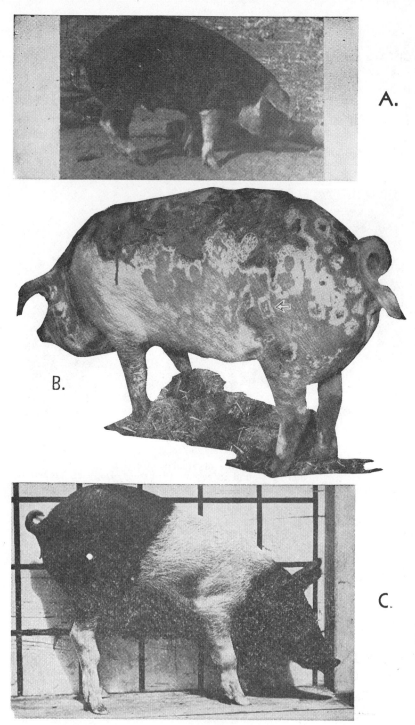

Fig. 11-6. Three forms of swine erysipelas: A, the acute form, showing hind feet "camped" up under the body giving evidence of pain; B, the diamond-skin form, showing typical skin lesions (see arrow showing diamond-skin lesion); and C, the chronic form, showing swelling on hind leg just below the hock. (Pictures A and C, courtesy, Dept. of Veterinary Pathology and Hygiene, College of Veterinary Medicine, University of Illinois; picture B, courtesy Dr. L. M. Forland, Northwood, Ia.)

to two weeks. The typical lesions are reddish rectangular plaques in the skin. Dry gangrene may affect the ears and tail, causing them partially to slough away. Unless complications set in, the animal usually recovers.

In the chronic form, the heart and/or the joints are usually the areas of localization. The joints of the knees and hocks are most commonly affected, showing enlargement and stiffness. Those pigs chronically affected are usually very poor and unthrifty.

CAUSE, PREVENTION, AND TREATMENT

Although the disease is somewhat difficult to reproduce with bacterial cultures, it is generally agreed that it is due to *Erysipelothrix insidiosa* (*rhusiopathiae*), a bacterium. This organism is often found in the tonsils, gall bladders, and intestines of apparently normal pigs. Infection usually takes place by ingestion.

Because the causative organism is able to propagate both in the animal and in the soil, prevention of the disease is very difficult. When an outbreak occurs, all the sick animals should be isolated and the herd examined daily for new cases; and antiserum alone may be used.

On infected farms, one should administer bacterin to (1) all pigs two weeks before or two weeks after weaning (or as early as one week of age if a break is encountered), and (2) all breeding stock each year. (In enzootic areas, some recommend that the bacterin be given breeding stock every 6 months.) A modified live bacterin is available for vaccinating pigs through the drinking water. The practicality of its application is being determined.

Foot-and-Mouth Disease

This is a highly contagious disease of cloven-footed animals (mainly swine, sheep, and cattle) characterized by the appearance of water blisters in the mouth (and in the snout in the case of hogs), on the skin between and around the claws of the hoof, and on the teats and udder. Fever is another symptom.

Man is mildly susceptible but very rarely infected, whereas the horse is immune.

Unfortunately, one attack does not render the animal permanently immune, but the disease has a tendency to recur perhaps because of the multiplicity of the causative virus.

The disease is not present in the United States, but there have been at least nine outbreaks (some authorities claim ten) in this country between 1870 and 1929, each of which was stamped out by the prompt slaughter of every affected and exposed animal. No United States outbreak has occurred since 1929, but the disease is greatly feared. Drastic measures are exercised in preventing the introduction of the disease into the United States, or, in the case of actual outbreak, in eradicating it.

Foot-and-mouth disease is constantly present in Europe, Asia, Japan, the Philippines, Africa, and South America. It has not been reported in New Zealand or Australia. Neither hogs nor uncooked pork products can be imported from any country in which it has been determined that foot-and-mouth disease exists.

In September, 1946, an outbreak of foot-and-mouth disease appeared in Mexico. From that date until Jan. 1, 1955, the Mexican-U. S. border was closed to imports of virtually all livestock and meat products most of the time. Likewise, the Canadian-U.S. border was closed, from February 1952, to March 1, 1953, due to an outbreak of the disease in Canada.

SYMPTOMS AND SIGNS

The disease is characterized by the formation of blisters (vesicles) and a moderate fever three to six days following exposure. These blisters are found on the mucus membranes of the tongue, lips, palate, cheeks, and on the skin around the claws of the feet, and on the teats and udder. In swine the blisters are usually found also on and above the snout.

Presence of these vesicles, especially in the mouth of cattle, stimulates a profuse flow of saliva that hangs from the lips in strings. Complicating or secondary factors are infected feet, caked udder, abortion, and great loss of weight. The mortality of adult animals is not ordinarily high, but the usefulness and productivity of affected animals is likely to be greatly damaged, thus causing great economic loss.

Fig. 11-7. Hog walking on his knees. Sore feet caused by foot-and-mouth disease. (Courtesy, USDA)

CAUSE, PREVENTION, AND TREATMENT

The infective agent of this disease is one of the smallest of the filtrable viruses. In fact, there are at least seven types, all of which are immunologically distinct from one another. Thus, infection with one does not protect against the other. The virus is present in the fluid and coverings of the blisters, in the blood, meat, milk, saliva, urine, and other secretions of the infected animal. The virus may be excreted in the urine for over two hundred days following experimental inoculation. The virus can also be spread through infected biological products, such as smallpox vaccine and hog cholera virus and serum, and by the cattle fever tick.

Except for the nine outbreaks mentioned, the disease has been kept out of the United States by extreme precautions, such as quarantine at ports of entry and assistance with eradication in neighboring lands when introduction appears imminent.

Two methods have been applied in control: the slaughter method and the quarantine procedure. Then, if the existence of the disease is confirmed by diagnosis, the area is immediately placed under strict quarantine; infected and exposed animals are

slaughtered and buried, with owners being paid indemnities based on their appraised value. Everything is cleaned and thoroughly disinfected.

Fortunately, the foot-and-mouth disease virus is quickly destroyed by a solution of the cheap and common chemical, sodium hydroxide (lye). Because quick control action is necessary, state or federal authorities should immediately be notified the very moment the presence of the disease is suspected.

Vaccines containing one or more immuno-types of the virus are manufactured in Europe and Argentina. The immunity produced from such vaccines lasts for only three to six months; hence, animals must be vaccinated three to four times per year. Vaccines have not been used in the outbreaks in the United States because they have not been regarded as favorable to rapid, complete eradication of the infection.

No attempt is made to treat animals that are known to be infected.

Influenza, Swine (or Hog "Flu")

This disease of swine resembles influenza of man, but the effects may be more serious. Swine influenza is an acute respiratory disease. The onset is rapid, and in most cases all swine in an infected herd show symptoms at the same time. The disease is usually first observed in the fall when the weather becomes cold.

SYMPTOMS AND SIGNS

The disease makes its appearance suddenly, following an incubation period of less than a week. High fever, loss of appetite, a cough, and discharge from the eyes and nose are seen. The animals seem reluctant to move but may sit up like dogs in an attempt to facilitate breathing which may in some cases be difficult.

CAUSE, PREVENTION, AND TREATMENT

The disease has an involved etiology. It is due to a combination of a bacteria (*Hemophilus influenzae suis*) and a virus. The bacteria alone cannot cause the disease but is able to exist in a recovered pig for an extended period. The virus, on the other

hand, can cause a mild infection alone but cannot be demonstrated to persist in a normal animal. Instead, the virus is found in the lungworm of the pig. The earthworm, however, serves as an intermediate host for the lungworm. That makes the life history as follows: The adult lungworm lays its eggs (containing the virus) in the lung of the infected pig, from which the eggs are coughed up, swallowed, and eliminated in the feces. Here the eggs hatch to larvae almost immediately. These larvae must then pass into (be eaten by) the earthworm before becoming infective. The pig then eats the earthworm that contains the lungworm larvae, which may in turn harbor the virus. These larvae then pass into the digestive tract, enter the lymph system, and migrate to the lungs. Here in the presence of the bacteria, the disease is initiated.

Because of its rapid spread, short duration, and low mortality, little thought has been given to the control of the disease. A logical approach is the use of dry and clean hog lots that are rotated, thus breaking up the life cycle of the lungworm. The only treatment seems to be the provision of warm, dry, clean quarters and minimum rations.

There is no known medical treatment, but some veterinarians believe that death losses from pneumonia due to secondary invading organisms can be lessened by the use of antibiotics or sulfa drugs, administered hypodermically or in the drinking water.

It is interesting to know that some believe the present virus of swine influenza is the surviving type of the agent that caused the big flu epidemic of 1918. The whole problem needs further investigation, but antibodies that neutralize human influenza virus have been found in pigs.

Leptospirosis

Leptospirosis was first observed in man in 1915-1916, in dogs in 1931, and in cattle in 1934. It has been recognized as an important disease of swine in this country only since about 1952, although it very probably has been present for a much longer period.

Human infections may be contracted through skin abrasions when handling or slaughtering infected animals, by swimming

in contaminated water, through consuming uncooked foods
that are contaminated, or through drinking unpasteurized milk.

SYMPTOMS AND SIGNS

Swine losses from leptospirosis are chiefly in baby pigs
that are aborted or born dead or weak, and in the unthriftiness of market hogs. Affected animals may refuse to eat, become mildly depressed, lose weight, and often run a high fever
for two or three days. Occasionally, there may be blood-stained
urine. Very frequently, however, the symptoms in growing-
finishing pigs are not apparent. Leptospirosis infection is
usually confirmed only by laboratory tests after abortions occur.

CAUSE, PREVENTION, AND TREATMENT

The most common cause of leptospirosis in swine in the
United States is *Leptospira pomona,* a corkscrew-shaped bacterium of the spirochete group. It can cause the disease in
swine, cattle, sheep, horses, and man, and it is readily transferred from one species to another.

The following preventive measures are recommended:

1. Blood test all animals prior to purchase, isolate for 30
days, and then retest prior to adding them to the herd.

2. Vaccinate annually.

If leptospirosis strikes in a swine herd—if it is positively
diagnosed—it may be brought under control by the following
procedure, which should be carried out under the supervision
of a veterinarian:

1. Spread animals out over a large area; avoid congestion
in a pen or barn.

2. Fence off water holes, ponds, or slow-running streams.

3. Isolate sick animals and new additions to the herd.

4. Discard milk from diseased cows.

5. Clean and disinfect barns; exterminate rodents.

6. Administer leptospirosis vaccine to all sows on problem
farms each year.

7. Keep different classes of livestock separated, because leptospirosis can be spread from one species to another.

Antibiotics are the treatment of choice. If afflicted animals
are treated promptly, fairly good results can be expected. To
help remove the carrier phase, feed high levels of the tetracycline

drugs (400 to 500 gm per ton in complete feeds for 14 days). Untreated, swine can remain carriers up to one year.

Mastitis-Metritis-Agalactia Complex (MMA Complex)

This is a disease of sows and gilts characterized by an inflammation of the mammary glands (mastitis), and inflammation of the uterus (metritis), and/or a failure to secrete milk (agalactia). The death rate in sows is low, but the loss of baby pigs may be high.

MMA appears to be a more serious problem in "multiple" and "confinement" farrowing than where portable houses on pasture are used.

SYMPTOMS AND SIGNS

The first signs of the disease usually appear within three days after farrowing, although symptoms can be seen before farrowing or before the pigs are weaned. A whitish or yellowish discharge of pus appears from the vagina of the infected animal and the temperature rises to 103° to 106° F. or higher. The sow goes off feed, stops milking, and the pigs often develop diarrhea. Sometimes the problem isn't recognized until the pigs starve to death.

CAUSE, PREVENTION, AND TREATMENT

The organisms commonly thought to cause the MMA syndrome include: *Escherichia coli, Streptococcus spp, Micrococcus,* and a PPLO organism called *Mycoplasma hyogenatalium*. It is particularly noteworthy that *E. coli* is also the most common organism isolated as the cause of diarrhea in baby pigs during the first three weeks of life. However, the disease is complex, and the actual cause is unknown.

Prevention revolves around sound management, good nutrition, superior sanitation, and proper swine husbandry. When sows are kept in confinement, it is especially important to avoid overfatness and constipation. The first condition can be controlled by limiting the ration, and the addition of 6 to 10 percent molasses to the ration will prevent constipation.

The list of treatments suggested by different people is long, confusing, and not always effective. Among them are:

1. Antibiotics or nitrofurans to eliminate infections.

2. Oxytocin, a hormone, to cause milk let-down.

3. Relief of constipation by (a) using a warm, soapy enema, (b) feeding a ration high in molasses or wheat bran, or (c) providing morning and evening exercise.

4. Supplemental milk and glucose to keep the baby pigs alive.

5. Oral antibiotic or nitrofuran for the baby pigs if diarrhea occurs.

6. Vaccination of sows with a bacterin prior to farrowing; preferably using an autogenous bacterin prepared from the strains of bacteria involved in the herd, or using a stock bacterin.

Mycoplasma Pneumonia (PPLO or Virus Pneumonia)

Mycoplasma pneumonia of pigs is one of the world's most important swine diseases. Economic losses in the United States are estimated at $120,000,000 annually; feed efficiency of affected pigs may be lowered by 25 percent.

SYMPTOMS AND SIGNS

Coughing is the first and most characteristic symptom manifested of mycoplasma pneumonia. It generally begins 10 to 16 days following exposure to diseased animals, and it may persist indefinitely. Coughing is most marked when pigs come out to feed in the morning or following vigorous exercise. Diarrhea usually occurs when pigs first begin to cough, but it lasts only two or three days. Temperatures are only slightly elevated, and even when they reach 105° F. the pigs do not look sick. In general, affected pigs eat well, but gains are slow and feed utilization poor.

If management is poor many pigs develop serious pneumonia due to secondary bacterial infection of the lungs. The age 14 to 26 weeks seems to be the most critical for such secondary lung complications.

CAUSE, PREVENTION, AND TREATMENT

The disease is caused by a small coccobacillary organism, *Mycoplasma.*

Since mycoplasma pneumonia is spread largely by direct contact from infected to normal animals, prevention consists in avoiding the purchase of animals from infected herds.

The disease is continued in infected herds by contact of young pigs with carrier sows, since about one in four sows remains a carrier. Two methods have been used for its eradication: (1) Specific pathogen free (SPF) pigs, and (2) farrowing old sows in isolation and ascertaining that the pigs are free of the disease before adding them to the herd.

Treatments will help control bacterial complications. Tylosin, tetracycline, and streptomycin have activity against PPLO organisms. Also, good nursing will help.

Pig Scours (*Colibacillosis*)

This is an acute, and often highly fatal, disease of suckling pigs. It has been estimated that between 7 and 10 million pigs in the United States die each year from scours.

SYMPTOMS AND SIGNS

The disease is characterized by creamy yellow or grayish green, watery feces. The pigs usually huddle together, are inactive, and may be dehydrated. Often the disease pattern is irregular; appearing, then disappearing, only to recur. It spreads from pig to pig within a litter, but less frequently from litter to litter. Sows are not affected.

CAUSE, PREVENTION, AND TREATMENT

Escherichia coli is the most commonly isolated organism among pigs with pig scours, but the causative agent or agents probably cannot be limited to one specific organism. The predisposing causes are poor sanitation, drafts, dust, dampness, chilling, insufficient bedding, improperly balanced or deficient creep rations, and iron deficiency anemia.

Prevention is best effected through management, especially by keeping visitors out of the farrowing house, strict sanitation, use of a good disinfectant, taking a break in the farrowing cycle—shutting down for three weeks, and dryness in the farrowing house. Also, when there is reason to believe that the sows are carriers of scour-causing bacteria, it may be well to treat them with antibiotics, nf-180, or a sulfa, using the product of choice according to the manufacturer's directions.

Immediate oral treatment with either neomycin or a nitro-

furan drug, repeated every 12 hours until four doses are given, is usually effective in those herds with diarrhea among newborn pigs. Also, such treatment appears to reduce the economic loss incurred as a result of incomplete recovery of pigs that develop diarrhea.

Pneumonia

Pneumonia is a widespread disease of all animals, including swine. If untreated, 50 to 75 percent of affected animals die.

SYMPTOMS AND SIGNS

Pneumonia is an inflammation of the lungs. It is ushered in by a chill, followed by elevated temperature. There is quick, shallow respiration, discharge from the nostrils and perhaps eyes, and a cough. Sick animals stand with their legs wide apart, and there is a drop in milk production, loss of appetite, constipation, crackling noises with breathing, and gasping for breath.

CAUSE, PREVENTION, AND TREATMENT

The causes of pneumonia are numerous, including (1) many microorganisms, (2) inhalation of water or medicines given by untrained persons as a drench, (3) virus, and (4) lungworms. When pneumonia is encountered, one should always try to establish what is causing it.

Preventive measures include providing good hygienic surroundings and practicing good, sound husbandry.

Sick animals should be segregated in quiet clean quarters away from drafts, and given easily digested nutritious feeds. Treatment, which should be by the veterinarian, may include antibiotics or sulfas.

Pox, Swine *(Variolla suilla)*

Swine pox is widely distributed in the Midwest, where it is an important disease of young pigs.

SYMPTOMS AND SIGNS

Swine pox is characterized by small red spots, which appear

over large parts of the body especially on the ears, neck, under-surface of the body, and inside of the thighs. These spots grow rapidly and reach the size of a dime. A hard nodule develops in the center of each. Several days later, small pea-sized vesicles (blisters) develop; at first these contain a clear fluid, but later the contents become puslike. Soon, these blisters dry up, leaving dark brown scabs, which fall off. Preceding these skin changes, some animals show fever, chills, and refusal to feed. Very few pigs die.

CAUSE, PREVENTION, AND TREATMENT

There are two types of swine pox, each caused by a different type of virus. Swine which recover from the disease are immune to further attacks from the specific type of virus that caused the disease, but not to attacks from the other virus. One type of virus is related to that causing pox in various other species of animals, but the other is not.

The disease appears to be transmitted primarily by lice, and less often by other insects and by contact. Therefore, lice control is the best preventive measure.

No treatment for swine pox is known. Good management and nursing will help.

When swine are infected with swine pox, they should never be vaccinated with a modified live virus for hog cholera, for heavy mortality may result.

Rabies (or Hydrophobia, "Madness")

Rabies (hydrophobia or "madness") is an acute infectious disease of all warm-blooded animals and man. It is characterized by deranged consciousness and paralysis, and terminates fatally. This disease is one that is far too prevalent and, if present knowledge were applied, it could be controlled. Complete eradication would be difficult to achieve because of the reservoir of infection in wild animals and bats.

When a human being is bitten by a dog that is suspected of being rabid, the first impulse is to kill the dog immediately. This is a mistake. Instead, it is important to confine the animal under the observation of a veterinarian until the disease, if it is present, has a chance to develop and run its course. If no recognizable symptoms appear in the animal within a period of two weeks

after it inflicted the bite, it is usually safe to assume that there was no rabies at the time. Death occurs within a few days after the symptoms appear, and the dog's brain can be examined for specific evidence of rabies. With this procedure, unless the bite is in the region of the neck or head, there will usually be ample time in which to administer treatment to exposed human beings. As the virus has been found in the saliva of a dog at least five days before the appearance of the clinically recognizable symptoms, the bite of a dog should always be considered potentially dangerous until proved otherwise. In any event, when people are bitten or exposed to rabies, they should see their local doctor. He may use a vaccine made of (1) killed virus (nervous tissue origin), or (2) killed virus (duck embryo or chick embryo origin). Also, new and promising vaccines have been developed and are being tested experimentally.

SYMPTOMS AND SIGNS

Rabies in swine is not very common. The disease usually manifests itself in two forms: the furious, irritable, or violent form, or the dumb or paralytic form. It is often difficult to distinguish between the two forms, however. The furious type usually merges into the dumb form because paralysis always occurs just before death.

In the early stages, rabid swine generally exhibit irritability as manifested by aimless wandering, hoarse grunting, gnawing or rubbing the bitten spot, and sudden jumping if disturbed. In the later stages, the pigs become paralyzed and death follows.

CAUSE, PREVENTION, AND TREATMENT

Rabies is caused by a filtrable virus which is usually carried into a bite wound by the infected saliva. The malady is generally transmitted to farm animals by dogs and certain wild animals, such as the fox and skunk.

Rabies can best be prevented by attacking it at its chief source, the dog. With the advent of an improved anti-rabies vaccine for the dog, it should be a requirement that all dogs be immunized. This should be supplemented by regulations governing the licensing, quarantine, and transportation of dogs.

When swine are bitten or exposed to rabies, see your veter-

inarian. After the disease is fully developed, there is no known treatment.

Shipping Fever

Shipping fever is a worldwide disease of all farm animals, including swine. It occurs most frequently among thin and poorly nourished young animals that are subjected to shipment by rail or truck during bad weather.

It is a serious problem to both shippers and receivers of animals. Death losses may be high in untreated areas.

SYMPTOMS AND SIGNS

The symptoms develop rapidly and last for a week or less. Usually there is high temperature, discharge from the eyes and nose, a hacking cough, difficulty in breathing, and there may be a swelling in the region of the neck. Sometimes there is diarrhea. In very acute forms, animals may die without showing symptoms.

Young animals are most susceptible, but animals of all ages are affected.

CAUSE, PREVENTION, AND TREATMENT

The cause is uncertain. But it generally occurs during the winter months when transportation takes several days and pigs are moved in unheated vehicles. The stress of transportation, which is sometimes accompanied by mishandling, overcrowding, lack of rest, and weather changes, lowers the resistance of pigs and creates conditions favorable to bacterial and, perhaps, virus infection.

Preventive measures include (1) eliminating as many as possible of the predisposing factors that lower the animal's resistance, and (2) isolating newly purchased animals two to three weeks before placing them in the main herd.

Affected animals should be isolated, and treatment should be handled by a veterinarian. In the early stages, the sulfa drugs or antibiotics will control the bacterial pneumonia.

When there is an outbreak of shipping fever, good feeding and management should be instituted.

Streptococcic Infection (or Streptococcic Septicemia)

This type of infection appears to be fairly common in swine. It is often confused with hog cholera, because, like cholera, it is characterized by sudden onset and death within twelve to eighteen hours.

SYMPTOMS AND SIGNS

All ages of swine are susceptible. Affected animals show weakness, prostration, and high temperature. Diarrhea and bloody urine may occur. It often localizes in the joints, causing chronic arthritis.

CAUSE, PREVENTION, AND TREATMENT

The disease is caused by a bacteria of the streptococcus group.

Good management, with emphasis on sanitation, constitutes the best control. Autogenous bacterins have proven helpful on some farms.

Antibiotics in the feed will help prevent this condition. Also, proper treatment of the navel with iodine at birth is an essential management practice.

Tetanus (or Lockjaw)

Tetanus is chiefly a wound infection disease that attacks the nervous system of horses (and other equines) and man, although it does occur in swine, cattle, sheep, and goats. In the Southwest, it is quite common in sheep after shearing and marking. In the central states, tetanus frequently affects lambs, pigs, and calves following castration or other wounds. It is generally referred to as lockjaw.

In the United States, the disease occurs most frequently in the South, where precautions against tetanus are an essential part of the routine treatment of wounds. The disease is world-wide in distribution.

SYMPTOMS AND SIGNS

The incubation period of tetanus varies from one to two weeks but may be from one day to many months. It is usually

associated with a wound but may not directly follow an injury. The first noticeable sign of the disease is a stiffness first observed about the head. The animal often chews slowly and weakly and swallows awkwardly; hence, the common designation "lockjaw." The animal then shows violent spasm or contractions

Fig. 11-8. Pigs with tetanus or lockjaw. Such infection usually follows castration or other wounds. (Courtesy, Dept. of Veterinary Pathology and Hygiene, College of Veterinary Medicine, University of Illinois)

of groups of muscles brought on by the slightest movement or noise, and usually attempts to remain standing throughout the course of the disease. If recovery occurs, it will take a month or more. In over 80 percent of the cases, however, death ensues, usually because of sheer exhaustion or paralysis of vital organs.

CAUSE, PREVENTION, AND TREATMENT

The disease is caused by an exceedingly powerful toxin (more than one hundred times as toxic as strychnine) liberated by the tetanus organism (*Clostridium tetani*). This organism is an anaerobe (lives in absence of oxygen) which forms the most hardy spores known. It may be found in certain soils, horse dung, and sometimes in human excreta. The organism usually causes trouble when it gets into a wound that rapidly heals or closes over it. In the absence of oxygen, it then grows and liberates the toxin which apparently passes by diffusion out into the surrounding medium or environment and then spreads to the

central nervous system where it seems to produce its most dire results.

The disease can largely be prevented by reducing the probability of wounds, by general cleanliness, proper wound treatment, and by vaccination with tetanus toxoid in the so-called " hot " areas. When an animal has received a wound from which tetanus may result, short term immunity can be conferred immediately by use of tetanus antitoxin, but it is of little or no value after the symptoms have developed. All valuable animals should be protected with tetanus toxoid.

All perceptible wounds should be properly treated, and the animals should be kept quiet and preferably should be placed in a dark quiet corner free from flies. Supportive treatment is of great importance and will contribute towards a favorable course. This may entail artificial feeding. The animal should be placed under the care of a veterinarian.

Transmissible Gastroenteritis (TGE)

This is a rapidly spreading disease accompanied by symptoms of inflammation of the stomach and intestine. The incubation period may be only 18 hours. Once the disease strikes, it spreads rapidly; the entire herd may become noticeably affected in two to three days.

SYMPTOMS AND SIGNS

It is characterized by marked scouring in all cases, by vomiting in some cases, and by high mortality in pigs less than seven to ten days of age. Usually, the body temperature remains normal. It affects swine of all ages, but the death loss in older swine is low.

CAUSE, PREVENTION, AND TREATMENT

It appears that the disease is caused by a virus.

The most effective preventive measure consists of exposing the sows to the disease before they farrow. They will then develop resistance or protection, and the pigs will get the antibodies from the milk. However, this procedure should be used only where it is inevitable that sows will be exposed at farrowing time and where there is no danger of spreading the disease to

neighboring herds. Isolation at farrowing time is also recommended.

No effective treatment is known, but good feeding and management will help. High level antibiotic feed supplements or sulfa drugs may minimize secondary bacterial complications.

Tuberculosis

Tuberculosis is a chronic infectious disease of man and animals. It is characterized by the development of nodules (tubercules) that may calcify or turn into abscesses. The disease spreads very slowly, and affects mainly the lymph nodes. There are three kinds of tubercle bacilli—the human, the bovine, and the avian (bird) types. As shown in Table 11-2, swine are subject to all three kinds, and practically every species of animal is subject to one or more of the three kinds.

TABLE 11-2

RELATIVE SUSCEPTIBILITY OF MAN AND ANIMALS TO THREE
DIFFERENT KINDS OF TUBERCULOSIS GERMS

Species	Susceptibility to Three Kinds of Tuberculosis Germs			Comments
	Human Type	Bovine Type	Avian (bird) Type	
Humans--------	Susceptible	Moderately susceptible	Questionable	Pathogenicity of avian type for humans is practically nil.
Cattle-----------	Slightly susceptible	Susceptible	Slightly susceptible	
Swine-----------	Moderately susceptible	Susceptible	Susceptible	Ninety percent of all swine cases are due to the avian type.
Chickens-------	Resistant	Resistant	Very susceptible	Chickens only have the avian type.
Horses and mules --------	Relatively resistant	Moderately susceptible	Relatively resistant	Rarely seen in these animals in the United States.
Sheep-----------	Fairly resistant	Susceptible	Susceptible	Rarely seen in these animals.
Goats -----------	Marked resistance	Highly susceptible	Susceptible	Rarely seen in these animals in the United States.
Dogs ------------	Susceptible	Susceptible	Resistant	Highly resistant to avian type.
Cats -------------	Quite resistant	Susceptible	Quite resistant	Usually obtained from milk of tubercular cows.

In general, the incidence of tuberculosis is steadily declining in the United States, both in animals and humans. In 1917, when a thorough nationwide eradication campaign was first initiated, 1 cow in 20 had the disease; whereas today the number is less than 1 in 400. Meanwhile, human mortality from tuberculosis has dropped from 150 per 100,000 in 1918 to well under 50 per 100,000. Some decline in the incidence of the disease in poultry and swine has also been noted, but the reduction among these species has been far less marked.

SYMPTOMS AND SIGNS

Tuberculosis may take one or more of several forms. Human beings get tuberculosis of the skin (lupus), of the lymph nodes (scrofula), of the bones and joints, of the lining of the brain (tuberculous meningitis), and of the lungs. For the most part, animals get tuberculosis of the lungs and lymph nodes; although in poultry the liver, spleen, and intestines are chiefly affected. In cows, the udder becomes infected in chronic cases. In swine, infection is most often contracted through ingestion of infected material; hence, the lesions often are in the abdominal cavity.

Fig. 11-9. Boar dying with the bovine type of tuberculosis. Though swine are susceptible to all three types of tuberculosis, 90 percent of all swine cases are due to the avian type. For the most part, hogs get tuberculosis of the lungs and lymph nodes. (Courtesy, Dept. of Veterinary Pathology and Hygiene, College of Veterinary Medicine, University of Illinois)

Many times an infected animal will show no outward physical signs of the disease. There may be a gradual loss of weight and condition and swelling of joints, especially in older animals. If the respiratory system is affected, there may be a chronic cough and labored breathing. Other seats of infection are lymph glands, udder, genitals, central nervous system, and the digestive system. The symptoms are similar, regardless of species.

CAUSE, PREVENTION, AND TREATMENT

The causative agent is a rod-shaped organism belonging to the acid-fast group known as *Mycobacterium tuberculosis*. The disease is usually contracted by eating food or drinking fluids contaminated with tuberculosis material. Hogs may also contract the disease by eating part of a tubercular chicken.

There are three principal methods of tuberculin testing—the intradermic, subcutaneous, and ophthalmic. The first of these is the method now principally used with swine. It consists of the injection of tuberculin into the dermis (the true skin), usually on the ear or back.

Upon injection into an infected animal, tuberculin will set up in the body a reaction characterized by a swelling at the site of injection. In human beings, the X ray is usually used for purposes of detecting the presence of the disease.

As a part of the federal-state tuberculosis eradication campaign of 1917, provision was made for indemnity payments on animals slaughtered.

An effective control program among swine embraces the following procedure: (1) disposing of tubercular swine, cattle, and poultry; (2) applying strict sanitation; and (3) rotating feedlots and pastures.

Preventive treatment for both humans and animals consists of pasteurization of milk and creamery by-products and the removal and supervised slaughter of reactor animals. Also, avoid housing or pasturing swine with chickens.

In human beings, tuberculosis can be arrested by hospitalization and complete rest, but in animals this method of treatment is neither effective nor practical. To date, medical treatment has been unsatisfactory, although beneficial results have been reported from giving streptomycin to affected humans.

Vesicular Exanthema

Vesicular exanthema is almost exclusively a disease of swine, but horses are slightly susceptible. It causes estimated average annual losses in swine of $1,032,000.[11]

The course of the disease is one to two weeks, and the morality is low. Pregnant sows often abort and nursing sows fall off noticeably in milk production.

SYMPTOMS AND SIGNS

The symptoms are similar to foot-and-mouth disease. Small vesicles (like water blisters) appear around the head, particularly on the snout, nose, or lips. Also these blisters appear on the feet where the hair and the horny part of the hoof meet, on the ball of the feet, on the dewclaws, between the toes, and on the udder and teats of nursing sows. Affected animals go lame, have a high temperature, and usually go off feed for 3 to 4 days.

In order to distinguish vesicular exanthema from foot-and-mouth disease, tests may be made with horses and cattle. Also guinea pigs may be infected with foot-and-mouth disease, but are resistant to the virus of vesicular exanthema.

CAUSE, PREVENTION, AND TREATMENT

Vesicular exanthema is caused by a virus. Usually symptoms appear 24 to 48 hours after contact with the virus.

No immunizing agents are available. Preventive measures consist of avoiding (1) the introduction of hogs from infested areas, and (2) the consumption of feed and water contaminated with the virus. Uncooked garbage that contains pork trimmings has often been the source of the virus.

Good nursing will help, but no treatment is entirely successful. Rigid quarantine of affected areas (applicable to both hogs and pork products) and the destruction of affected herds appears to constitute the best control and eradication. The virus that causes vesicular exanthema is readily killed when exposed to a 2% sodium hydroxide (lye) solution or a 4% sodium carbonate (soda ash) solution.

---

[11]*Losses in Agriculture*, Agriculture Handbook No. 291, ARS, USDA, 1965, p. 74.

PARASITES OF SWINE[12]

Hogs are probably more affected by parasites than any other class of livestock, with the possible exception of sheep. Infection with either internal or external parasites results in lack of thrift and poor development of young pigs. Moreover, feed is always too costly to give to parasites. A total of more than fifty species of worm and protozoan parasites have been reported as being found in swine throughout the world. Fortunately, a number of these species occur only infrequently in the swine of this country; and other species, although widespread, are not of major importance under ordinary conditions.

The losses due to internal parasites of swine are estimated at $65,739,000 annually;[13] and external parasites take an additional toll.

Fig. 11-10. Parasites made the difference! Two pigs of the same age, but the smaller one was stunted by worms and other hog-lot infections. (Courtesy, USDA)

---

[12]Several new and promising insecticides and vermifuges for controlling parasites are now on the market. However, further research is desirable in order to determine the value of many of these products. Where parasitism is encountered, therefore, it is suggested that the stockman obtain from local authorities the current recommendation relative to the choice and concentration of the drug to use.

[13]*Losses in Agriculture*, Agriculture Handbook No. 291, ARS, USDA, 1965, p. 79.

Fig. 11-11. Animals that are heavily parasitized cannot utilize feed to the best advantage. Here are shown worms which were expelled by a single animal after medicinal treatment. (Courtesy, USDA)

Any vermifuge that will get rid of the internal parasites of swine will also harm the host animal. Also, removal of parasites does not insure against reinfection; thus, if animals are kept on contaminated ground, the relief afforded by treatment may be only temporary. The prevention and control of parasites, therefore, is far more important than any treatment that may be prescribed, no matter how successful the latter may be. In order to initiate and carry out control measures successfully, the swine producer should have a clear understanding of how each parasite develops and where it lives, stage by stage, from the egg to the adult worm. When the life history and habits of the parasite are definitely known, then and only then can plans be made to break the life cycle at some point that will destroy it. The discussion that follows is especially designed to supply enlightened information which will be of value in preventing and controlling parasites.

At the outset, it should be emphasized that animals fed an adequate diet and kept under sanitary conditions are seldom

heavily infected with parasites. A discussion of the most damaging internal parasites of hogs follows.

Ascarids (or Large Intestinal Roundworm; *Ascaris lumbricoides*)

This is the most common and one of the most injurious

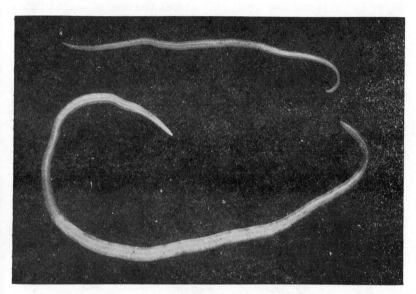

Fig. 11-12. Adult large intestinal roundworms (ascarids). They are usually yellowish or pinkish in color, 8 to 12 inches long, and almost the size of a lead pencil. (Courtesy, USDA)

parasites of swine and is identical in form and structure to the roundworm in man.

DISTRIBUTION AND LOSSES CAUSED BY ASCARIDS

The roundworm is widespread throughout the world. It is reported that in the United States from 20 to 70 percent or more of the hogs examined for this parasite have been found to be infected.[14] At times, especially in young pigs, the damage inflicted by roundworms may cause death of the animal. Lighter infections result in a stunting of growth and uneconomical

---

[14]Spindler, L. A. "Internal Parasites of Swine," *Keeping Livestock Healthy,* The Yearbook of Agriculture, 1942, USDA. p. 766.

gains. In total, ascarids cause estimated annual losses in swine of $34,812,000.[15]

LIFE HISTORY AND HABITS

Technically, the parasite is known as *Ascaris lumbricoides* var. *suis*. The adult worm is usually yellowish or pinkish in color, eight to twelve inches long, and almost the size of a lead pencil. The life history of the parasite may be briefly described as follows:

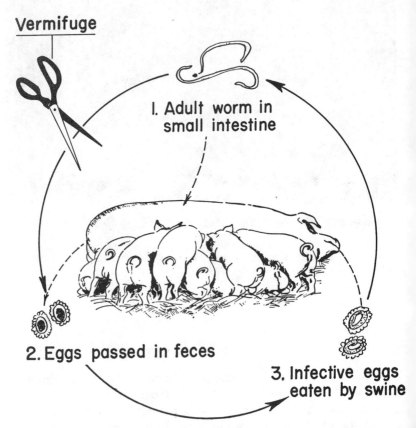

Vermifuge

1. Adult worm in small intestine

2. Eggs passed in feces

3. Infective eggs eaten by swine

Fig. 11-13. Diagram showing the life history and habits of the large intestinal roundworm. The application of the McLean County System of Swine Sanitation is the most effective preventive. (Drawing by R. F. Johnson)

---

[15]*Losses in Agriculture*, Agriculture Handbook No. 291, ARS, USDA 1965, p. 79.

1. The female worms lay eggs in the small intestines and these are eliminated with the feces. These eggs are extremely resistant to the usual destructive influences.

2. A small larva develops in the egg and remains there until the egg is swallowed by the pig along with contaminated feed or water. Then it emerges from its shell, bores through the wall of the intestine, and thence gets into the bloodstream—by means of which, after a brief sojourn in the liver, it is carried to the lungs.

3. In the lungs, the larvae break out of the capillaries, enter the windpipe, migrate to the throat. While in the throat, they are swallowed and lodge in the intestines where they develop into sexually mature worms, thus completing their life cycle.

DAMAGE INFLICTED; SYMPTOMS AND SIGNS OF AFFECTED ANIMALS

Except for the theft of nutrients, the damage inflicted by the adult worm is usually so slight as to be undetectable, but the larvae can cause serious lesions. The evident symptoms are exceedingly variable. Infected young pigs become unthrifty in appearance and stunted in growth. Because of the presence of the larvae in the lungs, coughing and "thumpy" breathing are usually characteristic symptoms. There may be a yellow color to the mucous membrane, due to blockage of the bile ducts.

PREVENTION, CONTROL, AND TREATMENT

Prevention consists of keeping the young pigs away from infection. The application of the McLean County System of Swine Sanitation has proved most effective in protecting pigs from the common roundworm infection. This system, devised by Drs. B. H. Ransom and H. B. Raffensperger of the U. S. Bureau of Animal Industry, was developed in McLean County, Illinois, as a result of a trial period of seven years, commencing in 1919. Though this program was worked out chiefly for the purpose of preventing infection of young pigs with the common roundworm, it is equally effective in lessening troubles from other parasites and in disease control, thus making possible cheaper and more profitable pork production. The system involves four simple steps:

1. **Clean the farrowing quarters.**—The house should be thoroughly cleaned and the walls and floors scrubbed with scalding lye water (1 pound of lye to 12 to 15 gallons of water).

2. **Wash sows before moving into farrowing quarters.**—The sows should be thoroughly scrubbed with soap and warm water, especially in the region of the sides, udder, and under surface of the body. This has as its purpose the removal of adhering parasite eggs. The sow and litter are confined to the clean farrowing quarters until moved.

3. **Haul the sow and litter to clean pasture.**—About two weeks after farrowing, the sow and litter should be hauled (not driven) to clean pasture. It is preferable that this should be a field that has been cultivated since last used by hogs.

4. **Keep the pigs on clean pasture until they are at least four months old.**—Experience has shown that pigs that are kept free from worms up to this age are little harmed by them.

Although worm infection can be prevented by following a strict sanitation program, sows should be routinely wormed 10 to 30 days before farrowing, and pigs should be wormed when between 7 and 10 weeks of age.

Many treatments have been and are being used for the removal of roundworms. The most commonly used and effective ones at the present time are:

1. **Dichlorvos** (Atgard V).—This is a prescription drug, which may be obtained through a veterinarian. It is reputed to remove more types of worms, and in greater numbers, than any other known single-dose pig wormer. Dichlorvos is mixed with the feed.

2. **Piperazines.**—Several piperazine compounds are on the market. They are quite effective in removing roundworms, but they are relatively ineffective for controlling nodular worms, whipworms, or strongyloides.

Administration depends on the particular piperazine compound selected; thus, they should be used according to the directions of the manufacturer. They may be fed in either wet or dry feed, or they may be given in the water.

3. **Thiabendazole.**—This drug is also effective. It should be used according to manufacturer's directions.

Blowfly

The flies of the blowfly group include a number of species that find their principal breeding ground in dead and putrifying flesh, although they sometimes infest wounds or unhealthy tissues of live animals and fresh or cooked meat. All the important species of blowflies except the flesh flies, which are grayish and have three dark stripes on their backs, have a more or less metallic luster.

DISTRIBUTION AND LOSSES CAUSED BY BLOWFLIES

Although blowflies are widespread, they present the greatest problem in the Pacific Northwest and in the South and southwestern states. Death losses from blowflies are not excessive, but they cause much discomfort to affected animals and lower production.

LIFE HISTORY AND HABITS

With the exception of the group known as gray flesh flies, which deposit tiny living maggots instead of eggs, the blowflies have a similar life cycle to the screwworm, except that the cycle is completed in about one-half the time. (See discussion of the screwworm later in this chapter.)

DAMAGE INFLICTED; SYMPTOMS AND SIGNS OF AFFECTED ANIMALS

The blowfly causes its greatest damage by infesting wounds and the soiled hair or fleeces of living animals. Such damage, which is largely limited to the black blowfly (or wool-maggot fly), is similar to that caused by screwworms. The maggots spread over the body, feeding on the dead skin and exudates, where they produce a severe irritation and destroy the ability of the skin to function. Infested animals rapidly become weak and fevered; and although they recover, they may remain in an unthrifty condition for a long period.

Because blowflies infest fresh or cooked meat, they are often a problem of major importance around packing houses or farm homes.

PREVENTION, CONTROL, AND TREATMENT

Prevention of blowfly damage consists of eliminating the pest and decreasing the susceptibility of animals to infestation.

As blowflies breed principally in dead carcasses, the most effective control is effected by promptly destroying all dead animals by burning or deep burial. The use of traps, poisoned baits, and electrified screens is also helpful in reducing trouble from blowflies. Suitable repellents, such as pine tar oil, help prevent the fly from depositing its eggs.

When animals become infested with blowfly maggots, clip well around the affected area. Then, using a paint brush or spray, apply to the affected area twice weekly either (1) Formula MS 62 (Smear 62), or (2) EQ-335 Screwworm Remedy diluted 1 part to 9 parts of water. Also, chloroform is frequently used to kill the larvae.

Coccidiosis

Coccidiosis—a parasitic disease affecting swine, cattle, sheep, goats, pet stock, and poultry—is caused by microscopic protozoan organisms known as coccidia, which live in the cells of the intestinal lining. Each class of domestic livestock harbors its own species of coccidia, thus there is no cross-infection between animals.

DISTRIBUTION AND LOSSES CAUSED BY COCCIDIOSIS

The distribution of the disease is worldwide. Except in very severe infections, or where a secondary bacterial invasion develops, infested farm animals usually recover. The chief economic loss is in lowered gains.

LIFE HISTORY AND HABITS

Infected animals or birds may eliminate daily with their droppings thousands of coccidia organisms (in the resistant oöcyst stage). Under favorable conditions of temperature and moisture, coccidia sporulate to maturity in three to five days, and each oöcyst contains eight infective sporozoites. The oöcyst then gains entrance into an animal by being swallowed with contaminated feed or water. In the host's intestine, the outer membrane

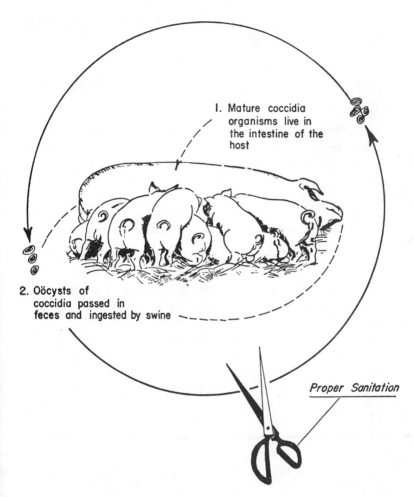

1. Mature coccidia
   organisms live in
   the intestine of the
   host

2. Oöcysts of
   coccidia passed in
   feces and ingested by swine

Proper Sanitation

Fig. 11-14. Diagram showing the life history and habits of coccidia, the organism that causes coccidiosis in swine. As noted (see scissors) proper sanitation is the key to prevention; thus protecting animals from feed or water that is contaminated with the protozoa that causes the disease. (Drawing by R. F. Johnson)

of the oöcyst, acted on by the digestive juices, ruptures and liberates the eight sporozoites within. Each sporozoite then attacks and penetrates an epithelial cell, ultimately destroying it. While destroying the cell, however, the parasite undergoes sexual multiplication and fertilization with the formation of new oöcysts. The parasite (oöcyst) is then expelled with the feces and is again in a position to infect a new host.

The coccidia parasite abounds in wet, filthy surroundings; resists freezing and ordinary disinfectants; and can be carried long distances in streams.

DAMAGE INFLICTED; SYMPTOMS AND SIGNS OF AFFECTED ANIMALS

A severe infection with coccidia produces diarrhea, and the feces may be bloody. The bloody discharge is due to the destruction of the epithelial cells lining the intestines. Ensuing exposure and rupture of the blood vessels then produces hemorrhage in the intestinal lumen.

In addition to a bloody diarrhea, affected animals usually show pronounced unthriftiness and weakness.

PREVENTION, CONTROL, AND TREATMENT

Coccidiosis can be prevented by protecting animals from feed or water that is contaminated with the protozoa that causes the disease. Prompt segregation of affected animals is important and should be done if practical. Manure and contaminated bedding should be removed daily. Low, wet areas should be drained. If possible, segregation and isolation of animals by age should be used in controlling the disease. All precautions should be undertaken to keep droppings from contaminating the feed. Although the oöcysts resist freezing and disinfectants and may remain viable outside the body for one or two years, they are readily destroyed by sunlight and drying.

Treatment should be undertaken mainly for the relief of symptoms. Some of the sulfonamide drugs may be employed as a drug treatment, but a veterinarian should be consulted. Good nursing is essential.

Kidney Worm *(Stephanurus dentatus)*

This is one of the most damaging worm parasites affecting swine in the southern United States. It causes estimated annual swine losses of $17,059,000.[16] The kidney worm, technically known as *Stephanurus dentatus,* is a thick-bodied black-and-

---

[16]*Losses in Agriculture,* Agriculture Handbook No. 291, ARS, USDA, 1965, p. 79.

white worm which, when fully grown, may attain a length of 2 inches. Though especially harmful to swine, cattle may become infected when running with hogs.

DISTRIBUTION AND LOSSES CAUSED BY THE KIDNEY WORM

The kidney worm is one of the most serious obstacles to profitable swine production in the South. Although it causes initial loss to the farmer because of inefficient gains and lowered reproduction, the carcass also is affected, with damage to the liver, kidney, loin, leaf fat, and even the ham. This necessitates severe trimming or even condemnation of the carcass. All such carcass losses are ultimately borne by the swine producer in the form of lowered market prices. In certain areas of the South where swine infections with kidney worms are notoriously heavy, a blanket reduction in price is made on all market hogs coming from the infected area in anticipation of the usual damage to the carcass.

LIFE HISTORY AND HABITS

Adult kidney worms may be found around the kidneys and in cysts in the ureters (tubes leading from the kidneys to the bladder). The mature female worms lay numerous eggs that are discharged with the urine. It has been estimated that as many as one million eggs may be passed in the urine of a moderately infected hog in one day. When eggs fall on moist, shaded soil, a tiny larva hatches from each egg in twenty-four to forty-eight hours, depending on temperature conditions. In another three to five days, the larva develops into the infective stage. Hogs then obtain kidney worms by swallowing the infective larvae with contaminated feed and by rooting and hunting for feed in litter that is allowed to accumulate on pastures and in lots.

Kidney worm larvae can also enter the bodies of pigs through the skin, though this is not considered a great source of infection. Regardless of the way in which the larvae enter the body, they get into the blood and migrate to the liver, lungs, and other organs—some of them finally reaching the kidneys. Upon reaching maturity, which may be 12 to 14 months after the pigs ingest the larvae, the adult female kidney worms begin producing eggs, thus completing the life cycle.

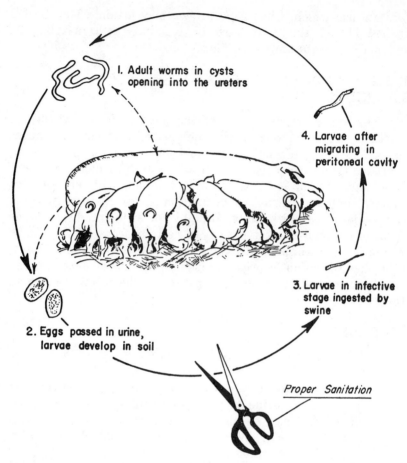

Fig. 11-15. Diagram showing the life history and habits of the kidney worm. As noted (see scissors) effective control of kidney worms in swine is obtained through proper sanitation; thus avoiding infestation with the larvae. There is no known drug treatment for removing kidney worms. (Drawing by R. F. Johnson)

DAMAGE INFLICTED; SYMPTOMS AND SIGNS OF AFFECTED ANIMALS

There are no definite symptoms ascribable to kidney worm infection. The growth rate is markedly retarded, and health is impaired. Frequently, infected animals discharge pus in the urine. Diagnosis is only positively made by microscopically discovering the presence of eggs in the urine.

PREVENTION, CONTROL, AND TREATMENT

The "gilt-only method," first proved at the Coastal Plain Experiment Station, Tifton, Georgia, constitutes the most effective prevention and control. With this method, gilts are bred only once; then, after farrowing and weaning off their first litter, they are sent to slaughter before mature kidney worms develop. This system is based on the fact that it may take the kidney worm as long as a year to reach the egg-laying stage. By following this system for two years, kidney worms may be completely eliminated.

There is no known drug treatment for removing kidney worms.

Lice

The louse is a small, flattened, wingless insect parasite of which there are several species. Hog lice, which are the largest species, may range up to one-fourth inch in length. The two main types are sucking lice and biting lice. Of the two groups, the sucking lice are the most injurious.

Most species of lice are specific for a particular class of animals; thus, hog lice will not remain on the other farm animals, nor will lice from other animals usually infest hogs. Lice are always more abundant on weak, unthrifty animals and are more troublesome during the winter months than during the rest of the year.

DISTRIBUTION AND LOSSES CAUSED BY LICE

The presence of lice upon animals is almost universal, but the degree of infestation depends largely upon the state of animal nutrition and the extent to which the owner will tolerate parasites. The irritation caused by the presence of lice retards growth, gains, and/or production of milk; and diseases may be transmitted by lice.

Swine lice and mites cause an estimated average annual loss of $3,000,000.[17]

LIFE HISTORY AND HABITS

Lice spend their entire life cycle on the host's body. They

---

[17]*Losses in Agriculture*, Agriculture Handbook No. 291, ARS, USDA, 1965, p. 82.

Fig. 11-16. Male hog louse *(Haematopinus suis)*. This is a small, flattened, wingless insect parasite. Hog lice may range up to one-fourth inch in length. (Courtesy, USDA)

attach their eggs or "nits" to the hair near the skin where they hatch in about two weeks. Two weeks later the young females begin laying eggs, and after reproduction they die on the host. Lice do not survive more than a week when separated from the host; but under favorable conditions, eggs clinging to detached hairs may continue to hatch for two or three weeks.

DAMAGE INFLICTED; SYMPTOMS AND SIGNS OF AFFECTED ANIMALS

Infestation shows up most commonly in winter in ill-nourished and neglected animals. There is intense irritation, restlessness, and loss of condition. As many lice are blood suckers, they devitalize their host. There may be severe itching and the animal may be seen scratching, rubbing, and gnawing at the skin. The

hair may be rough, thin, and lack luster; and scabs may be evident. In pigs, the skin of infested animals becomes thick, cracked, tender, and sore. In some cases, the symptoms may resemble that of mange; and it must be kept in mind that the two may occur simultaneously.

With the coming of spring, when the hair sheds and the animals go to pasture, lousiness is greatly diminished.

PREVENTION, CONTROL, AND TREATMENT

Because of the close contact of domesticated animals, especially during the winter months, it is practically impossible entirely to prevent herds and flocks from becoming slightly infested with the pests. Nevertheless, lice can be kept under control.

For effective control, all members of the herd must be treated simultaneously, and this is especially necessary during the fall months about the time they are placed in winter quarters. Spraying or dipping during freezing weather should be avoided, however. It is also desirable to treat the housing and bedding.

If a power sprayer is used, from 100 to 200 pounds pressure is adequate for spraying hogs.

Dusting is less effective than spraying or dipping, but may be preferable when few animals are to be treated or during the winter months.

Treating the bedding with 5 percent ronnel (Korlan) granules at the rate of ½ pound per 100 square feet will eliminate lice.

Table 11-3 (next page) contains recommendations for the control of lice of swine.

Several new and promising insecticides are now on the market. However, further research is desirable in order to determine the value of many of these products. Where hog lice are encountered, therefore, it is suggested that the producer obtain from local authorities the current recommendations relative to the choice and concentration of the insecticide to use.

Lungworms *(Metastrongylus elongatus, M. pudendotectus,* and *M. salmi)*

Lungworms are among the most widespread of the parasites

TABLE 11-3

HANDY SPRAY AND DIP GUIDE FOR CONTROL OF LICE OF SWINE[1]

Use Pesticides Safely—Follow the Label

Insecticide	Tolerance (p. p. m. in fat unless otherwise indicated)	Min. Days from Last Application to Slaughter	Formulation and Strength[2]	Amount of Formulation per Animal Unless Otherwise Indicated	Where and When to Apply	Safety Restrictions
Carbaryl	—	7	WP, 0.5% S	1 qt.	Spray thoroughly. Repeat as needed.	Do not apply carbaryl more often than once every 4 days or Ciodrin more often than once a week.
Ciodrin	—	—	EC, 0.5-1% S	1 pt. 1% or 2 pt. 0.5%	Spray thoroughly. Repeat once a week or as necessary.	
			EC, 0.15-0.3% S	1-4 qt.		
			EC, 0.1-0.25% S	1-2 gal. (1 gal. 0.25%)	Repeat application after 7 days.	
Coumaphos	1 meat and fat	—	WP, 0.06% S	Depending on size of animals and amount of hair.	Immerse, spray, or dust thoroughly. Use lindane dusts and DDT dusts and sprays only once, but repeat other treatments after 2 to 3 weeks if needed.	Do not use coumaphos on animals less than 3 months old. Spray animals 3 to 6 months old only lightly. Do not use with synergized pyrethrins, allethrin, or synergist. Do not spray animals for 10 days before or after shipping or weaning or after exposure to disease. Do not apply in conjunction with oral drenches *(Continued)*

(Continued)

(Continued)

Footnotes on last page of table.

Table 11-3 (Continued)

Insecticide	Tolerance (p. p. m. in fat unless otherwise indicated)	Min. Days from Last Application to Slaughter	Formulation and Strength[2]	Amount of Formulation per Animal Unless Otherwise Indicated	Where and When to Apply	Safety Restrictions
Coumaphos (continued)						or other medications, such as phenothiazine or with other organic phosphates.
DDT	7	30	EC or WP, 0.5% dip or S 10% D			
Dioxathion	1	—	EC, 0.15% dip or S			Do not reapply dioxathion or ronnel within 2 weeks. Do not dip animals less than 3 months old in dioxathion. Withdraw bedding treated with ronnel 14 days before slaughter. Do not apply ronnel to animals receiving organic phosphate treatment from any other source.
Lindane	4	30 (S) 60 (dip) 30 (D)	EC or WP, 0.05-0.06% dip or S 1% D			Do not treat young animals with dips or sprays containing more than 0.03% lin- *(Continued)*
(Continued)						

Footnotes on last page of table.

(Continued)

TABLE 11-3 (Continued)

Insecticide	Tolerance (p.p.m. in fat unless otherwise indicated)	Min. Days from Last Application to Slaughter	Formulation and Strength[2]	Amount of Formulation per Animal Unless Otherwise Indicated	Where and When to Apply	Safety Restrictions
Lindane (continued)						dane. Do not dip, spray, or dust animals less than 3 months old with lindane. Do not treat sows within 2 weeks of farrowing or for at least 3 weeks thereafter.
Malathion	4 meat	—	EC or WP, 0.5% dip or S 4-5% D			Do not use malathion on animals less than 1 month old.
Methoxychlor	3	—	EC or WP, 0.5% dip or S			
Ronnel	—	42	EC, 0.25% S			
		14	5% G	0.5 lb./100 sq. ft. bedding		
Toxaphene	7	28	EC or WP, 0.5% S	Depending on size of animals and amount of hair	Spray thoroughly. Repeat after 2 to 3 weeks, if needed.	Do not use toxaphene on animals less than 3 months old.

[1]This table was taken from *Suggested Guide for the Use of Insecticides to Control Insects Affecting Crops, Livestock, Households, Stored Products, Forests, and Forest Products*-1968 Agri. Handbook No. 331, USDA, with the permission of ARS, USDA.
[2]The following abbreviations are used:D=dust; EC=emulsifiable concentrate; G=granules; and S=spray.

that infect swine. Three species are common in hogs in this country; namely, *M. elongatus, M. pudendotectus,* and *M. salmi.* All lungworms are threadlike in diameter, one to one and a half inches in length, and white or brownish in color. As the name would indicate, they are found in the bronchi, or air passages, of the lungs. Sheep and cattle also have lungworms.

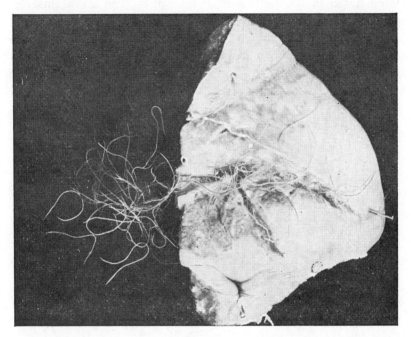

Fig. 11-17. Lower portion of a swine lung, partially cut open to show the nest of lungworms. Lungworms are threadlike in diameter, one to one and a half inches in length, and white or brownish in color. (Courtesy, USDA)

DISTRIBUTION AND LOSSES CAUSED BY LUNGWORMS

The lungworm is found in all sections of the United States, but the heaviest infection of swine occurs in the southeastern states. In addition to the usual economic losses and lowered growth and feed efficiency caused by the lungworm, there is evidence to indicate that this parasite may be instrumental in the spread of swine influenza and cholera.

Lungworms cause estimated average annual losses in swine of $3,584,000.[18]

---

[18]*Losses in Agriculture*, Agriculture Handbook No. 291, ARS, USDA, 1965, p. 79.

LIFE HISTORY AND HABITS

Female lungworms produce large numbers of thick-shelled eggs, each containing a tiny larva. The eggs are coughed up, swallowed, and eliminated with the feces of the pig. Earthworms, the intermediate hosts, feed on the feces, then swallow the eggs, which hatch in the earthworms' intestines. The larva then develops in the earthworm for three to four weeks, after which it is capable of producing an infection. Infection of the pig results from the swallowing of the earthworm, which it usually acquires by rooting and feeding in places where earthworms

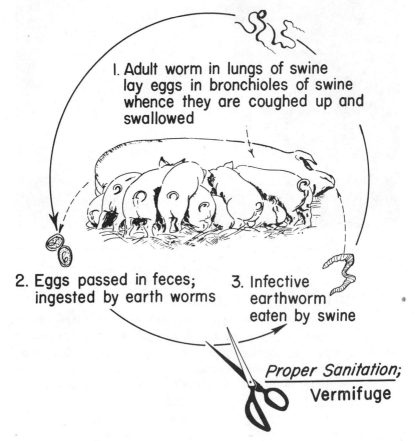

Fig. 11-18. Diagram showing the life history and habits of lungworms. As noted (see scissors) effective control of lungworms in swine is obtained through proper sanitation. (Drawing by R. F. Johnson)

abound—manure piles; rich, feces-contaminated soil; under trash; and in moist places. After ingestion by the pig, the lungworm larvae are liberated from the earthworm and migrate by way of the lymphatic and blood circulatory systems to the lungs. There they become localized, complete development, and begin to produce eggs in about one and one-half months, thus completing the life cycle.

The female lungworm produces an incredibly large number of eggs. It is estimated that as many as three million eggs may be eliminated in the droppings of a heavily infected pig in a period of twenty-four hours. More than two thousand larvae have been found in a single earthworm collected in a hog lot.

DAMAGE INFLICTED; SYMPTOMS AND SIGNS OF AFFECTED ANIMALS

Pigs heavily infected with lungworms become unthrifty, stunted, and are subject to spasmodic coughing. Positive diagnosis is made only by fecal examination or by postmortem examination. A cross section of the lungs exposes the white thread-like worms in the air tubes.

PREVENTION, CONTROL, AND TREATMENT

Prevention of lungworm infection consists of keeping hogs away from those areas where earthworms are likely to abound. Removal of manure piles and trash and the drainage of low places will help. In brief, the swine producer should provide clean, dry, well-drained lots—conditions which are not conducive for the intermediate host, the earthworm. Ringing the snout will also help in that it will prevent rooting.

Cyanacethydrazide has been used to a limited extent for the control of lungworms of swine, but its efficacy is unknown.

Mites (or Mange)

Mites produce a specific contagious disease known as mange (or scabies, scab, or itch). These small insect-like parasites, which are almost invisible to the naked eye, constitute a very large group. They attack members of both the plant and animal kingdom.

Each species of domesticated animals has its own peculiar

species of mange mites; and, with the exception of the sarcoptic mites, the mites from one species of animals cannot live normally and propagate permanently on a different species. The sarcoptic mites are transmissible from one class of animals to another and, in the case of the sarcoptic mite of the horse and cow, from animals to man. There are two chief forms of mange: sarcoptic mange, caused by burrowing mites, and psoroptic mange, caused by mites that bite the skin and suck blood but do not burrow. The sarcoptic form is most damaging; for, in addition to their tunneling, the mites secrete an irritating poison. This combination results in severe itching.

Mites are responsible for the condition known as mange (scabies) in swine, sheep, cattle, and horses. The disease appears to spread most rapidly among young and poorly nourished animals.

DISTRIBUTION AND LOSSES CAUSED BY MITES

Injury from mites is caused by irritation and blood sucking and the formation of scabs and other skin affections. In a severe attack, the skin may be much less valuable for leather. Growth is retarded, and production of meat and milk is lowered.

LIFE HISTORY AND HABITS

The mites that attack livestock and poultry breed exclusively on the bodies of their hosts, and they will live for only two or three weeks when removed therefrom. The female mite which produces sarcoptic mange—the most severe form of scabies—lays from ten to twenty-five eggs during the egg-laying period, which lasts about two weeks. At the end of another two weeks, the eggs have hatched and the mites have reached maturity. A new generation of mites may be produced every fifteen days.

The disease is more prevalent during the winter months, when animals are confined and in close contact with each other.

DAMAGE INFLICTED; SYMPTOMS AND SIGNS OF AFFECTED ANIMALS

Infested animals do not eat properly and, as a result, they do not gain at normal rates.

When the mite pierces the skin to feed on cells and lymph, there is marked irritation, itching, and scratching. Exudate forms on the surface, and this coagulates, crusting over the surface. The crusting is often accompanied or followed by the for-

Fig. 11-19. Pig with sarcoptic mange, caused by sarcoptic mites. Note the thickening, wrinkling and harshness of the skin. (Courtesy, Dept. of Veterinary Pathology and Hygiene, College of Veterinary Medicine, University of Illinois)

mation of a thick, tough, wrinkled skin. Often there are secondary skin infections. The only certain method of diagnosis is to demonstrate the presence of the mites.

PREVENTION, CONTROL, AND TREATMENT

Prevention consists of avoiding contact with diseased animals or infested premises. In case of an outbreak, the local veterinarian or livestock sanitary officials should be contacted.

Mites can be controlled by spraying or dipping infested animals with suitable insecticidal solutions. For recommended insecticides, see Table 11-4. Because new insecticides are constantly being developed, when hog mites are encountered it is suggested that the producer obtain from local authorities the current recom-

Fig. 11-20. Spraying hogs for the control of lice and mites, using a power sprayer. (Courtesy, University of Idaho)

mendations relative to the choice and concentration of the insecticide to use.

Nodular Worm

These parasites are most numerous in southeastern United States. A parasitic survey conducted in North Carolina showed the nodular worm to be second to strongyloides in incidence.

They are called nodular worms because of the nodules or lumps they cause in the large intestine. Four species occur in swine, but all of them are slender, whitish to grayish in color, and ⅓ to ½ inch in length.

TABLE 11-4

HANDY SPRAY AND DIP GUIDE FOR CONTROL OF SWINE MITES[1]

Insecticide	Tolerance (p.p.m. in fat unless otherwise indicated)	Min. Days from Last Application to Slaughter or Use of Milk	Formulation and Strength	Amount of Formulation per Animal unless Other- wise Indicated	Where and When to Apply
Lime-sulfur			2% "sulfide sulfur" spray or dip	Spray: 2-4 qts./animal, depending on the size.	Make two ap- plications 10-14 days apart.
Nicotine			0.05% nicotine spray or dip	Do	Do
Lindane	4	30 (S)	0.05-0.06% spray or dip	Do	Do
Toxaphene	7	28	0.5-0.6% spray or dip	Do	Do
Malathion	4		1 gal. of 50-57% emulsifiable conc. plus 1 lb. of non- foaming detergent /100 gallons of water.	Do	Do

[1]This table was authoritatively reviewed by a staff member of the federal regulatory division charged with the control of scabies; namely, Dr. Charles R. Omer, Chief Staff Veterinarian, Animal Health Division, Agricultural Research Service, USDA, Federal Center Building, Hyattsville, Maryland.

DISTRIBUTION AND LOSSES CAUSED BY
THE NODULAR WORM

Nodular worms are widely distributed, but damage is heaviest in the southeastern states. In addition to the usual lack of thrift that accompanies parasite infections, the intestines of severely infected animals are not suited for either sausage or as food (in some sections of the country, the intestines of pigs are marketed for human food under the trade name of chitterlings). Thus, the presence of nodular worms often results in considerable loss to the meat industry—a loss that is passed back to the swine producer in the form of lower market prices.

Nodular worms cause average annual swine losses of $6,836,-000.[19]

LIFE HISTORY AND HABITS

The four species of nodular worms affecting swine have similar life histories. The adult worms are localized in the large intestine of the host animal. The female worms deposit large numbers of partly developed eggs that become mixed with the intestinal contents and are eliminated with the droppings. With favorable conditions of temperature and moisture, a larva emerges from each egg in one to two days. After another three to five days of development, the larvae are infective to swine. Pigs then become infected by swallowing the larvae while feeding on contaminated ground or grazing on contaminated pastures. In the digestive system of the host, the larvae travel to the large intestine where they penetrate into the wall and grow for the next two to three weeks. They then move into the lumen, or cavity, of the large intestine where they continue development. Within five to seven weeks after ingestion by the pig, the worms are fully grown and have mated and are producing eggs, thus starting a new cycle.

DAMAGE INFLICTED; SYMPTOMS AND SIGNS
OF AFFECTED ANIMALS

No specific symptoms can be attributed to the presence of

---

[19]*Losses in Agriculture*, Agriculture Handbook No. 291, ARS, USDA, 1965, p. 79.

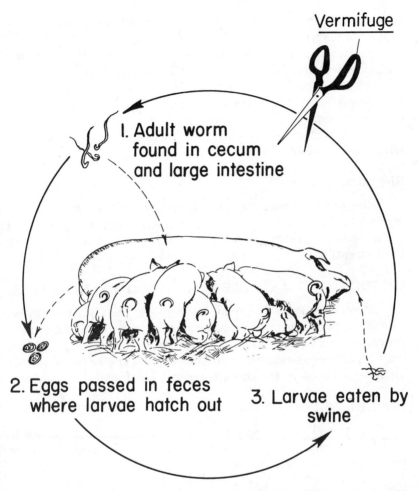

Fig. 11-21. Diagram showing the life history and habits of the nodular worm. As noted (see scissors) pigs may be dewormed by administering a vermifuge. Rigid sanitation, accompanied by pasture rotation, constitutes the only successful and practical preventive measure. (Drawing by R. F. Johnson)

nodular worms. Weakness, anemia, emaciation, diarrhea, and general unthriftiness have all been reported as due to infection with these parasites.

PREVENTION, CONTROL, AND TREATMENT

A strict program of swine sanitation, accompanied by pas-

ture rotation, constitutes the only successful and practical preventive measure.

Pigs may be dewormed by administering dichlorvos, a prescription drug available through veterinarians; mixing the drug in the feed according to manufacturer's directions. Dichlorvos is a broad spectrum worm medicine, which is effective in the control of ascarids, whipworms, and strongyloides, in addition to nodular worms. Parvex and the antibiotic hygromycin are also effective in nodular worm control.

Ringworm

Ringworm, or barn itch, is a contagious disease of the outer layers of skin. It is caused by certain microscopic molds or fungi (*Trichophyton*, *Achorion*, or *Microsporon*). All animals and man are susceptible.

DISTRIBUTION AND LOSSES CAUSED BY RINGWORM

Ringworm is widespread throughout the United States. Though it may appear among animals on pasture, it is far more prevalent as a barn disease. It is unsightly, and affected animals may experience considerable discomfort; but the actual economic losses attributed to the disease are not too great.

LIFE HISTORY AND HABITS

The period of incubation for this disease is about one week. The fungi form seed or spores that may live eighteen months or longer in barns or elsewhere.

DAMAGE INFLICTED; SYMPTOMS AND SIGNS OF AFFECTED ANIMALS

Round, scaly areas almost devoid of hair appear mainly in the vicinity of the eyes, ears, side of the neck, or the root of the tail. Crusts may form, and the skin may have a gray, powdery, asbestos-like appearance. The infested patches, if not checked, gradually increase in size. Mild itching usually accompanies the disease.

PREVENTION, CONTROL, AND TREATMENT

The organisms are spread from animal to animal and

through the medium of contaminated fence posts, curry combs, and brushes. Thus, prevention and control consists of disinfecting everything that has been in contact with infested animals. The affected animals should also be isolated. Strict sanitation is an essential in the control of ringworm.

The hair should be clipped, the scabs removed, and the area brushed and washed with mild soap. The diseased parts should be painted with tincture of iodine or salicylic acid and alcohol (one part in ten) every three days until cleared up. Certain proprietary remedies available only from veterinarians have proved very effective in treatment.

Screwworm (*Callitroga hominivorax*)

Among all the insect pests on this earth, those which raise their maggots in the living flesh of animals—such as the screwworm—are peculiarly loathsome. True screwworms seldom get through the unbroken skin, but will penetrate moist pockets like the prepuce of a gelding and the dimple in front of a cow's udder.

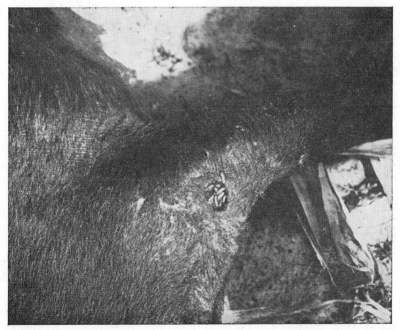

Fig. 11-22. Screwworm injury to the front leg of year old sow. (Courtesy, USDA)

They are not found in cold-blooded animals such as turtles, snakes, and lizards.

Man-made wounds resulting from shearing, branding, castrating, dehorning, and docking afford a breeding ground for this parasite. Add to this the wounds from some types of vegetation, from fighting, and from blood-sucking insects; and ample places for propagation are provided.

DISTRIBUTION AND LOSSES CAUSED BY SCREWWORMS

Normally, the primary screwworm fly is confined to the southern and southwestern states, including Arizona and the southern half of California. Occasionally, under exceptionally favorable weather conditions or through the shipping of infested animals from further south, destructive outbreaks of the pest have occurred in some of the Corn Belt states.

In infested areas, the screwworm is undoubtedly the greatest enemy of all the insect species with which the livestock owner must contend. For example, in the Southwest, where it inflicts the most injury, many stockmen report that 50 percent of their normal annual livestock losses are caused by this parasite.

LIFE HISTORY AND HABITS

The primary screwworm fly is bluish green in color, with three dark stripes on its back and reddish or orange color below the eyes. The fly generally deposits its eggs in shingle-like masses on the edges or the dry portion of wounds. From 50 to 300 eggs are laid at one time, with a single female being capable of laying about 3,000 eggs in a lifetime. Hatching of the eggs occurs in eleven hours, and the young whitish worms (larvae or maggots) immediately burrow into the living flesh. There they feed and grow for a period of four to seven days, shedding their skin twice during this period.

When these larvae have reached their full growth, they assume a pinkish color, leave the wound, and drop to the ground, where they dig beneath the surface of the soil and undergo a transformation to the hard-skinned, dark-brown, motionless pupa. It is during the pupa stage that the maggot changes to the adult fly.

After the pupa has been in the soil from seven to sixty days, the fly emerges from it, works its way to the surface of the ground, and crawls up on some nearby object (bush, weed, etc.) to allow its wings to unfold and otherwise mature. Under favorable conditions, the newly emerged female fly becomes sexually mature and will lay eggs five days later. During warm weather, the entire life cycle is usually completed in twenty-one days, but under cold, unfavorable conditions the cycle may take as many as eighty days or longer.

DAMAGE INFLICTED; SYMPTOMS AND SIGNS OF AFFECTED ANIMALS

The injury caused by this parasite is inflicted chiefly by the maggots. Unless proper treatment is administered, the great destruction of many tissues kills the host in a few days.

PREVENTION, CONTROL, AND TREATMENT

Prevention in infested areas consists mainly of keeping animal wounds to a minimum and of protecting those that do materialize.

As the primary screwworm must have living, warm-blooded animals in which to breed and in order to survive, it must produce a new generation during each four-month period. It is evident, therefore, that the most effective control measures can be effected during the winter months. During this season, the life cycle is slowed down, and it is difficult for the fly to live and breed. Thus, the most effective control consists of preventing infestation of wounds and of killing all possible maggots during the winter and spring months. Additional control is effected through timing as much as possible those farm and ranch operations that necessarily produce wounds during the winter season when the flies are least abundant and least active. The use of Burdizzo pincers or other similar instruments in castration, the dehorning of animals at an early age and during the proper season, the eradication of plants that cause injuries, breeding so that young will arrive during the seasons of least fly activity, and avoidance of anything else that might produce wounds will all aid greatly in screwworm control. In brief, the elimination of wounds or injuries to the host constitutes effective control.

If possible there should be facilities available for handling

and treating infested animals. It is highly desirable to have a
screened, fly-proof area available for wounded or infested animals. All wounds should be treated with a smear or spray containing diphenylamine, lindane, or ronnel to prevent the invasion of
tissue by fly larvae.

The screwworm eradication program, by sterilization, has
been very effective. This consists in sterilizing male screwworms
in the pupal stages with X rays or gamma rays. Male screwworms
mate repeatedly, but females mate only once. Thus, when a female
mates with a sterilized male, only infertile eggs are laid. The release of millions of sterilized males has led to the near eradication
of screwworms from most of the United States.

Stomach Worms (*Ascarops strongylina, Physocephalus sexalatus,* and *Hyostrongylus rubidus*)

Three species of small stomach worms infect swine. Two of
the species, *A. strongylina* and *P. sexalatus,* are commonly
known as "thick stomach worms." These parasites are reddish
in color and nearly an inch long in the adult stage. The third
species, *H. rubidus,* commonly known as the "red stomach worm,"
is a small, delicate, slender, reddish worm about one-fifth
inch in length.

DISTRIBUTION AND LOSSES CAUSED BY STOMACH WORMS

The occurrence of the stomach worm is widespread in hogs
throughout the United States. In certain of the midwestern
states, as many at 90 percent of the animals examined have been
found to harbor the worms, and, in the southeastern states, 50 to
80 percent.[20] However, it is noteworthy that this parasite is no
problem on farms where a good parasite control program is followed.

LIFE HISTORY AND HABITS

It has been definitely established that the ordinary dung
beetle serves as the intermediate host for the thick stomach

---

[20]Spindler, L. A., "Internal Parasites of Swine," *Keeping Livestock
Healthy,* the Yearbook of Agriculture, 1942, USDA, p. 752.

worm. The female worm deposits eggs in the stomach of the
pig, with each egg containing a tiny embryo. The eggs pass with
the feces to the outside of the body of the pig, then hatch, and
the tiny larvae enter the body cavity of various species of dung
beetles, the intermediate hosts.

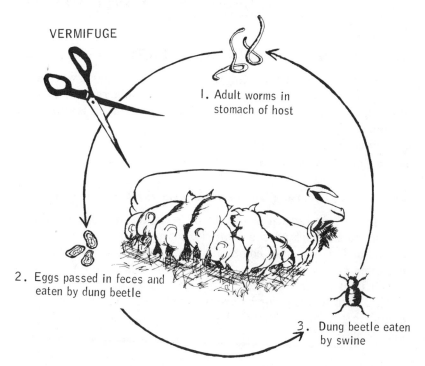

Fig. 11-23. Diagram showing the life history and habits of the thick
stomach worm. As noted (see scissors) the vermifuge treatment is
effective; though it is not entirely satisfactory. The application of the
McLean County System of Swine Sanitation is the most effective preventive. (Drawing by R. F. Johnson)

After developing for about a month in the beetle, the
larvae arrive at a stage infective to swine. Hogs feeding on contaminated ground then swallow the beetles. In the stomach of
the pig, the parasites are liberated from the beetles and make
their way into the mucus membrane of the stomach, where they
grow to maturity. The life history of the red stomach worm
differs from that of the thick stomach worms in that no intermediate host is necessary, the infections being directly acquired.

DAMAGE INFLICTED; SYMPTOMS AND SIGNS OF AFFECTED ANIMALS

Because of the burrowing tendency of this parasite, inflammation and gastric ulcers usually follow. In external appearance, the affected animals usually become unthrifty and show a marked loss in appetite.

PREVENTION, CONTROL, AND TREATMENT

Preventive measures for the control of stomach worms are similar to those advocated for the control of ascarids; namely, the application of the McLean County System of Swine Sanitation.

Parvex is the treatment of choice. It should be administered under the direction of the veterinarian.

Thorn-headed Worm *(Macracanthorhynchus hirudinaceus)*

The thorn-headed worm is of considerable importance in the southern part of the United States. It may be easily distinguished from the common intestinal roundworm by the presence of rows of hooks—a spiny proboscis (snout)—through which it attaches itself to the wall of the small intestine of the host. Thorn-headed worms are milk white to bluish in color and cylindrical to flat in shape, the largest being about the size of a lead pencil.

DISTRIBUTION AND LOSSES CAUSED BY THORN-HEADED WORMS

The thorn-headed worm is not a common parasite of hogs grown in the Corn Belt states, but it is of considerable economic importance in the deep South. In addition to the usual slow growth, inefficient feed utilization, and death losses resulting from other parasites, thorn-headed worms weaken the intestine and make it unfit for sausage casings. This causes a financial loss to the packer that is passed along to the swine producer in the form of lowered meat prices.

LIFE HISTORY AND HABITS

Adult female thorn-headed worms produce numerous thick-

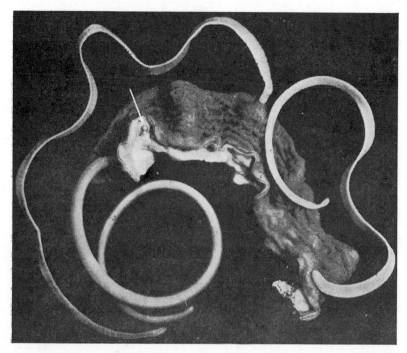

Fig. 11-24. Thorn-headed worms of swine. These worms are milk white to bluish in color and cylindrical to flat in shape, with the largest being about the size of a lead pencil. (Courtesy, USDA)

shelled brownish eggs, each containing a fully developed larva. Each female may produce as many as 600,000 eggs per day at the peak of her egg-producing capacity. The eggs, which pass out with the manure, are very resistant to destruction.

White grubs, the larvae of June bugs (or May beetles), serve as the intermediate hosts. The grubs, feeding on infected manure or contaminated soil, swallow the parasite eggs. The eggs hatch in the bodies of the grubs and in seven to twelve weeks develop to a stage that is infective to swine.

Pigs rooting in manure or trash piles, rich soil, or low-lying pastures swallow the grubs, of which they are very fond. The young thorn-headed worms then escape from the bodies of the grubs or adult beetles through the process of digestion and develop to egg-laying maturity.

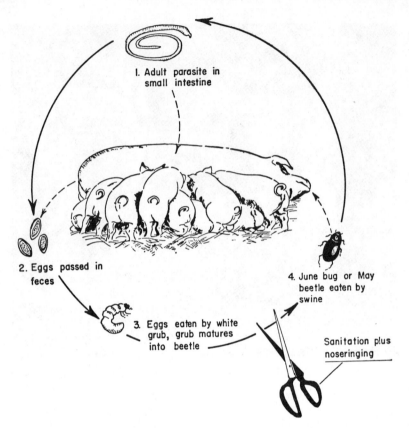

1. Adult parasite in
   small intestine

2. Eggs passed in
   feces

3. Eggs eaten by white
   grub, grub matures
   into beetle

4. June bug or May
   beetle eaten by
   swine

Sanitation plus
noseringing

Fig. 11-25. Diagram showing the life history and habits of the thorn-headed worm. As noted (see scissors), sanitation plus nose-ringing are effective preventive measures, keeping pigs from consuming the white grub or June bug. No known drug treatment is entirely satisfactory for removing thorn-headed worms. (Drawing by R. F. Johnson)

DAMAGE INFLICTED; SYMPTOMS AND SIGNS OF AFFECTED ANIMALS

No special symptoms have been attributed to swine infected with thorn-headed worms, although these parasites are decidedly injurious. Infected swine exhibit the general unthriftiness that is commonly associated with parasites. A heavy infestation may even kill young pigs. Upon autopsy, a swelling or nodule may be evident at the point of attachment, and the intestinal wall may exhibit great weakness.

PREVENTION, CONTROL, AND TREATMENT

Prevention consists of keeping pigs from feeding in areas where they might obtain the white grub of the June bug. Thus, sanitation, clean ground, and noseringing are effective preventive measures. No known drug treatment is entirely satisfactory for removing thorn-headed worms.

Threadworm *(Strongyloides ransomi)*

The pig is the only known host of *S. ransomi*. These worms are tiny; females are 3.33 to 4.49 mm long.

DISTRIBUTION AND LOSSES CAUSED BY THREADWORMS

The importance of the threadworm is attested to by the fact that it causes estimated average annual swine losses of $2,731,-000.[21] It is the most important swine parasite in the South.

LIFE HISTORY AND HABITS

The life cycle is as follows: Small, embryonated eggs are passed in the feces; at room temperature, they hatch in 12 to 18 hours; the larvae develop into the infective stage 22 to 24 hours after hatching; the infective larvae penetrate the skin and proceed to the lungs via the bloodstream, thence from the alveoli of the lungs to the bronchi, esophagus, stomach, and small intestine, where they become adults about seven days after infection. Also, it has been shown that (1) oral ingestion of the infective larvae can produce infection, and (2) *S. ransomi* is capable of developing a free living generation of adult males and females, which, in turn, develop infective parasitic larvae.

DAMAGE INFLICTED; SYMPTOMS AND SIGNS OF AFFECTED ANIMALS

Diagnosis is best made upon autopsy. However, hogs with threadworms are usually restless and irritable, and show reduced growth rate, diarrhea, vomiting, and even death.

---

[21]*Losses in Agriculture*, Agriculture Handbook No. 291, ARS, USDA, 1965, p. 79.

PREVENTION, CONTROL, AND TREATMENT

Prevention is best achieved through (1) a program of strict sanitation, and (2) selecting dry, unshaded areas for swine lots. There is no effective treatment at the present time.

Trichinosis *(Trichinella spiralis)*

This is a parasitic disease of human beings caused by *T. spiralis*.[22] The main source of the disease is infected pork, eaten raw or imperfectly cooked. Although the parasite is present in the muscle tissue of swine, it does not induce symptoms in this species.

DISTRIBUTION AND LOSSES CAUSED BY TRICHINOSIS

This disease appears to be worldwide, with the highest incidence occurring in areas where uncooked garbage is fed to hogs. Old studies (conducted prior to enactment of state laws requiring that garbage be cooked before feeding to swine) showed (1) less than 1 percent of pork from grain fed hogs infected with trichinosis, and (2) 5 to 6 percent infection of pork in hogs fed uncooked garbage.

LIFE HISTORY AND HABITS

The life cycle of trichina may be summarized as follows:

1. The adult parasite, which is a round worm from 1.5 to 4 mm in length, lives in the small intestine of man, hogs, rats, and other animals. The female worms penetrate into the lining of the intestines where they produce numerous young or larvae.

2. The larvae pass from the wall of the intestine into the lymph stream, thence into the bloodstream, and finally into the muscle cells.

3. In the muscles, the larvae grow until they are about 1/25 of an inch long, then roll into a characteristic spiral shape, and

---

[22]For the whole United States, there were only 13 deaths due to trichinosis in the three-year period 1955-57 (4 in 1955; 5 in 1956; 4 in 1957), according to a report entitled "National Summaries, Mortality from Each Cause, 1955-57," issued January 9, 1959, by the Public Health Service, National Office of Vital Statistics, U. S. Department of Health, Education, and Welfare.

become surrounded by a capsule. In this environment and stage of development, these larvae may live for years or until the raw or improperly cooked muscle tissue is eaten by man or other species of meat eaters.

4. Upon gaining entrance to the intestines of another host, the worm starts a new life cycle.

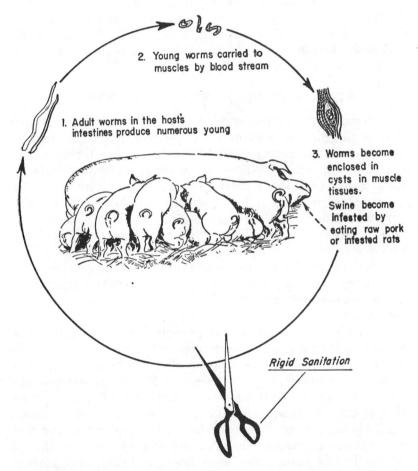

Fig. 11-26. Diagram showing the life history and habits of trichina, the parasite that causes trichinosis. As noted (see scissors) effective control of trichinosis in swine is obtained through rigid sanitation, including (1) destruction of rats, (2) proper carcass disposal of dead hogs, and (3) cooking all garbage and offal from slaughtering houses. The surest and best protection now available to human pork consumers consists of cooking or freezing pork at the temperatures specified. (Drawing by R. F. Johnson)

DAMAGE INFLICTED; SYMPTOMS AND SIGNS OF AFFECTED ANIMALS

Trichinosis in pigs is never diagnosed for the reason that other fever-producing diseases of swine are characterized by similar clinical manifestations.

The symptoms in man vary depending upon the degree of parasite infection. The disease is usually accompanied by a fever, digestive disturbances, swelling of infected muscles, and severe muscular pain (in the breathing muscles as well as others). A specific skin test may also be applied to aid in the diagnosis in man. Normally, the symptoms begin about ten to fourteen days after eating infected pork.

PREVENTION, CONTROL, AND TREATMENT

Fortunately, a considerable amount of the trichinosis pork that is slaughtered is noninfective by the time it reaches the consumer. In processing, much of it is made safe through heating, freezing, etc. Nevertheless, a small amount of infected pork is sold over the counter, and the only certain protection to man is to cook pork and pork products to 140° F. internal temperature. Thus, prevention consists of the thorough cooking of all pork before it is eaten, either by humans or swine. Trichina is also destroyed by refrigeration for a continuous period of not less than twenty days at a temperature of not higher than 5° F.

Microscopic examination of pork is the only way in which to detect the presence of trichina, but such a method is regarded as impractical.

Trichinosis in swine may be prevented by (1) destruction of all rats on the farm, (2) proper carcass disposal of hogs that die on the farm, and (3) cooking of all garbage and offal from slaughtering houses at a temperature of 212° F. for 30 minutes.[23] But as all these preventive measures may not be feasible or practical or carried out with care, the surest and best protection now available to pork consumers consists of cooking or freezing pork at the temperatures specified. It is noteworthy, however, that all 48 contiguous states now have laws requiring that garbage be cooked.

---

[23]Only a very small proportion of U.S. hogs are now garbage-fed; to be exact, in 1960 only 1.85 percent of the nation's hogs were fed garbage; and all 48 contiguous states require that it be cooked prior to feeding.

Whipworm *(Trichuris suis)*

Whipworms are usually found attached to the walls of the cecum (blind gut) and large intestine of swine. They are 1 to 2 inches in length. The worms have a very slender anterior portion and much enlarged posterior. The anterior resembles the lash of a whip and the posterior the handle, hence the name whipworm.

DISTRIBUTION AND LOSSES CAUSED BY THE WHIPWORM

Little factual information is available relative to the prevalence of this particular parasite. It appears, however, that the heaviest infection of swine occurs in the southeastern states. Also, there is ample evidence that the whipworm is increasing in the Corn Belt. One well-known practicing Iowa veterinarian is authority for the statement that "the whipworm is second only to the large intestinal roundworm (ascarids) in swine" in his particular area.

Whipworms cause annual swine losses of $717,000.[24]

LIFE HISTORY AND HABITS

The life cycle of the whipworm is simple and direct; that is, no intermediate host is necessary to complete the life cycle. The eggs, which are produced in large numbers, are eliminated with the feces. An infective larva develops in the shell, and swine become infected by swallowing the eggs when feeding on soil where they are present. The eggs hatch in the stomach and intestine, and the larvae make their way to the blind gut, where they grow to maturity in about ten weeks or longer.

DAMAGE INFLICTED; SYMPTOMS AND SIGNS OF AFFECTED ANIMALS

Infected animals may develop a diarrhea, and in heavy infections the diarrhea becomes bloody. In massive infections, growth may be noticeably retarded, and the animal may become weak and finally die.

---

[24]*Losses in Agriculture*, Agriculture Handbook No. 291, ARS, USDA, 1965, p. 79.

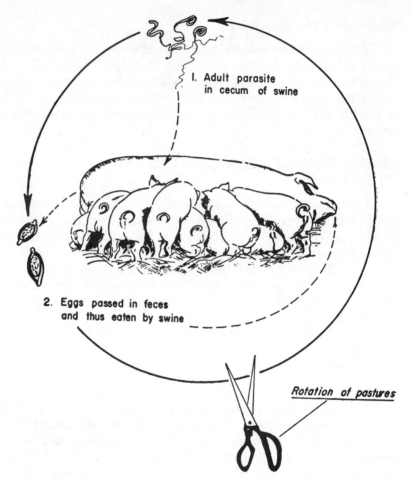

1. Adult parasite
in cecum of swine

2. Eggs passed in feces
and thus eaten by swine

Rotation of pastures

Fig. 11-27. Diagram showing the life history and habits of the whip-worm. As noted (see scissors) rotation of clean, well-drained pastures, and plenty of sunlight are the key to the prevention of the whipworm. Dichlorvos is effective in whipworm treatment. (Drawing by R. F. Johnson)

PREVENTION, CONTROL, AND TREATMENT

Clean well-drained pastures, rotation grazing, and plenty of sunlight are the key to the prevention and control of the whip-worm. Dichlorvos is effective in whipworm treatment.

How to Prepare Sprays or Dips

In most cases several concentrations of both wettable pow-ders and emulsions of each insecticide are on the market. Because

of this, the recommended concentrations of sprays and dips in Tables 11-3 and 11-4 are in terms of percentage concentration of the active ingredient in the finished spray or dip.

In preparing sprays and dips, most stockmen rely almost entirely on the directions found on the container. With products manufactured by reputable companies, this is probably satisfactory. However, any stockman can easily prepare an insecticide of any desired strength (1) by referring to Table 11-5, or (2) by following the simple mathematical formula which follows Table 11-5.

TABLE 11-5

HANDY GUIDE FOR MAKING DESIRED STRENGTH OF INSECTICIDES[1]

Type and Percentage of Insecticide in Concentrate	Amount of Concentrate to Add to Water to Make Different Percentage Strengths in Finished Spray or Dip			
	For 5 Gallons		For 100 Gallons	
	0.5 Percent	2.5 Percent.	0.5 Percent	2.5 Percent
Wettable Powder:				
25%	12 oz.	----------	16 lbs.	----------
40%	8 oz.	2.5 lbs.	10 lbs.	50 lbs.
50%	6½ oz.	2.0 lbs.	8 lbs.	40 lbs.
75%	4 oz.	1¼ lbs.	5⅓ lbs.	26½ lbs.
Emulsion:				
25%	1½ cups	2 qts. (7½ c.)	2 gals.	10 gals.
50%	¾ cup	1 qt. (3¾ c.)	1 gal.	5 gals.

[1]To make 0.25 percent strengths, use half the amount given in Table 11-5 for the 0.5 percent strength. To make 5 percent strength, use two times the amount given in Table 11-5 for the 2.5 percent strengths.

Where Table 11-5 is not applicable, the number of pounds of any given insecticide wettable powder or emulsion—regardless of its concentration—to add in order to make a desired number of gallons of spray or dip of the desired strength may be computed readily and accurately as shown in the following example:

Example: How many pounds of 50 percent wettable DDT powder are required in order to prepare 100 gallons of 0.5 percent finished DDT spray for the control of flies?

Answer:

$$\frac{\text{(gallons of finished spray or dip desired)} \times \text{(wt. of 1 gal. of water)} \times \text{(percentage of active ingredient desired in finished spray or dip)}}{\text{(percentage active ingredient in insecticide)}} \text{ or } \frac{100 \times 8^2 \times 0.5}{50} = 8 \text{ pounds}$$

To be more exact, this figure is 8.337, but 8.0 is close enough for all practical purposes.

Use Chemicals Safely

Agricultural chemicals are as vital to the health of animals as modern medicines are to the health of people. Stockmen depend on chemicals—insecticides, herbicides, fungicides, and similar materials—to control the pests that attack their animals or damage

their feed crops; and, when necessary, they use biologics for the prevention or treatment of animal diseases.

Registered materials for the protection of livestock and feed crops are safe when used as recommended. But some of them can be hazardous if they are improperly applied or administered. Misuse can bring serious financial loss and/or lower the quality of products.

Observance of the following guidelines will assure the profitable and safe use of chemicals:[25]

1. Use chemicals economically

a. Don't use more than the recommended amount of a pesticide. Follow directions on the container label. Most of the materials are expensive. Overdosage is wasteful and often hazardous.

b. Use only the chemicals that competent authorities recommend as both safe and effective for your specific purpose.

c. Store chemicals carefully, for safety and economy. Avoid spillage.

d. Prevent waste of chemicals by keeping application equipment in perfect working condition. Calibrate the equipment so it will dispense the recommended dosage.

2. Don't poison livestock

a. Be sure chemicals are always properly labeled. Prevent misuse by referring to the label each time a chemical is used. Don't transfer chemicals from the original containers to unlabeled containers.

b. Use only chemicals that are registered or licensed as suitable for the particular purpose intended.

c. Place covers over feed and water containers when applying chemicals on or near areas occupied by livestock.

d. Keep chemicals thoroughly mixed when applying them to livestock. Otherwise, some animals may receive too much of the active ingredient for safety, or too little to accomplish the desired purpose.

e. Don't use a spray or dip if an oily or gummy film appears on its surface after it has been mixed; the chemical

---

[25]These guidelines were prepared by the Agricultural Research Service, USDA and issued June 1966, in USDA PA-727.

may have deteriorated and consequently the active ingredient may not be evenly distributed in the mixture.

f. Don't use food or drink containers for measuring or storing pesticides.

3. Don't contaminate products

The residues of some chemicals may accumulate in the bodies of animals. Under federal and state laws, meat containing illegal pesticide residue is condemned and may not be sold as food. To prevent illegal residues from being present in the meat of slaughtered animals, observe these measures:

a. Follow label directions when treating animals with pesticides.

b. When soils are treated, on which will be grown feed or forage, use only a chemical that will not contaminate the crop.

c. Clean application equipment thoroughly before using it to apply a different pesticide.

d. Don't feed animals wastes from canneries or food processing plants unless it is ascertained that these wastes will not cause illegal pesticide residues in the meat.

e. Allow the prescribed number of days to elapse between the last application of a chemical and the harvesting or grazing of feed crops.

f. After spraying, dipping, or dusting animals with pesticides, observe the prescribed number of days' interval between the last treatment and slaughter. Refer to the container labels for the information.

g. When preparing back rubbers, use only the recommended chemicals and carriers. Don't use waste motor oil as a carrier; it may contain poisonous material. Allow the prescribed number of days to elapse between last use of back rubbers and slaughter.

4. General pesticide precautions

a. Follow the directions and heed all precautions on pesticide container labels.

b. Keep pesticides in closed, well-labeled containers in a dry place. Store them where they will not contaminate food or feed, and **where children and animals cannot reach them.** Keep empty containers away from children and animals; dispose of containers as promptly as possible.

c. When handling a pesticide, wear clean, dry clothing.

d. Avoid repeated or prolonged contact of pesticide with your skin.

e. Wear protective clothing or equipment if the container label states that it is needed. Avoid prolonged inhalation of pesticide dusts or mists. Don't spray into the wind.

f. Avoid spilling pesticide concentrate on your skin, and keep it out of your eyes, nose, and mouth. If you spill any on your skin, wash it off immediately with soap and water. If you get it in your eyes, flush the eyes with water for 15 minutes; get medical attention. If you spill it on your clothing, change the clothing at once and launder it before wearing it again.

g. After handling a pesticide, don't eat, smoke, or drink until you have washed your hands and face. Wash your hands and face and any other exposed skin immediately after applying pesticide.

h. To protect water resources, fish, and wildlife, don't contaminate lakes, streams, or ponds with pesticide. Don't clean spraying equipment or dump unwanted spray material near such water.

i. To protect honey bees and other pollinating insects that are necessary in the production of many crops, treat crops at times when these insects are not visiting the plants. This may be before or after flowering, or it may be at night.

j. Avoid drift of pesticide to nearby livestock, crops, or bee yards. Ground sprayers do not permit as much drift as other types of application equipment.

k. Dispose of empty pesticide containers at a sanitary land-fill dump or bury them at least 18 inches deep in a level, isolated place where they will not contaminate water supplies. If you have trash collection service, you may wrap small containers in heavy layers of newspapers and place them in the trash can.

DISINFECTANTS[26]

Under ordinary conditions, proper cleaning of barns removes most of the microorganisms, along with the filth, thus eliminat-

---

[26]The author had the benefit of the authoritative review and suggestions of Dr. R. W. H. Gillespie, Professor of Veterinary Microbiology, Washington State University, in the preparation of this section and Table 11-6.

ing the necessity of disinfection. In case of a disease outbreak, however, the premises must be disinfected.

Effective disinfection depends on five things:

1. Thorough cleaning before application.

2. The phenol coefficient of the disinfectant, which indicates the killing strength of a disinfectant as compared to phenol (carbolic acid). It is determined by a standard laboratory test in which the typhoid fever germ is used as the test organism.

3. The dilution at which the disinfectant is used.

4. The temperature; most disinfectants are much more effective if applied hot.

5. Thoroughness of application and time of exposure.

Disinfection must in all cases be preceded by a very thorough cleaning, for organic matter serves to protect disease germs and otherwise interferes with the activity of the disinfecting agent.

Sunlight possesses disinfecting properties, but it is variable and superficial in its action. Heat and some of the chemical disinfectants are more effective.

The application of heat by steam, by hot water, by burning, or by boiling is an effective method of disinfection. In many cases, however, it may not be practical to use heat.

In choosing a chemical disinfectant, it should be realized that not all disease-producing bacteria are susceptible to the same chemical agents. Table 11-6 gives a summary of the limitations, usefulness, and strength of some common disinfectants.

POISONS

Hogs are seldom poisoned. When trouble is encountered, the owner or caretaker should promptly call a veterinarian. In the meantime, the animal(s) should be (1) placed where adequate care and treatment can be given, (2) protected from excessive heat and cold, and (3) allowed to eat only feeds known to be safe.

Cocklebur Poisoning

Of the numerous poisonous plants, the cocklebur is the only one likely to poison hogs; although cases have been reported of swine being poisoned by black night shade, buttercup, St. Johnswort, buckeyes, and water hemlock.

The cocklebur grows in fields and waste areas in eastern

TABLE 11-6

HANDY DISINFECTANT GUIDE

(Chemical agents should not be relied upon to destroy spores; controlled and prolonged heat is required to kill spores.)

Kind of Disinfectant	Usefulness	Strength	Limitations and Comments
Alcohol	Effective against the less resistant disease germs provided there is adequate exposure.	70 percent alcohol—the content usually found in "rubbing" alcohol.	Limited application. Not recommended for general use. Often used as a local antiseptic in obtaining blood samples or making hypodermic injections. Not reliable for sterilization of instruments.
Bichloride of Mercury (mercuric chloride; corrosive sublimate)	Destroys less resistant bacteria under favorable conditions. Tends to prevent growth rather than actually destroy bacteria. Organic mercurials, sometimes used as local antiseptics, are less poisonous and more reliable.	Tablets used in a dilution of 1 to 1,000.	Unreliable as a germ killer in the presence of organic matter. Also, cattle are especially susceptible to mercury poisoning. For farm disinfection, bichloride of mercury is inferior to synthetic phenols, lye, saponified cresols, and the new cationic bactericides.
Boric acid[1]	As wash for eyes, and other sensitive parts of the body.	1 oz. in 1 pt. water (about 6% solution).	It is a weak antiseptic. It may cause harm to the nervous system if absorbed into the body in large amounts. For this and other reasons, antibiotic solutions and saline solutions are fast replacing it.
Cationic bactericides (many commercial products available, including QAC, i.e., quarternary ammonium compounds)	Primarily detergents but some are actively bactericidal. Often used in sanitizing dairy or other equipment and utensils. **Use only as recommended by a sanitarian.**	Concentration varies with different products and under different conditions. Follow authoritative recommendations.	They have only a slight toxicity and are non-irritant and odorless. They are neutralized by soap, anionic detergents and even by mineral content of some waters. Superior to chlorine compounds in the presence of organic matter. They are not effective against T.B. organisms and spores.

(Continued)

Footnote on last page of table.

TABLE 11-6 (Continued)

Kind of Disinfectant	Usefulness	Strength	Limitations and Comments
Cresols (many commercial products available)	A generally reliable class of disinfectant. Effective against brucellosis, shipping fever, swine erysipelas, and tuberculosis.	4 oz. per gal.; or according to the directions found on the container.	Cannot be used where odor may be absorbed, and, therefore, not suited for use around milk and meat.
Heat (by steam, hot water, burning, or boiling)	In the burning of rubbish or articles of little value, and in disposing of infected body discharges. The steam "Jenney," is effective for disinfection if properly employed—particularly if used in conjunction with a phenolic germicide.	10 min. exposure to boiling water is usually sufficient.	Exposure to boiling water will destroy all ordinary disease germs, but sometimes fails to kill the spores of such diseases as anthrax and tetanus. Moist heat is preferred to dry heat, and steam under pressure is the most effective. Heat may be impractical or too expensive.
Hypochlorites (chlorine compounds)	For deodorizing manure, sewers, drains, and for disinfecting milk cans and bottles and around dairy barns.	200 parts available chlorine per million of water. Unstable; replace solution frequently as recommended.	Excellent for disinfection, but with following limitations: Not effective against the T.B. organism and spores. Its effectiveness is greatly reduced in presence of organic matter, such as milk, even in small quantities. Hypochlorites deteriorate rapidly when exposed to air.
Iodine[1]	Extensively used as skin disinfectant, for minor cuts and bruises.	Generally used as tincture of iodine 2% or 7%.	Never cover with a bandage. Clean skin before applying iodine.

Footnote on last page of table.

TABLE 11-6 (Continued)

Kind of Disinfectant	Usefulness	Strength	Limitations and Comments
Iodophor (iodine complexed with a detergent which releases free iodine at a controlled rate)	For disinfecting milk cans and bottles around dairy barns and for area disinfection where large quantities of organic soil are not present.	75 parts available iodine per million is minimum under ideal circumstances. 150 ppm is recommended for most practical uses. Unstable—replace solution frequently.	An excellent disinfectant but with the following practical limitations: Germicidal agent rapidly consumed by organic matter necessitating frequent replacement. Functions best in a highly acid range. Solution strength must be increased to get necessary available iodine when mixture is made with alkaline water. Iodine slowly volatilizes from solution. Considerable control should be exercised.
Lime (quick-lime; burnt lime; calcium oxide)	As a deodorant when sprinkled on manure and animal discharges; or as a disinfectant when sprinkled on the floor or used as a newly made "milk of lime" or as a whitewash.	Use as a dust; as "milk of lime"; or as a whitewash but use fresh.	Not effective against organism of T.B. and the spore formers. Wear goggles when adding water to quicklime.
Lye (sodium hydroxide or caustic soda)	On concrete floors; in milk houses because there is no odor; against microorganisms of brucellosis and the viruses of foot-and-mouth disease, hog cholera, and vesicular exanthema. In strong solution (5%) effective against anthrax and blackleg.	1 can (13 oz.) to 12 to 15 gals. water. To prepare a 5% solution, add 5 (13 oz.) cans to 10 gals. water.	Damages fabrics, aluminum, and painted surfaces. Be careful, for it will burn the hands and face. Not effective against organism of T.B., or Johne's disease, or strangles, or most spores. When used in hog houses, lye should be mixed with hot water, as the heat of the water will destroy the worm eggs. *Diluted vinegar can be used to neutralize lye.*

(Continued)

TABLE 11-6 (Continued)

Kind of Disinfectant	Usefulness.	Strength	Limitations and Comments
Phenolic germicides, synthetic (those containing odorless nontoxic phenols such as orthophenyl phenol or orothobenzyl parachlorophenol)	A very reliable class of disinfectants effective against all disease-producing fungi and bacteria including the T.B. organism.	Varies with different formulations; follow directions on manufacturer's label.	Excellent for disinfection. They are not inactivated by soap, anionic detergents, hard water or organic matter. They are effective against all bacteria and fungi including the T.B. organism but not the spores of anthrax and tetanus.
Sal soda	It may be used in place of lye against foot-and-mouth disease and vesicular exanthema.	10½% solution (13½ oz. to 1 gal. water).	
Soap	Its power to kill germs is very limited. Greatest usefulness is in cleansing and dissolving coatings from various surfaces, including the skin, prior to application of a good disinfectant.	As commercially prepared.	Although indispensable for sanitizing surfaces, soaps should not be used as disinfectants. They are not regularly effective; staphylococci and the organisms which cause diarrheal diseases are resistant.
Soda ash (or sodium carbonate)	It may be used in place of lye against foot-and-mouth disease and vesicular exanthema.	5% solution (1 lb. to 3 gals. water). Most effective in hot solution.	Commonly used as a cleansing agent, but has disinfectant properties, especially when used as a hot solution.

¹Sometimes loosely classed as a disinfectant but actually an antiseptic and practically useful only on living tissue.

United States. and in low wet places in the western part of the country. The plant is palatable and dangerous in the seedling or two-leaf stage, mostly in the spring or early summer.

Affected animals show prostration, rapid and weak pulse, low temperature, and vomiting. Death, if it occurs, follows in 24 hours. On autopsy, the stomach is very inflamed.

Emergency treatment consists in giving the animal—by mouth or through a stomach tube—such fatty substances as raw linseed oil—mineral oil, lard, cream, or whole milk.

Preventive measures are: (1) keep swine out of cocklebur-infested pastures during late spring and early summer when cocklebur seeds are sprouting, and (2) lessen cocklebur infestation by mowing or chopping plants before they seed.

Lead Poisoning

Paint containing lead; discarded storage batteries; and contaminated vegetation, containers, or water are the main sources of lead poisoning.

Symptoms develop rapidly in young pigs but may be slow in onset in mature hogs. There is loss of appetite and evidence of gastroenteritis. The feces may become very dark gray and be tinged with blood. There is salivation, champing of the jaws, frenzy, blindness, convulsions, coma, and death. Mature animals usually have diarrhea and show incoordination, especially in the hind limbs, and prostration. Lead poisoning can be diagnosed positively by analyzing the blood or tissue for lead content.

Prevention consists in avoiding the source of lead. If damage to tissues has been extensive, treatment is of little value; in any event, the veterinarian should determine the latter. The best chemical antidote is protein (milk, eggs, blood serum).

Mercury Poisoning

Most of the mercury poisoning of hogs results from the consumption of seed grains treated with fungicides that contain mercury. This happens because mercury is the active principle of many fungicides employed in the control of fungous diseases of oats, wheat, barley, and flax. Both dry and liquid preparations, containing approximately 2 to 3 percent mercury equivalent, are available and used for this purpose; with only a small

amount of the fungicide mixed with the grain. Either because of not realizing the hazard or through negligence, frequently some of the leftover mercury-treated grain is fed to hogs.

Gastrointestinal, renal, and nervous disturbances are usually manifested by swine suffering from mercury poisoning. It is not possible, however, on the basis of symptoms, to differentiate mercury from other poisons. The ultimate diagnosis depends upon demonstrating the presence of mercury in the tissues, especially of the kidneys and liver. However, a case history which reveals that some of the grains the pigs were consuming had been treated with a mercurial fungicide should be considered as strong circumstantial evidence.

Treatment has not been satisfactory. The best chemical antidote is protein (milk, eggs, blood serum).

Seed grains that have been treated with a mercury-containing fungicide must not be fed to swine, or to other livestock. Any surplus of treated grain should be burned and the ash buried deep in the ground.

Pitch Poisoning (Clay Pigeon Poisoning)

This is an acute, highly fatal disease of swine characterized, clinically, by depression and, pathologically, by striking liver lesions.

The vast majority of cases of this disease result from swine eating expended clay pigeons, which contain pitch. Pastures contaminated with clay pigeons are dangerous for many years; deaths having been reported 35 years after the last known time that the pasture was used for trapshooting.

Instances of pitch poisoning have also been reported as a consequence of consuming other pitch- or bitumen-containing products, including roofing material, certain types of tar paper, and plumbers' pitch.

There is no known treatment for this disease.

Salt Poisoning

The Indians and the pioneers of this country handed down many legendary stories about huge numbers of wild animals that killed themselves simply by gorging at a newly found salt lick after having been salt starved for long periods of time. However, such salt-starved conditions seldom prevail among domestic ani-

mals; and, some opinions to the contrary, salt poisoning is relatively rare in swine.

If hogs have not previously been fed salt for a very long time, they should first be hand-fed salt, and the daily allowance should be increased gradually until they start leaving a little in the mineral box. When the latter point is reached, self-feeding may be followed.

Hogs will not normally eat sufficient salt to be harmful. Exceptions have been reported where brine (as from cured meats) and wet salt have killed hogs, and where large amounts of salt or brine have been mixed in a slop.

Protein Poisoning

Despite occasional diagnosis of protein poisoning in swine, and other animals, there is no proof that heavy feeding of high protein feeds is harmful, provided that the ration is balanced out in all other respects and the animal does not have a kidney ailment. At Washington State University, growing-finishing pigs on a Sudangrass pasture were successfully fed a grain ration composed of 98.5 percent cull peas (averaging 24 percent digestible protein) plus a mineral supplement.

In a high protein ration, any amino acids that are left over after the protein requirements have been met, are deaminated or broken down in the body. In this process, a part of each amino acid is turned into energy, and the remainder is excreted via the kidneys.

Generally speaking, feeds of high protein content are more expensive than those high in carbohydrates or fats, with the result that there is the temptation to feed too little of them.

REGULATIONS RELATIVE TO DISEASE CONTROL

Certain diseases are so devastating that no individual swine producer could long protect his herd against their invasion. Moreover, where human health is involved, the problem is much too important to be entrusted to individual action. In the United States, therefore, certain regulatory activities in animal-disease control are under the supervision of various federal and state organizations. Federally, this responsibility is entrusted to the following agency:

Animal Health Division
Agricultural Research Service
U. S. Department of Agriculture
Federal Center Building
Hyattsville, Maryland

Most states have state veterinarians, or comparable officials, who also direct their effort to livestock sanitary and regulatory problems.

Many highly infectious diseases are prevented by quarantine from (1) gaining a foothold in this country, or (2) spreading. *By quarantine is meant (1) segregation and confinement of one or more animals in the smallest possible area to prevent any direct or indirect contact with animals not so restrained; or (2) regulating movement of animals at points of entry.* When an infectious disease outbreak occurs, drastic quarantine must be imposed to restrict movement out of an area or within areas. The type of quarantine varies from one involving a mere physical examination and movement under proper certification to the complete prohibition against the movement of animals, produce, vehicles, and even human beings.

Where certain animal diseases are involved, the swine producer can obtain financial assistance in eradication programs through federal and state sources. Information relative to indemnities paid to owners by the federal government may be secured from the federal agency just listed, and similar information pertaining to each state can be secured by writing to the respective state departments of agriculture.

QUESTIONS FOR STUDY AND DISCUSSION

1. Why are such publications as (a) the 1942 Yearbook of Agriculture entitled *Keeping Livestock Healthy,* and (b) the 1956 Yearbook of Agriculture entitled *Animal Diseases* of value to swine producers?
2. What is the normal temperature, pulse rate, and breathing rate of hogs, and how would you determine each?
3. Select a specific farm (either your own or one with which you are familiar) and outline (in 1, 2, 3, order) a program of swine health, disease prevention, and parasite control.

4. Obtain the following publications from the Animal Health Division, Agricultural Research Service, USDA, Federal Center Building, Hyattsville, Maryland: Subchapter B. Title 9, of the Code of Federal Regulations, parts 51 and 53. Also, write to your state department of agriculture for information about indemnity payments. Then determine the indemnity payments that you could expect were you to encounter an outbreak of foot-and-mouth disease.

5. Assume that a specific contagious disease (you name it) has broken out in your herd. What steps would you take to meet the situation (list in 1, 2, 3, order; be specific)?

6. Assume that a specific parasite (you name it) has become troublesome in your herd. What steps would you take to meet the situation (list in 1, 2, 3, order; be specific)?

7. Assume that you have, during a period of a year, encountered swine death losses from three different diseases. What kind of disinfectant would you use in each case?

8. Assume that you have encountered death losses from a poison (you name it). What steps would you take to meet the situation (list in 1, 2, 3, order; be specific)?

9. Why do we have federal and state regulatory officials? How can they be of assistance to the individual swine producer?

SELECTED REFERENCES

Title of Publication	Author(s)	Publisher
Anatomy & Physiology of Farm Animals	R. D. Frandsen	Lea & Febiger, Philadelphia, Pa., 1965.
Animal Diseases	Yearbook of Agriculture, 1956	U. S. Department of Agriculture, Washington, D. C.
Animal Sanitation and Disease Control	R. R. Dykstra	The Interstate Printers & Publishers, Inc., Danville, Ill., 1961.
Brucellosis	A symposium— 1949	American Assn. for the Advancement of Science, 1515 Massachusetts Ave., N.W., Washington, D. C.
Diseases of Swine	H. H. Dunne (edited by)	The Iowa State University Press, Ames, Ia., 1958.
Diseases of Swine	C. G. Grey C. N. Dale	Farmers' Bul. 1914, U. S. Department of Agriculture, Washington, D. C.
Farmer's Veterinary Handbook, The	J. J. Haberman	Prentice-Hall, Inc., New York, N.Y., 1953.

Title of Publication	Author(s)	Publisher
Home Veterinarian's Handbook, The	E. T. Baker	The Macmillan Company, New York, N. Y., 1949.
Infectious Diseases of Domestic Animals, The	W. A. Hagan D. W. Bruner	Comstock Publishing Associates, Ithaca, N. Y., 1957.
Insecticide Recommendations	Agricultural Handbook No. 331	U. S. Department of Agriculture, Washington, D. C., 1968.
Keeping Livestock Healthy	Yearbook of Agriculture, 1942	U. S. Department of Agriculture, Washington, D. C.
Livestock Health Encyclopedia	Rudolph Seiden	Springer Publishing Co., New York, N. Y., 1951.
Merck Veterinary Manual, The		Merck & Co., Rahway, N. J., 1967.
Principles of Veterinary Science	F. B. Hadley	W. B. Saunders Co., Philadelphia, Pa., 1949.
Progress in Swine Practice	Edited by J. F. Smithcors, DVM E. J. Catcott, DVM	American Veterinary Publications, Inc., Wheaton, Ill., and Santa Barbara, Calif., 1966.
Stockman's Handbook, The	M. E. Ensminger	The Interstate Printers & Publishers, Inc., Danville, Ill., 1970.
Veterinary Drugs in Current Use	Rudolph Seiden	Springer Publishing Co., Inc., New York, N. Y., 1960.
Veterinary Guide for Farmers	G. W. Stamm	Windsor Press, Chicago, Ill., 1950.
Veterinary Medicine	D. C. Blood J. A. Henderson	The Williams & Wilkins Company, Baltimore, Md., 1960.

In addition to these selected references, valuable publications on different subjects pertaining to swine diseases, parasites, disinfectants, and poisonous plants can be obtained from the following sources:

Division of Publications
Office of Information
U. S. Department of Agriculture
Washington, D. C.

Your state agricultural college.

Several biological, pharmaceutical, and chemical companies.

Chapter XII

MARKETING AND SLAUGHTERING HOGS

Contents   **Page**

Livestock marketing embraces those operations beginning with loading animals out on the farm and extending until they are sold to go into processing channels.

Marketing—along with breeding, feeding, and management —is an integral part of the modern livestock production process.

It is the end of the line; that part which gives point and purpose to all that has gone before. Market receipts constitute the only source of reimbursement to the producer for his work; market day is the producer's payday—hence, it is the most important single day of operation to him. The importance of hog marketing is further attested by the following facts:

1. In 1967, 85,528,000 hogs were marketed in the U.S.[1]

2. In 1967, U.S. farmers received 8.9 percent of their cash farm marketing income from hogs.[2]

3. Livestock markets establish values of all animals, including those down on the farm or ranch. On January 1, 1969, there were 57,205,000 head of hogs in the U.S. (including Alaska and

Fig. 12-1. Hogs being driven to market. This was a common scene in the early 1900's. Truck transportation of livestock was first started in 1911. (Photo by J. C. Allen and Son, West Lafayette, Ind.; courtesy American Feed Manufacturers Association, Inc.)

---

[1]*Livestock and Meat Statistics*, June 1968, Agricultural Marketing Service, USDA, Supplement to Statistical Bul. No. 333.
[2] *Agricultural Statistics*, 1968, USDA, pp. 478 and 479.

Hawaii), with an aggregate value of $1,822,963,000 or $31.90 per head.[3]

It is important, therefore, that the swine producer know and follow good marketing practices.

THE CHANGING HOG MARKET

In the good old days, farm produce marketing was relatively simple. On Saturdays, the farmer toted to town and sold to the corner produce store a basket of eggs, a gunny sack of old hens or fryers, and a jar of sour cream. Surplus hogs were usually sold to local buyers. The farmer did little figuring as to the best time

LIGHT HOGS ARE MORE PROFITABLE

20 HOGS AT 225 LBS
4500 LBS.

15 HOGS AT 300 LBS.
4500 LBS.

WILL PRODUCE   **WILL PRODUCE**

 560 lbs. lard   720 lbs. lard

2660 lbs. meat   2670 lbs. meat

FROM   **FROM**

 18500 lbs. feed   20625 lbs. feed

Fig. 12-2. Lighter hogs produce less lard and a larger proportion of the valuable cuts, and there is a saving in feed. (From "The Little Woman Is Changing the Hog Market," University of Minnesota, Extension Folder 151)

---

[3]*Livestock and Poultry Inventory, January 1, Number, Value, and Classes*, Statistical Reporting Service, Crop Reporting Board, USDA, pp. 3 and 9.

to sell his animals; his chief worry was in growing rather than in selling his stuff. He could be successful if he knew how to breed, feed, and manage his stock. Today, this is not enough; pre-considered, if not prearranged, markets are essential.

Consumer preference has dictated, and will continue to dictate, changes in market hogs. In recent years, the consumer has been demanding (1) less lard, (2) smaller cuts with less fat and more lean, and (3) a larger proportion of the valuable cuts. These requirements are met by meat type hogs that are slaughtered at light weights. Further, from the producers' standpoint, there is a saving in feed in marketing at lighter weights. These facts are clearly illustrated in Fig. 12-2.

Recognition of consumer preference is reflected in the comparative market prices prevailing for light and heavy weight hogs. In turn, market changes have caused a lowering of show-ring weight classifications for barrows, and a shift in emphasis in swine type conferences.

METHODS OF MARKETING HOGS

The hog producer is confronted with the perplexing problem

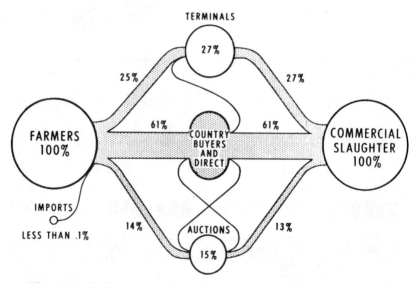

Fig. 12-3. U. S. market channels for slaughter hogs, 1963. (From: *Organization and Competition in the Livestock and Meat Industry*, Tech. Study No. 1, National Commission on Food Marketing, June 1966, p. 6, Fig. 1-4)

of determining where and how to market his animals. Usually there is a choice of market outlets, and the one selected often varies between classes and grades of hogs and among sections of the country. Thus, the method of marketing usually differs between slaughter hogs and feeder pigs, and both of these differ from the marketing of purebreds.

Most hogs and pigs are sold through the following channels: (1) direct, country dealers, etc., (2) terminal markets, or (3) auction markets.

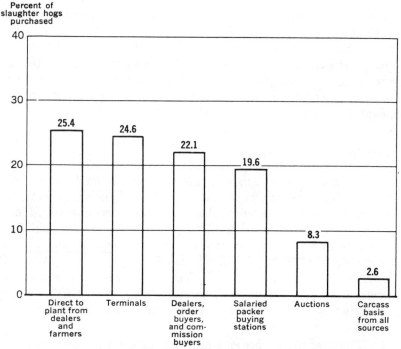

Fig. 12-4. Hog procurement channels of the 40 largest U. S. hog packers in 1964. (From: *Organization and Competition in the Livestock and Meat Industry*, Tech. Study No. 1, National Commission on Food Marketing, p. 136, Fig. 10-1)

In 1967, the U.S. Department of Agriculture reported that farmers sold hogs and pigs through different market outlets in about the proportions shown in Table 12-1.

In comparison with the marketing of cattle and sheep, the marketing of hogs differs in the following respects: (1) there has

TABLE 12-1

MARKET AVENUES FOR HOGS AND PIGS, 1967[1]

	1,000 Head	Percent
Direct, country dealers, etc.--	50,948	65.7
Terminal markets --	14,540	18.8
Auction markets --	12,019	15.5
Total---	77,509	100.0

[1]*Packers and Stockyards Résumé*, Consumer and Marketing Service, USDA, Vol. VI, No. 10, Nov. 8, 1968.

been a greater proportionate increase in direct marketing of hogs with the advent of improved highways and truck transportation; (2) relatively few hogs are taken out of the market for further feeding because of parasite and disease problems; and (3) the proportion of hogs slaughtered on farms far exceeds that of cattle or sheep because of the greater ease of slaughtering and the adaptation of pork to home-curing.

Terminal Public Markets

Terminal public markets (also referred to as terminal markets, central markets, public stockyards, and public markets) are livestock trading centers, where livestock are assembled at a single geographic location in large numbers to be sold on a "private treaty basis," and which possess complete facilities for receiving, caring for, handling, and selling livestock. About 50 U. S. markets are so classified. Various numbers of commission firms, depending on the size of the market, sell livestock at these markets; and all buyers and sellers of livestock are privileged to use these facilities.

The first of the present terminal public markets was established at Chicago in 1865. Most of the larger terminal markets operating today were established in the latter half of the nineteenth century.

Up through World War I, the majority of slaughter livestock in the United States was sold through terminal public markets directly by farmers or by local buyers shipping to them. Since then, the importance of these markets has declined in relation to other outlets (see Fig. 12-5). In 1923, federally inspected slaughterers purchased 77 percent of their hogs in central mar-

kets;[4] in 1950, 40 percent;[5] and, in 1967, 18.8 percent.[6] But these figures do not tell the whole story; when the total slaughter at all commercial slaughtering establishments is considered, the percentage bought at terminal markets is somewhat less. The latter situation is so because nonfederally inspected slaughterers tend to buy larger proportions of their livestock at markets other than terminal markets.

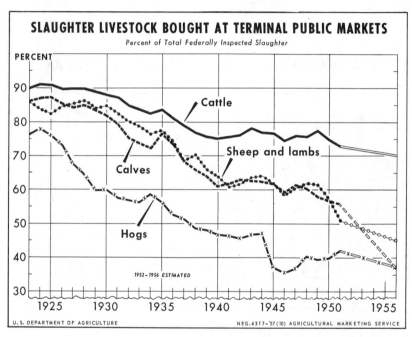

SLAUGHTER LIVESTOCK BOUGHT AT TERMINAL PUBLIC MARKETS

Percent of Total Federally Inspected Slaughter

Fig. 12-5. This shows that terminal public markets have declined in relative importance.

LEADING TERMINAL HOG MARKETS

As would be expected, the leading hog markets of the United States are located in or near the Corn Belt—the area of densest hog population. With the advent of the motor truck and improved highways, the pork packing plants were moved nearer the areas

---

[4] Phillips, Victor B., and Gerald Engleman, *Market Outlets for Livestock Producers*, USDA, Marketing Research Report No. 216, p. 5.

[5] *Food From Farmer to Consumer*, Report of the National Commission on Food Marketing, June 1966 p. 22.

[6] See Table 12-1.

of hog raising. Thus, during the past three decades, local or interior packers have increased in numbers. In order to meet this added competition, the large packers at more distant points resorted to direct buying and the purchase of interior plants.

The rank of the major hog markets shifts considerably according to feed supplies and general economic conditions. The ten largest hog markets, by rank, and their receipts are listed in Table 12-2.

TABLE 12-2

TOTAL RECEIPTS OF TEN LEADING TERMINAL HOG MARKETS, BY RANK, 1967[1]

Market	Average Hog Receipts 1967
	(no.)
Omaha, Nebr.	2,101,227
St. Louis National Stock Yards, Ill.	1,860,454
Sioux City, Iowa	1,844,258
South St. Paul, Minn.	1,604,772
Chicago, Ill.	1,333,016
St. Joseph, Mo.	1,317,647
Indianapolis, Ind.	1,152,239
Kansas City, Mo.	1,039,983
Peoria, Ill.	854,581
Sioux Falls, S.D.	834,975
U.S. Total—52 markets	17,776,871

[1]*Livestock and Meat Statistics*, June 1968, USDA, Supp. for 1967 to Statistical Bul. No. 333, p. 38.

CHARGES AT TERMINAL PUBLIC MARKETS

Hog producers need to be acquainted with livestock marketing costs. Although commission and yardage rates vary slightly (1) according to size of consignment and (2) between markets, Table 12-3 summarizes the typical charges at a terminal market for trucked-in hog shipments. On the average, it costs producers about $1.00 per head to market hogs through a terminal market, exclusive of farm to market shipping charges.

Livestock Auction Markets

Livestock auctions (also referred to as sales barns, livestock auction agencies, community sales, and community auctions) are trading centers where animals are sold by public bidding to the

TABLE 12-3

CHICAGO TERMINAL PUBLIC MARKET CHARGES ON HOGS PER HEAD
PAID BY PRODUCERS IN 1966[1]

	Hogs (per head)
Commission[2]	$ .50
Yardage[2]	.42
Corn	.10
Services[3]	.03
Marketing cost per head	$1.05
Marketing cost per cwt.	.42

[1]Figures provided by *The Drovers Journal,* in a personal communication to the author from Allan W. McGhee, Editor, *The Drovers Journal.*
[2]Rates vary slightly according to the size of consignment and also between markets.
[3]Includes bedding.

buyer who offers the highest price per hundredweight or per head.

This method of selling livestock in this country is very old, apparently being copied from Great Britain where auction sales date back many centuries.

Apparently the auction method of selling was used in many of the colonies as a means of disposing of property, imported goods, secondhand household furnishings, farm utensils, and animals. According to available records, the first U. S. public livestock auction sale was held in Ohio in 1836, by the Ohio Company, whose business was importing English cattle.

Although there are some records of occasional livestock auctions sales during the nineteenth century, there is no indication of any auction market that continued operation throughout the period of the greatest development of terminal public stockyards markets. It is within the current century that present auction development had its beginnings. In fact, livestock auction markets have had their greatest growth since 1930, both in numbers established and the extensiveness of the area over which they operate.

Fig. 12-6 shows the growth in numbers of livestock auctions from 1900 to 1955. About 200 auctions were operating by 1930; by 1937, this number had increased to 1,345. The peak in numbers was reached in 1952, when over 2,500 different livestock auctions were holding sales; but, by 1958, the total number had declined to 2,350.

Several factors contributed to the phenomenal growth in

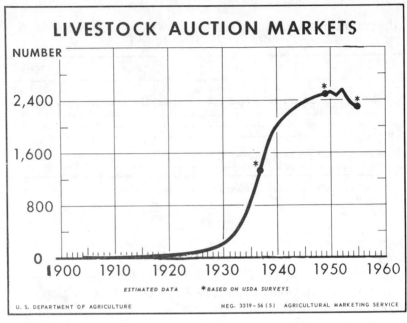

Fig. 12-6. Number of livestock auctions.

auction markets during the thirties, chief of which were the following:

1. The decentralization of markets. Associated with this was the improvement and extension of hard surfaced roads accompanied by the increased use of trucks as a means of transporting livestock to and from the market place. Use of trucks increased flexibility in the handling of various sized lots of livestock and in the direction of movement, and, with the advent of better roads, trucks could be used for transporting livestock moderate distances both quickly and economically. Also, growing numbers of small packers, located at distant points from terminal markets, were able to procure livestock more efficiently at auction markets.

2. The development of more uniform class and grade classifications for livestock.

3. Improvements made by the federal government in providing more extensive collection and dissemination of market news.

4. The greater convenience afforded in disposing of small

lots of livestock and in purchasing stockers, feeders, and breeding animals.

5. The recognized educational value of these nearby markets, which enabled producers to keep currently informed of local market conditions and livestock prices.

6. The Depression of 1930-1933. When livestock prices are low—such as was true during the depression years—transportation and other marketing expenses comprise a greater part of the total gross value received from the sale of livestock. Since, at this time the commission charges at most auctions were based on a percentage of the gross sale value of the animal, marketing expenses at auctions tended to be low when prices were low. Also, with the proximity of auctions to producing areas, out-of-pocket transportation expenses were less for livestock sent to local auctions than for shipments to more distant market outlets.

7. The abnormal feed distribution caused by the droughts of 1934 and 1936 in the western Corn Belt and range states created conditions favoring increased sales at auctions. Some immature and unfinished stock in these areas were sold at nearby auctions to farmers having a plentiful supply of feed on hand. Also, stocker and feeder cattle were shipped out of the drought sections to auctions located in areas where feed supplies were more abundant.

8. The desire to sell near home. By contrast to large public terminal markets which receive some livestock from considerable distances, auction markets draw their supplies largely from the communities in which they are located.

Prior to the advent of community livestock auctions, the small livestock operator had two main market outlets for his animals—(1) shipping them to the nearest terminal public market, or (2) selling them to buyers who came to his farm or ranch. Generally, the first method was too expensive because of the transportation distance involved and the greater expense in shipping small lots. The second method pretty much put the producer at the mercy of the buyer, because he had no good alternative to taking the price he was offered, and often he did not know the value of his animals. By contrast, the big operator is not particularly concerned about these things. Because of his large scale, usually he can take advantage of any of several terminal markets, and he knows enough about values that he can deal satisfactorily with buyers who come to his farm or ranch. Thus, the community

livestock auctions are really of greatest importance to the small operator.

A larger proportion of the hogs sold through auctions go back to the farm than of those sold on terminal markets.

CHARGES AT AUCTIONS

Rates charged for marketing livestock vary at different auctions. Services for which charges are levied may include sellings, yardage, weighing, insurance, brand inspection, and health inspection. Many auctions do not provide all these services. A commission or selling fee, however, is charged at all markets and is the primary source of income to auction operators. At some auctions, the commission covers yardage and weighing, in addition to the selling service. Some operators levy a separate charge for each service provided, while others charge a single rate to cover all services.

Auction operators levy their charge on a per head basis, on a percentage of gross value, or by a combination of the two methods.

Straight per head charges on hogs vary considerably. However, the national average is 65 to 75 cents per head. For auctions reporting straight percentage charges, the most usual charge on hogs is 3 percent.[7]

Direct Selling

Direct selling refers to producers' sales of livestock direct to packers or country dealers without the support of commission men, selling agents, buying agents, or brokers.

Prior to the advent of terminal public markets in 1865, country selling accounted for virtually all sales of livestock. Sales of livestock in the country declined with the growth of terminal markets until the latter method reached its peak of selling at the time of World War I. But country selling was accelerated by the large nationwide packers following World War I in order to meet the increased buying competition of the small interior packers.

Like auction selling, direct selling has a certain appeal, inasmuch as it permits producers to observe and exercise some

---

[7]*Livestock Auction Markets in the United States*, March 1958, Agricultural Marketing Service, USDA, Marketing Research Report No. 223, p. 2.

control over selling while it takes place; whereas consignment to distant terminal public markets at times represents an irreversible commitment to sell. Larger and more specialized livestock farmers feel competent to sell their livestock direct.

Improved highways and trucking facilitated the growth of direct selling. Farmers were no longer tied to outlets located at important railroad terminals or river crossings. Livestock could move in any direction. Improved communications, such as the radio and telephone, and an expanded market information service, also aided in the development of direct selling of livestock, especially in sales direct to packers.

Direct selling to meat packers is an important outlet for slaughter hogs in many areas. It is the dominant method of marketing hogs and pigs in the North Central Region, the most highly concentrated area of hog production in the United States. Some packers buy hogs direct from producers at the plant; others send their buyers into the country, from farm to farm, where they make bids on the livestock that they inspect.

Country dealers operate in all parts of the nation. These include country buying operations by local buyers, by contract buyers for later delivery, by buyers purchasing on orders for others, and by a variety of speculative buyers. Speculative buyers are known by a variety of names in different parts of the country; they are sometimes called livestock buyers, traders, scalpers, truck buyers, stock buyers, pinhookers, and scavengers. Some of these country buyers purchase livestock at fixed establishments similar to packer-owned country buying points.

Carcass Grade and Weight (Yield) Selling

Carcass grade and weight (yield) selling is that type of transaction in which the packer makes a price bid contingent on the quality of the carcass as well as its weight.

This is the most common method of marketing hogs in Denmark, Sweden, and Canada, but only limited selling on this basis has been followed in the United States—only 3.2 percent in 1967.[8]

In general, farmers who produce superior animals benefit from selling on the basis of carcass grade and weight, whereas the producers of lower quality animals usually feel that this method unjustly discriminates against them. In countries where

---

[8]*Packers and Stockyards Resume*, Vol. VI, No. 10, Nov. 8, 1968, Table 6.

rail grading has been used extensively, there has been an un-
mistakable improvement in the breeding and feeding of swine.
Denmark, Sweden, and Canada have effectively followed this
type of program in producing high quality bacon, chiefly for
export to the London market. Although Canadians made great
strides in improving the quality of their market hogs prior to
initiating compulsory carcass grade and weight marketing in
1940, it is noteworthy that by 1958 it was estimated that 71 percent of Canada's market hogs would grade U. S. No. 1, whereas it
was estimated that only 15 to 30 percent of all U. S. slaughter
barrows and gilts would grade U. S. No. 1.[9]

The factors favorable to selling on the basis of carcass grade
and weight may be summarized as follows:

1. It encourages the breeding and feeding of quality hogs.

2. It provides the most unassailable evaluation of the product.

3. It eliminates wasteful filling on the market.

4. It makes it possible to trace losses from condemnations,
bruises, and soft pork to the producer responsible for them.

5. It is the most effective approach to animal improvement.

The factors unfavorable to selling on the basis of carcass
grade and weight are:

1. The procedure is more time consuming than the conventional basis of buying.

2. From the standpoint of the meat packer, there is less
flexibility in the operations.

3. The physical difficulty of handling the vast United States
volume of hogs on this basis is great.

4. There is delay in returns to the shipper.

5. Decreased bargaining power exists on the part of the
producer or his agent.

6. Grading in the presence of the buyer and absence of the
seller, opens the way to fraud—sometimes suspected by the seller.

Broiler producers are already producing to specification a
top grade bird of a specific weight—a product which meets the
demands of the consumer and in which there is repeatability

---

[9]*Marketing Meat-Type Hogs*, April 1958, Agricultural Marketing
Service, USDA, Marketing Research Report No. 227, p. III.

(subsequent purchases having about the same eating qualities). Perhaps the producers of four-footed meat animals need to emulate the broiler producers. How did they achieve their present status? Essentially, all concerned segments of the chicken industry got together and agreed on the "chicken of tomorrow"— a bird that would meet the demands of the consumer. Then, with the aid of research and practical producers, they took the necessary steps to reach their goal. Swine producers can emulate broiler producers. To this end, all segments of the industry should get together and decide on the "hog of tomorrow." Then, with the aid of research scientists and practical operators, we should progress toward these goals through improved breeding and feeding. Granted, it will take longer with hogs, because of their slower reproduction than chickens, but it can be done.

REGULATIONS FOR CARCASS GRADE AND WEIGHT TRANSACTIONS

In 1968, the U. S. Department of Agriculture issued the following uniform regulations where meat packers buy hogs (or other species) on the basis of carcass grade, carcass weight, or a combination of the two:

1. Make known to the seller, before sale, significant details of the purchase contract.

2. Maintain identity of each seller's livestock and carcass.

3. Maintain sufficient records to substantiate settlement for each purchase transaction.

4. Make payment on the basis of actual carcass weight.

5. Use hooks, rollers, gambrels and similar equipment of uniform weight in weighing carcasses for the same species of livestock in each packing plant; and include only the weight of this equipment in the actual weight of the container.

6. Make payment on the basis of final USDA carcass grades or furnish the seller with detailed written specifications for any other grades used in determining final payment.

7. Grade carcasses by the close of the second business day following the day of slaughter.

Choice of Market Outlets

Marketing is dynamic; thus, changes are inevitable in types

of market outlets, market structures, and market services. Some outlets have gained in importance; others have declined.

The choice of a market outlet represents the seller's evaluation of the most favorable market among the number of alternatives available to him. No simple and brief statement of criteria can be given as a guide to the choice of the most favorable market channel. Rather, an evaluation is required of the contributions made by alternative markets in terms of available services offered, selling costs, the competitive nature of the pricing process, and ultimately the producer's net return. Thus, an accurate appraisal is not simple.

From time to time, producers can be expected to shift from one type of market outlet to another. Because price changes at different market outlets do not take place simultaneously, nor in the same amount, nor even in the same direction, one market may be the most advantageous outlet for a particular class and grade of hogs at one time, but another may be more advantageous at some other time. The situation may differ for different classes and kinds of livestock and may vary from one area to another.

Regardless of the channel through which the producer markets his livestock, in one way or another, he pays or bears, either in the price received from the livestock or otherwise, the entire cost of marketing. Because of this, he should never choose a market because of convenience of habit, or because of personal acquaintance with the market and its operator. Rather, the choice should be determined strictly by the net returns from the sale of his livestock; effective selling and net returns are more important than selling costs.

Selling Purebred Hogs

Selling purebred animals is a highly specialized and scientific business. Purebred animals are usually sold either at private treaty directly to other purebred breeders or to commercial producers or through auctions which may either be sponsored by one or a few breeders (joint sales or consignment sales).

In general, the vast majority of boars saved for breeding purposes go into commercial herds. Only the elite sires are retained with the hope of affecting further breed improvement in purebred herds. On the other hand, the sale of purebred females is fairly well restricted to meeting the requirements for replace-

ment purposes in existing purebred herds or for establishing new purebred herds.

Most consignment sales are sponsored by a breed association, either local, statewide, or national in character. Such auctions, therefore, are usually limited to one breed. Purebred auction sales are conducted by highly specialized auctioneers. In addition to being good salesmen, such auctioneers must have a keen knowledge of values and must be familiar with the blood lines of the breeding stock.

IMPROVEMENT AND EXPANSION OF MARKET NEWS REPORTING

Accurate and rapid market news reporting is essential to the efficient marketing of livestock, to keep both sellers and buyers well informed regarding supplies and prices. Decentralization of marketing has made market news reporting much more difficult; terminal markets are no longer the "price barometer" for the nation. The real challenge is to cover a multitude of widely scattered livestock auctions and country selling promptly and accurately, better to reflect what is going on. It appears that livestock may soon find itself facing somewhat the same problem as the butter, egg, and broiler markets; of these products, so little is now moving through terminals that for all practical purposes prices are really made at many scattered points over the country, thereby making it very difficult to report and know what is going on.

For market news to be meaningful, sales must also be reported accurately from the standpoint of grades and weights. Also, market reports should reflect consumer preferences back to producers, to the benefit of everyone in the agribusiness chain. It is a fair statement of fact that completely accurate, reliable, and understandable communication of livestock marketing has not yet been achieved.

Should there be further carcass grade and weight buying along with the decline of terminal markets, as now seems inevitable, wholesale meat reporting will take on greater significance. From the producer's standpoint, it will be more important that he be able to translate carcass prices of various weights and grades to a live animal basis.

PREPARING AND SHIPPING HOGS[10]

Improper handling of hogs immediately prior to and during shipment may result in excessive shrinkage; high death, bruise, and crippling losses; disappointing sales; and dissatisfied buyers. Unfortunately, many swine producers who do a superb job of producing hogs, dissipate all the good things that have gone before by doing a poor job of preparing and shipping. Generally speaking, such omissions are due to lack of know-how, rather than any deliberate attempt to take advantage of anyone. Even if the sale is consummated prior to delivery, negligence at shipping time will make for a dissatisfied customer. Buyers soon learn what to expect from various producers and place their bids accordingly.

In addition to the important specific considerations covered in later sections, the following general considerations should be accorded in preparing hogs for shipment and in transporting them to market:

1. **Select the best suited method of transportation.**—The hog producer should decide between truck and rail transportation on the basis of which method best suits his particular situation. Distance of haul is the greatest single factor for consideration in this regard; generally shorter hauls are made by truck and greater distances by rail, but modern trucks and improved highways have extended the distance of truck shipments. Hogs are now being provided with deluxe truck transportation from Omaha, Sioux City, and other markets to the West Coast. Some of these aluminum "palace trucks" are air conditioned, insulated, provided with sprinklers, and cleaned by steam. Railroads are also operating with vastly improved handling and hauling facilities and expedited schedules. Hogs never had it so good.

Today, truck shipments account for the majority of receipts at terminal stockyards, practically all hogs sold at auction markets, and most hogs shipped direct to packers.

Regardless of the transportation facility selected—truck or rail—it is important that sufficient prior notification be given

---

[10]This section, and the section entitled "How to Prevent Bruises, Crippling, and Death Losses," were authoritatively reviewed by the following: Mr. Don K. Spalding, Executive Vice President and General Manager, St. Joseph Stock Yard Co., South Saint Joseph, Mo.; and Mr. Joe W. Jarvis, Supervisor of Livestock and Agriculture, Union Pacific Railroad Co., Omaha, Neb.

the carrier regarding the date, time, and destination of shipment, in order that cars or trucks will be spotted or ready for loading. Size and type (single or double deck) facilities should be specified; also, any special equipment (partitions, linings, etc.) should be requested at that time.

All major operators clean, disinfect, and bed facilities prior to loading, but it is always well that the shipper make his own inspection to make sure that these matters have been handled to his satisfaction. Generally hogs are bedded with about one inch of sand, and in the wintertime straw is placed on top of the sand. If the shipper desires a type of bedding other than supplied by the carrier, he may provide it at his own expense.

To avoid any misunderstanding, it is recommended that all requests for hauling facilities either be requested or confirmed in writing.

2. **Avoid drafts and suffocation.**—Check the car or truck to avoid heavy wind drafts which will cause the hogs to pile up. At the same time be sure that there is enough ventilation to prevent suffocation. During extremely cold weather, the sides of stock cars or trucks should be papered or slatted.

3. **Feed properly prior to loading out.**—Never ship hogs on an excess fill. Instead, either (a) feed lightly (not over a half-feed), or (b) withhold feed entirely for 7 hours before loading (omit one feed).

Hogs that are too full of feed (especially slop or other wet feed) or water at the time of loading will scour and urinate excessively. As a result, the floors become dirty and slippery and the animals befoul themselves. Such hogs undergo a heavy shrink and present an unattractive appearance when unloaded.

4. **Keep hogs quiet.**—Prior to and during shipment, hogs should be handled carefully. Hot, excited animals are subject to more shrinkage and more death and injury.

Although loading may be exasperating at times, take it easy; never lose your temper. Avoid hurrying and striking. Never beat an animal with such objects as pipes, sticks, canes, or forks; instead, use either (a) a flat, wide canvas slapper with a handle, (b) a broom, or (c) an electric prod (the latter judiciously).

5. **Consider health certificates and permits in interstate shipments.**—When hogs are to be shipped into another state,

the shipper should check into and comply with the state regulations relative to health certificates and permits. Generally health certificates are not required where hogs are consigned to a public stockyard or packing plant for immediate slaughter. Usually, the local veterinarian or railroad agent will have this information. Should there be any question about the health regulations, however, the state livestock sanitary board (usually located at the state capital) of the state of destination should be consulted. Knowledge of and compliance with such regulations well in advance of shipment will avoid frustrations and costly delays.

6. **Comply with the 28-hour law in rail shipments.**[11]— Actually, the shipper has no alternative to taking advantage of feed and rest stops during long hauls by rail, for, by federal law, passed in 1873, livestock cannot be transported by rail for a longer period than twenty-eight consecutive hours without unloading for the purpose of giving feed, water, and rest for a period of at least five consecutive hours before resuming transportation. The period may be extended to thirty-six hours upon written request from the owner of the animals, and most experienced hog shippers routinely so request. With less than carload lots (LCL shipments), the owner may provide feed and water in the car with instructions that the animals be fed and watered enroute.

The shipper may instruct the railway company on the kind and amount of feed to be given in transit, with these instructions written on the waybill or on the livestock contract which each shipper signs. If no such instructions are given by the owner of the hogs, the amount of feed prescribed by the USDA is given at the livestock feeding yards (see Table 12-4). The feeding is done by the railway company crew, and charge is made to the shipper for the amount of feed consumed.

Where two or more cars of hogs are shipped, the railroad will provide a free *ticket* for a caretaker, including return to the point of origin. When shipping by rail and where possible, it is recommended that the shipper take advantage of this arrangement. When this is done, the caretaker can make certain that the animals are properly fed and given access to clean water at the stops enroute; also, under certain circumstances, it may be wise to allow hogs to make as much as a 12-hour rest stop and to feed twice before reloading.

---

[11]No such law applies to truck transportation of animals.

TABLE 12-4

AMOUNT OF CORN (OR THE EQUIVALENT IN OTHER SUITABLE FEED)
TO BE FED TO HOGS IN TRANSIT TO MEET THE MINIMUM
REQUIREMENTS OF THE 28-HOUR LAW[1]

Live Weight of Animals	Amount to Be Fed	
	At First Feeding Station	At Subsequent Feeding Station
(lb.)	(bu.)	(bu.)
18,000 or less ---	2	2
18,001 to 21,000---	2½	2½
21,001 to 24,000---	3	3
24,001 to 27,000---	3½	3½
27,001 to 30,000---	4	4
30,001 and over---	(Footnote 2)	(Footnote 2)

[1]T. W. Cole, USDA Leaflet No. 38, Table 1, p. 6.
[2]Proportionately larger amounts.

7. **Use partitions when necessary.**—When mixed loads (consisting of hogs, cattle, and/or sheep) are placed in the same truck or car, partition each class off separately. Also, boars, stags, sows, crippled and weak animals should be properly partitioned.

8. **Avoid shipping during extremes in weather.**—Whenever possible, avoid shipping when the weather is either very hot or very cold. During such times, shrinkage and death losses are higher than normal. During warm weather, avoid transporting hogs during the heat of the day; travel at night or in the evening or early morning. In hot weather, wet the sand; and it may even be wise to distribute some ice on the floor of the car or truck.

How to Prevent Bruises, Crippling, and Death Losses

Losses from bruising, crippling, and death that occur during the marketing process represent a part of the cost of marketing livestock; and, indirectly, the producer foots most of the bill.

The following precautions are suggested as a means of reducing hog market losses from bruises, crippling, and death:

1. Remove projecting nails, splinters, and broken boards from feeding areas and fences.

2. Keep feedlots free from old machinery, trash, and any obstacle that may bruise.

3. Do not feed slop or wet feeds heavily just prior to loading.

4. Use good loading chutes; not too steep.

5. Bed with sand free from stones, to prevent slipping.

6. Cover sand with straw in cold weather, but do not use straw in hot weather.

7. Wet the sand bedding in summer before loading hogs and while enroute. Drench when necessary.

8. Partition all packing sows from lightweight butchers.

9. Provide covers for trucks to protect from sun in summer and cold in winter.

10. Always partition mixed loads into separate classes.

11. Remove protruding nails, bolts, or any sharp objects in truck or car.

12. Load slowly to prevent crowding against sharp corners and to avoid excitement. Do not overload.

13. Use canvas slappers instead of clubs or canes.

14. Partition boars, stags, and cripples.

15. Drive trucks carefully; slow down on sharp turns and avoid sudden stops.

16. Back truck slowly and squarely against unloading dock.

17. Unload slowly. Do not drop animals from upper to lower deck; use cleated inclines.

All these precautions are simple to apply, yet all are violated every day of the year.

Number of Hogs in a Railroad Car and in a Truck

Overcrowding of market animals causes heavy losses. Sometimes a railroad car or a truck is overloaded in an attempt to effect a saving in hauling charges. More frequently, however, it is simply the result of not knowing space requirements. The suggested number of animals should be tempered by such factors as distance of haul, class of livestock, weather, and road conditions. The space requirements by rail and by truck follow:

1. **By rail.**—Normally, railroad cars are either 36 or 40 feet in length. The size of the car and the class and size of animals determine the number of head that can be loaded in a given car. For comfort in shipping, the car should be loaded heavily enough so that the animals stand close together, but overcrowding is to be avoided. Table 12-5 gives some indication as to the number of market hogs that may be loaded in a railroad car.

TABLE 12-5

HOGS PER RAILROAD CAR[1]

Car Size	Hogs, 225 pounds
36 foot car---------------------------------------	73
40 foot car---------------------------------------	82

[1]Hogs per single deck.

2. By truck.—Tables 12-6 and 12-7 show the number of swine for safe trucking.

TABLE 12-6

NUMBER OF HOGS FOR SAFE LOADING IN A SINGLE-DECK TRUCK[1]

Floor Length	100 lb.	150 lb.	175 lb.	200 lb.	225 lb.	250 lb.	300 lb.	350 lb.	400 lb.
(ft.)									
8	27	21	19	18	16	14	13	11	9
10	33	26	24	22	20	18	16	14	12
12	40	31	28	26	24	22	19	17	14
15	50	39	36	33	30	27	24	21	17
18	60	47	43	40	36	33	28	25	21
20	67	52	48	44	40	35	32	28	24
24	80	62	57	52	48	44	38	34	28
28	93	72	67	61	56	51	44	39	33
30	100	77	72	66	60	55	47	42	35
32	107	83	76	70	64	58	51	44	38
36	120	94	86	79	72	66	57	50	42
42	140	109	100	92	84	77	63	55	49

[1]Authoritative recommendations of Livestock Conservation, Inc., Exchange Building, Union Stock Yards, Chicago, Ill.

TABLE 12-7

NUMBER OF HOGS FOR SAFE LOADING IN A DOUBLE-DECK TRUCK[1]
(Divide equally between decks)

Floor Length	100 lb.	150 lb.	175 lb.	200 lb.	225 lb.	250 lb.	300 lb.	350 lb.	400 lb.
(ft.)									
8	43	33	31	29	27	24	21	18	16
10	53	41	38	36	33	30	26	23	20
12	63	50	46	43	40	36	31	28	24
15	79	62	56	54	50	45	39	34	30
18	95	75	70	65	60	55	46	41	36
20	105	83	77	72	67	61	52	46	40
24	127	100	93	87	80	73	62	55	48
28	148	116	109	101	93	86	73	64	56
30	158	125	116	108	100	91	78	68	60
32	169	133	130	115	107	97	83	73	64
36	190	150	140	130	120	110	94	82	72
42	220	172	164	151	142	128	109	96	80

[1]Authoritative recommendations of Livestock Conservation, Inc., Exchange Building, Union Stock Yards, Chicago, Ill.

Kind of Bedding to Use for Hogs in Transit

Among the several factors affecting livestock losses, per-

haps none is more important than proper bedding and footing in transit. This applies to both rail and truck shipments, and to all classes of animals.

Footing, such as sand, is required at all times of the year, to prevent the car or truck floor from becoming wet and slick, thus predisposing to injury of animals by slipping or falling. Bedding, such as straw, is recommended for warmth in the shipment of swine during extremely cold weather, and as cushioning for dairy cows, breeding stock, or other animals loaded lightly enough to permit their lying down. During warm weather, the sand should be wet down prior to loading, for it has been well said that a hog with a wet belly is a live hog all the way to market. Recommended kinds and amounts of bedding and footing materials are given in Table 12-8.

TABLE 12-8

HANDY GUIDE RELATIVE TO BEDDING AND FOOTING MATERIAL
WHEN TRANSPORTING LIVESTOCK[1]

Class of Livestock	Kind of Bedding for Moderate or Warm Weather; Above 50° F.	Kind of Bedding for Cool or Cold Weather; Below 50° F.
Swine	Sand, ½ inch to 2 inches	Sand covered with straw
Cattle	Sand, 2 inches	Sand; for calves use sand covered with straw
Sheep and Goats	Sand	Sand covered with straw
Horses and Mules	Sand	Sand

[1]Straw or other suitable bedding (covered over sand) should be used for protection and cushioning breeding stock that are loaded lightly enough to permit their lying down in the car or truck.
Sand should be clean and medium-fine, and free from brick, stones, coarse gravel, dirt, or dust.
Fine cinders may be used as footing for cattle, horses and mules, but not for sheep or hogs. They are picked up by and damage the wool of sheep, and they damage hog casings.
In hot weather, wet sand down before loading. Never apply water to the backs of hot hogs; it may kill them.

Shrinkage in Marketing Hogs

The shrinkage (or drift) refers to the weight loss encountered from the time animals leave the feedlot until they are weighed over the scales at the market. Thus, if a hog weighed 200 pounds at the feedlot and had a market weight of 196 pounds, the shrinkage would be 4 pounds or 2.0 percent. Shrink is usually expressed in terms of percentage. Most of this weight loss is due to excretion, or in the form of feces and urine and the moisture in the expired air. On the other hand, there is some

tissue shrinkage, which results from metabolic or breakdown changes.

The most important factors affecting shrinkage are:

1. **The fill.**—Naturally, the larger the fill animals take upon their arrival at the market, the smaller the shrinkage.

2. **Time in transit.**—The longer the animals are in transit and the greater the distance, the higher the total shrinkage. Reducing the total time in marketing will do more to reduce shrink than anything else, so long as time is not minimized in ways that increase excitement or confinement.

3. **Truck vs. rail transportation.**—Based on practical experience and observation, most stockmen are of the opinion that (a) truck shipments result in less shrinkage than rail shipments for short hauls, and (b) rail shipments result in less shrinkage than truck shipments for long hauls. This may be due to the fact that hogs hauled by rail have a feed and rest stop while those moved by truck usually do not.

4. **Season.**—Extremes in temperature, either very hot or very cold weather, result in higher shrinkage. Shrink is at a minimum between 20 and 60 degrees. When the temperature is above 80° F., hogs in transit, via either rail or truck, should be sprinkled.

5. **Age and weight.**—Young animals of all species shrink proportionally more than older animals.

6. **Overloading or underloading.**—Either overloading or underloading always results in abnormally high shrinkage.

7. **Rough ride, abnormal feeding, and mixed loads.**—Each of these factors will increase shrinkage.

On the average, hogs shrink from 1 to 2 percent, which is the lowest of any class of livestock.

MARKET CLASSES AND GRADES OF HOGS

The market classes and grades of swine were developed in much the same manner as the classifications of cattle were developed and brought into use. They also serve much the same purpose. Swine classes and grades do differ from those used in cattle and sheep in that: (1) there are no age divisions by years (*e.g.*, cattle are classified as yearling and two-year-old and over);

(2) only a limited number of hogs are returned to the country as feeders for further growth or finishing; and (3) rarely are hogs of any kind purchased on the market for use as breeding animals. As in the classification of market cattle, the class of market hogs indicates the use to which the animals are best adapted, whereas the grade indicates the degree of perfection within the class.

The generally accepted market classes and grades of hogs are summarized in Table 12-9.

Factors Determining Market Classes of Hogs

The market class of hogs is determined by the following factors: (1) hogs and pigs, (2) use selection, (3) sex, and (4) weight.

HOGS AND PIGS

All swine are first divided into two major groups according to age: hogs and pigs. Although actual ages are not observed, the division is made largely by weight in relation to the apparent age of the animal. Young animals weighing under 120 pounds (under about four months of age) are generally known as pigs, whereas those weighing over 120 pounds are called hogs.

USE SELECTION OF HOGS AND PIGS

Hogs and pigs are each further divided into two subdivisions as slaughter animals and feeders. Slaughter swine are hogs and pigs that are suitable for immediate slaughter. The demand for lightweight slaughter pigs is greatest during the holiday season when they are in demand as roasting pigs for hotels, clubs, restaurants, steamships, and other consumers. Such pigs weigh from 15 to 20 pounds, are dressed shipper style (with the head on), and must produce a plump and well-proportioned carcass. Slaughter hogs (the older animals) are in demand throughout the year.

Feeder swine include those animals that show ability to take on additional weight and finish. The feeder group is relatively small. Moreover, because of the greater disease hazard with hogs, this class is under very close federal supervision. Before being released for return to the country, feeder swine must be inspected

TABLE 12-9

THE MARKET CLASSES AND GRADES OF HOGS[1]

Hogs or Pigs	Use Selection	Sex Classes	Weight Divisions (pounds)	(kg)	Commonly Used Grades
Hogs	Slaughter Hogs	Barrows and Gilts (Hogs in this class often called "butcher hogs")	120-140	55-64	U.S. No. 1, U.S. No. 2. U.S. No. 3, U.S. No. 4, U.S. Utility
			140-160	64-73	
			160-180	73-82	
			180-200	82-91	
			200-220	91-100	
			220-240	100-109	
			240-270	109-123	
			270-300	123-136	
			300-330	136-150	
			330-360	150-163	
			360-400	163-182	
			400 lbs. up	182-up	
		Sows (or packing sows)	270-300	123-136	U.S. No. 1, U.S. No. 2, U.S. No. 3, U.S. No. 4, U.S. Utility
			300-330	136-150	
			330-360	150-163	
			360-400	163-182	
			400-450	182-204	
			450-500	204-227	
			500-600	227-272	
			600 lbs. up	272-up	
		Stags	All Weights		Ungraded
		Boars	All Weights		Ungraded
	Feeder Hogs	Barrows and Gilts	120-140	55-64	U.S. No. 1, U.S. No. 2, U.S. No. 3, U.S. No. 4, U.S. Utility, Cull
			140-160	64-73	
			160-180	73-82	

(Continued)

Footnote on last page of table.

TABLE 12-9 (Continued)

Hogs or Pigs	Use Selection	Sex Classes	Weight Division		Commonly Used Grades
Pigs	Slaughter Pigs	Barrows, Gilts, and Boars	Under 30 30-60	13.6 13.6-27.2	Ungraded
		Barrows and Gilts	60-80 80-100 100-120	27.2-36.3 36.3-45.4 45.4-54.5	Ungraded
	Feeder Pigs	Barrows and Gilts	80-100 100-120	36.3-45.4 45.4-54.5	U.S. No. 1, U.S. No. 2, U.S. No. 3, U.S. No. 4, U.S. Utility, Cull

This section was authoritatively reviewed by Mr. John C. Pierce, Livestock Division, Consumer Marketing Service, USDA.

from a health standpoint, and then either sprayed or dipped as a precautionary measure to prevent the spread of disease germs or parasites.

THE SEX CLASSES

The sex class is used only when it affects the usefulness and selling price of animals. In hogs, this subdivision is of less importance than in cattle. Thus, barrows and gilts are always classed together in the case of both slaughter and feeder hogs. This is done because the sex condition affects their usefulness so little that a price differentiation is not warranted. In addition, because the carcass is not affected, no sex differentiations are made for slaughter pigs under 60 pounds in weight. The terms barrow, gilt, sow, boar, and stag are used to designate the sex classes of hogs. The definition of each of these terms follows:

Barrow—*A castrated male swine animal that was castrated at an early age—before reaching sexual maturity and before developing the physical characteristics peculiar to boars.*

Gilt—*A female swine that has not produced pigs and which has not reached an evident stage of pregnancy.*

Sow—*A female swine that shows evidence of having produced pigs or which is in an evident stage of pregnancy.*

Boar—*An uncastrated male swine animal of any age.* Mature boars should always be stagged and fed three weeks or longer (until the wound heals) before being sent to market. The market value of boars is necessarily low, for a considerable number are condemned as unfit for human consumption, primarily because of odor.

Stag—*A stag is a male swine animal that was castrated after it had developed the physical characteristics of a mature boar.* Because of relatively thick skins, coarse hair, and heavy bones, stags are subject to a dockage. When marketed direct, stags are usually not docked in weight but are purchased at a price that reflects their true value from a meat standpoint.

WEIGHT DIVISIONS

Occasionally, the terms light, medium, and heavy are used to indicate approximate weights, but most generally the actual

range in weight in pounds is specified both in trading and in market reporting. Moreover, hogs are usually grouped according to relatively narrow weight ranges because variations in weight affect (1) the dressing percentage, (2) the weight and desirability of the cuts of meat, and (3) the amount of lard produced (heavier weights produce more lard). Boars and stags are not usually subdivided according to weights.

The Federal Grades of Hogs

The market grade for swine, as for other kinds of livestock, is a specific indication of the degree of excellence within a given class based upon conformation, finish, and quality. The two chief factors which serve to place a hog in a specific grade are: degree of fatness and amount of muscling. While no official grading of live animals is done by the U.S. Department of Agriculture, market grades do form a basis for uniform reporting of livestock marketings. It is intended that the grade of slaughter hogs on foot be correlated with the carcass grade.

The Federal market grades of slaughter barrows and gilts are: U. S. No. 1, U. S. No. 2, U. S. No. 3, U. S. No. 4, and U. S. Utility. As will be noted, the market grades of swine differ from the grades of cattle in that: (1) hogs possess five grades instead of the eight common to cattle; (2) the top grade of hogs is U. S. No. 1 instead of Prime; and (3) no Cutter or Canner designations are used in hogs, instead the lowest grade is known as a U. S. Utility.

The five grades for slaughter barrows and gilts may be described as follows:

U. S. No. 1.—Slaughter barrows and gilts in this grade will produce carcasses with acceptable lean quality and acceptable belly thickness, and a high percentage of lean cuts.

U. S. No. 2.—Slaughter barrows and gilts in this grade will produce carcasses with acceptable lean quality and acceptable belly thickness, and a slightly high percentage of lean cuts.

U. S. No. 3.—Slaughter barrows and gilts in this grade will produce carcasses with acceptable lean quality and acceptable belly thickness, and a slightly lower percentage of the four lean cuts.

U. S. No. 4.—Slaughter barrows and gilts in this grade will

produce carcasses with acceptable lean quality and acceptable belly thickness. However, they are fatter and less muscular and will have a lower carcass yield of the four lean cuts than those in the U. S. No. 3 grade.

U. S. Utility.—Barrows and gilts typical of this grade will have a thin covering of fat. The sides are wrinkled and the flanks are shallow and thin. They will produce carcasses with unacceptable lean quality and/or unacceptable belly thickness.

The Federal grades of slaughter sows are: U. S. No. 1, U. S. No. 2, U. S. No. 3, U. S. No. 4, and U. S. Utility. These are the same grade designations used for barrows and gilts, and the general characteristics of each grade are also similar. The grades are based on differences in yields of lean cuts and fat cuts and differences in quality of pork.

As a rule, slaughter pigs that weigh under 60 pounds are not graded because they have not reached sufficient maturity for variations in their conformation, finish, and quality to affect the market value materially.

Most packer buyers are now making a sincere effort to pay price differentials that reflect their appraisal of the degree of finish and muscling of market hogs. It is noteworthy, however, that meat packers in Canada pay price differentials between grades 2½ or 3 times wider than have been thought possible in the United States.[12]

The grades of feeder pigs are closely correlated with the standards for slaughter barrows and gilts. These are given in Table 12-9. The standards on which these grades are based embrace two general value-determining characteristics of feeder pigs—(1) their logical slaughter potential and (2) their thriftiness. For example, if a feeder pig is graded U. S. No. 1, it has the potential for developing into a U. S. No. 1 slaughter hog that will produce a U. S. No. 1 carcass. Thriftiness indicates the ability of a feeder pig to gain weight rapidly and efficiently.

OTHER HOG MARKET TERMS AND FACTORS

In addition to the rather general terms used in designating the different market classes and grades of hogs, the following terms and factors are frequently of importance.

---

[12]*Marketing Meat-Type Hogs*, April, 1958, Agricultural Marketing Service, **USDA**, Marketing Research Report No. 227, p. IV.

SLAUGHTER BARROWS and GILTS
U. S. GRADES

U.S. NO. 1

U.S. NO. 2

U.S. NO. 3

U.S. NO. 4

Fig. 12-7. The four U.S. top market grades of slaughter barrows and gilts. (Courtesy, John C. Pierce, Director, Livestock Division, Consumer and Marketing Service, USDA)

Roasters

Roasters refer to fat, plump, suckling pigs, weighing 15 to 50 pounds on foot. These are dressed shipper style (with the head on). When properly roasted and attractively served with the traditional apple in the mouth, roast pig is considered a great delicacy for the holiday season.

Roughs (or Throw-outs)

The term "roughs or throw-outs" is frequently applied to coarse, rough hogs lacking in condition. Carcasses from such hogs are used for the cheaper class of trade, both as cured and fresh pork.

Governments

Governments are suspicious animals that federal inspectors tag at the time of the ante-mortem inspection to indicate that more careful scrutiny is to be given in the post-mortem inspection. If the carcass is deemed unfit for human consumption, it is condemned and sent to the inedible tank.

Cripples

Cripples are hogs that are not able to walk and that must be hauled to the packing plants in cripple carts.

Dead Hogs

Dead hogs are those that arrive dead at the market. These carcasses are sent to the tanks for conversion into inedible grease, fertilizer, etc.

SOME HOG MARKETING CONSIDERATIONS

Enlightened and shrewd marketing practices generally characterize the successful hog enterprise. Among the considerations of importance in marketing hogs are those which follow.

Cyclical Trends in Market Hogs

The price cycle as it applies to livestock may be defined as that period of time during which the price for a certain kind of

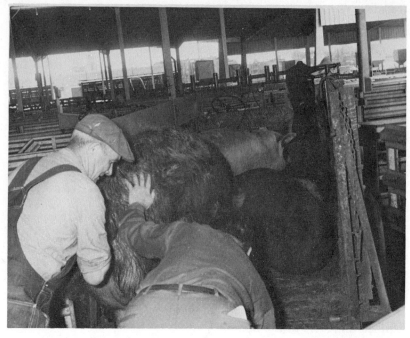

Fig. 12-8. Badly crippled hogs unable to walk into pens unassisted on arrival at market. Such badly crippled animals are hauled in the cripple cart, and are generally bought subject to inspection. The National Livestock Loss Prevention Board is authority for the statement that there is an annual loss of $81,300,000 accruing from bruises, crippling, and death losses in marketing animals. (Courtesy, Union Stock Yard and Transit Co. of Chicago)

livestock advances from a low point to a high point and then declines to a low point again. In reality, it is a change in animal numbers that represents the stockman's response to prices. Although there is considerable variation in the length of the cycle within any given class of stock, over a period of time it has been observed that the price cycle of the different classes of animals is about as follows: hogs, 3 to 5 years; sheep, 9 to 10 years; and cattle, 10 to 12 years (see Fig. 12-9).

The species cycles are a direct reflection of the rapidity with which the numbers of each class of farm animals can be shifted under practical conditions to meet consumer meat demands. Thus, litter-bearing and early-producing swine can be increased in numbers much more rapidly than either sheep or cattle.

When market hog prices are favorable, established swine

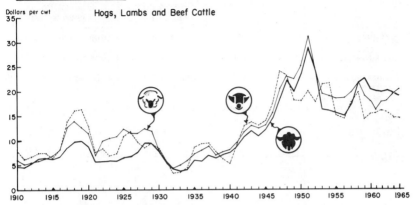

Fig. 12-9. Average price received by U.S. farmers for each class of livestock, 1910 to 1965. In general, this shows that the price cycle of each class of animals is approximately as follows: hogs, 3 to 5 years; sheep, 9 to 10 years; and cattle, 10 to 12 years. (Based on data obtained from USDA. Drawing by Steve Allured)

enterprises are expanded, and new herds are founded, so that about every 3 to 5 years, on the average, the market is glutted and prices fall, only to rise again because too few hogs are being produced to take care of the demand for pork. Normal cycles are disturbed by droughts, wars, general periods of depression or inflations, and federal controls.

The normal price cycles of hogs can be made less acute— that is, prices may be made more stable year after year—by (1) applying technological advances to get away from seasonal breeding and farrowing, (2) informing producers of build-ups and shortages, and (3) contracting for delivery at specified times.

Seasonal Changes in Market Hogs

Hog prices vary seasonally with marked regularity due to the variation in market receipts, as shown in Table 12-10, and in Figures 12-10 and 12-11. Consideration is given herein to slaughter barrows and gilts and to sows.

1. **Barrows and gilts.**—Fig. 12-10 shows the seasonal variation in barrow and gilt prices. From this and other market information, the following conclusions are drawn:

    a.   Market hogs will usually hit the highest markets in June through August, and the lowest markets in November to May. Due to increased multiple farrowing

TABLE 12-10
WHEN TO BUY AND WHEN TO SELL HOGS[1]

Class of Animal	Lowest Prices (when to buy)	Highest Prices (when to sell)
Slaughter barrows and gilts	Nov. to May	June through August
Sows (packing)	December	June to Oct.
Feeder pigs[2]	July	February through April

[1]Based on averages.
[2]Coppersmith, R. L., *Producing and Marketing Feeder Pigs*, Circ. 349, p. 5, Kansas State University, 1965.

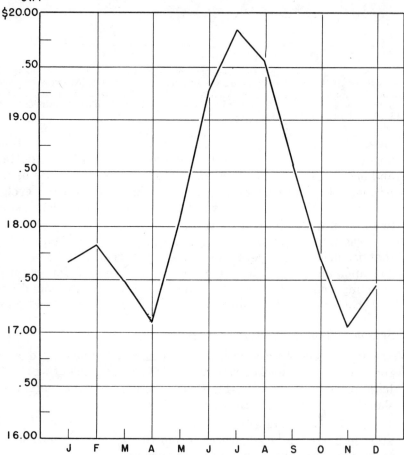

Fig. 12-10. Monthly average prices of barrows and gilts (eight markets combined) for the 10-year period, 1958 to 1967. This shows the seasonal variation in barrow and gilt prices. (Data from *Livestock and Meat Statistics*, USDA, Statistical Bul. No. 333 and Supplements. Drawing by R. F. Johnson)

and improved nutrition, there are less drastic seasonal fluctuations than formerly.

b.   The bulk of spring and early summer farrowed pigs are marketed from November to May, which generally causes a seasonal depression in prices.

c.   In order to take advantage of higher price periods, the hog producer may do two things:
(1) Regulate the farrowing dates of the sows; and/or
(2) Use either forced or delayed feeding in order to bring hogs to market weight during high price periods.

d.   Most consumers prefer lighter cuts of meat, and fat pork and lard have become a "drug" upon the market. This accounts for the spread in price between light and heavy weights of hogs.

2.   **Sows.**—Fig. 12-11 shows the seasonal variation in sow prices. From this and other market information, the following conclusions are made:

a.   Sows do not follow the same seasonal pattern as market barrows and gilts.

b.   An initial high is reached in February and March, when the bulk of spring farrowing is under way; then, following weaning, many sows are marketed. In August and September, sows are again farrowing or about to farrow, with the result that few are marketed and sow prices hit a peak at that time before falling to a December low.

The shifting of farrowing dates, including multiple farrowing, and the application of technological advances offer a practical means of reducing extreme seasonal price drops of market animals.

Wherever possible, the producer should plan his culling and marketing operations accordingly.

Short-time Changes

Day-to-day variations in swine prices usually are caused by uneven distribution of receipts on a given market because of such factors as weather, interference with transportation, strikes, uncertain or threatened federal policies, and stock mar-

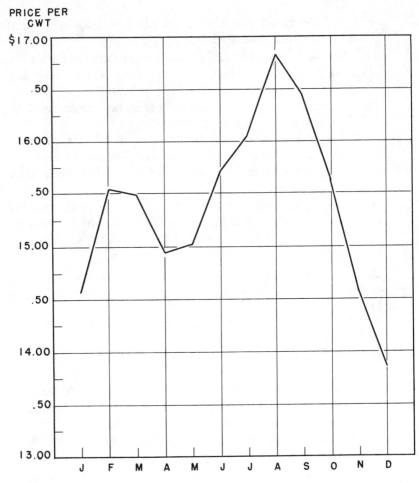

Fig. 12-11. Monthly average prices of packing sows (eight markets combined) for the 10-year period, 1958 to 1967. This shows the seasonal variation in sow prices. (Data from *Livestock and Meat Statistics*, Statistical Bul. No. 333 and Supplements. Drawing by R. F. Johnson)

ket fluctuations. Although such changes are not large, the shrewd producer and market specialist is quick to take advantage of fluctuations that are in his financial interest.

The Monday Market

Traditionally, terminal markets have been plagued with heavy runs on Monday (Fig. 12-12). Where a market operates

to capacity only one day a week, the fixed costs for the balance of the week must be carried largely by that single day's operations.

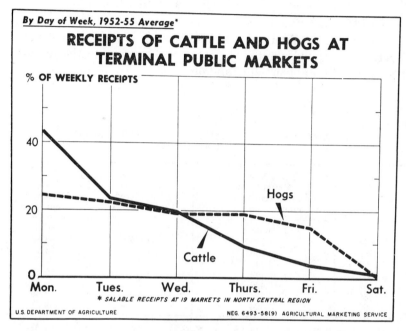

By Day of Week, 1952-55 Average*

RECEIPTS OF CATTLE AND HOGS AT TERMINAL PUBLIC MARKETS

% OF WEEKLY RECEIPTS

Hogs

Cattle

Mon. Tues. Wed. Thurs. Fri. Sat.

* SALABLE RECEIPTS AT 19 MARKETS IN NORTH CENTRAL REGION

U.S. DEPARTMENT OF AGRICULTURE   NEG. 6493-58(9) AGRICULTURAL MARKETING SERVICE

Fig. 12-12. Terminal markets have always been plagued by heavy Monday runs.

Dockage

The value of some market animals is low because dressing losses are high, or because part of the product is of low quality. Some common dockages on livestock markets are:

1. **Piggy sows.**—Usually docked 40 pounds, but it may range from 0 to 50 pounds, depending on the market.

2. **Stags (hogs).**—Usually docked 70 pounds, but it may range from 40 to 80 pounds, depending on the market.

PACKER SLAUGHTERING AND DRESSING OF HOGS

Hog slaughtering is unique in that the carcasses are seldom sold, such as is the case with beef, veal, mutton, and lamb. In-

stead, hogs are reduced to the wholesale cuts at the place of slaughter. Also, much more pork is cured than is the case with beef or lamb; and pork fat (lard) is not classed as a by-product, although the surplus fats of beef, veal, mutton, and lamb are in the by-product category.

Table 12-11 shows the proportion of hogs slaughtered in federally inspected plants. The total figure refers to the number dressed in all establishments and on farms.

TABLE 12-11

PROPORTION OF HOGS SLAUGHTERED COMMERCIALLY
1960 THROUGH 1966[+]

Year	Total Number Slaughtered (commercially and noncommercially)	Number Slaughtered Commercially	Percent Slaughtered Commercially
	(1,000 head)	(1,000 head)	(%)
1960	84,196	79,036	93.87
1961	82,050	77,335	94.25
1962	83,543	79,334	94.96
1963	87,252	83,324	95.50
1964	86,420	83,019	96.06
1965	76,394	73,784	96.58
1966	75,324	74,011	98.25

[1]*Livestock and Meat Statistics*, USDA, Supp. for 1965 to Statistical Bul. No. 33, June 1967, p. 63.

Although modern equipment may be lacking, the slaughtering procedure on the farm or in a small local plant is much the same as that followed in a large federally inspected plant. Only the procedure used in a modern commercial packing plant will be discussed, however.

After purchase, hogs are driven from the holding pens to the packing plant where they are given a shower and are held temporarily in a small pen while awaiting slaughter.

Steps in Slaughtering and Dressing Hogs

The chain method of slaughtering is used in killing and dressing hogs. In this method, the following steps are carried out in rapid succession:

1. **Rendering insensible.**—The hogs are rendered insen-

sible[13] by use of a captive bolt stunner, gunshot, electric current, or carbon dioxide.

2. **Shackling and hoisting.**—The hogs are shackled just above the hoof on the hind leg and are then hoisted to an overhead rail.

3. **Sticking.**—The sticker sticks the hog just under the point of the breast bone, severing the arteries and veins leading to the heart. The animal is allowed to bleed for a few minutes.

4. **Scalding.**—The animals are next placed in a scalding vat for about four minutes. By means of automatically controlled steam jets, the temperature of the water in the vats is maintained at 142° to 145° F. The scalding process loosens the hair and scurf.

5. **Dehairing.**—After scalding, the animals are elevated into a dehairing machine which scrapes them mechanically. In modern packing plants a single dehairing machine will handle up to five hundred hogs per hour. Most large plants are equipped with twin machines which provide a scraping capacity of a thousand hogs per hour.

6. **Returning to overhead tracks.**—As the animals are discharged from the dehairing machine, the gam cords of the hind legs are exposed; and gambrel sticks are inserted in the cords. Then the carcass is again hung from the rail.

7. **Dressing.**—A conveyor then moves the carcass slowly along a prescribed course where attendants perform the following tasks:

    a. Washing and singeing.
    b. Removing the head.
    c. Opening the carcass and eviscerating.
    d. Splitting or halving the carcass with a cleaver or electric saw.
    e. Removing the leaf fat.
    f. Exposing the kidneys for inspection and facing the

---

[13] By Federal law (known as the Humane Slaughter Act) passed in 1958 and effective June 30, 1960, unless a packer uses humane slaughter methods, he forfeits the right to sell meat to the government. The law lists the following methods as humane: by rendering insensible to pain by a single blow or gunshot or an electrical, chemical, or other means that is rapid and effective, before being shackled, hoisted, thrown, cast, or cut.

hams (removing the skin and fat from the inside face or cushion of the ham).

g. Washing the carcass and sending it to the coolers where the temperature is held from 31° to 38° F. (Rapid chilling is desirable.)

During the dressing process, federal inspectors carefully examine the head, viscera, and carcass. If the carcass gives no evidence of disease, it is stamped "U.S. Inspected and Passed" prior to being sent to the coolers. If it shows evidence of a diseased condition and is not considered wholesome, it is stamped "U.S. Condemned" and is sent to the inedible tank room along with the viscera. There the carcass is cooked under steam pressure in sealed tanks until all the disease germs are destroyed.

Packer Versus Shipper Style of Dressing

The two common styles of dressing hogs in packing plants are: packer style and shipper style. In general, the packer style is followed, and this system is used almost exclusively when car-

Fig. 12-13. Packer (left) vs. shipper (right) style of dressing. Both hogs dressed 75 percent shipper style, but subsequent removal of the head, leaf fat, and kidneys from the carcass to the left—in preparing it packer style—lowered the dressing percentage of this carcass a further 4 percent. (Courtesy, Washington State University)

casses are to be converted into the primal cuts. In packer-style dressing, the backbone is split full length through the center; the head, without the jowl, is removed; and the kidneys and the leaf fat are removed and the hams faced.

The shipper style is ordinarily limited to lightweight slaughter pigs that are sold as entire carcasses to the wholesale trade. In this style of dressing, the carcass is merely opened from the crotch to the tip of the breastbone; the backbone is left intact; the leaf fat is left in; and the entire head is left attached. Roasting pigs are dressed shipper style and prior to cooling are placed in a trough with front legs doubled back from the knee joints and the hind legs extending straight back from the hams.

When dressed packer style, the carcass yields are 4 to 8 percent less than can be obtained shipper style. The lower yield is due to the removal of the head, leaf fat, kidneys, and ham facings.

The Dressing Percentage of Hogs

Dressing percentage may be defined as the percentage yield of chilled carcass in relation to the weight of the animal on foot. For example, a hog that weighed 200 pounds on foot and yielded a carcass weighing 140 pounds may be said to have a dressing percentage of 70.

Because hogs have a smaller digestive capacity, fill is less important in determining their dressing percentage than is the case with cattle. The degree of fatness and the style of dressing are the important factors affecting dressing percentage in hogs. U.S. No. 1 hogs dressed packer style (with head, leaf fat, and kidneys removed) dress about 69 percent, whereas hogs dressed shipper style (head left on, and leaf fat and kidneys in) dress 4 to 8 percent higher.

Table 12-12 gives the approximate percentages that may be expected from the different grades of barrows and gilts. It is generally recognized that fat, lardy type hogs give a higher dressing percentage than can be obtained with meat type or bacon type animals. Because lard frequently sells at a lower price than is paid for hogs on foot, an excess yield of lard very obviously represents an economic waste of feed in producing the animals and is undesirable from the standpoint of the processor. Accordingly, many producers and slaughterers are slowly

TABLE 12-12

APPROXIMATE DRESSING PERCENTAGE OF BARROWS
AND GILTS, BY GRADE[1]

Grade	Range	Average
U.S. No. 1..	67-71	69
U.S. No. 2..	68-72	70
U.S. No. 3..	69-73	71
U.S. No. 4[2]...	65-69	67
U.S. Utility[2]..	63-67	65

[1]Dressing percentages, based on chilled weights and packer-style dressing (ham facings, leaf fat, kidneys, and head removed), provided by Livestock Division Consumer and Marketing Service, USDA.
[2]Effective June 1, 1968, Medium was changed to U.S. No. 4, and Cull was changed to U.S. Utility. No doubt, the dressing percentages of all grades will change slightly with the new standards.

arriving at the conclusion that attaching great importance to the projected dressing percentage of hogs is outmoded. The more progressive buyers are now focusing their attention on the cut-out value of the carcass, especially on the maximum yield of the more sought primal cuts of high quality.

Hogs have a relatively smaller barrel and chest cavity than cattle and sheep. In addition, they are dressed with their skin and shanks on. Consequently, they dress higher than other classes of slaughter animals.

The average live weight of hogs, dressed shipper and packer styles by federally inspected commercial meat packing plants, and their percentage yield in meat for 1966 was as shown in Table 12-13.

TABLE 12-13

AVERAGE LIVE WEIGHT, CARCASS YIELD, AND DRESSING PERCENTAGES
OF ALL HOGS COMMERCIALLY SLAUGHTERED IN THE U.S. IN 1966[1]

Average Live Weight		Average Dressing Weight[2]		Dressing Percent
(lb.)	(kg)	(lb.)	(kg)	(%)
242 •	110	151	69	62.39

[1]Livestock and Meat Statistics, USDA, Supp. for 1966 to Statistical Bul. No. 333, June 1967, pp. 89 and 103.
[2]Carcass weight excluding lard.

QUESTIONS FOR STUDY AND DISCUSSION

1. Define livestock marketing.

2. Why is hog marketing important?

3. Since World War I, terminal public markets have declined in importance, while livestock auction markets and country selling have increased. Why has this happened?

4. What method of marketing (what market channel) do you consider most advantageous for the hogs sold off your home farm (or a farm with which you are familiar), and why?

5. How do you account for the fact that Canada has compulsory carcass grade and weight selling of hogs, whereas this method has been little used in the U. S.?

6. Why do Canadian hogs grade higher than U. S. hogs?

7. Of all meat, why does pork have the most immediate need for a system that will get the consumer's preferences reflected through to the producer?

8. How does the marketing of hogs differ from the marketing of cattle and sheep?

9. Does each market channel give adequate assurance of honesty, of sanitation, and of humane treatment of animals?

10. Why is it important that a hog producer know the leading hog markets?

11. Which is the more important to the hog producer: (a) low marketing costs, or (b) effective selling and net returns?

12. In what ways does the selling of purebred hogs differ from the selling of commercial hogs?

13. Outline, step by step, how you would prepare and ship hogs.

14. Discuss practical ways and means of lessening shrinkage in market hogs.

15. Define on-foot market (a) classes and (b) grades of hogs and tell of their value.

16. Why are grade names and specifications changed from time to time?

17. Discuss practical ways through which the hog producer can make (a) cyclical trends and (b) seasonal changes less acute.

18. What is the Humane Slaughter Act, and how does it affect hog slaughtering?

SELECTED REFERENCES

Title of Publication	Author(s)	Publisher
American Live Stock Market, The, How It Functions	A. C. Davenport	Drovers Journal Print, Chicago, Ill., 1922.
Animal Science	M. E. Ensminger	The Interstate Printers & Publishers, Danville, Ill., 1969.
Charting the Seasonal Market for Meat Animals	H. F. Breimyer Charlotte Jause	Agri. Handbook No. 83, U. S. Department of Agriculture, Washington, D. C., 1955.
Essentials of Marketing Livestock	R. C. Ashby	(For the National Live Stock Exchange) Morningside College, Sioux City, Ia.
Export Market for Pork and Lard, The	A. A. Dowell R. E. Olson O. B. Hesness	Agri. Expt. Sta. Bul. 418, University of Minnesota, St. Paul, Minn., June 1953.
Farm to Market Hog Shrinkage	T. T. Stout C. B. Cox	Research Bul. No. 685, Purdue University, Lafayette, Ind., 1959.
Food from Farmer to Consumer	National Commission on Food Marketing	U. S. Government Printing Office, Washington, D. C., June 1966.
Hired Truck Transportation in Marketing Livestock	Marketing Research Report No. 297	U. S. Department of Agriculture, Washington, D. C.
Improving Livestock Marketing Efficiency	I. M. Stevens R. L. Fox	General Report No. 39, Farmer Cooperative Service, U. S. Department of Agriculture, Washington, D. C.
Livestock Auction Markets in the Southeast	G. E. Turner C. F. Brasington	Marketing Research Report No. 141, U. S. Department of Agriculture, Washington, D. C., 1956.
Livestock Auction Markets in the United States	Gerald Engelman Betty Sue Pence	Marketing Research Report No. 223, U. S. Department of Agriculture, Washington, D. C.
Livestock Marketing	A. A. Dowell Knute Bjorka	McGraw-Hill Book Co., New York, N. Y., 1941.
Livestock Marketing in the United States	H. H. Smith	Agri. Ext. Serv. Bul. 422-A, Colorado State University, Fort Collins, Colo.
Livestock Shipping Guide and Directory		Department of Traffic, Union Pacific Railroad, Omaha, Neb.
Livestock Terminal Markets in the United States	Marketing Research Report No. 299	U. S. Department of Agriculture, Washington, D. C.
Looking Over the Hog Buyer's Shoulder		Agricultural Research Dept., Swift & Co., Chicago, Ill.

Title of Publication	Author(s)	Publisher
Losses of Livestock in Transit in Midwestern and Western States	J. E. Rickenbacker	Marketing Research Report No. 247, Farmer Cooperative Service, U. S. Department of Agriculture, Washington, D. C.
Maintaining the Health of Livestock in Transit	T. W. Cole	Leaflet No. 38, U. S. Department of Agriculture, Washington, D. C.
Marketing Hogs in Northeastern Indiana	Agri. Expt. Sta. Bul. 561	Purdue University, Lafayette, Ind.
Marketing Livestock in the Corn Belt Region	Knute Bjorka	Agri. Expt. Sta. Bul. 365, South Dakota State College, Brookings, S. Dak., 1942
Marketing Meat-Type Hogs	Marketing Research Report No. 227	Agricultural Marketing Service, U. S. Department of Agriculture, Washington, D. C.
Marketing of Livestock and Meat, The	S. H. Fowler	The Interstate Printers & Publishers, Inc., Danville, Ill., 1961.
Market Outlets for Livestock Producers	Marketing Research Report No. 216	Agricultural Marketing Service, U. S. Department of Agriculture, Washington, D. C.
Organization and Competition in the Livestock and Meat Industry. Technical Study No. 1.	National Commission On Food Marketing	U. S. Government Printing Office, Washington, D. C., June 1966.
Pork Marketing Margins and Costs	Misc. Pub. No. 711	Agricultural Marketing Service, U. S. Department of Agriculture, Washington, D. C., April 1956.
Relationship of Type, Grade, Weight and Price of Market Hogs, The	C. N. Haugse Warren Dekrey V. K. Johnson	Bul. No. 421, Department of Animal Husbandry, North Dakota State University, Fargo, N. Dak.
Sprinkling Hogs in Trucks to Reduce Losses from Heat	R. H. Hinds, Jr. R. F. Gulfoy, Jr.	Marketing Research Report No. 374, U. S. Department of Agriculture, Washington, D. C., 1959.
Stockman's Handbook, The	M. E. Ensminger	The Interstate Printers & Publishers, Inc., Danville, Ill., 1970.
Trade in Western Livestock at Auctions: 1. Development Relative Importance Operations	Harold Abel D. A. Broadbent	Utah Agri. Expt. Sta. Bul. 352, University of Utah, Logan, Utah, 1952.
Trade in Western Livestock at Auctions: 2. Analysis of Livestock Marketings	C. R. Harston E. C. Voorhies	Wash. Agri. Expt. Sta. Bul. 537, Washington State University, Pullman, Wash., 1952.
What Governs Livestock Prices?	F. A. Kutish	Agricultural Research Dept., Swift & Co., Chicago, Ill.
Why Not Sell Quality Hogs?	C. R. Harston W. M. Chase	Circ. 219, Montana Agri. Expt. Sta., Montana State University, Bozeman, Mont.

Chapter XIII

PORK AND BY-PRODUCTS FROM HOG SLAUGHTER

Contents   Page

Pork over the counter is the ultimate objective in producing hogs; it is the end product of all breeding, feeding, care and management, marketing, and processing. It is imperative, therefore, that the progressive hog producer, the student, and the swine scientist have a reasonable working knowledge of pork and of the by-products from hog slaughter. Such knowledge

Fig. 13-1. A modern self-service counter in a food store. Pork over the counter is the ultimate objective in producing swine. (Courtesy, Mrs. Marie Kiefer, Executive Director, National Association of Retail Grocers of the United States, 360 N. Michigan Ave., Chicago, Ill.)

will be of value in selecting animals and in determining policies relative to their handling. To this end, this chapter is presented.

Of course, the type of animals best adapted to the production of meat over the block has changed in a changing world. Thus, in the early history of this country, the very survival of animals was often dependent upon their speed, hardiness, and ability to fight. Moreover, long legs and plenty of bone were important attributes when it came time for animals to trail as drovers took them to market. The Arkansas razorback was adapted to these conditions.

With the advent of rail transportation and improved care and feeding methods, the ability of animals to travel and fight diminished in importance. It was then possible, through selection and breeding, to produce meat animals better suited to the needs of more critical consumers. With the development of large cities, artisans and craftsmen and their successors in industry required fewer calories than those who were engaged in the more arduous tasks of logging, building railroads, etc.

Simultaneously, the American family decreased in size. The demand shifted, therefore, to smaller and less fatty cuts of meats; and, with greater prosperity, high quality hams, bacons, and chops were in demand. To meet the needs of the consumer, the producer gradually shifted to the breeding and marketing of younger animals with maximum cut-out value of the primal cuts. The need was for meat type hogs.

Thus, through the years, consumer demand has exerted a powerful influence upon the type of hogs produced. To be sure, it is necessary that such production factors as prolificacy, economy of feed utilization, rapidity of gains, size, etc., receive due consideration along with consumer demands. But once these production factors have received due weight, hog producers—whether they be purebred or commercial operators—must remember that pork over the counter is the ultimate objective.

Now, and in the future, hog producers need to select and feed so as to obtain increased red meat without excess fat. Production Testing programs and livestock shows have been reoriented to give greater emphasis to these consumer demands.

WORLD PORK CONSUMPTION

In general, pork consumption (and production) is highest in the temperate zones of the world, and in those areas where the population is relatively dense. In many countries, such as China, pigs are primarily scavengers; in others, hog numbers are closely related to corn, barley, potato, and dairy production. As would be expected, the per capita consumption of pork in different countries of the world varies directly with its production and availability (see Table 13-1). Food habits and religious restrictions also affect the amount of pork consumed.

It is noteworthy that, in 1967, the United States produced over 34 billion pounds of meat, or about 27.5 percent of the total world production. This was almost twice the production of the U.S.S.R. (Russia), the world's second largest meat producer.

Table 13-2 gives a summary of per capita meat consumption in the leading meat-eating countries of the world and shows the position of pork. It is noteworthy that pork is in an especially favored position in West Germany, France, and the United Kingdom.

TABLE 13-1

MEAT PRODUCTION (1967)[1] AND PER CAPITA CONSUMPTION (1966)[2]
IN SPECIFIED COUNTRIES

Country (leading countries by rank of total meat production)	Total Meat Production 1967[1]		Pork Production 1967[1]		Percent Pork of All Meat	Per Capita Consumption of All Meat 1966[2]	
	(million)		(million)				
	(lb.)	(kg)	(lb.)	(kg)	(percent)	(lb.)	(kg)
United States ---------	34,210	15,550	12,550	5,705	36.7	171	78
U.S.S.R. ----------------	17,150	7,795	7,300	3,318	42.6	76	35
France-------------------	7,696	3,498	3,170	1,441	41.2	152	69
West Germany--------	7,010	3,186	4,332	1,969	61.8	123	56
Argentina---------------	6,727	3,058	474	215	7.0	207	94
Brazil -------------------	4,468	2,031	1,218	554	27.3	54	25
United Kingdom------	4,426	2,012	1,815	825	41.0	138	63
Australia---------------	3,564	1,620	313	142	8.8	198	90
Canada------------------	3,076	1,398	1,195	543	38.8	148	67
Italy---------------------	2,658	1,208	914	415	34.4	64	29
Denmark ---------------	2,031	923	1,622	737	80.0	120	55
New Zealand ---------	1,886	857	80	36	4.2	229	104
Netherlands -----------	1,876	853	1,193	542	63.6	109	50
Mexico ------------------	1,779	809	557	253	31.3	40	18

[1]*Foreign Agriculture Circular*, USDA, Foreign Agricultural Service, FLM 7-68, June, 1968, pp. 6 and 7.
[2]*Foreign Agriculture Circular*, USDA, Foreign Agricultural Service, FLM 11-67, Nov., 1967, p. 7.

TABLE 13-2

PER CAPITA MEAT CONSUMPTION IN SPECIFIED COUNTRIES, 1966[1]

Country (leading countries by rank of all meats)	All Meats		Pork		Percent Pork of All Meats
	(lb.)	(kg)	(lb.)	(kg)	(%)
New Zealand ------------------------------	229	104	31	14	13.5
Uruguay ------------------------------------	224	102	18	8	8.0
Argentina----------------------------------	207	94	20	9	9.7
Australia-----------------------------------	198	90	26	12	13.1
United States -----------------------------	171	78	58	26	33.9
France--------------------------------------	152	69	66	30	43.4
Canada--------------------------------------	148	67	48	22	32.4
United Kingdom--------------------------	138	63	62	28	44.9
Paraguay -----------------------------------	133	60	27	12	20.3
West Germany-----------------------------	123	56	73	33	59.3

[1]*Foreign Agriculture Circular*, USDA, Foreign Agricultural Service, FLM 11-67, Nov., 1967, pp. 4 and 7.

UNITED STATES PORK CONSUMPTION

Although comprising less than 6 percent of the world's population and having only 10.2 percent of its hogs, the people of the United States eat 24 percent of the total world production of pork.

The story of U. S. pork consumption is further presented in Table 13-3 and Figs. 13-2 and 13-3. From these, the following conclusions may be drawn:

TABLE 13-3

U.S. PER CAPITA MEAT CONSUMPTION[1]

Year	All Meats		Pork		Percent Pork of All Meats
	(lb.)	(kg)	(lb.)	(kg)	(%)
1957	158.7	72.1	61.1	27.8	38.5
1958	151.6	68.9	60.2	27.4	39.7
1959	159.5	72.5	67.6	30.7	42.4
1960	161.4	73.4	65.2	29.6	40.4
1961	161.0	73.2	62.2	28.3	38.6
1962	163.5	74.3	63.7	29.0	39.0
1963	170.0	77.3	65.6	29.8	38.6
1964	175.1	79.6	65.5	29.8	37.4
1965	167.4	76.1	58.8	26.7	35.1
1966	170.3	77.4	58.0	26.3	34.0
10 year ave.	163.9	74.5	62.8	28.5	38.4

[1] Agricultural Statistics 1967, USDA, p. 425.

1. Pork ranks second as the preferred red meat in the United States, beef having replaced pork in first position in the early 1950's.

2. Until 1937, the longtime trend in meat consumption was downward; since then it has been upward.

3. Meat—along with fruit and vegetables, dairy products, and eggs—continues to be the preferred food. By contrast, the consumption of cereals and potatoes has declined.

PORK IMPORTS AND EXPORTS

Hog producers are prone to ask why the United States, with a swine population second only to China, buys pork and hogs abroad. Conversely, consumers sometimes wonder why we export pork. Occasionally, there is justification for such fears, on a temporary basis and in certain areas, but as shown in Tables 13-4 and 13-5, this nation neither imports nor exports large quantities of pork. Also, only negligible numbers of live hogs are imported or exported. During the five-year period, 1962 to 1966, we imported an average of only 9,969 live hogs per year;

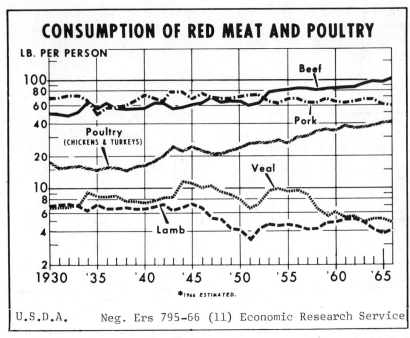

Fig. 13-2. Per capita meat consumption in the United States, by kind of meat. As noted, the amount of meat consumed in this country varies from year to year. In recent years, the average American has consumed less pork than beef.

in this same period, we exported only 9,125 live hogs per year.[1]

Table 13-4 reveals that the United States imports more pork than it exports. But, as shown in Table 13-5, total pork imports actually constitute a very small percentage of the available U. S. pork.

The amount of pork imported from abroad depends to a substantial degree on (1) the level of U. S. meat production, (2) consumer buying power, (3) hog prices, and (4) tariffs. (See Table 2-7, Chapter II, for tariffs on pork and live hogs.) When hog prices are high, more pork is imported (see Fig. 13-4).

Because tariffs have always been in politics and are subject to change, we need constantly to increase efficiency of production as a means of meeting foreign competition (see Chapter II, under

---

[1] *Livestock and Meat Statistics*, Supp. for 1966 to Statistical Bul. No. 333, p. 148, Tables 215 and 216, June 1967.

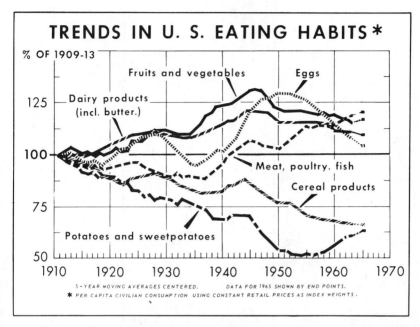

TRENDS IN U. S. EATING HABITS *

% OF 1909-13

Fruits and vegetables

Eggs

125 — Dairy products (incl. butter.)

100

Meat, poultry, fish

Cereal products

75

Potatoes and sweetpotatoes

50

1910 1920 1930 1940 1950 1960 1970

5-YEAR MOVING AVERAGES CENTERED. DATA FOR 1965 SHOWN BY END POINTS.
* PER CAPITA CIVILIAN CONSUMPTION USING CONSTANT RETAIL PRICES AS INDEX WEIGHTS.

Fig. 13-3. Trends in our per capita consumption of major food groups, with projections to 1975. Until 1937, the longtime trend in meat consumption was downward; since then it has been upward. (Courtesy, Agricultural Marketing Service, USDA)

"The Future of the American Swine Industry," for current duties).

The amount of pork exported from this country is dependent upon (1) the volume of meat produced in the United States, (2) the volume of meat produced abroad, and (3) the relative vigor of international trade, especially as affected by buying power and trade restrictions.

Our pork imports come principally from Canada, Netherlands, Denmark, and Poland. Neither swine nor the fresh, chilled, or frozen meat from hogs can be imported from any country in which it has been determined that rinderpest or foot-and-mouth disease exists.

We export pork to Canada, Venezuela, Bahamas, Jamaica, France, and Mexico. We export more lard than any other nation; in 1966, U. S. exports of lard as a percent of world lard exports were 26 percent. The United Kingdom is our leading lard customer.

TABLE 13-4

U.S. IMPORTS AND EXPORTS OF PORK AND OTHER MEATS[1]

	IMPORTS						EXPORTS				
Year	Pork		All Meats		Percent Pork of All Meats		Pork		All Meats		Percent Pork of All Meats
	(1000)		(1000)		(%)		(1000)		(1000)		(%)
	(lb.)	(kg)	(lb.)	(kg)			(lb.)	(kg)	(lb.)	(kg)	
1962	203,788	92,631	1,252,373	569,260	16.3		63,679	28,945	222,857	101,299	27.9
1963	212,554	96,615	1,420,870	645,850	15.0		138,126	62,785	330,200	150,090	41.8
1964	215,163	97,801	1,062,068	482,758	20.3		132,988	60,449	430,567	195,712	30.9
1965	267,329	121,513	1,011,987	459,994	26.4		47,654	21,661	331,508	150,685	14.4
1966	304,340	138,336	1,276,379	580,172	23.8		50,885	23,130	309,902	140,864	16.4
5-yr. ave.	240,635	109,379	1,204,735	547,607	20.0		86,666	39,394	325,007	147,730	26.7

[1]*Agricultural Statistics 1967*, USDA, pp. 421 and 422.

TABLE 13-5

IMPORTS OF PORK COMPARED WITH U.S. PRODUCTION[1]

Year	Pork Imports		Pork Production		Pork Imports as Percent of Production
	(1000)		(1000)		
	(lb.)	(kg)	(lb.)	(kg)	(%)
1962	203,788	92,631	11,819,000	5,372.273	1.7
1963	212,554	96,615	12,419,000	5,645,000	1.7
1964	215,163	97,801	12,503,000	5,683,182	1.7
1965	267,329	121,513	11,132.000	5.060,000	2.4
1966	304,340	138,336	11,328,000	5,149,090	2.7
5-yr. ave.	240,635	109,379	11,840,000	5,381,909	2.0

[1]Agricultural Statistics 1967, USDA, pp. 418 and 422.

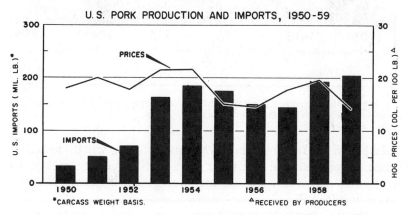

Fig. 13-4. U. S. hog prices and imports go up and down together.

QUALITIES IN PORK DESIRED BY THE CONSUMER

Until 30 years ago, big lardy hogs were preferred; families were large and engaged in strenuous outdoor occupations, there was a lively export for lard, and lard was in demand for use as shortening and for the manufacture of soaps and munitions. But times have changed! Vegetable oils have largely replaced lard as a shortening, and we have lost much of our export market. From a position of minor importance in 1946, synthetic detergents now have about two-thirds, by weight, of our combined soap-detergent sales. As a result of these changes, there has been a rather constant widening of the gap between the prices of the primal lean cuts of pork (hams, loins, picnics, and

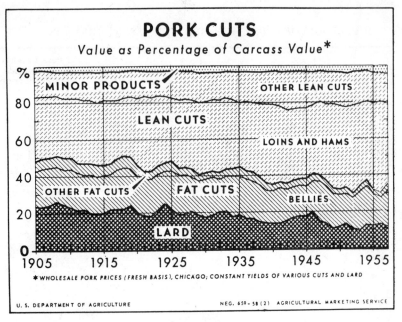

Fig. 13-5. In recent years, lean cuts of pork have become relatively more valuable than fat cuts and lard.

butts) and of fat for lard. Whereas fat was worth nearly as much as lean cuts in the early part of the century, today, the lean cuts, pound for pound, are worth almost three times as much as fat.

Because consumer preference is such an important item in the production of pork, it is well that the farmer, the packer, and the meat retailer be familiar with these qualities, which are summarized as follows:

1. **Palatability.**—First and foremost, people eat pork because they like it. Palatability is influenced by the tenderness, juiciness, and flavor of the fat and lean.

2. **Attractiveness.**—The general attractiveness is an important factor in selling pork to the housewife. The color of the lean, the degree of fatness, and the marbling are leading factors in determining buyer appeal. Most consumers prefer a white fat and a light or medium red color in the lean.

3. **Maximum muscling; moderate fat.**—Maximum thickness of muscling influences materially the acceptability by the

Fig. 13-6. A pork chop-apple-sauerkraut combination ready for serving. (Courtesy, American Meat Institute)

consumer. Also, consumer resistance to fat on all meats, particularly on pork, has been very marked in recent years.

4. **Small cuts.**—Most purchasers prefer to buy cuts of meat that are of a proper size to meet the needs of their respective families. Because the American family has decreased in size, this has meant smaller cuts. This, in turn, has had a profound influence on the type of animals and on market age and weight.

5. **Ease of preparation.**—In general, the housewife prefers to select pork that will give her the greatest amount of leisure time; thus, she selects those cuts that can be prepared with the greatest ease and the least time.

6. **Tenderness.**—The consumer wants a piece of meat which, when properly cooked and served, can be cut and eaten with ease. With pork, lack of tenderness is seldom a problem.

7. **Repeatability.**—The housewife wants to be able to secure

a standardized product; meat of the same tenderness and other eating qualities as her previous purchase.

If these seven qualities are not met by pork, other products will meet them. Recognition of this fact is important, for competition is keen for space on the shelves of a modern retail food outlet.

To this end, we need to conduct more experimental studies on consumer preference and demand; then we need accurately to reflect this information in price differentials at the market place, and, in turn, in production.

HOW TO PRODUCE HIGHER QUALITY PORK

Excess fat is the greatest single factor causing undesirable pork carcasses. Experimental work indicates that the producer can help alleviate this condition through the following:

1. By selecting breeding stock with bred-in meat quality.
2. By restricting the rate of gain of pigs to about 1.5 pounds daily after a live weight of 125 pounds. This can be easily accomplished by using a lighter, bulkier finishing ration—one containing about one-third of some such suitable feed as bran, oats, or alfalfa.
3. By slaughtering at lighter live weights, preferably not over 200 pounds.

It is also noteworthy that barrows normally yield fatter carcasses than gilts at equal marketing weights. Also, contrary to the opinion held by some, level of protein in the hog ration has no direct effect on carcass excellence, although it does affect the growth of the pig.

THE FEDERAL GRADES OF PORK CARCASSES

The grade of a pork carcass may be defined as, a measure of its degree of excellence based chiefly on quality of lean and the expected yield of trimmed major wholesale cuts. It is intended that the specifications for each grade shall be sufficiently definite to make for uniform grades throughout the country and from season to season, and that on-hook grades shall be correlated with on-foot grades.

Both producers and consumers should know the federal grades of pork and have reasonably clear understanding of the

Fig. 13-7. Hog producers should evaluate the carcasses that they produce. This picture shows Dr. O. D. Butler, Texas A & M, evaluating pork carcasses. (Courtesy, Texas A & M University)

specifications of each grade. From the standpoint of producers—including both purebred and commercial operators—this is important, for, after all, meat over the counter is the ultimate objective. From the standpoint of consumers, especially the housewife who buys most of the meat, this is important, because (1) in these days of self-service prepackaged meats there is less opportunity to secure the counsel and advice of the meat cutter when making purchases, and (2) the average consumer is not the best judge of the quality of the various kinds of meats on display in the meat counter.

The grades of barrow and gilt carcasses are based on two general considerations: (1) the quality-indicating characteristics of the lean, and (2) the expected combined yields of the four lean cuts (ham, loin, picnic shoulder, and Boston butt). Although the quality of the lean is best evaluated by a direct observation

of its characteristics in a cut surface, in grading carcasses such observations are impractical. Thus, in carcasses, the quality of the lean is evaluated indirectly, on the bases of such quality-indicating characteristics as firmness of the fat and lean, amount of feathering between the ribs, color of lean, and belly thickness determined primarily by the thickness of the belly pocket.

Research has shown that the actual average thickness of backfat in relation to carcass length is a rather reliable guide to the yield of the four lean cuts. Therefore, in determining the grade of pork carcasses, the actual average thickness of backfat and the carcass length are considered. This relationship is illustrated in Figure 13-8 for carcasses 27 to 36 inches in length. By extending the lines in Figure 13-8, average backfat thickness requirements for carcasses of other lengths can be obtained.

The Federal grades of pork carcasses are: U. S. No. 1, U. S. No. 2, U. S. No. 3, U. S. No. 4, and U. S. Utility. The market grades of pork differ from the grades of beef in that (1) pork possesses five grades instead of the eight common to beef, because it is more uniform in quality, and, therefore, fewer grades are needed; (2) the top grade of pork is U. S. No. 1, instead of Prime; and (3) no Cutter or Canner designations are used in pork, instead the lowest grade is known as U. S. Utility.

The expected yield of the four lean cuts for each of the four top grades of pork are:

Grade	Expected yield of ham, loin, picnic shoulder, and Boston butt, based on chilled carcass weight
U.S. No. 1	53% and over
U.S. No. 2	50 to 52.9%
U.S. No. 3	50 to 49.9%
U.S. No. 4	Less than 47%

These yields are based on the cutting and trimming methods used by the U.S. Department of Agriculture in developing the standards.

The five grades of pork carcasses (barrows and gilts) may be described as follows:

U.S. No. 1.—Carcasses in this grade have an acceptable quality of lean, a high yield of lean cuts, and a low yield of fat cuts. In carcasses grading U.S. No. 1, the maximum average thickness of backfat increases from 1.3 to 1.6 inches with in-

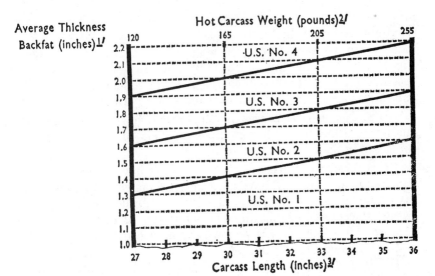

Average Thickness Backfat (inches)[1]

Hot Carcass Weight (pounds)[2]

Carcass Length (inches)[3]

[1]An average of three measurements including the skin made opposite the first and last ribs and the last lumbar vertebra. It also reflects adjustment, as appropriate, to compensate for variations-from-normal fat distribution.

[2]Carcass weight is based on a hot packer style carcass.

[3]Carcass length is measured from the anterior point of the aitch bone to the anterior edge of the first rib.

Fig. 13-8. Relationship between average thickness of backfat, carcass length or weight, and grade for carcasses with muscling typical of their degree of fatness. (From Federal Register, March 28, 1968; courtesy, John C. Pierce, Director, Livestock Division, USDA, Consumer and Marketing Service)

creases in carcass length from 27 to 36 inches (see Fig. 13-8); but, within limitations, superior muscling may compensate for fatness in excess of that indicated in Figure 13-8, and, conversely, low fatness may compensate for some lack of muscling—so long as the latter is moderately thick or better.

U.S. No. 2.—Carcasses in this grade have an acceptable quality of lean, a slightly high yield of lean cuts, and a slightly low yield of fat cuts. In carcasses grading U.S. No. 2, the maximum average thickness of backfat increases from 1.6 to 1.9 inches with increases in carcass length from 27 to 36 inches (see Fig. 13-8); but, within limitations, superior muscling may compensate for fatness in excess of that specified, and the reverse type of compensation is also permitted.

U.S. No. 3.—Carcasses in this grade have an acceptable quality of lean, a slightly low yield of lean cuts, and a slightly

high yield of fat cuts. In carcasses grading U.S. No. 3, the maximum average thickness of backfat increases from 1.9 to 2.2 inches with increases in carcass length from 27 to 36 inches (see Fig 13-8). Also, within limitations, muscling superior to that specified for U.S. No. 3 may compensate for some excess fatness, and the reverse type of compensation is also permitted.

U.S. No. 4.—Carcasses in this grade have an acceptable quality of lean, but a lower expected yield of lean cuts than carcasses in the U.S. No. 3 grade.

U.S. Utility.—Carcasses in this grade have characteristics which indicate they will have a lesser development of lean quality than required as minimum for the four top grades. Also, regardless of other quality-indicating characteristics, all carcasses which (1) are soft or oily, or (2) do not have an acceptable belly thickness are graded U.S. Utility.

Unlike meat inspection, government grading is purely voluntary, on a charge basis.

DISPOSITION OF THE PORK CARCASS

Almost all hog carcasses are cut up at the slaughtering plant and are sold in the form of wholesale cuts. In most parts of the country, not more than 1 percent of the pork in large packing plants is sold in carcass form. The whole-carcass trade is largely confined to roasting and slaughter pigs.

The handling of pork differs further from that of beef and lamb in that only a relatively small percentage—about 30 percent—of the pork is sold fresh. The remaining 70 percent is cured by various methods, is rendered into lard, or is manufactured into meat products. In general, loins, shoulders, and spareribs are most likely to be sold as fresh cuts. But it must be remembered that practically every pork cut may be cured, and, under certain conditions, is cured. Because pork is well adapted to curing, it has a decided advantage over beef and mutton, which are sold almost entirely in the fresh state. The hog market is stabilized to some extent by this factor.

THE HOG CARCASS AND ITS WHOLESALE CUTS

A minimum of twenty-four hours chilling at temperatures ranging from 31° to 38° F. is necessary to remove properly the animal heat and give the carcasses sufficient firmness to make

Fig. 13-9. Dry-salting bacon for curing. The cuts are thoroughly rubbed with salt, after which they are piled closely in layers and resalted at intervals. Salting, which is still the chief method of curing meats, has been practiced since the fifth century B. C. and possibly longer. (Courtsey, H. A. Rothra, Ed., *Meat Magazine*)

possible a neat job of cutting. After chilling, the carcasses are brought to the cutting floor where they are reduced to the wholesale cuts.

The method of cutting varies somewhat according to the value of lard and the relative demand for different cuts. Despite some variation, the most common wholesale cuts of pork are: ham, bacon, loin, picnic shoulder, Boston butt, jowl, spareribs, and feet.

Market hogs weighing from 180 to 200 pounds will have about 45.5 percent of their live weight in the four primal cuts: the ham, shoulder, loin, and bacon belly. Yet, because of the relatively higher value per pound of these cuts, they make up three-quarters of the value of the entire carcass.

LARD

Lard is the fat rendered (melted out) from fresh, fatty pork tissue. From 10 to 25 percent—with an average of 15 percent—of the hog carcass is made into lard in the large packing houses.

Fig. 13-10. Hams in dry cure (or dry-sugar cure). After the curing formula is added, most packers allow 15 to 45 days to cure a ham and 17 to 30 days to cure bacon. Most dry-cured pork is smoked following the formula treatment. (Courtesy, H. A. Rothra, Ed., *Meat Magazine*)

The proportion varies with the type, weight, and finish of the hogs, and the relative price of lard and the cuts of meat. Lard is considered a primary product of hog slaughter and not a by-product.

Kinds of Lard

Lard is classified according to the part of the animal from which the fat comes and the method of rendering.

KETTLE-RENDERED LEAF LARD

Kettle-rendered leaf lard is made from leaf fat only. It is rendered in a steam-jacketed open kettle at a temperature of 230° to 250° F. It is very white in color, fine textured, and possesses excellent keeping qualities and a pleasing flavor. It is the highest grade of lard.

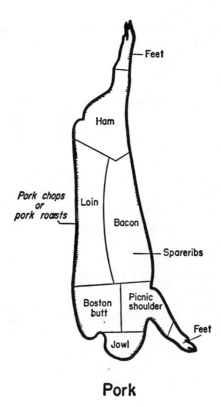

Feet

Ham

Pork chops
or
pork roasts

Loin

Bacon

Spareribs

Boston
butt

Picnic
shoulder

Feet

Jowl

Pork

Fig. 13-11. Wholesale cuts of pork. (Drawing by R. F. Johnson)

KETTLE-RENDERED LARD

Kettle-rendered lard is made from back fat and leaf fat, usually in equal amounts. It is also rendered in a steam-jacketed open kettle but at a temperature of 240° to 260° F. Kettle-rendered lard has good keeping qualities, but it is likely to be somewhat darker than kettle-rendered leaf lard, to which it ranks second in grade.

PRIME STEAM LARD

Probably 85 percent of packing house lard is of the prime steam type. It is made from killing and cutting fats that are rendered in a closed tank under steam pressure of from 30 to 50 pounds and at a temperature of 285° F. It is somewhat milder in

flavor and odor and lighter in color than lard produced by dry rendering.

NEUTRAL LARD

Neutral lard is made entirely from leaf fat that is rendered at a very low temperature of about 120° F. It is used almost entirely in the manufacture of oleomargarine.

DRY-RENDERED LARD

Dry-rendered lard is essentially a kettle-rendered lard, except that the fat is melted in a closed container, usually under reduced pressure. This method of rendering gives a product that has a fine flavor and excellent keeping quality.

NEW PROCESS LARD (OR DEODORIZED OR HYDROGENATED LARD)

New process lard is deodorized lard to which extra atoms of hydrogen and a stabilizing agent (inhibitors of vegetable origin) have been added. Such lard is bland, has a high melting point, and is less subject to rancidity than ordinary lard. New-process lard was first placed on the market in 1941.

LARD SUBSTITUTES

Lard substitutes, which are sometimes used in place of lard, are made from: (1) lard and other animal fats mixed with vegetable oils, (2) vegetable oils alone, and (3) hydrogenated vegetable oils, the most prominent of which are cottonseed, soybean, and coconut oil.

CURING PORK ON THE FARM

Farm meat curing other than freezing is largely confined to pork, primarily because of the keeping qualities and palatability of cured pork products.

The secret of pork curing is to use good sound meat, the correct curing method and formula, clean containers, and to be fortunate enough to secure cool curing weather.

The primary meat curing ingredients and the functions of each are:

1. **Salt.**—It preserves by inhibiting or retarding the bacteria that cause spoilage. In excess quantities, salt makes meat less palatable.

2. **Sugar.**—Sugar is used to counteract the hardening of the muscles caused by salt and to enhance the flavor of the meat.

3. **Saltpeter** (nitrate of potash).—It is used to enhance the bright red color of the lean meat.

Table 13-6 is a Handy Pork Curing Guide.

PORK RETAIL CUTS AND HOW TO COOK THEM

The method of cutting pork is practically the same in all sections of the United States. Figure 13-12 illustrates the common wholesale and retail cuts of pork, and gives the recommended method or methods for cooking each. This informative figure may be used as a guide to wise buying, in dividing the pork carcass into the greatest number of desirable cuts, in becoming familiar with the types of cuts, and in preparing each type of cut by the proper method of cookery.

It is important that meat be cooked at low temperature, usually between 300 and 325° F. At this temperature, it cooks slowly, and as a result is juicier, shrinks less, and has a better flavor than when cooked at high temperatures.

The methods used in meat cookery depend on the nature of the cut to which it is applied. In general, the types of meat cookery may be summarized as follows:

1. **Dry-heat Cooking.**—Dry-heat cooking is used in preparing the more tender cuts, those that contain little connective tissue. This method of cooking consists of surrounding the meat by dry air in the oven or under the broiler. The common methods of cooking by dry heat are (a) roasting, (b) broiling, and (c) panbroiling (see Fig. 13-13).

    a. How to Roast:
        (1) Season with salt and pepper, if desired.
        (2) Place fat side up on rack in open roasting pan.
        (3) Insert meat thermometer.
        (4) Roast in preheated oven at 300° F.
        (5) Do not add water, nor cover, nor baste.
        (6) Roast until the meat thermometer registers rare, medium, or well-done, as desired.

TABLE 13-6
HANDY PORK CURING GUIDE

Curing Method and Formula	Kind of Cuts to Which Adapted	Curing Directions	Comments
1. Dry-salting: Salt only	Backs, sides, and other cuts of pork; especially heavy fat backs and bacons.	Rub and sprinkle over the cuts 7 to 10 pounds of salt per 100 pounds of meat. Pile meat closely in layers and resalt at intervals. Let cure for 3 to 4 weeks. A curing temperature of about 40° F. is preferable.	Dry-salting was formerly the most common method of preserving farm pork, but, for the most part, it has now been replaced by the dry-cure and sweet-pickle methods.
2. Dry-cure (or dry-sugar cure): Mixture per 100 pounds meat: 8 pounds table salt 3 pounds sugar (brown or granulated sugar) 3 ounces saltpeter (nitrate of potash)	Hams, bacons, and shoulders.	**For bacon,** (1) rub on 1 oz. of the dry-cure mix per pound of bacon (sprinkling any surplus of this amount on the rib side), and (2) let cure 7 days per inch of thickness (thus a side of bacon 2 inches thick would be left in cure 14 days). **For hams** (1) rub on 1 oz. (if hams weigh over 20 pounds use 1¼ to 1½ ozs.) of the dry-cure mix per pound of ham, applying in 3 rubbings at three- to five-day intervals, and (2) let cure 7 days per inch of thickness (as measured directly back of the aitchbone). **For shoulders,** (1) rub on 1 oz. of the dry-cure mix per pound of shoulders, applying in 2 rubbings at three- to five-day intervals, and (2) let cure 7 days per inch of thickness. Meats in cure should be placed on a clean shelf, on a table, or in a barrel with a drain at the bottom so the juice can drain off.	The dry-cure produces more palatable products than dry-salting. In comparison with the sweet-pickle cure, the dry-cure is more rapid, requires less equipment, results in a higher shrink, and gives a stronger cure. It is the preferred cure in warm areas. Curing should not be attempted where the temperature is over 50° F., because spoilage is apt to take place before the cure can penetrate the ham or shoulder.
3. Sweet-pickle Cure: Mixture per 100 pounds meat: 8 pounds table salt 3 pounds sugar (brown or granulated sugar) 3 ounces saltpeter (nitrate of potash) 6 gals. water (8 pounds/gal.: boiling water or unboiled, cold water—depending on its purity) As noted, the ingredients are the same in the dry-cure and in the sweet-pickle cure; *(Continued)*	Hams, bacons, and shoulders.	Weigh out the ingredients of the formula (water may be measured), and stir until thoroughly mixed. Pack the meat skin side down into either a crock or a clean, well-soaked, odorless, hardwood barrel. Place the thicker and heavier cuts in the bottom of the container Pour cool pickle or brine over the meat until the liquid just covers it. Four to five gals. of pickle will cover 100 pounds of meat. Place a weight, such as a lid, on top of the meat to hold it under the liquid, and weight it down *(Continued)*	A combination of salt and water is called a brine or pickle, and, with the addition of sugar, it is known as a sweet-pickle cure. In comparison with the dry-cure, the sweet-pickle cure results in a milder flavor and gives less shrink. For best results, the curing-room temperature should not rise above 40° F.; temperatures above 50° F. are too high for safe pickle curing. A salometer, or salinometer, is a ballasted glass vacuum tube graduated in degrees, which is sometimes used for testing the strength or salinity *(Continued)*

(Continued)

TABLE 13-6 (Continued)

Curing Method and Formula	Kind of Cuts to Which Adapted	Curing Directions	Comments
the difference being that in the dry-cure the mixture is applied directly to the meat while in the brine cure the mixture is dissolved in water and the meat submerged in it.		with a clean stone or other suitable object. Let the meat cure in the pickle 11 days per inch of thickness. Thus, the thinner and lighter cuts on the top of the container must be removed first. When large vats are used, overhauling (meaning the rehandling or repacking) of the meat is recommended in order to permit a more uniform distribution of the pickle, but this is not necessary with the small quantities cured on most farms. If the brine should spoil (as evidenced by cloudiness), remove all the cuts, wash them with cold water, and place them in a new brine with 2/3 of the original ingredients.	of pickle. A test of about 75° is preferred under most conditions.
4. Pumping, followed by either dry-cure or sweet-pickle cure: By means of a plunger-type syringe, sweet-pickle cure (see formula under "sweet-pickle cure") is injected into the ham or shoulder; and Then the ham or shoulder is subjected to either the dry-cure or sweet-pickle cure for the balance of the curing.	Hams.	Mix the sweet-pickle formula as directed under "sweet-pickle cure." Inject into the center of the ham an amount of sweet-pickle cure equivalent to 8 to 10 percent of the weight of the cut. Following pumping, complete the curing process by either the dry-cure or sweet-pickle cure methods, but lessen the curing time by one-third.	Pumping hastens the curing process in the center of the cut and lessens spoilage. Meat packers use a modified pumping method for hams, known as the artery cure. In this process, the sweet-pickle is injected into the femoral artery under 40 to 50 pounds of pressure, and the subsequent dry-cure or sweet-pickle cure is limited to 2 weeks. The advantages of the artery cure are speed and uniform flavor.
5. Smoking: Hickory, oak, hard maple, and apple are favorite smoke woods. Hardwood sawdust is also satisfactory. Two methods of smoking are: For light mahogany smoke, smoke 24 to 48 hours at a temperature of approximately 125° to 135° F. For meat that is to be stored for summer use, smoke at a temperature of 80° to 100° F., at intervals of approximately 5 to 10 days, over a period of several weeks.	Hams, bacons, and shoulders.	If the meat has been either dry-cured or sweet-pickle cured, prior to smoking, it should be (1) soaked from ½ to 3 hours in cold water (using the longer soaking period for the heavier cuts), (2) scrubbed with a clean stiff brush, and (3) hung to dry overnight in the smoke house. This removes the excess salt on the outside and alleviates the formation of salt streaks. Hang the cuts so that they will not touch each other, since this will cause streaking. After meat is smoked, many people like to season it heavily with black pepper.	Smoking is a common practice in the home-curing of pork, and most packer dry-cured and sweet-pickle cured pork cuts are smoked, as well as many items of sausage. Smoking adds flavor, makes for a more desirable appearance, and improves the keeping qualities of meats. The higher the temperature the greater the absorption of smoke and the darker the color. After the smoked meat has cooled, it should be carefully wrapped with heavy parchment paper, put into muslin bags, and hung in a dry, dark, cool, well-ventilated place.

the Identification of Pork Cuts

Meat Cuts and How to Cook Them

PORK CHART

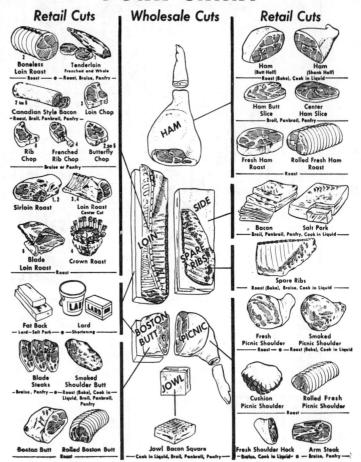

Fig. 13-12. The common wholesale and retail cuts of pork, and the recommended method or methods of cooking each. (Courtesy, National Live Stock and Meat Board)

For best results, a meat thermometer should be used to test the doneness of roasts (and also for thick steaks and chops). It takes the guesswork out of meat cooking. Allowing a certain number of minutes to the pound is not always accurate; for ex-

Dry-heat Cooking

A. Roasting

B. Broiling

C. Panbroiling

Moist-heat Cooking

D. Braising

E. Cooking in liquid

Fig. 13-13. Common methods of meat cookery. (Drawing by R. F. Johnson)

ample, rolled roasts take longer to cook than ones with bones.

The thermometer is inserted into the cut of meat so that the bulb reaches the center of the largest muscle, and so that it is not in contact with fat or bone. Naturally, frozen roasts need to be partially thawed before the thermometer is inserted, or a metal skewer or ice pick will have to be employed in order to make a hole in frozen meat.

As the oven heat penetrates, the temperature at the center

Fig. 13-14. Roast pork loin. Perhaps most people eat meats simply be-cause they like them. For flavor, variety, and appetite appeal, pork is un-surpassed. (Courtesy, National Livestock and Meat Board)

of the meat gradually rises and is registered on the thermometer. Most meat can be cooked as desired—rare, medium, or well-done, but pork should always be cooked well-done.

    b. How to Broil:

       (1) Set the oven regulator for broiling.

       (2) Place meat on the rack of the broiler pan and cook 2 to 3 inches from heat.

       (3) Broil until the top of meat is brown.

       (4) Season with salt and pepper.

       (5) Turn the meat and brown the other side.

       (6) Season and serve at once.

    c. How to Panbroil:

       (1) Place meat in a heavy, uncovered frying pan. Cook slowly.

       (2) Do not add fat or water.

       (3) Turn at intervals to insure even cooking.

(4) If fat accumulates, pour it off.

(5) Brown meat on both sides.

(6) Do not overcook. Season.

2. **Moist-heat Cooking.**—Moist-heat cooking is generally used in preparing the less tender cuts, those containing more connective tissues that require moist heat to soften them and make them tender. In this type of cooking the meat is surrounded by hot liquid or steam. The common methods of moist-heat cooking are: (a) braising, and (b) stewing or cooking in water (see Fig. 13-13).

    a. How to Braise:

       (1) Brown the meat on all sides in a small amount of hot fat in a heavy utensil.

       (2) Season with salt and pepper.

       (3) Add small amount of liquid, if necessary.

       (4) Cover tightly.

       (5) Cook at simmering temperature, without boiling, until tender.

    b. How to Cook-in-liquid:

       (1) Cut meat into 1 to 2 inch cubes.

       (2) Brown on all sides in hot lard, if desired.

       (3) Season with salt and pepper.

       (4) Cover with water and cover kettle tightly.

       (5) Cook at simmering temperature, without boiling.

       (6) If desired, add vegetables just long enough to be cooked before serving.

THE NUTRITIVE QUALITIES OF PORK

Perhaps most people eat pork simply because they like it. They derive a rich enjoyment and satisfaction therefrom.

But pork is far more than just a very tempting and delicious food. From a nutritional standpoint, it contains certain essentials of an adequate diet: high quality proteins, calories, minerals, and vitamins. This is important, for how we live and how long we live are determined in large part by our diet.

It is estimated that the average American gets the following percentages of his food nutrients from meat:[2]

----

[2]From a study conducted by the USDA. The percentages of daily dietary allowance are based on recommendations of the National Research Council for an average 154-lb. sedentary man.

63% of his protein   42% of his vitamin B₁ (thiamine)
47% of his iron   24% of his vitamin B₂ (riboflavin)
28% of his phosphorus   79% of his niacin

Plus generous amounts of other B vitamins—including the important B_{12}.

Effective pork promotion necessitates full knowledge of the nutritive qualities of meats, the pertinent facts of which follow:

1. **Proteins.**—The word protein is derived from the Greek word "proteous," meaning "in first place." Protein is recognized as a most important body builder. Fortunately, meat contains the proper quantity and quality of protein for the building and repair of body tissues. On a fresh basis, pork contains 15 to 20 percent protein. Also, it contains all of the amino acids, or building stones, which are necessary for the making of new tissue; and the proportion of amino acids in meat almost exactly parallels that in human protein.

2. **Calories.**—Pork is a good source of energy, the energy value being dependent largely upon the amount of fat it contains.

3. **Minerals.**—Minerals are necessary in order to build and maintain the body skeleton and tissues and to regulate body functions. Pork is a rich source of several minerals, but is especially good as a source of phosphorus and iron. Phosphorus combines with calcium in building the bones and teeth. Phosphorus also enters into the structure of every body cell, helps to maintain the alkalinity of the blood, is involved in the output of nervous energy, and has other important functions.

Iron is necessary for the building of blood, and its presence protects against nutritional anemia. It is a constituent of the hemoglobin or red pigment of the 25 trillion or more body corpuscles. Thus, it helps to carry the life-giving oxygen to every part of the body. The average adult would be assured an adequate supply of iron if two servings of meat were taken daily along with one serving of liver each week.

4. **Vitamins.**—Thousands of years ago, people knew that certain foods possessed unique nutritive properties. For example, as early as 1500 B. C., the Egyptians and Chinese hit upon the discovery that eating liver would improve one's vision in dim light. We now know that liver furnishes vitamin A, a very important factor for night vision. In fact, medical authorities

recognize that night blindness, glare blindness, and poor vision in dim light are all common signs pointing to the fact that the person so affected is not getting enough vitamin A in his diet.

Meat is one of the richest sources of the important B group of vitamins, especially thiamine, riboflavin, niacin, and vitamin B_{12} (see Table 13-7). Pork is much higher than beef or lamb in thiamine content.

TABLE 13-7

VITAMIN CONTENT OF FRESH PORK[1]

Muscle Cuts Medium Grade	Thiamin	Ribo-flavin	Niacin	B_6	Panto-thenic Acid	Biotin	Choline	B_{12}	Folic Acid
	(mg./ 100g)	(mg / 100g)	(mg / 100g)	(mg / 100g)	(mg / 100g)	(mg./ 100g)	(mg / 100g)	(mg / 100g)	(mg / 100g)
Ham	.74	.18	4.0	.33	.72	5.3	120	0.9	.009
Loin or loin chops	.80	.19	4.3	.50	2.0	5.5	77		.007
Picnic	.94	.18	4.0						
Spareribs	.92	.18	3.9						

[1]*A Summary of the Nutrient Content of Meat*, American Meat Institute Foundation Bul. No. 30, Sept. 1956, Table 10.

These B vitamins are now being used to reinforce certain foods and are indispensable in our daily diet. Thiamine is needed for growth, for the utilization of carbohydrates, and for the proper functioning of the heart, nerves, and digestive tract; a marked deficiency of thiamine causes beriberi. Riboflavin is essential for growth, health of the skin and mouth, and functioning of the eyes; it is popularly called the anti-old age vitamin because a diet rich in this essential seems to promote a longer life, a longer prime of life, and greater freedom from disease. Niacin is essential for the health of the skin and nerves and normal functioning of the digestive tract; it is the factor which prevents and cures the disease pellagra. Vitamin B_{12} stimulates the appetite, increases the rate of growth and the efficiency of food utilization, and is necessary for normal reproduction. Indeed, one of the reasons for the rapid decline in B-vitamin deficiencies in America may well be the increased amount of meat and other B vitamin-containing foods in the daily diet.

5. **Digestibility.**—Finally, in considering the nutritive qualities of meats, it should be noted that this food is highly digestible. About 97 percent of meat proteins and 96 percent of meat fats are digested. The statement often is heard that "pork is

hard to digest." This is not true. Being somewhat fatter than other meats, it may remain in the stomach a longer period, but pork, in common with all meats, is well utilized by the body.

We come to realize, therefore, the important part that pork is playing in the nutrition of the nation.

PORK PRICES AND SPREAD

During those periods when pork is high in price, especially the choicest cuts, there is a tendency on the part of the consumer to blame either or all of the following: (1) the farmer, (2) the packer, (3) the meat retailer, or (4) the government; and these four may blame each other. Vent to such feelings is sometimes manifested in political campaign propaganda, consumer boycotts, sensational news stories, and the chain-type telephone meat strike.

Also, some folks are prone to compare what the packer is paying for hogs on foot to what they are paying for a pound of pork over the counter. Then they scream, "Why 80-cent pork chops from 20-cent hogs?"

Is there any real justification for this often vicious criticism? Who or what is to blame for high meat prices and for the spread? If good public relations are to be maintained, it is imperative that each member of the meat team—the producer, the packer, and the meat retailer—be fully armed with documented facts and figures with which to answer such questions and to refute such criticisms. Also, the consumer should know the truth of the situation. The sections which follow are designed to ferret out the facts relative to pork prices and spread.

What Determines Pork Prices?

Pork prices are determined by the laws of supply and demand; that is, the price of meat is largely dependent upon what the consumers as a group are able and willing to pay for the available supply.

THE AVAILABLE SUPPLY OF PORK

Because pork is a perishable product, the supply of this food is very much dependent upon the number and weight of hogs available for slaughter at a given time. In turn, the

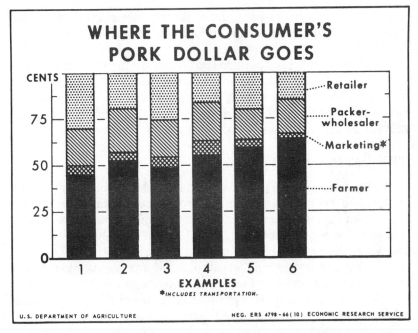

Fig. 13-15. Price spread for pork. Based on six examples which illustrate the actual steps and specific costs involved in marketing hogs from farm to retail. (From: *Price Spreads for Pork*, Misc. Pub. No. 1051, Fig. 9, p. 17, Economic Research Service, USDA, Jan. 1967)

number of market animals is largely governed by the relative profitability of the swine enterprise in comparison with other agricultural pursuits. That is to say, farmers—like other good businessmen—generally do those things that are most profitable to them. Thus, a short supply of market animals at any given time usually reflects the unfavorable and unprofitable production factors that existed some months earlier and which caused curtailment of breeding and feeding operations.

Historically, when short pork supplies exist, pork prices rise, and the market price on slaughter hogs usually advances, making hog production more profitable. But, unfortunately, swine breeding and feeding operations cannot be turned on and off like a spigot.

History also shows that if hog prices remain high and feed abundant, the producer will step up his breeding and feeding operations as fast as he can within the limitations imposed by nature, only to discover when market time arrives that too

many other producers have done likewise. Overproduction, disappointingly low prices, and curtailment in breeding and feeding operations are the result.

Nevertheless, the operations of livestock farmers do respond to market prices, producing so-called cycles. Thus, the intervals of high production, or cycles, in hogs—which are litter bearing, breed at an early age, have a short gestation period, and go to market at an early age—occur every 3 to 5 years.

THE DEMAND FOR PORK

The demand for pork is primarily determined by buying power and competition from other products. Stated in simple terms, demand is determined by the spending money available and the competitive bidding of millions of housewives who are the chief home purchasers of meats. On a nationwide basis, a high buying power and great demand for meats exist when most people are employed and wages are high.

It is also generally recognized that in boom periods—periods of high personal income—meat purchases are affected in three ways: (1) more total meat is desired; (2) there is a greater demand for the choicest cuts; and (3) because of the increased money available and shorter working hours, there is a desire for more leisure time, which in turn increases the demand for those meat cuts or products that require a minimum of time in preparation (such as pork chops and hams). In other words, during periods of high buying power, people not only want more meats, but they compete for the choicer and more easily prepared cuts of meats.

Because of the operation of the old law of supply and demand, when the choicer and more easily prepared cuts of pork are in increased demand, they advance proportionately more in price than the cheaper cuts. This results in a great spread in prices, with some pork cuts very much higher than others. Thus, while pork chops may be selling for four or five times the cost per pound of the live animal, less demanded cuts may be priced at less than half the cost of the more popular cuts. This is so because a market must be secured for all the cuts.

Thus, when the national income is exceedingly high, there is a demand for the choicest but limited cuts of pork from the very top but limited grades. This is certain to make for high prices, for the supply of such cuts is limited, but the demand is

great. Under these conditions, if prices did not move up to balance the supply with demand, there would be a marked shortage of the desired cuts at the retail counter.

Who Controls Pork Prices; Are Profits Excessive?

On the surface, this heading appears to pose a very controversial subject. Actually, much of it is due to misunderstanding; most folks know too little about the other fellow's business. The following sections are designed to ferret out the facts relative to pork prices and profits.

PORK PRICES AND PRODUCERS' PROFITS

It is preposterous to think that U.S. hog producers could control prices, for producers are well-known individualists and the competition between them is too great. However, some consumers feel that producers, as a group, make excess profits—that they are responsible for the high price of pork. They hear that sows farrow litters of 10 each, and that these pigs sell on the market at $40.00 per head 5 to 6 months later; so they decide that it is, indeed, a lucrative business.

Unfortunately, all too many pork consumers fail to realize that a gilt cannot be bred until she is about 8 months of age, that the pregnancy period requires another 114 days, and, finally, that the young are usually grown and finished 6 months before marketing. Thus, under the most favorable conditions, this process, which is under biological control and cannot be speeded up, requires about 18 months in which to produce a new generation of market hogs. Most of these critics also fail to realize that, for various reasons, only an average of 6 out of each 10 pigs farrowed reach market age and weight; that in addition to breeding stock and feed costs, there are shipping charges, interest on borrowed money, death losses, marketing charges, taxes, and numerous other costs, before the hog finally reaches the packer.

For the hogs, and all the expenses and services that go into their production, the producer gets from 44 to 63 cents of the consumer's pork dollar.[3] But these figures do not tell the whole

---

[3] *Price Spreads for Pork*, Misc. Pub. No. 1051, Economic Research Service. USDA, pp. 18 to 23, Jan. 1967. Also see Fig. 13-15 in this chapter.

story! They do not relate the bedeviling effect of well-meant, imposed or threatened legislation, the shivering hours spent in the farrowing quarters as numb fingers attempt to bring life into a newborn pig; they do not tell of disease problems or of the sweat of a long work week which begins at 40 hours.

Thus, it is perfectly clear that the farmer is not receiving excessive profits in pork production. With knowledge of these facts, and considering the longtime risks involved, it is doubtful if very many people will object to the occasional good years when the producer has a chance to recoup the losses he suffers during the lean years.

PORK PRICES AND MEAT PACKERS' PROFITS

Of course, meat packing companies, like other businesses, are owned and operated by people; and all people want to be paid for their work. Therefore, they are entitled to a fair and reasonable profit; otherwise, they would not stay in business. The only question is—do they control prices and are they making too lush profits? Here are the pertinent facts on which to base an answer to this question:

1. Packers do not and cannot control prices because there is too intensive competition between them; there are more than 4,000 meat packers in the United States.

2. From 1960 to 1967, meat packers' net earnings amounted to 0.84 cents per dollar of sales, or less than 1 cent per dollar of sales; which is not enough. By comparison, it is noteworthy that the net earnings per dollar of sales of 17 individual companies[4] in the United States averaged 9.3 cents in 1967.[5]

3. From 1965 to 1967, the net profit of packing companies per 100 pounds of live animal averaged 29 cents[6] and for 100 pounds of dressed meat, it averaged 46 cents.[7] Thus, on the average, for each 200-pound hog purchased, the packer netted about 58

---

[4] *Financial Facts About the Meat Packing Industry 1967*, published by the American Meat Institute, Chicago, Ill.

In 1967, each of 17 individual companies in the United States made more money than the entire meat packing industry. As a whole, the net earnings of these 17 companies amounted to $10,308.2 million, compared to the net earnings of $192 million made by all the meat packers; hence, the net income of these 17 companies was 54 times greater than the meat industry's earnings.

[5] *Ibid.*

[6] *Ibid.*

[7] *Ibid.*

cents in profit. Certainly this is a reasonable and legitimate earning. Of course, the volume of sales (the number of animals processed in a year), the efficiency of operations, and the utilization of by-products makes it possible for the industry to operate on these comparatively small margins.

Actually, the packers' profits are so small that, were they eliminated entirely, they would have practically no effect on the ultimate selling price of the retail cuts. The truth of the matter is that the meat packer is in the middle of an impossible situation; on the one hand, the nation's hog producers want high prices for all the animals that they can sell while, on the other, more than 190 million consumers desire to buy as much meat as they wish at low prices.

PORK PRICES AND MEAT RETAILERS' PROFITS

Finally, let us consider the meat retailer. Like the producer and the packer, he, too, is in business to make money; thus, he buys pork carcasses at as low a price as possible and he sells the retail cuts at as high a price as consumers will pay. But does he control meat prices, and is he making excessive profits? Here are the facts:

1. There are about 278,616 grocery stores in the United States, most of which handle meat, plus about 23,844 meat markets; or a total of about 300,000 retail meat outlets.[8]

2. On the average, year after year, the meat retailer nets less than 1.5 cents after taxes on each $1.00 of sales.[9]

3. There is much competition between the 300,000[10] U.S. retail outlets that sell meat. As a result, no meat retailer can keep his prices out of line for very long; otherwise, consumers will just quit patronizing his market.

4. There is an old axiom in the meat business which says, "You sell it or you smell it." This simply refers to the fact that, as a perishable product, it must be moved promptly into consumption channels and sold for whatever it will bring. If the retailer attempted to get a higher price than the market

---

[8]Data provided, in a personal communication to the author, by Dr. S. Kent Christensen, Vice President and Agricultural Counsel, National Association of Food Chains, Washington, D. C. Grocery store numbers from 1963 census, and meat markets from 1958 census.

[9] Same as Footnote 8.

[10] Same as Footnote 8.

afforded, the amount of the product demanded would diminish, the meat would not be sold, and it would soon spoil.

THE HOUSEWIFE CONTROLS PORK PRICES

From the previous discussion, it should be obvious that neither the producer, the packer, nor the meat retailer controls pork prices. Unknowingly, the person who really dictates the

Mrs. Homemaker casts her "vote" at the meat counter.

Fig. 13-16. The housewife controls pork prices. (Courtesy, Swift & Co.)

price of hogs on-foot, the price of dressed hogs, and the price of retail cuts is the little wife. She actually puts the price tag on the retail cuts. For purposes of illustrating her impact on pork and hog prices, let us assume the following vital statistics: That the producer sells the packer a U. S. No. 1 hog at 20¢ per pound, that the packer sells the retailer the on-the-hook carcass at 32¢ per pound, and that the retailer prices center cut pork chops at 80¢ per pound.

When the housewife walks along the counter, she, and she alone, determines what she will buy. If she feels that 80¢ a pound is too much to pay for the pork chops, she may buy a pork roast or pork sausage or perhaps move down the counter a few feet and buy some broilers or perhaps some fish. She does not

say anything to the retailer about his price of 80¢ being too high for the pork chops. There is no organized boycott on the part of the housewives, but it does not take the retailer long to discover that his price on pork chops is out of line.

If pork chops will not sell at 80¢, the retailer will lower the price to 75 or to 70¢ a pound. He probably will try to raise the prices on some other pork cuts to take care of the loss on pork chops. If he is unable to make up the deficit, there is only one thing to do and that is to tell the packer that he cannot afford to pay 32¢ a pound for pork carcasses. He may tell the packer that he will pay 30¢ a pound, and in all probability the packer will refuse this offer; so the retailer will buy three pork carcasses instead of six; and he may double his order for beef and poultry. Then, in two or three days, as pork carcasses begin to back up in his coolers, the packer will probably call the retailer and make a deal with him. They may compromise on 31¢ a pound instead of 30¢ or 32¢, and the retailer starts buying his normal quantity of pork carcasses.

If the packer cannot get 32¢ a pound for pork carcasses, it does not take him very long to tell his hog buyers that he cannot afford to pay 20¢ a pound for live hogs and that they will have to cut the price to 19¢. If the run is heavy, the packer may be able to buy all the hogs he needs at 19¢. But if the run is light, he may be forced to pay 20¢, realizing that he will lose less money by paying 20¢ for hogs than he will lose by not having enough work to keep his employees busy. The packer faces a dilemma; he must keep enough livestock coming into the plant to keep it in operation, but he must also buy livestock at low enough prices so that the dressed meat can be sold at a profit.

From this, it is apparent that, as in the case of all other commodities on a free market, meat prices are determined by the laws of supply and demand; by what the consumers as a group are able and willing to pay for the available supply. In plain simple terms, this means that what you and your neighbor and all America eat tonight will determine tomorrow's pork prices.

What Determines the Spread Between On-foot Hog Prices and Retail Pork Prices?

When a hog producer receives a check for $40.00 for a

200-pound hog—20¢ a pound—and on the way home stops at a retail meat market and buys pork chops at 80¢ per pound, he is prone to think that he is on the wrong side of the counter; that he ought to be a meat packer or meat retailer.

Why is there so much spread between the price of a hog on-foot and the price of a pound of pork chops? This is a straightforward question which deserves a straightforward answer. Here are the facts.

A HOG IS NOT ALL PORK CHOPS

Hogs are not all pork, and pork is not all chops. It is important, therefore, that those who produce and slaughter animals and those who purchase wholesale and/or retail cuts know the approximate (1) percentage yield of chilled carcass in relation to the weight of the animal on foot, and (2) yield of different retail cuts. For example, the average hog weighing 210 pounds on foot will only yield 135 pounds of retail cuts (the balance consists of internal organs, etc.). Thus, only about 60 percent of a live hog can be sold as retail cuts of pork.

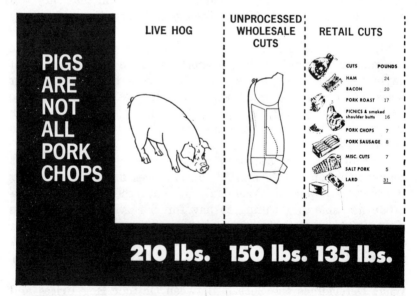

Fig. 13-17. Pigs are not all pork chops! This shows the approximate (1) percentage yield of chilled carcass in relation to the weight of the animal on-foot, and (2) yield of different retail cuts. (Courtesy, American Meat Institute)

In other words, the price of pork at retail would have to be nearly double the live cost even if there were no processing and marketing charges at all. Secondly, the higher priced cuts make up only a small part of the carcass. Thus, this 135 pounds will cut out only about 7 pounds of center cut pork chops. The other cuts retail at lower prices than do these choice cuts; also, there are bones, fat, and cutting losses which must be considered. To make bad matters worse, if the moneyed buyer insists on buying only the top grade of pork, namely U. S. No. 1, it must be remembered that only 15 to 30 percent of slaughter barrows and gilts produce carcasses of this top grade. To be sure, the lower grades are equally wholesome, but they are simply graded down because the carcass is somewhat deficient in conformation or quality.

Table 13-8 shows the wide variation in the retail price of specified pork cuts.

TABLE 13-8

RETAIL PRICE PER POUND OF SPECIFIED
PORK CUTS, U.S. AVERAGE, AUGUST 1966[1]

Pork Cut	Price per Pound
	(dollars)
Fresh:	
Center cut pork chops	1.09
Loin-end roast	.73
Rib-end roast	.67
Spareribs	.80
Neckbones	.31
Butts	.69
Pork sausage, bulk	.59
Cured:	
Bacon, sliced	.95
Bacon, squares	.59
Hams, whole	.71
Ham, shank end	.61
Ham, butt end	.69
Ham, center slices	1.25
Picnics	.53

[1]*Price Spreads for Pork*, Economic Research Service, USDA, 1967, Misc. Pub. No. 1051, Table 1, p. 3.

INCREASED SERVICES AND ATTRACTIVENESS

Since about 60 percent of the nation's working women are

married and the other 40 percent are spending more time at the club, it is understandable why they want more convenience. They desire that food purchases be largely prepared for immediate cooking, for their kitchen time is limited. Thus, when the housewife buys meat, she also buys many unseen services such as trimming, boning, packaging, and freezing. All of these services have increased the farm-to-consumer spread.

The trend toward "convenience foods" is increasing fast.

Fig. 13-18. Convenience foods make for higher prices. (Photo courtesy, Swift & Co.)

MARKETING AND PROCESSING CHARGES AND PROFITS

Everyone and everything connected with the meat industry influences the spread between on-foot and retail prices. Investment capital is not free; it must yield returns comparable with other industries which compete for the use of capital. In addition, there are costs for labor, rent, supplies, transportation, and equipment. Over and above these costs, there should be a reasonable and fair profit.

What about decreasing margins by reducing the profits of the marketing agencies? The two major organizations involved are the meat packing industry and the retail stores. As previously stated, the average net profit of each—the meat packer and the meat retailer—amounting to less than 1 and 2 percent, respectively, on each $1.00 of sales—is very small. Were profits from both businesses eliminated entirely—and if

producers received all of this additional amount—hog prices would be raised about ½ cent a pound.

Producers and consumers also need to recognize that when the demand or the supply changes for pork, there is of necessity much more change in the price of live hogs than there is in the price of pork over the counter. This is so because of the tendency for marketing margins to be more fixed—that is, the costs of labor, rent, supplies, transportation, and equipment do not fluctuate rapidly.

Other Factors Affecting Pork Prices and Spread

This includes those forces other than supply and demand, *per se,* which affect pork prices and help to explain why pork chops may cost four times the price of hogs on-foot.

CONSUMERS WITH HIGH INCOMES DEMAND CHOICE CUTS AND TOP GRADES

In periods of prosperity—when incomes are rising—consumers place a premium on the preferred kind, cut, and quality of meat, rather than any marked increase in total meat consumption. Also, people on higher incomes eat more beef, veal, and lamb and less pork (Fig. 13-19), and they eat more of the expensive cuts of pork, such as chops and hams, and fewer roasts and less sausage.

Also, due to the increased money available and shorter working hours, there is a desire for more leisure time, which, in turn, increases the demand for those meat cuts or products which require the minimum time in preparation. In many respects, these two factors operate together; in other words, with high buying power, people hunt the choicer and more easily prepared cuts of meat—chops and ham.

All this suggests that producers of meat animals and processors and distributors have much to gain in periods of good times by taking steps to provide the desired kind and quality of products; by breeding for increased carcass quality, by feeding hogs to enhance grade, by selling at lighter weights, and by processing and preparing a higher quality and more attractive product.

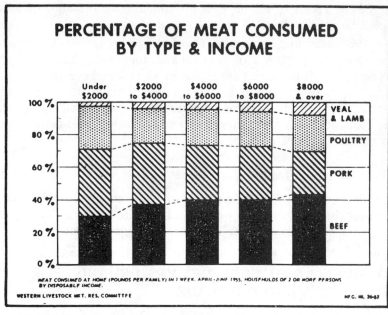

Fig. 13-19. This shows that folks in the higher income brackets prefer beef to pork.

NATURE MAKES FEW CHOICE CUTS AND TOP GRADES

But the novice may wonder why these choice cuts are so scarce; even though people are able and willing to pay a premium for them. The answer is simple; nature does not make many choice cuts or top grades, regardless of price. Hogs are born with only two hams; and only two loins (a right and left one) can be obtained from each carcass upon slaughter. The balance of the cuts are equally wholesome and nutritious, but they are better adapted for use as roasts, etc. To make the situation even worse, not all hogs are of a quality suitable for the production of chops—for example, the meat from most stags is not sold over the block. To be sure, the lower grades are equally wholesome and nutritious; they are simply graded down because the carcass is somewhat less desirable in conformation, finish, and quality.

Thus, when the national income is exceedingly high, there is a demand for the choicest but limited cuts from the very top but limited grades of meats. This is bound to make for

extremely high prices for such grades—for the supply is limited, but the demand is great.

CONSUMER TREND TO LESS PORK AND MORE BEEF

Another underlying trend which depresses the price of pork is the shift in consumer preference from pork to beef. Expenditures for pork dropped from around $3\frac{1}{4}$ percent of the consumer income in the early 1930's to about 2 percent in 1957; whereas, during this same period, consumer expenditures for beef increased from $2\frac{1}{3}$ percent to $2\frac{2}{3}$ percent.[11]

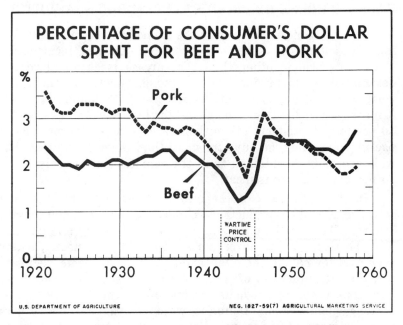

Fig. 13-20. About 1950, U.S. consumer preference shifted from pork to beef.

Competition with Other Food Products and Services

Meat must compete with other products for the consumer's dollar. Thus, in addition to preference, relative price is an important factor.

[11]Engleman, Gerald and R. L. Gaarder, *Marketing Meat-Type Hogs*, Agricultural Marketing Service, USDA, Marketing Research Report No. 227.

Also, meat must compete with certain non-food items, for there are people who would go hungry in order to be able to spend their money for other purposes. On the average, consumers spend 5 to 6 percent of their disposable income, or about 25 percent of their food budget, for meat.

Finally, sometimes the consumer is prone to blame his budget troubles on food, and meat in particular, simply because he forgets that he is spending part of his income on things which he did not have before—including such things as TV sets, automatic dryers, and two automobiles.

PACKING HOUSE BY-PRODUCTS FROM HOG SLAUGHTER

The meat or flesh of hogs is the primary object of slaughtering. The numerous other products are obtained incidentally. Thus, all products other than the carcass meat and lard are designated as by-products, even though many of them are wholesome and highly nutritious articles of the human diet. Yet it must be realized that upon slaughter hogs yield an average of 30 percent of products other than carcass meat. When a meat packer buys a hog, he buys far more than the cuts of meat that will eventually be obtained from the carcass; that is, only about 70 percent of a hog is meat.

In the early days of the meat packing industry, the only salvaged animal by-products were hides, wool, tallow, and tongue. The remainder of the offal was usually carted away and dumped into the river or burned or buried. In some instances, packers even paid for having the offal taken away. In due time, factories for the manufacture of glue, fertilizer, soap, buttons, and numerous other by-products sprang up in the vicinity of the packing plants. Some factories were company-owned; others were independent industries. Soon much of the former waste material was being converted into materials of value.

Naturally, the relative value of carcass meat and by-products varies both according to the class of livestock and from year to year. For the three-year period, 1963-65, hog by-products averaged 12.8 percent of the on-foot slaughter price.[12] The longtime trend for by-product values has been downward relative to the value of the live animal, due largely to technolog-

---

[12]*Agricultural Markets in Change*, USDA Report No. 95, July 1966.

ical progress in competitive products derived from non-animal sources.

The complete utilization of by-products is one of the chief reasons why large packers are able to compete so successfully with local butchers. Were it not for this conversion of waste material into salable form, the price of meat would be higher than under existing conditions.

It is not intended that this book should describe all of the by-products obtained from hog slaughter. Rather, only a few of the more important ones will be listed and briefly discussed (see Fig. 13-21).

1. **Skins.**—Pig skins from domestic sources are virtually nonexistent because, for the most part, they are sold along with the pork cuts. The main source of so-called pigskin leather is the peccary, a pig-like mammal of Central America, which provides leather for wallets, sport shoes, saddles, gloves, and razor strops. However, the pig skins that are available from meat packing are used for shoe manufacture, razor strops, belts, and other leather goods.

2. **The fats.**—The inedible fats (not including lard) are used in the manufacture of soaps, animal feeds, lubricants, leather dressing, candles, fertilizer, shaving cream, salves, and chemicals from fats.

3. **Variety meats.**—The edible by-products include the liver, brains, kidneys, stomach, ears, pork skins, snout, gullet, and weasand meat. All these are sold over the counter as variety meats or fancy meats. They represent about 3½ percent of the live weight of a hog; the inedible by-products represent about 2½ percent of the live weight of a hog.

Some edible hog by-products which are known as meat and not meat by-products, but which come under the "variety meats" classification, are head and cheek meat, tongue, heart, tail, and feet.

4. **Hair.**—Hair from hogs is used in tooth brushes; mattresses; upholstery for furniture, automobiles, and passenger planes; insulation boards for refrigeration; air filters; baseball mitts; parachute seat pads; etc.

5. **Hoofs.**—At one time considered a nuisance, the hoofs are now converted into fertilizer and plaster retarder.

6. **Blood.**—The blood is used in the refining of sugar; and printing calico; in making blood sausage and stock feeds; in making buttons and shoe polish; and in medicine.

7. **Meat scraps and muscle tissue.**—After the grease is removed from meat scraps and muscle tissue, they are made into meat-meal or tankage.

8. **Bones.**—The bones and cartilage are converted into stock feed, fertilizer, glue, and bone oil.

9. **Intestines and bladders.**—Intestines and bladders are used as sausage, lard, cheese, snuff, and putty containers.

10. **Glands.**—Various glands of the body are used in the manufacture of numerous pharmaceutical preparations. People afflicted with diabetes, pernicious anemia, arthritis, and many other diseases are treated by their doctors with insulin, liver extract, and many other medicines made in whole or in part from the glands of hogs.

Proper preparation of glands requires quick chilling and skillful handling. Moreover, a very large number of glands must be collected in order to obtain any appreciable amount of most of these pharmaceutical products. For example, about 1,600 pounds of hog pituitaries are required to make 1 pound of ACTH; and it takes pancreas glands from 7,500 hogs (or 1,500 cattle) to produce one precious ounce of insulin. But, fortunately, only minute amounts of insulin are required—the insulin from two hogs per day, or from 750 hogs per year, will suffice for each diabetic.

It is estimated that the glands removed from hogs have a value of 5½ to 7 cents per animal; the exact amount, of course, varies because of fluctuations in the value of specific glands and organs.

11. **Collagen.**—The collagen of the connective tissues—sinews, lips, head, knuckles, feet, and bones—is made into glue and gelatin. The most important uses for glues are in the woodworking industry; as coated abrasives, in the match industry; and as a binder for ignition chemicals. Gelatin is used in canning hams and other large cuts, and in baking, ice cream making, capsules for medicine, coating for pills, photography, culture media for bacteria, etc.

12. **Contents of the stomach.**—Contents of the stomach are used in making fertilizer.

Fig. 13-21. It is not within the scope of this book to picture and describe all of the products which are manufactured from by-products obtained from slaughter. Instead, this figure is presented in order to show some of the more important items for which by-products are used; items which contribute to the convenience, enjoyment, and health of people in all walks of life. (Courtesy, American Meat Institute)

1. Bone for bone china.
2. Horn and bone handles for carving sets.
3. Hides and skins for leather goods.
4. Rennet for cheese making.
5. Gelatin for marshmallows, photographic film, printers' rollers.
6. Stearin for making chewing gum and candies.
7. Glycerin for explosives used in mining and blasting.
8. Lanolin for cosmetics.
9. Chemicals for tires that run cooler.
10. Binders for asphalt paving.
11. Medicines such as various hormones and epinephrine, ACTH, cortisone; and surgical sutures.
12. Drumheads and violin strings.
13. Animal fats for soap.
14. Wool for clothing.
15. Camel's hair (actually from cattle ears) for artists' brushes.
16. Cutting oils and other special industrial lubricants.
17. Bone charcoal for high-grade steel, such as ball bearings.
18. Special glues for marine plywoods, paper, matches, window shades.
19. Curled hair for upholstery. Leather for fine furniture.
20. High-protein livestock feeds.

Thus, in a modern packing plant, there is no waste; literally speaking, "everything but the squeal" is saved. These by-products benefit the human race in many ways. Moreover, their utilization makes it possible to slaughter and process pork at a lower cost.

But scientists are continually striving to find new and better uses for packing house by-products in an effort to increase their value.

PORK PROMOTION

Effective pork promotion—which should be conceived in a broad sense and embrace research, educational, and sales approaches—necessitates full knowledge of the nutritive qualities of the product. To this end, we need to recognize that (1) pork contains 15 to 20 percent high quality protein, on a fresh basis; (2) pork is a rich source of energy, the energy value being dependent largely upon the amount of fat it contains; (3) pork is a rich source of several minerals, but it is especially good as a source of phosphorus and iron; (4) pork is one of the richest sources of the important B group of vitamins, especially thiamine, riboflavin, niacin, and vitamin B_{12}; and (5) pork is highly digestible, about 97 percent of meat proteins and 96 percent of meat fats are digested. Thus, pork is one of the best foods with which to alleviate human malnutrition; a most important consideration when it is realized that (1) Selective Service records show that one out of eight draftees of World War II was turned down because of ailments directly or indirectly traceable to malnutrition, and (2) it is estimated that 35 to 40 percent of the U. S. population is now failing to receive an adequate diet.

Also, it is noteworthy that the per capita consumption of meat in four countries exceeds that of the United States; by rank, these are: New Zealand, 229 lbs.; Uruguay, 224 lbs.; Argentina, 207 lbs.; and Australia, 198 lbs.[13]

Thus, based on (1) its nutritive qualities, and (2) the per capita consumption in those four countries exceeding us, it would appear that there is a place and a need for increased pork promotion; thereby increasing pork consumption and price.

There is considerable controversy as to how pork promotion funds should be raised, whether by voluntary deductions (check offs) or otherwise. There can be no doubt, however, that all segments of the meat industry would benefit by working together in a unified approach.

---

[13] From Table 13-2 of this chapter.

QUESTIONS FOR STUDY AND DISCUSSION

1. Why should hog producers have a reasonable working knowledge of the end product, pork?

2. What are the primary factors determining the per capita consumption of pork in the various countries?

3. Should the U. S. import pork? Should we have hog and pork quotas and tariffs?

4. Should the U. S. export pork?

5. Consumer studies indicate the following transition in preferences relative to pork:
   a. Preference for more red meat and less fat.
   b. Preference for more highly processed meat; that is, meat that is boned-out, trimmed, etc., prior to purchase.
   c. Preference for more frozen meat.
   Discuss the impact of each of these trends from the standpoint of the producer, the processor, and the consumer.

6. What qualities do you desire in pork? Are these qualities reflected adequately in the top federal grades of pork?

7. Do you feel that we should have more federal grading of pork? Justify your answer.

8. How and why does the disposition of the pork carcass differ from that of beef and lamb?

9. Discuss the leading methods of curing pork on the farm.

10. Discuss the relationship of choice of retail pork cuts and method of cookery.

11. What facts relative to the nutritive qualities of pork are important in effective pork promotion?

12. What determines pork prices?

13. Choose and debate either the affirmative or negative to each of the following questions:
    a. Pork prices are controlled by (1) the producers, (2) the packers, or (3) the retailers.
    b. Excessive profits are made by (1) the producers, (2) the packers, or (3) the retailers.

14. Discuss the factors that determine the spread between on-foot hog prices and retail pork prices.

15. What factors contributed to pork losing its lead to beef in U. S. per capita consumption?

16. How can small local slaughterers without the benefit of modern by-product processing facilities compete with large packers?

SELECTED REFERENCES

Title of Publication	Author(s)	Publisher
Adventures in Diet	Vilhjalmur Stefansson	Reprinted from *Harper's* Magazine by the Institute of American Meat Packers (now American Meat Institute) 59 East Van Buren St., Chicago, Ill.
Animal Science	M. E. Ensminger	The Interstate Printers & Publishers, Inc., Danville, Ill. 1969.
By-Products in the Packing Industry	R. A. Clemen	University of Chicago Press, Chicago, Ill., 1927.
Financial Facts About the Meat Packing Industry		American Meat Institute, 59 East Van Buren St., Chicago, Ill.
Food from Farm to Consumer	National Commission on Food Marketing	Supt. of Documents, U.S. Govt. Printing Office, Wash., D. C., June 1966.
Inspection Stamp as a Guide to Wholesome Meat, The	Ag. Information Bul. 92	U. S. Department of Agriculture, Washington, D. C.
Marketing of Livestock and Meat, The	S. H. Fowler	The Interstate Printers & Publishers, Inc., Danville, Ill., 1961.
Meat for the Table	Sleeter Bull	McGraw-Hill Book Co., New York, N. Y., 1951.
Meat Inspection, Regulations Governing the, of the United States		U. S. Department of Agriculture, Washington, D. C.
Meat Reference Book		American Meat Institute, 59 East Van Buren St., Chicago, Ill.
Meat We Eat, The	P. T. Ziegler	The Interstate Printers & Publishers, Inc., Danville, Ill., 1966.
Nutritional Observatory	B. H. Schweigert	Vol. 14, No. 2, April 1953, p. 37.
Official United States Standards for Grades of Pork Carcasses		U. S. Department of Agriculture, Washington, D. C.
Organization and Competition in the Livestock and Meat Industry, Tech. Study No. 1	National Commission on Food Marketing	Supt. of Documents, U. S. Govt. Printing Office, Washington, D. C., June 1966.

Title of Publication	Author(s)	Publisher
Pork Marketing Margins and Costs		Agricultural Marketing Service, Misc. Pub. No. 711, U. S. Department of Agriculture, April 1956.
Price Spreads for Pork, Misc. Pub. No. 1051	J. Bruce Bullock Richard Eisenberg Duane Hacklander	Economic Research Service, U.S. Department of Agriculture, 1967.
Spread Between Prices of Livestock and Meat, The	J. C. Bottum	Agricultural Research Department, Swift & Co., Chicago, Ill.
Stockman's Handbook, The	M. E. Ensminger	The Interstate Printers & Publishers, Inc., Danville, Ill., 1970.
Ten Lessons on Meat for Use in Schools	Department of Home Economics	National Live Stock and Meat Board, 407 South Dearborn St., Chicago, Ill.

Also, literature on meats may be secured by writing to meat packers and processors and trade organizations; in particular, the following two trade organizations:

American Meat Institute
59 East Van Buren Street
Chicago, Ill.

National Live Stock and Meat Board
407 South Dearborn Street
Chicago, Ill.

CHAPTER XIV

SWINE MANAGEMENT

Contents   Page

Although it is not possible to arrive at any over-all, certain formula for success, in general those swine producers who have made money have paid close attention to the details of management. In a general sort of way, the principles of good management are much the same. Without attempting to cover all management practices, some facts relative to, and methods of accomplishing, certain swine management practices follow.

SWINE MANAGEMENT SYSTEMS AND PRACTICES

Swine management systems and practices vary widely between areas and individual swine producers; they are in-

fluenced by size of operations; available land and its value for alternate uses; markets; available capital, labor and feed; and the individual whims of producers.

Pasture Versus Confinement Hog Production

It has long been recognized that hogs are better adapted to confinement rearing than other classes of four-footed farm animals. In fact, in many countries of the world this is the accepted practice.

Recently,[1] U.S. swine producers, especially the larger commercial operators, have shown a pronounced trend away from pasture rearing of swine, toward confinement production. By 1967, it was reported that 35 percent, or slightly more than a third, of Illinois hog producers were using confinement feeding—all or in part, with 13 percent of this group using totally enclosed, insulated buildings as contrasted to the major bulk depending on sheds and outside concrete lots.[2] This shift to confinement has gone hand in hand with (1) greater knowledge of nutrition, (2) improved disease prevention and parasite control, (3) improvements in buildings and equipment, and (4) the growth of large-scale, highly specialized operations. Contrary to the opinion held by some, this does not mean that the use of pastures for hog production is antiquated. Rather, there now exists two alternatives for the management of swine, instead of just one; and the able manager will choose wisely between them.

Although more cost studies are needed, it appears that, on a per hog basis, the total cost of confinement and pasture production does not differ greatly. Despite this fact, a number of motivating forces have caused, and will continue to cause, more and more confinement production. Among the **factors favorable** to confinement production are:

1. It permits substituting capital for labor, primarily because it facilitates automatic feeding and watering.

2. It facilitates manure handling.

3. It frees land for more remunerative uses—most Corn Belt

---

[1] The confinement system started evolving about 1955. By 1960, it was estimated that 3 to 5 percent of the market hogs of the country were being produced in confinement.

[2] From *Feedstuffs*, March 1967, and *National Hog Farmer*, April 1967. Survey made by the Illinois Crop Reporting Service.

producers can make more money from growing corn and soy-beans than from hog pasture.

4. It allows hog producers to intensify their operations without enlarging their farms.

5. It results in hogs reaching market weight at an earlier age, thereby decreasing labor, risk, and production expense.

6. It requires less time and labor in vaccinating, castrating, worming, and loading for the market.

7. It makes for less distance to transport feed.

8. It facilitates sorting and lotting groups for size and uniformity.

9. It makes for environmental control.

10. It makes it possible to employ superior management, because of the sheer size of such operations.

11. It enhances the application of the latest in research, and the best in breeding, feeding, management, marketing, and business.

12. It mitigates against the hogs being accorded the neglect of a minor enterprise, simply because it's big business, and usually treated as such.

13. It generally makes for more favorable feed prices, due to purchases of quantity lots.

On the other hand, the following **factors favor conventional, pasture production,** all or in part, over confinement production:

1. Lower building and equipment costs.

2. Lower feed costs, because hogs on pasture (a) require less feed per pound of gain, and (b) are usually provided lower cost feeds, due to requiring less exacting and expensive protein, vitamin, and mineral.

3. The use of pasture often makes for the most desirable land use, crop rotation, and soil conservation.

4. Pasture swine operations are more flexible than confinement programs—an important consideration where renters are involved.

5. Pastures are especially valuable for the breeding herd—providing a combination of needed exercise, forage, and nutrients.

6. There are usually fewer disease problems where animals are spread out.

7. Fewer cases of tail biting, primarily caused by the stress and boredom of confinement, occur among hogs on pasture.

8. It does not require as high levels of skill and management as are necessary to make confinement production work.

Also, it is recognized that the monetary value of pastures varies rather widely; being affected by (1) the quality and quantity of the forage, (2) length of pasture season, (3) relative price of protein supplements, and (4) class and age of hogs.

In summary, therefore, confinement production fits where there is (1) adequate capital but limited labor, (2) superior managerial skill, (3) a long-term swine enterprise, without need for flexibility in buildings, and (4) maximum use of buildings and equipment, over and over again—conditions which usually go hand in hand with larger operations. In Illinois, for example, it was found that 63 percent of the producers raising over 500 hogs per year were using some confinement as compared with 25 percent of the group producing less than 100 hogs per year.[3]

The hog producer had best stick to a pasture system if (1) labor is more plentiful than capital, (2) there is rolling land, of which the highest and best use is for pasture, (3) conventional buildings are already available, and (4) the future of the hog business on the particular farm is uncertain.

It would appear, therefore, that confinement systems will not put good pasture systems out of business, but that they will increase in number and become more competitive for the bottom two-thirds of pasture systems.

Without doubt, many swine producers can advantageously combine pasture and confinement production—using pastures for the breeding herd and confinement production for the growing-finishing pigs. Also, it is recognized that well managed farm herds of up to 60 sows will be competitive for a long time to come, and that large, highly specialized swine enterprises will not drive all small producers out of business, although it is expected that they will become increasingly competitive.

Gilts Versus Older Sows

Controlled experiments and practical observations, in which gilts have been compared with older (tried) sows, bear out the following facts: (1) gilts have fewer pigs in their litters than do older sows, and (2) the pigs from gilts average slightly smaller in weight at birth and also tend to make somewhat slower gains.

---

[3] *Ibid.*

Despite these disadvantages, gilts have certain advantages, especially for the commercial pork producer. Their chief superiority lies in the fact that they continue to grow and increase in value while in reproduction. Although overweight young sows bring less on the market than prime barrows, from this standpoint alone they generally return a handsome profit when the price of pork is sufficiently favorable. Many practical commercial producers, who probably are less close to the herd at farrowing time than purebred breeders, are of the opinion that the smaller gilts crush fewer pigs than do older and heavier sows.

In no case is it recommended that the purebred breeder rely only on gilts. Tried sows that are regular producers of large litters with a heavy weaning weight and that are good mothers and producers of progeny of the right type should be retained in the herd as long as they are fertile.

Two-litter System Versus One-litter System

Whether to have each sow farrow two litters or one litter per year is a problem that each individual swine producer must decide. Where climatic conditions, facilities, and feeds are favorable to the two-litter system, it has the following distinct **advantages**:

1. Maximum use is made of the capital invested in facilities and equipment.

2. More certain and rapid improvement can be effected in the breeding herd through maintaining outstanding tried sows throughout their useful lives. The two-litter system is conducive to retaining such sows.

3. There is a better distribution of labor.

4. Pigs are marketed at two different times of the year, thereby distributing risks.

5. There is better distribution of farm income.

On the other hand, in the northern latitudes where suitable facilities and feeds may not always be available, the following **disadvantages** often apply to the two-litter system:

1. It is necessary that the spring-farrowed litter arrive reasonably early, often during inclement weather. Young pig losses, under such conditions, are higher than is usually encountered in a one-litter system.

2. Except in the South where nearly year-round pastures

are available, fall-farrowed pigs require more concentrates and high-priced protein supplement than pigs born earlier in the year and run on pastures. Because of inadequate nutrition, most fall pigs also are less thrifty and make slower gains than pigs born in the spring or early summer, although this need not be so with our present knowledge of nutrition.

Because of the high cost in maintaining tried sows for a whole year to raise one litter of pigs, the one-litter system is usually based chiefly or entirely on the use of gilts that are finished and marketed soon after weaning their litters.

The **advantages** of the one-litter system are:

1. There are fewer management problems; it is easier to keep on schedule.
2. Less total capital is tied up in hog buildings and equipment.
3. Less grain storage is required.
4. The weather is usually more favorable at farrowing time.
5. Less labor and hard work are required.

The **disadvantages** of the one-litter system are:

1. Buildings and equipment are not used to the maximum.
2. It limits the rapidity of improvement that can be made in the breeding herd; sows are usually sold after one litter only, or if retained there is only one litter per year.
3. The labor requirements are not distributed throughout the year.
4. Farm income is not distributed throughout the year.

Multiple Farrowing

Multiple farrowing refers to that type of program in which there is a scheduling of breeding so that the litters arrive in a greater number of farrowing periods throughout the year than is the case in the conventional one- and two-litter systems.

There is nothing mysterious or complicated about multiple farrowing. It does, however, entail some planning and close attention to management details. In practice, it generally means that the sow herd is split into either two or three groups, with each group farrowing twice each year. If two groups of sows are used, pigs are farrowed every three months. If three groups

are used, pigs can be farrowed every other month. Should a sow fail to conceive, she can be set back to another group.

As shown in Fig. 12-10 of Chapter XII, on the average, the highest price paid for slaughter barrows and gilts occurs in June through August when the receipts are low, and the lowest price occurs during the months of October to March. Increased multiple farrowing will help alleviate these rather sharp fluctuations in hog receipts and prices and prove beneficial both to producers and packers.

Among the **factors favorable** to multiple farrowing are:

1. It makes for a more stable hog market, with fewer high and low market receipts and price fluctuations.

2. It distributes the work load for the swine producer.

3. It makes for better use of existing buildings and equipment; for example, the farrowing house can accommodate more litters because of the longer farrowing season.

4. It provides a more sustained flow of hogs to market, which, from the standpoint of the packer, is desirable because— (1) it makes for more complete use of labor and plant capacity, and (2) it enables the processor more nearly to meet the demands of the retailer and consumer. Also, the producer's income is distributed throughout the year.

5. It provides retailers with a steady supply of pork for their trade.

6. It avoids sharp price rises, which the consumer dislikes.

Among the **factors unfavorable** to multiple farrowing are:

1. The swine enterprise is more confining for a longer period of time, for the reason that competent help must be available over a more prolonged farrowing season.

2. The possibility of a disease break may be increased because of the possible build-up of pathogenic organisms. That is, with multiple farrowing, it is not possible to clean out and air out for a long period of time.

3. Farrowing in seasons of extreme cold or heat increases building and equipment costs.

4. It requires more management know-how.

No one expects the seasonal pattern of hog production to be completely eliminated, but, because of the several recognized advantages of multiple farrowing to both the processor and the

producer, it is likely that it will increase sufficiently to make for a lessening of some of the market gluts of the past.

Weaning

Pigs are usually weaned when they are five to eight weeks of age. If creep feeding has been practiced, weaning will result in very little disturbance or setback. The separation should be complete and final, preferably with no opportunity for the pigs to hear or see their dam again. In no case should the sow be returned to the pigs once the separation has been made. Such practice will only prolong the weaning process and give rise to digestive disorders in the pigs.

The feed of the sow should be decreased a few days prior to the separation, and should be more bulky for a few days after the removal of the pigs, and until the udder has dried up.

EARLY WEANING

At the present time, there is much interest in weaning pigs at early ages; under six weeks. The practice has many advantages; and, no doubt, it will increase. For successful early weaning, superior nutrition and management are essential; and the earlier the weaning age the more exacting these requirements.

Among the **advantages** of early weaning are:

1. **It produces heavier and more uniform pigs, with fewer runts.**—If a well-balanced, highly palatable prestarter or starter ration is fed, early weaned pigs will get more nutrients than if left with the sow until 8 weeks of age; this is so because the milk production of the sow usually declines after the fourth week. To achieve these results, however, it is very necessary that the ration of early-weaned pigs be well fortified with protein, minerals, vitamins, and antibiotics.

2. **It saves more pigs per litter.**—Early weaning lessens the number of pigs laid on or crippled by the sow, and lessens runt losses. Also, early weaning must be resorted to under special conditions—such as raising orphan pigs.

3. **It provides for optimum nutrition.**—With our present knowledge of nutrition, it is possible to improve upon the sow's milk (except for colostrum). Thus, with a palatable, highly

fortified ration, optimum nutrition for maximum growth and development is assured.

4. It saves in feed.—A heavy milking sow needs 6 to 10 pounds more feed when nursing a litter. Also, pigs under 8 weeks of age will make 1 pound of gain from each $1\frac{3}{4}$ to 2 pounds of feed.

The feed efficiency per pound of gain is definitely in favor of early weaning. The Purdue station reported[4] that pigs weaned at 5 weeks of age were 9 percent more efficient in feed utilization than pigs weaned at 8 weeks of age. The Illinois station found[5] that pigs weaned at 30, 20, and 10 days, respectively, when compared to pigs weaned at 42 days of age, were 32, 45, and 64 percent more efficient in their feed utilization. The Ralston Purina Company found[6] that pigs weaned at 6 weeks of age were 16 percent more efficient than those weaned at 9 weeks of age.

5. It may permit rebreeding or selling sows sooner after farrowing.—As is generally known, many sows will come in heat and accept the boar 3 to 5 days after farrowing, regardless of the weaning date. However, sows so bred will not conceive.

Very early weaning (at less than a week of age) will result in sows rebreeding at 30 to 40 days after farrowing; thus making for a maximum average of 2.4 litters per year—and not 3 litters as sometimes has been claimed.

6. It saves weight loss in the sow.—Where sows are to be marketed following farrowing—such as is always done in the one-litter system—early weaning prevents sows from getting suckled down.

7. It lessens disease transmittance from sow to baby pigs.—Where certain diseases or parasites that are transmitted from dam to offspring are encountered, this may be an important consideration.

8. It saves space.—With the sows removed, more pigs can be housed and cared for properly in less space.

------

[4] Conrad, J. H., and W. M. Beeson, "A Comparison of Weaning Pigs at Five and Eight Weeks of Age Using Different Creep Feeds," Purdue Mimeo. A. H. 153, 1955.
[5] Jensen, A. H. *et al.* "Effect of Weaning Age on Performance of Pigs to Six Weeks of Age," Illinois Swine Growers Day Report, As-420, 1955.
[6] "Early Weaning of Pigs," from *Nutrition News Bulletin*, Vol. 12, No. 1, Jan. 1956, published by the Ralston Purina Company.

Among the **disadvantages** of early weaning are:

1. **It necessitates superior management and know-how.**—The presence of the sow can compensate, in part at least, for deficiencies in management practices, inadequate rations, and failure to feed and water regularly. With early weaning, these factors cannot be neglected.

2. **It makes for higher feed costs.**—Even though early-weaned pigs utilize feed more efficiently—require less feed per pound of gain—because the required rations are more expensive (due to being highly fortified with protein, minerals, vitamins, and antibiotics) generally the total feed cost is higher. With more experiments and experience, no doubt satisfactory rations for very young pigs will be compounded with less expensive ingredients.

3. **Labor, equipment, and overhead costs may be higher.**—Because warm, clean, disease-free quarters are essential, it is probable that labor, equipment, and other overhead costs may be higher with early weaning.

Under certain conditions, other advantages and limitations to early weaning may accrue. Everything considered, based on experiments and on the experiences of swine producers, it appears (1) that even the better operators should not plan on weaning earlier than 2 to 3 weeks of age, and (2) that producers with average management ability, know-how, and equipment should not try to wean earlier than 5 to 6 weeks of age.

For early-weaned pigs, warm, dry, well-ventilated, draft-free housing is essential, and supplemental heat (such as a heat lamp) and special feeders and waterers are recommended; at its best, this entails an extra building—a nursery. Also, the conditions listed in Table 14-1 should prevail.

TABLE 14-1

RECOMMENDED CONDITIONS FOR EARLY WEANING

Conditions	Age in Weeks				
	1	2	3	4	5
Minimum pig wt., lbs.	5	9	12	15	21
Farrowing house temperature, °F.	80-90	80-85	75	70	70
Minimum floor space/pig, sq. ft.	4	4	4	5	5
Minimum no. of pigs/linear ft. of feeder space	5	5	4	4	4
Maximum no. of pigs/linear ft. of water space	12	12	12	10	10
Maximum no. of pigs of uniform size/group	10	10	10	20	25

Grouping; Separating Hogs of Different Sexes, Ages, and Sizes

Although there is a paucity of experimental work upon which to base intelligent recommendations relative to proper grouping or separating of hogs of different sexes, ages, and sizes, observant producers recognize that this is a most important part of management. The following practices are generally followed and advocated by successful producers:

1. **Gilts to be retained for the breeding herd.**—Gilts to be retained for the breeding herd should be separated from market hogs at 4 to 5 months of age.

2. **Pregnant gilts and sows.**—Gilts and sows should be kept separate during the gestation period, unless they are self-fed a bulky ration.

3. **Boars of different ages.**—Junior and mature boars should not be run together. Boars of the same age or size can be run together during the off-breeding season.

4. **Adjusting size of litter.**—Where possible, the size of litters should be adjusted to the number of functioning teats or nursing ability of the sow. Transferring pigs from sow to sow should be done as early as possible; three to four days after farrowing is usually the maximum length of time that this can be done, unless the odor of the pigs is masked, when it may be possible to transfer at a later date.

5. **Running sows and litters together.**—Pigs should be about two weeks old before placing sows and litters together, although small groups may be put together as early as one week. The age difference between such litters should not be more than one week in a central farrowing house or two weeks on pasture. Not more than four sows and litters should be grouped together in a central farrowing house; and not more than six on pasture.

6. **Creep feeding.**—A maximum of 40 pigs per creep may be allowed.

7. **Early weaning.**—In early weaning, not over 10 pigs should be placed together up to 3 weeks of age; 20 may be placed together at 3 to 4 weeks of age; and 25 at 5 weeks of age.

8. **Pigs of different weights.**—Growing-finishing pigs of varying weights should not be run together. It is recommended

Fig. 14-1. Twenty to 25 finishing hogs in each group (pen) in the commercial swine barn operated by Guy Gosserand, Dodge City, Kansas. (Courtesy, Wilbur L. Plager, American Yorkshire Club, Inc., Lafayette, Ind.)

that the range in weight should not exceed 20 percent above or below the average.

FEEDER PIG PRODUCTION

Feeder pig production refers to the production and sale of weanling pigs, usually throughout the year, for growing and finishing on other farms. It makes for a two-phase system in swine production, similar to the two-phase system so well known in the cattle industry where some operators specialize in the cow-and-calf system (the production of feeder cattle) and others in finishing cattle. Until recent years, it was generally assumed that a two-phase system lends itself more logically to beef cattle than to swine because of the western range and of fewer disease problems. But several important scientific and technological developments which occurred in the swine industry in the 1950's and early 1960's ushered in considerable two-phase production of hogs. Among such developments were: (1) Specific Pathogen Free (SPF) herds and other improved disease control measures; (2) confined and continuous production—which increased special-

ization in breeding, in farrowing, and in finishing; and (3) increased mechanization. As a result, by 1963 it was estimated that 15 percent of the nation's hogs started life on one farm but were fed out on another, as compared to only 5 percent a decade earlier.[7]

In comparison with finishing hogs, feeder pig production requires less grain per dollar of product sold, but more labor.

Among the **advantages** of raising feeder pigs as compared to growing-finishing pigs are:

1. It provides an opportunity to use efficiently a maximum amount of labor, for about two-thirds of the labor of raising hogs occurs by the time pigs reach weaning age.

2. It requires less grain per dollar of product sold. To maintain a brood sow and raise a litter of pigs to 40 pounds requires only 20 to 25 percent as much feed as is needed to feed them to market weight of 200 pounds.

3. It makes good use of available pasture for the sow herd.

4. It allows a rapid turnover in the volume of pigs that can be handled each year. In a feeder pig operation, it takes 6 months from the time the sows are bred until feeder pigs are sold, whereas the growing-finishing stage, from weaning to marketing, requires about 4 months more.

The main **disadvantage** to feeder pig production is that producers must depend on those engaged in growing-finishing operations for a market; hence, they are somewhat limited as to time of marketing and volume of sales.

Knowledge of the following pointers is pertinent to successful feeder pig production:

1. **Basic requirements.**—The two most important requirements of a good feeder pig program are:

    a. **High level of management.**—Since one-fourth to one-third of the pigs born never reach weaning age, the importance of good management during this critical period is obvious.

    b. **Dependable market.**—Most feeder pig producers are not equipped to feed out hogs from weaning to market. Also, modern systems of multiple farrowing make it necessary to market pigs on schedule to make room for younger pigs to

---

[7] *The Wall Street Journal*, Feb. 19, 1963.

be farrowed and raised to weaning weights. Thus, if a dependable market is not available, a feeder pig producer can find himself in the unenviable position of having unsold pigs on his hands and more of them on the way.

2. **Variation in feeder pig prices.**—Feeder pig prices are more erratic than slaughter hog prices—they move upward and downward more than slaughter hog prices, and they do so more rapidly. This is attributed to the fact that there is no well organized nationwide system of marketing feeder pigs where dependable price information is available.

3. **Methods of marketing feeder pigs.**—There are four methods of marketing feeder pigs; namely—

a. **Farmer-to-farmer agreements.**—This refers to the sale of feeder pigs from one farmer to another. More pigs are sold by such agreements than by any other method. The method has the advantages of (1) spreading fewer diseases, because the pigs are moved directly from one farm to another, and (2) assuring the buyer of a steady supply of pigs he wants, while providing the seller with a steady market. However, it does have two major disadvantages: (1) if a disease outbreak affects either the buyer's or seller's hogs, the production and marketing schedule of both parties is thrown off, and (2) extreme price fluctuations in either direction may make for dissatisfaction on the part of one party.

b. **Local and special auctions.**—The auction method of selling feeder pigs appears to be increasing in popularity. Well-conducted auctions provide the advantages of (1) uniform lots in type, color, and size; (2) selling a large number of pigs quickly and at reasonable cost; (3) buyers who are interested in various sizes, qualities, and numbers; and (4) a competitive market.

On the other hand, auctions may have the following disadvantages: (1) spreading diseases if considerable caution is not exercised; (2) insufficient buyers at those auctions where volume is small and inconsistent; and (3) inefficient operation due to inefficient or indifferent management.

c. **Private treaty sale.**—In this method, feeder pig producers hire a specialized pig salesman to sell by private treaty.

d. **Specialized contract marketing.**—This involves a contract between a producer of feeder pigs and a cooperative marketing agency, with the producer agreeing to market all his pigs through the agency. In return, the marketing agency agrees, for a fee deducted from the sale price, to (1) furnish field services on production problems, (2) secure a market for the pigs, (3) sort the pigs into uniform lots, (4) provide facilities for weighing and assembling, (5) deliver the pigs to buyers from the assembly point, and (6) guarantee the buyer against loss by death for a specified period following delivery.

Regardless of the method of marketing used, the producer of feeder pigs will find the following "to do" list helpful:

1. Build a reputation as an honest supplier of good feeder pigs.
2. Distribute farrowings so as to permit sales throughout the year and help level out price fluctuations.
3. Sort pigs into groups of uniform size and quality.
4. Have pigs clean and presentable when shown to a buyer.
5. Keep contact with buyers of your pigs and see what results they get with them.
6. Price pigs realistically and in keeping with the market—neither too high nor too low.
7. Castrate all boar pigs and vaccinate all pigs as far in advance of sale as possible.
8. Furnish buyers with a herd health and inspection statement from your veterinarian.
9. Furnish buyers written recommendations on handling feeder pigs on arrival at the new location.
10. Assist buyers in arranging transportation of pigs to their farms.

Buyer of feeder pigs should observe the following "to do" list:

1. Buy from a reputable company or individual.
2. Choose a dependable source of supply—a firm or individual that can consistently supply you with feeder pigs when you need them.
3. Beware of pigs at bargain prices—there's usually something wrong with them and you may be buying a disease and death loss problem.

4. Give special care during the first few days after arrival on your farm to avoid death losses. See Chapter XI of this book, part V under the section "A Program of Swine Health, Disease Prevention and Parasite Control," for details.

5. Abide by the legal health regulations of your state—these laws are for your protection, so you should respect and appreciate them. Information about the health regulations of each state may be obtained by writing to the Livestock Sanitary Commissioner.

6. Decide what you can afford to pay for feeder pigs before making an offer. With this information at hand, you can take them or leave them.

7. Buy the right size pigs for your needs. Normally, feeder pigs should weigh between 40 and 50 pounds at purchase. If you wish to use them to clean up cornfields, they should be 60 pounds and up.

Pig Hatcheries

A pig hatchery is another name for an establishment which specializes in producing and selling feeder pigs. In comparison with chicken hatcheries, the term "pig hatchery" is really a misnomer, for the former seldom maintain breeding animals, and they sell at an earlier age.

Like so many developments, pig hatcheries were ushered in by the impetus of something new, and by a few well written magazine articles and news releases glamorizing the new method of mass producing weaner pigs. The commercial production of synthetic milk followed closely in period of time, and the boom was on. Unfortunately, there was a paucity of experimental work and practical experience on which to base decisions relative to their operation. As a result, many of them failed.

Eventually, many of the early-day mistakes in the operation of pig hatcheries were rectified, largely through trial and error; and their fundamental soundness was established. With this transition, the use of the name pig hatchery largely gave way to the more accurate term "feeder pig production."

GROWING AND FINISHING HOGS

This refers to the stage from weaning to marketing. It is the simplest phase, or system, of hog production—it involves the

least amount of both equipment and managerial ability of all types.

The producer who raises and feeds out his own pigs for market usually experiences fewer problems in the growing-finishing stage than the one who buys feeder pigs. However, the grower-finisher who buys his pigs from a reputable source and follows good management practices will generally do well.

Growing and finishing pigs may be, and are, handled under either of two systems—pasture or confinement. If properly managed, both systems are satisfactory and will produce good results.

The main requisites for a successful growing-finishing program are:

1. A pasture or a confined area for the hogs.
2. Adequate housing.
3. Facilities for cooling hogs in hot weather.
4. A satisfactory source of feeder pigs, either purchased or raised.
5. A readily available supply of feed.
6. Balanced rations.
7. Adequate feed and water facilities and space per pig.
8. Control of diseases and external and internal parasites.
9. Vaccination against the diseases prevalent to the area.
10. A suitable market for finished hogs.
11. Accurate records upon which to base managment decisions.

Pig Parlors (or Pig Corrals)

The terms "pig parlor," or "pig corral," refer to a system of finishing market hogs in confinement. The advocates like the name "pig parlors," because, so they claim, "the idea is to make things as conducive as possible for pigs to make hogs out of themselves." There are all types and sizes of pig parlors, but in all of them emphasis is on sound management, careful sanitation, and good feeding of pigs from weaning to market *in a confined area*.

Generally, they consist of a sloping (¼ to ½″ to the foot) concrete (rough finish) floor, with a fence around it and an iron or aluminum roof. For winter use, they are boxed in.

A 22′ x 30′ parlor will accommodate 50 hogs (a load of market hogs for a 30′ trailer), from 45 to 75 pounds up to market weight; allowing 13 square feet of floor space per pig. Generally, these units are equipped with automatic waterers (2 to 3 waterers placed on the high side of the concrete floor) and a 10 to 16 hole self-feeder. At their best, such operations combine proper feeding and good management on concrete, with built-in labor savers and quick turnover.

If pigs are available, 3 to 4 crops per year can be fed out in a pig parlor—a new bunch every 60 to 90 days. Pigs may either be raised or bought. If raised, 12 sows can provide enough pigs to keep a pig parlor busy; by breeding 6 sows every 3 months on a two-litter system, 200 weaned pigs should be available.

Pig parlors, and the various promotional aspects that accompany them, are affecting swine production in three ways: (1) increasing swine numbers through getting new producers in the business and expanding existing operations, (2) shifting the geography of production, into the South and West, and (3) encouraging multiple farrowing and year-round, rather than seasonal, marketing.

ESSENTIAL SKILLS FOR THE SWINE PRODUCER

The essential skills include those routine things which the producer must do with his hands, whereas systems and practices are activities involving policies and programs. In order to be successful and to get satisfaction from producing swine, the operator should be able to perform the skills which follow.

Clipping the Boar's Tusks

It is never safe to allow the boar to have long tusks, for they may inflict injury upon other boars or even prove hazardous to the caretaker. Above all, such tusks should be removed well in advance of the breeding season, at which time it is necessary to handle the boar a great deal. The common procedure in preparation for removing the tusks consists of drawing a strong rope over the upper jaw and tying the other end securely to a post or other object. As the animal pulls back and the mouth opens, the tusks may be cut with a bolt clipper.

Removing the Needle Teeth

Newborn pigs have eight small, tusk-like teeth (so-called needle or black teeth), two on each side of both the upper and lower jaw. As these are of no benefit to the pig, most swine producers prefer to cut them off soon after birth. This operation may be done with a small pair of pliers or with forceps made especially for the purpose. In removing the teeth, care should be taken to avoid injury to the jaw or gums, for injuries may provide an opening for germs; for this reason only the tips of needle teeth should be clipped.

The needle teeth are very sharp and are often the cause of pain or injury to the sow, particularly if the udder is tender. Moreover, the pigs may bite or scratch each other, and infection may start and cause serious trouble.

Marking or Identifying Swine

The common method of marking or identifying swine consists of ear notching the litters. Pigs are generally marked at the same time that the needle teeth are removed. Pureberd breeders find it necessary to employ a system of marking so that they may determine the parentage of the individuals for purposes of registration and herd records. Even in the commercial herd, a system of identification is necessary if the gilts are to be selected from the larger and more efficient litters. The ear notches are usually made with a special ear marker or an ordinary harness punch. No universal system is employed; each individual producer has his own ideas upon the subject. Most of the breed associations are in position to recommend a satisfactory marking system; a few registry associations even specify a specific marking system.

Table 14-2, Handy Marking or Identifying Guide for Registered Swine, summarizes the pertinent regulations of the swine associations relative to marking or identifying.

Castration

Castration is the removal of the testicles from the male and the ovaries from the female. In this country, female swine usually are not castrated (spayed).

Male pigs are castrated to maintain the quality of the meat, to prevent uncontrolled breeding, and to prevent the development

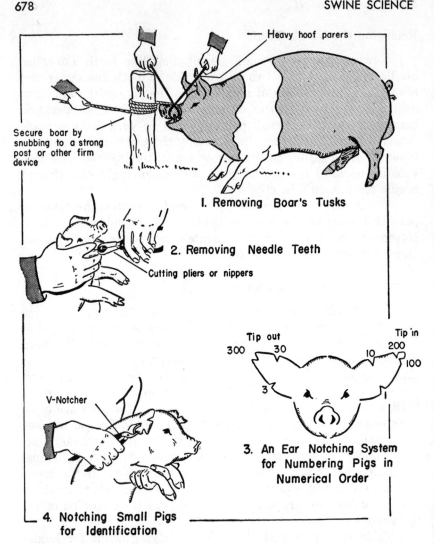

Heavy hoof parers

Secure boar by
snubbing to a strong
post or other firm
device

1. Removing Boar's Tusks

2. Removing Needle Teeth

Cutting pliers or nippers

Tip out   Tip in
300   30   10   200
                                                100

V-Notcher

3   1

3. An Ear Notching System
for Numbering Pigs in
Numerical Order

4. Notching Small Pigs
for Identification

Fig. 14-2. Diagrams showing some essential skills: (1) removing boar's
tusks, (2) removing needle teeth, (3) an ear notching system for numbering
pigs in numerical order, and (4) notching small pigs for identification.
(Drawing by R. F. Johnson)

of the boar odor or flavor that occurs in the cooked meat of a
boar. As a result of castration, male pigs take on the conformation of a sow rather than a boar.

Boars that are no longer useful in a breeding program may
be castrated to remove the boar odor before marketing; such

TABLE 14-2

HANDY MARKING OR IDENTIFYING GUIDE FOR REGISTERED SWINE

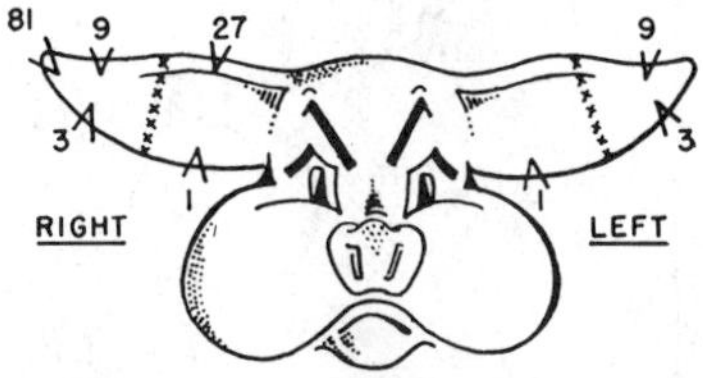

Breed	Association Rules Relative to Marking

81 9   27   9

3   3

RIGHT   LEFT

Fig. 14-3. Standard ear-notching system used, or recommended, by most swine registry associations. The right ear is used for litter mark, and the left ear is used for individual pig number. Up to 161 litters can be marked with this system.

Breed	Association Rules Relative to Marking
American Landrace	The Association accepts either ear notching or tattoo, or both. The Association recommends, but does not require, the standard notching system shown in Fig. 14-3.
Berkshire	The Association recommends the standard notching system shown in Fig. 14-3.
Chester White	The Association requires the standard notching system shown in Fig. 14-3.
Duroc	The Association recommends, but does not require, the standard notching system shown in Fig. 14-3.
Hampshire	The Association requires the system shown in Fig. 14-3.
Hereford	Ear notches or tattoo required.
Inbreds Breeds (Registered by Inbred Livestock Association)	The diagram which follows shows all the notches used in this system. Of course, no one pig would have all the notches indicated. Provision is made for individual notching of ears and numbering the pigs individually from 0 to 999. The left ear carries the litter number and the right ear carries the individual pig number. For example, pig number 118 carries the litter mark 100 and 10 and the individual mark within the litter is 8; thus his number is 118. The system provides for the identification of the litters by 10's, starting with litter 0 (no marks) and continuing to 990. The pigs within each litter are marked individually starting with 0 (no marks) and running to 9. This takes care of 10 pigs. If there are more than 10 pigs in the litter, the others are marked by means of a notch called x.

(Continued)

TABLE 14-2 (Continued)

Breed	Association Rules Relative to Marking
	Fig. 14-4
OIC	Animals must be ear notched and the position of the notch indicated on pedigree when sent for record. All pigs in the same litter must receive and bear the same ear mark, except by permission for experimental purposes.
Poland China	The Association requires the standard notching system shown in Fig. 14-3.
Spotted	All pigs must be ear marked, and each litter must be marked differently. The Association suggests the standard notching system shown in Fig. 14-3.
Tamworth	The Association requires the standard notching system shown in Fig. 14-3.
Yorkshire	The Association recommends the system herewith illustrated. The right ear is used to identify the litter, whereas the left ear is used to identify the individual pigs within a litter. Fig. 14-5

an operation is known as stagging. By the time the castration wound has healed (in 3 to 4 weeks), the odor usually disappears enough to allow the stag to be marketed.

All male pigs that are not to be used for breeding purposes should be castrated while they are still sucking their dams. They should be castrated early enough to allow plenty of time

for the wounds to heal thoroughly (the incision usually heals in 2 to 3 weeks) before weaning; and the operation should not be done at the same time that the pigs are vaccinated. Generally this means that castration should be done within the first 4 weeks (some castrate 5-day-old pigs); pigs that are weaned at 4 weeks of age or earlier should not be castrated within one week of the time of weaning. In preparation for the operation, the pigs should be kept off feed a short time.

Castrating Swine

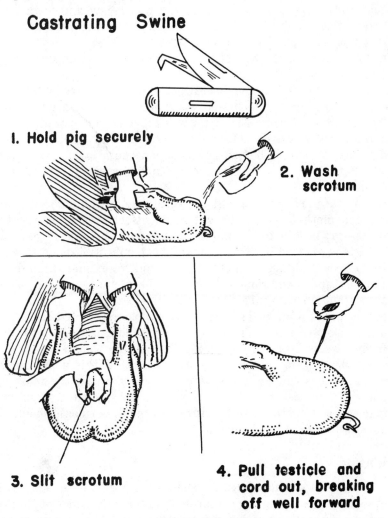

1. Hold pig securely

2. Wash scrotum

3. Slit scrotum

4. Pull testicle and cord out, breaking off well forward

Fig. 14-6. Swine are castrated with a knife, by following the four steps herewith illustrated. (Drawing by R. F. Johnson)

The best way to restrain, or hold, swine that are to be castrated depends on the age and size of the animal and the number of helpers available. A young pig is generally either (1) suspended by its hind legs with the back toward the helper (the helper also clamps his knees against the pig's ribs, near the shoulders), or (2) held on its back on the top of a table (this requires either (a) a castration crate or rack, or (b) two helpers —one grasping the front legs and the other the rear legs). Large boars are usually snared around the upper jaw and behind the tusks, with the free end of the snare tied to a post; then further restraint is applied by either tying all four legs or by hoisting the hind legs, with the animal castrated in either a standing or lying position.

Before starting the operation, the hands should be thoroughly washed with soap and water and rinsed in a good disinfectant. If the scrotum is dirty, wash it with soapy water, using a coarse fiber brush. After washing, disinfect the area. Also, disinfect the knife before and between operations. A 2-percent solution of cresol is a satisfactory disinfectant for these purposes.

With a sharp knife, slit the scrotum on each side (the one-incision method—with the cut made directly between the testicles—is satisfactory, and is preferred by some), as each testicle is pressed outward. Extend both cuts well down to allow for proper drainage, and cut deep enough to extend through the scrotum and membrane (if desired, the membrane need not be slit; simply remove it along with the testicle). Pull the cord out, or break it off well forward (with tension directed backward; otherwise, the inguinal ring may be torn and evisceration follow). In fly season, apply an insect repellant to the wound.

Some swine producers routinely handle this management phase, others call upon the veterinarian; perhaps the most important thing is that it be done at the proper time. Pigs with undescended testicles or ruptures (scrotal hernias) should be operated on by a veterinarian.

Ringing

By instinct most hogs do some rooting, but it is likely to be especially damaging to pastures where animals are on limited rations or some nutritive deficiencies exist. Also, older animals are more prone to root than young pigs.

When rooting starts, the herd should be "ringed"; and this applies to all hogs past weaning age. Older animals can be restrained by a rope or instrument placed around the snout, whereas young pigs can be held.

Many types of rings can be and are used, but the fish-hook type is most common. Rings (usually 1 to 3 rings) are usually placed in the snout, just back of the cartilage but away from the bone; although some producers prefer to use a ring that is placed through the septum (the partition of the nose). Others cut the cartilage on top of the snout, but this causes a rather severe setback and should be practiced with caution.

SANITATION

In order to reduce the possibility of disease, the hog producer must adopt certain management practices relative to the environment of animals. It has been well said that domestication and increased animal numbers imply sort of a contract. In fulfilling this obligation for services rendered, man must protect his animals from the elements, parasites, and diseases, and furnish them sanitary quarters and suitable rations. Abuse leads to the reduction of profit—a case in which money and decency are on the same side of the ledger.

Hogs require sanitary quarters. In the wild state, they had access to plenty of fresh air, clean feed, and plenty of room. They are naturally of clean habits and if given the choice will not voluntarily consume contaminated feed nor lie in filth.

Clean and Disinfect Buildings; Keep Idle

All swine buildings should be emptied of animals for a minimum period of two weeks each year, to permit thorough cleaning, disinfecting, and drying out. Better yet, this operation should be repeated before putting in each new bunch of pigs. See Chapter XI relative to the choice of a disinfectant and the method of using it.

The McLean County System of Swine Sanitation

The McLean County system of swine sanitation, the principles of which are fully described in Chapter XI (under Ascarids), was worked out especially for the purpose of preventing

infestation of young pigs with the common roundworm. The application of these principles is usually effective in reducing trouble from other parasites and in disease control—thus making possible cheaper and more profitable pork production (see Fig. 14-7).

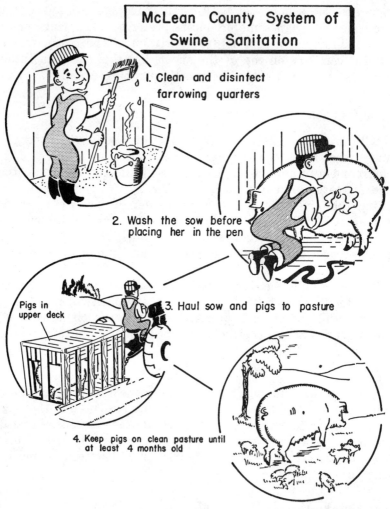

Fig. 14-7. The McLean County System of Swine Sanitation involves the four simple steps shown in the diagram; namely: (1) Cleaning and disinfecting the farrowing quarters, (2) washing the sow before placing her in the farrowing quarters, (3) hauling the sow and pigs to clean pasture, and (4) keeping the pigs on clean pasture until they are at least four months old. (Drawing by R. F. Johnson)

BEDDING SWINE

Bedding or litter is used primarily for the purpose of keeping animals clean and comfortable. But bedding has the following added values from the standpoint of the manure:

1. It soaks up the urine which contains about one-half the total plant food of manure.

2. It makes manure easier to handle.

3. It absorbs plant nutrients, fixing both ammonia and potash in relatively insoluble forms that protects them against losses by leaching. This characteristic of bedding is especially important in peat moss, but of little significance with sawdust and shavings.

Currently, there is a trend to eliminate bedding, especially in some of the larger, confinement-type operations, primarily because it reduces costs and makes cleaning easier. This is being accomplished by the use of slotted floors.

Kind and Amount of Bedding

The kind of bedding material selected should be determined primarily by (1) availability and price, (2) absorptive capacity, and (3) plant nutrient content. In addition, a desirable bedding should not be dusty, should not be excessively coarse, and should remain well in place and not be too readily kicked aside. Table 14-3 summarizes the characteristics of some common bedding materials.

TABLE 14-3

CHARACTERISTICS OF BEDDING MATERIALS[1]

	Bedding Required to Absorb 100 Pounds of Liquid	Ability to Absorb Ammonia Nitrogen per Ton of Bedding	Plant Food Content per Ton of Air-Dry Material		
			Nitrogen	Phosphoric Acid (P_2O_5)	Potash (K_2O)
	(lbs.)	(lbs.)	(lbs.)	(lbs.)	(lbs.)
Wheat straw	45	4.5	11	4	20
Oat straw	35	7.1	12	4	26
Rye straw	45	3.4	12	6	17
Chopped straw	20-30	—	—	—	—
Cornstalks (shredded)	25-35	5.3	15	8	18
Sawdust	25	0	4	2	4
Wood shavings	25-45	0	4	2	4
Peat moss (sphagnum)	10	40	16	2	3

[1]*Soils and Men*, the Yearbook of Agriculture, 1938, Table III, page 451.

In addition to the bedding materials listed in Table 14-3, many other products can be and are successfully used for this purpose, including low quality hays, peanut hulls, leaves of many kinds, spent tanbark, tobacco stalks, buckwheat hulls, oat hulls, and cocoa shells.

Naturally the availability and price per ton of various bedding materials varies from area to area, and from year to year. Thus, in the New England states shavings and sawdust are available, whereas other forms of bedding are scarce, and straws are more plentiful in the central and western states.

Table 14-3 shows that bedding materials differ considerably in their relative capacities to absorb liquid. Thus, 45 pounds of wheat straw will absorb about 100 pounds of liquid; whereas 10 pounds of peat moss have the same absorptive capacity. This means that, on the average, 1 pound of peat moss will absorb as much liquid as 4½ pounds of wheat straw. Also, it is noteworthy that cut straw will absorb more liquid than long straw; ordinary long straw will take up to 2 to 3 times its weight in water, whereas cut straw will absorb about 5 times its weight in water. But there are disadvantages to chopping; chopped straws do not stay in place, and they may be dusty.

Table 14-3 also shows that bedding materials contain valuable plant foods, and that there is considerable difference between them in this respect. From the standpoint of the value of plant food nutrients per ton of air dry material, peat moss is the most valuable bedding, and wood products (sawdust and shavings) the least valuable.

The suspicion that sawdust or shavings will hurt the land is rather widespread, but unfounded. It is true that these products decompose slowly. But this process can be expedited by the addition of nitrogen fertilizers.

The minimum desirable amount of bedding to use is the amount necessary to absorb completely the liquids in manure. Some helpful guides to the end that this may be accomplished follow:

1. Per 24-hours confinement, the minimum bedding requirements of hogs, based on uncut wheat or oats straw, is one-half to one pound. With other bedding materials, the quantities will vary according to their respective absorptive capacities (see Table 14-3). Also, more than these minimum quantities of bed-

ding may be desirable where cleanliness and comfort of the animal are important. Comfortable animals lie down more and utilize a higher proportion of the energy of the feed for productive purposes.

2. Under average conditions, about 500 pounds of bedding are used for each ton of excrement.

3. Where the liquid excrement is collected separately in a cistern or tank, less bedding is required than where the liquid and solid excrement are kept together.

MANURE

The term "manure" refers to a mixture of animal excrements (consisting of undigested feeds plus certain body wastes) and bedding. From the standpoint of soils and crops, barnyard manure contains the following valuable ingredients:

1. **Organic matter.**—It supplies valuable organic matter which cannot be secured in chemical fertilizers. Organic matter —which constitutes 3 to 6 percent, by weight, of most soils— improves soil tilth, increases water-holding capacity, lessens water and wind erosion, improves aeration, and has a beneficial effect on soil microorganisms and plants. It is the "lifeblood" of the land.

2. **Plant food.**—It supplies plant food or fertility—especially nitrogen, phosphorus, and potassium. In addition to these three nutrients, manure contains organic matter, calcium, and trace elements such as boron, manganese, copper, and zinc. A ton of well-preserved hog manure, free of bedding, contains plant-food nutrients equal to about 100 pounds of 10-2-7 fertilizer (see Table 14-4). Thus, spreading manure at the rate of 8 tons per acre supplies the same amounts of nutrients as 800 pounds of a 10-2-7 commercial fertilizer.

Amount, Composition, and Value of Manure Produced

The quantity, composition, and value of manure produced vary according to species, weight, kind and amount of feed, and kind and amount of bedding. The author's computations are on a fresh manure (exclusive of bedding) basis. Table 14-4 presents data by species per 1,000 pounds live weight, whereas Table 14-5 gives yearly tonnage and value.

TABLE 14-4

QUANTITY, COMPOSITION, AND VALUE OF FRESH MANURE
(FREE OF BEDDING) EXCRETED BY 1,000 POUNDS LIVE WEIGHT
OF VARIOUS KINDS OF FARM ANIMALS

| Animal | Tons Excreted Year/1,000 Lbs. Live Weight[1] | Composition and Value of Manure on a Tonnage Basis[2] | | | | | | |
		Excre-ment	Lbs./ Ton[3]	Water	N	P[4]	K[4]	Value/ Ton[5]
				(%)	(lb.)	(lb.)	(lb.)	($)
Swine	16	Liquid	800					
		Solid	1,200					
		Total	2,000	75	10.0	2.8	7.6	2.19
Sheep	6	Liquid	660					
		Solid	1,340					
		Total	2,000	65	28.0	4.2	20.0	5.36
Cows	12	Liquid	600					
		Solid	1,400					
		Total	2,000	79	11.2	2.0	10.0	2.32
Steers (finishing cattle)	8.5	Liquid	600					
		Solid	1,400					
		Total	2,000	80	14.0	4.0	9.0	2.98
Horses and foals	8	Liquid	400					
		Solid	1,600					
		Total	2,000	60	13.8	2.0	12.0	2.76
Chickens	4.5	Total	2,000	54	31.2	8.0	7.0	5.68

[1]*Manure Is Worth Money—It Deserves Good Care.* University of Illinois Circ. 595, 1953, p. 4.
[2]Last 5 columns on the right from: *Farm Manures,* University of Kentucky Circ. 593, 1964, Table 2, p. 5.
[3]From: Reference Material for 1951 Saddle and Sirloin Essay Contest, p. 43, compiled by M. E. Ensminger, data from *Fertilizers and Crop Production,* by Van Slyke, published by Orange Judd Publishing Co.
[4]Phosphorus (P) can be converted to P_2O_5 by multiplying the figure given by 2.29, and potassium (K) can be converted to K_2O by multiplying by 1.2.
[5]Calculated on the assumption that nitrogen (N) retails at 12¢, phosphorus (P) at 19¢, and potassium (K) at 6¢ per pound in commercial fertilizers.

The data in Table 14-4 and Figure 14-8 are based on animals confined to stalls the year around. Actually, the manure recovered and available to spread where desired is considerably less than indicated because (1) animals are kept on pasture and along roads and lanes much of the year, where the manure is dropped, and (2) losses in weight often run as high as 60 percent when manure is exposed to the weather for a considerable time.

As shown in Figure 14-9, about 75 percent of the nitrogen,

TABLE 14-5

TONNAGE AND VALUE OF MANURE (EXCLUSIVE OF BEDDING) EXCRETED IN 1967 BY U. S. LIVESTOCK

Class of Livestock	Produced by Animals Maintained Throughout Year[1]	Produced by Animals That Died During Year[2]	Produced by Animals Slaughtered During Year[3]	Total by Class of Livestock	Total Value of Manure[4]
	(tons)	(tons)	(tons)	(tons)	($)
Swine	217,052,000	1,264,392	160,834,912	379,151,304	830,341,355.76
Cattle (beef and dairy)	1,077,248,700	446,913	cattle 192,032,258 calves 7,862,024	1,277,589,895	2,964,008,556.40
Sheep	16,591,500	37,650	3,949,392	20,578,542	205,785.42
Horses	53,400,000	—		53,400,000	147,384,000.00
Chickens	95,523,750	2,653,344	2,392,902	154,632,258	878,311,225.44
Turkeys	7,216,110		46,846,152		
Totals	1,467,032,060	4,402,299	413,917,640	1,885,351,999	4,820,250,923.02

[1]Basis January 1, 1968, animal numbers.
[2]Computed basis ½ year.
[3]Computed basis ½ year. Average slaughter weights used.
[4]Computed on the basis of the value/ton given in the right-hand column of Table 14-4.

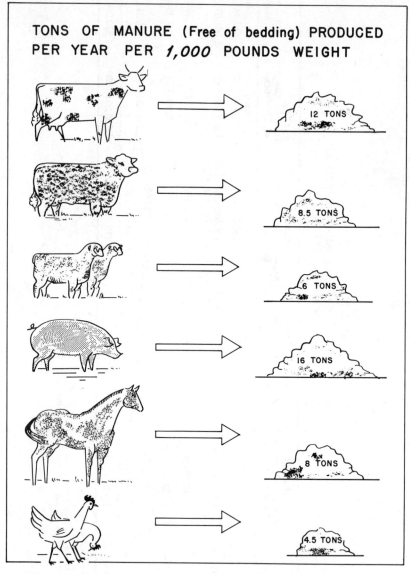

Fig. 14-8. On the average, each class of stall-confined animals produces per year per 1,000 pounds weight the tonnages shown above. (Drawing by R. F. Johnson)

80 percent of the phosphorus, and 85 percent of the potassium contained in animal feeds are returned as manure. In addition, about 40 percent of the organic matter in feeds is excreted as

manure. As a rule of thumb, it is commonly estimated that 80 percent of the total nutrients in feeds are excreted by animals as manure.

A ton of fresh barnyard manure has approximately the composition shown in Figure 14-10.

The urine makes up 40 percent of the total weight of the excrement of hogs, and 20 percent of that of horses; these figures

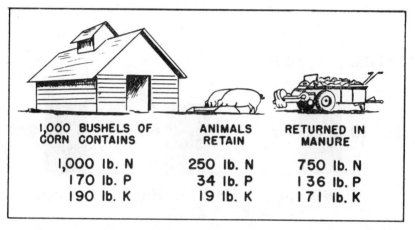

1,000 BUSHELS OF CORN CONTAINS	ANIMALS RETAIN	RETURNED IN MANURE
1,000 lb. N	250 lb. N	750 lb. N
170 lb. P	34 lb. P	136 lb. P
190 lb. K	19 lb. K	171 lb. K

Fig. 14-9. Animals retain about 20 percent of the nutrients in feed; the rest is excreted in manure. (Drawing by Steve Allured)

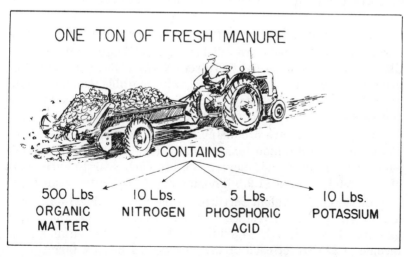

ONE TON OF FRESH MANURE

CONTAINS

500 Lbs ORGANIC MATTER	10 Lbs. NITROGEN	5 Lbs. PHOSPHORIC ACID	10 Lbs. POTASSIUM

Fig. 14-10. The contents of one ton of average fresh manure. (Drawing by Steve Allured)

represent the two extremes in farm animals. Yet the urine, or liquid manure, contains nearly 50 percent of the nitrogen, 6 percent of the phosphorus, and 60 percent of the potassium of average manure; roughly one-half of the total plant food of manure (see Fig. 14-11). Also, it is noteworthy that the nutrients in liquid manure are more readily available to plants than the nutrients in the solid excrement. These are the reasons why it is important to conserve the urine.

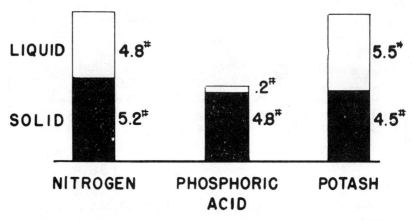

Fig. 14-11. Distribution of plant nutrients between liquid and solid portions of a ton of average farm manure. As noted, the urine contains about half the fertility value of manure. (Drawing by Steve Allured)

The actual monetary value of manure can and should be based on (1) increased crop yields, and (2) equivalent cost of a like amount of commercial fertilizer. Numerous experiments and practical observations have shown the measurable monetary value of manure in increased crop yields. Tables 14-4 and 14-5 give the equivalent cost of a like amount of commercial fertilizer.

Currently, we are producing manure (exclusive of bedding) at the rate of 1.8 billion tons annually (see Table 14-5). That is sufficient manure to add nearly one ton each year to every acre of the total land area (1.9 billion acres) of the United States.

Based on equivalent fertilizer prices (see Table 14-4, right-hand column), and livestock numbers (Table 14-5), the yearly manure crop is worth $4.8 billion. That is a potential annual income of $1,518 for each of the nation's 3.1 million farms.

Of course, the value of manure cannot be measured alone in

terms of increased crop yields and equivalent cost of a like amount of commercial fertilizer. It has additional value for the organic matter which it contains, which almost all soils need, and which farmers and ranchers cannot buy in a sack or tank.

Also, it is noteworthy that, due to the slower availability of its nitrogen and to its contribution to the soil humus, manure produces rather lasting benefits, which may continue for many years. Approximately one-half of the plant nutrients in manure are available to and effective upon the crops in the immediate cycle of the rotation to which the application is made. Of the unused remainder, about one-half, in turn, is taken up by the crops in the second cycle of the rotation; one-half of the remainder in the third cycle, etc. Likewise, the continuous use of manure through several rounds of a rotation builds up a backlog which brings additional benefits, and a measurable climb in yield levels.

Swine producers sometimes fail to recognize the value of this barnyard crop because (1) it is produced whether or not it is wanted, and (2) it is available without cost.

Modern Ways of Handling Manure

Modern handling of manure involves maximum automation and a minimum loss of nutrients. Among the methods being used are scrapers, power loaders, conveyors, industrial-type vacuums, slotted floors with the manure stored underneath or emptying into irrigation systems, storage vats, spreaders (including those designed to handle liquids alone or liquids and solids together), dehydration, and lagoons. Actually, there is no one best manure management system for all situations; rather, it is a matter of designing and using that system which will be most practical for a particular set of conditions.

Objectionable Features of Manure

Despite the recognized virtues of manure, it does possess the following objectionable features:

1. **It may propagate insects.**—Unless precautions are taken, often manure is the preferred breeding place for flies and other insects. It is noteworthy, however, that comparatively few house flies are reared in cow manure.

2. **It may spread disease and parasites.**—Where animals

Fig. 14-12. Flat-bottomed gutter with mechanical manure conveyors located at the outer edge of a concrete floor. (Courtesy, James Mfg. Co., Fort Atkinson, Wisconsin)

Fig. 14-13. Liquid manure tank spreader in operation. In this system, the manure is stored in a container, pumped into a spreader, and spread on fields. (Courtesy, Harold Boucher, Executive Secretary, Hampshire Swine Registry)

are allowed to come in contact with their own excrement, there is always danger of infections from diseases and parasites.

3. **It may produce undesirable odors.**—Where manure is stored improperly, there may be a nuisance from odors.

4. **It may scatter weed seeds.**—Even when fermented, manure usually contains a certain quantity of viable weed seeds which may be scattered over the land.

QUESTIONS FOR STUDY AND DISCUSSION

1. Define and discuss the advantages and disadvantages, and the future of each of the following:
   a. Confinement hog production.
   b. Gilts versus older sows.
   c. Multiple farrowing.
   d. Early weaning of pigs.
   e. Feeder pig production.
   f. Growing-finishing operations.

2. How do you account for the paucity of experimental work on the subject of grouping and separating hogs of different sexes, ages, and sizes?

3. How can the average establishment move hogs about so that each building may be cleaned, disinfected, and kept idle for two weeks each year, or preferably two weeks before each new group of hogs is added?

4. Is the application of the McLean County System of Swine Sanitation as important to successful swine production currently as it was at the time it originated?

5. In your area, what kind of bedding would you use, and why; or would you eliminate bedding entirely?

6. Can you justify the expense of saving and spreading hog manure, or would it be cheaper to buy a commercial fertilizer and either give away the manure or wash it into a lagoon?

7. How would you recommend that each (a) a small operator, and (b) a large operator handle and dispose of hog manure?

SELECTED REFERENCES

Title of Publication	Author(s)	Publisher
Approved Practices in Swine Production	G. C. Cook E. M. Juergenson	The Interstate Printers & Publishers, Inc., Danville, Ill., 1962.
Farrowing Systems	R. C. Wallstrom R. F. Wilson Turner Wright	Agri. Expt. Sta. Bul. 437, South Dakota State College, Brookings, S. Dak., May 1954.
Hog Castration	Leaflet No. 473	U. S. Department of Agriculture, Washington, D. C., June 1960.
Hogs; One- and Two-Litter Systems Compared	L. S. Hardin R. N. Weigle H. S. Wann	Agri. Expt. Sta. Bul. 565, Purdue University, Lafayette, Ind., November 1951.
Meat Hog, The	C. H. Hinman	Claude H. Hinman, Grand Junction, Colo., 1955.
More Swine Dollars from Multiple Farrowing		American Meat Institute, 59 East Van Buren St., Chicago, Ill., August 1957.
Multiple Farrowing (in Armour's Analysis)	C. E. Hughes	Armour's Livestock Bureau, Chicago, Ill., April 1956.
Pig Parlors (The Purina pig parlor way to farrow, grow, and finish hogs)		The Ralston Purina Co., Checkerboard Square, St. Louis, Mo., 1957.
Pork Production	W. W. Smith	The Macmillan Company, New York, N. Y., 1952.
Raising Swine	G. P. Deyoe J. L. Krider	McGraw-Hill Book Co., New York, N. Y., 1952.
Southern Hog Growing	C. C. Scarborough	The Interstate Printers & Publishers, Inc., Danville, Ill., 1958.
Stockman's Handbook, The	M. E. Ensminger	The Interstate Printers & Publishers, Inc., Danville, Ill., 1970.
Swine Production	W. E. Carroll J. L. Krider F. N. Andrews	McGraw-Hill Book Co., New York, N. Y., 1962.
Swine Production	C. E. Bundy R. V. Diggins	Prentice-Hall, Inc., Englewood Cliffs, N. J., 1956.

CHAPTER XV

BUSINESS ASPECTS OF SWINE PRODUCTION

Contents   Page

As swine enterprises get bigger and more complex, the business aspects become increasingly important. More capital is required, risks are greater, margins become smaller, greater effici-

ency of production is essential, and competent management is in demand. The net results is that those engaged in swine production must treat it as the big business that it is, and become more sophisticated; otherwise, they won't be in business very long.

CAPITAL

Hog producers should never invest money, either their own or borrowed, unless they are reasonably certain that it will make money. Capital will be needed for land, buildings, machinery and equipment, hogs, feed, supplies, labor, and miscellaneous items.

Whether establishing or enlarging a swine enterprise, the most common question, a two-pronged one, is—how much money will it take, and what can I make? This information is needed by both hog producers and lenders. Unfortunately, a simple answer cannot be given. However, the following guides will be helpful:

1. **Kind of swine enterprise.**—Feed costs represent 80 to 85 percent of the total cost of a finishing operation, but only 55 to 60 percent of the total cost of producing feeder pigs. On the other hand, feeder pig production requires more labor, land, and buildings than a growing-finishing operation. Thus, growing-finishing fits where large acreages of corn, or other grain, are available; where facilities for farrowing pigs are not available but where there are other buildings, perhaps initially constructed for uses other than hogs, which can be adequately remodeled to achieve labor efficiency and sanitation. Feeder pig production is suited to small farms which have sufficient labor and good management ability.

2. **Size of swine enterprise.**—Generally speaking, larger hog enterprises contribute to increased profits for the following reasons:

    a. They result in fewer hours of labor per hog.

    b. They are more apt to be used to capacity. For example, if for a 400-head facility the depreciation, interest, repairs, insurance, and taxes cost $1,224 annually, that's $3.06 per pig. If the same facility were used twice a year, thereby accommodating 800 head instead of 400, the cost would be $1.53 per pig. If used for 1,200 head, the cost would be $1.02 per pig. This shows how multiple farrowing reduces the building and equipment costs per sow.

Table 15-1 shows initial and yearly resource requirements for three different kinds of swine enterprises, each of average efficiency. This will serve as a useful guide. Individual hog farm adjustments can be made better to reflect local feed costs, building and equipment costs, etc.

TABLE 15-1

INITIAL AND YEARLY RESOURCE REQUIREMENTS OF THREE SYSTEMS OF HOG PRODUCTION[1]

Item	Producing Feeder Pigs. Multiple Farrowing, 2 sets of Sows Farrowing Twice/yr. (Hence, farrowing facilities used 4 times/yr.) Self-fed, 7 pigs/litter, sold at 40 lb.	Raising & Finishing Market Hogs. One set of Sows Farrowing Twice/year. Self-fed, 7 pigs/litter, sold @ 220 lb.	Finishing Purchased Feeder Pigs. Three Groups/yr., 180 lb. Gain/Pig.
	(one sow and two litters)	(one sow and two litters)	(10 pigs)
Corn (or equivalent cereal grain)-------(bu.)	47.	185.	102.
Alfalfa hay-----------(tons)	.30	.65	.26
Supplements and minerals -----------($)	24.00	70.00	34.00
Cash operating expense[2]-------------($)	27.00	60.00	26.00
Building cost (initial)--------------($)	117.00[3]	327.00[4]	100.00[5]
Equipment cost (initial)---------------($)	32.00	57.00	12.00
Breeding stock cost-------------------($)	90.00	90.00	—
Labor-----------------(hrs.)	16-30	25-50	6-16

[1]From: *Tooling Up For Swine Production*, College of Agriculture, University of Wisconsin, Special Circular 120, p. 3, 1966.
[2]Feed grinding and miscellaneous cash expenses, including bedding.
[3]Central farrowing house plus sow and replacement housing, 4 farrowings per year.
[4]Central farrowing house plus confined finishing hog house, 4 farrowings per year.
[5]Confined finishing hog house, 3 groups per year.

Guidelines Relative to Facility and Equipment Costs

Overinvestment is a mistake. Some producers invest more in land and buildings than reasonably can be expected to make a satisfactory return; others invest too much in feed mills and equipment. Sometimes small producers fail to recognize that it may cost half as much to mechanize for a 20-sow unit as it does for a 100-sow unit.

In order to lessen the hazard of overinvestment, guidelines are useful. Here are two:

1. **Guideline No. 1**—The break-even point on how much you

can afford to invest in equipment to replace hired labor can be arrived at by the following formula:

Annual saving
in hired labor
from new
equipment

$$\frac{\text{}}{.15} = \text{amount you can afford to invest}$$

Example:
If hired labor costs $3,600 per year, this becomes—

$$\frac{\$3,600}{.15} = \$24,000, \text{ the break-even point on new equipment.}$$

Thus, if it costs more than $24,000 to mechanize in order to replace one laborer, you should not do so. However, since labor costs are going up faster than machinery and equipment costs, it may be good business to exceed this limitation under some circumstances. Nevertheless, the break-even point, $24,000 in this case, is probably the maximum expenditure that can be economically justified at the time.

2. **Guideline No. 2**—Assuming an annual cost plus operation of power machinery and equipment equal to 20 percent of new cost, the break-even point to justify replacement of one hired man is as follows:

If Annual Cost of One Hired Man is—[1]	The Break-Even Point on New Investment is—
$2,500 (20%) × 5	$12,500
3,500 (20%) × 5	17,500
4,500 (20%) × 5	22,500

Example:
Assume that the new cost of added equipment comes to $1,500, that the annual cost is 20 percent of this amount, and that the new equipment would save one hour of labor per day for six months of the year. Here's how to figure the value of labor to justify an expenditure of $1,500 for this item:

$1,500 (new cost) × 20% = $300

---

[1] This is assuming that the productivity of men at different salaries is the same, which may or may not be the case.

$300 (annual ownership
use cost) + 180 hrs. (labor saved) = $1.67/hour.

So, if labor costs less than $1.67/hour, you probably shouldn't buy the new item.

CREDIT IN THE SWINE BUSINESS

Total farm assets are estimated at $300 billion, while farm debt is about $55 billion. This means that, in the aggregate, farmers have nearly an 82 percent equity in their business, and 18 percent borrowed capital. Perhaps they have been too conservative, for it is estimated that one-fourth to one-third of American farmers could profit from the use of more credit in their operations.

Credit is an integral part of today's hog business. Wise use of it can be profitable, but unwise use of it can be disastrous. Accordingly, producers should know more about it. They need to know something about the lending agencies available to them, the types of credit, how to go about obtaining a loan, and methods of computing interest.

The common lending sources of farm credit are: commercial banks, Production Credit Associations, Federal Land Banks, individuals and other private lenders, life insurance companies, merchants and dealers, and Farmers Home Administration.[2]

Data are not available to show the amount of money borrowed by hog producers. However, it is known that farmers and ranchers borrow over $6 billion a year (which is about one-sixth of the credit which they use) from the Farm Credit System—which includes the Federal Land Banks, the Federal Intermediate Credit Banks, Production Credit Associations, and Banks for Cooperatives. Also, it is reported that, on January 1, 1964, commercial banks held 85 percent of the reported non-real estate loans to farmers in California, production credit associations held 12 percent, and all other sources had only 3 percent.[3] Grain companies, feed companies, and various other suppliers, are also important sources of credit to hogmen.

---

[2]Information relative to each of these credit sources is given in *The Stockman's Handbook*, 4th ed., Sec. XVII.
[3]*Cattle Feeding in California*, Bank of America, Economic Research Department, Feb. 1965, p. 29.

Types of Credit

Following are the three general types of agricultural credit to consider, based on length of life and type of collateral needed:

1. **Short-term or production credit.**—This is used for one production period or up to one year. It is used for purchase of feeders, feed, and operating expenses; and it's repaid when the hogs are sold.

2. **Intermediate credit.**—This type of credit may be for one to seven years. It is used for the purchase of breeding stock, machinery, equipment, and semi-permanent investments. Repayment is made from the profits over several production periods.

3. **Long-term credit.**—This type of credit is used for land and major farm buildings, and physical plant construction. Repayments are made over several years from profits.

Credit Factors Considered and Evaluated by Lenders

Potential money borrowers sometimes make their first big mistake by going in "cold" to see a lender, without adequate facts and figures, with the result that they have two strikes against getting the loan to begin with.

When considering and reviewing hog loan requests, the lender tries to arrive at the repayment ability of the potential borrower. Likewise, the borrower has no reason to obtain money unless it will make money.

Lenders need certain basic information in order to evaluate the soundness of a loan request. To this end, the following information should be submitted:

1. **Analysis and feasibility study.**—Lenders are impressed with a borrower who has a written-down program; showing where he is now, where he is going, and how he expects to get there. In addition to spelling out the goals, this should give assurance of the necessary management skills to achieve them. Such an analysis of the present and projection into the future is imperative in big operations.

2. **The applicant, farm, and financial statement.**—It is the borrower's obligation, and in his best interest, to present the following information to the lender:

a. **The applicant:**

(1) Name of applicant and wife; age of applicant.
(2) Number of children (minors, legal age).
(3) Partners in business, if any.
(4) Years in area.
(5) References.

b. **The farm:**

(1) Owner or tenant.
(2) Location; legal description and county, and direction and distance from nearest town.
(3) Type of hog enterprise; producing feeder pigs, raising and finishing market hogs, or finishing purchased feeder pigs.

c. **Financial statement.**—This document indicates the borrower's financial record and current financial position, his potential ahead, and his liability to others. The borrower should always have sufficient slack to absorb reasonable losses due to such unforeseen happenstances as storms, droughts, diseases, and poor markets; thereby permitting the lender to stay with him in adversity and to give him a chance to recoup his losses in the future. The financial statement should include the following:

(1) **Current assets:**

(a) Livestock.
(b) Feed.
(c) Machinery.
(d) Cash (there should be reasonable cash reserves, to cut interest costs, and to provide a cushion against emergencies).
(e) Bonds or other investments.
(f) Cash value of life insurance.

(2) **Fixed assets:**

(a) Real property, with estimated value:
(i) Farm property.
(ii) City property.
(iii) Long term contracts.

(3) **Current liabilities:**

(a) Mortgages.
(b) Contracts.
(c) Open account—to whom owed.
(d) Co-signer or guarantor on notes.

(e) Any taxes due.

(f) Current portion of real estate indebtedness due.

(4) **Fixed liabilities.**—amount and nature of real estate debt:

(a) Date due.

(b) Interest rate.

(c) To whom payable.

(d) Contract or mortgage.

3. **Other factors.**—Shrewd lenders usually ferret out many things, among them—

a. **The potential borrower.**—Most lenders will tell the potential borrower that he is the most important part of the loan. Lenders consider his—

(1) Character.

(2) Honesty and integrity.

(3) Experience and ability.

(4) Moral and credit rating.

(5) Age and health.

(6) Family cooperation.

(7) Continuity, or line of succession.

Lenders are quick to sense the "high-liver"—the fellow who lives beyond his means; the poor manager—the kind who would have made it except for hard luck, and to whom the hard luck happened many times; and the dishonest, lazy, and incompetent.

In recognition of the importance of the man back of the loan, "key man" insurance on the owner or manager should be considered by both the lender and the borrower.

b. **Production records.**—This refers to a good set of records showing efficiency of production. Such records should show weight and price of hogs sold, pig-crop percentage and weaning weight, efficiency of feed utilization and rate of gain on growing-finishing hogs, gilt replacement program, depreciation schedule, average crop yield, and other pertinent information. Lenders will increasingly insist on good records.

c. **Progress with previous loans.**—Has the borrower paid back previous loans plus interest; has he reduced the amount of the loan, thereby giving evidence of progress?

d. **Profit and loss (P&L).**—This serves as a valuable guide to the potential ahead. Preferably, this should cover the previous three years. Also, most lenders prefer that this

be on an accrual basis (even if the hogman is on a cash basis in reporting to the Internal Revenue Service).

e. **Physical plant:**

(1) Is it an economic unit?

(2) Does it have adequate water, and is it well balanced in feed and livestock?

(3) Is there adequate diversification?

(4) Is the right kind of livestock being produced?

(5) Are the right crops and varieties grown; and are approved methods of tillage and fertilizer practices being followed?

(6) Is the farmstead neat and well kept?

f. **Collateral (or security):**

(1) Adequate to cover loan, with margin.

(2) Quality of security:

(a) Grade and age of livestock.

(b) Type and condition of machinery.

(c) If grain storage is involved, adequacy to protect from moisture and rodents.

(d) Government participation.

(3) Identification of security:

(a) Ear marks on hogs.

(b) Serial numbers on machinery.

4. **The loan request.**—Swine producers are in competition for money from urban businessmen. Hence, it is important that their request for a loan be well presented and supported. The potential borrower should tell the purpose of the loan; how much money is needed, when it is needed, and what it is needed for; the soundness of the venture; and the repayment schedule.

Credit Factors Considered by Borrowers

Credit is a two-way street; it must be good for both the borrower and the lender. If a borrower is the right kind of person and on a sound basis, more than one lender will want his business. Thus, it is usually well that a borrower shop around a bit; that he be familiar with several sources of credit and see what they have to offer. There are basic differences in length and type of loan, repayment schedules, services provided with the loan, interest rate, and the ability and willingness of lenders to stick by the borrower in emergencies and times of adversity. Thus,

interest rates and willingness to loan are only two of the several factors to consider. Also, if at all possible, all borrowing should be done from one source; a one-source lender will know more about the borrower's operations and be in a better position to help him.

Helpful Hints for Building and Maintaining a Good Credit Rating

Swine producers who wish to build up and maintain good credit are admonished to do the following:

1. **Keep credit in one place, or in few places.**—Generally, lenders frown upon "split financing." Shop around for a creditor (a) who is able, willing, and interested in extending the kind and amount of credit needed, and (b) who will lend at a reasonable rate of interest; then stay with him.

2. **Get the right kind of credit.**—Don't use short-term credit to finance long-term improvements or other capital investments.

3. **Be frank with the lender.**—Be completely open and aboveboard. Mutual confidence and esteem should prevail between borrower and lender.

4. **Keep complete and accurate records.**—Complete and accurate records should be kept by enterprises. By knowing the cost of doing business, decision-making can be on a sound basis.

5. **Keep annual inventory.**—Take an annual inventory for the purpose of showing progress made during the year.

6. **Repay loans when due.**—Borrowers should work out a repayment schedule on each loan, then meet payments when due. Sale proceeds should be promptly applied on loans.

7. **Plan ahead.**—Analyze the next year's operation and project ahead.

Calculating Interest

The total cost of using credit varies according to (1) rate of and method of computing interest, and (2) length of time the loan is needed. There are four commonly used methods of calculating interest; namely—

1. **Flat rate of interest** (or simple interest) **method.**—In which a specified rate of interest is paid on the original amount

of the loan. For example, if $1,000 is borrowed for 12 months at 6 percent interest, the total interest will be $60.

2. **Added-on interest method.**—In which the interest is added to the principal at the time the loan is made. Thus, if the loan is repaid in 12 equal monthly installments, the true interest rate will be approximately 12 percent, because the interest is charged on the total original amount of the loan and does not decrease with each successive payment.

3. **Unpaid balance method.**—In which interest is paid only on the amount which has not been repaid. Thus, if $1,000 is borrowed for 12 months at 6 percent interest, but half the original loan is repaid at the end of six months, six month's interest would be saved on $500. Hence, the interest on this $500 would be 3 percent, whereas the interest on the remaining $500 not repaid until the end of the 12 months would be 6 percent. Thus, the total interest cost would be $45.

4. **Discount method.**—In which the lender discounts the loan in advance. For example, with a $1,000 loan for 12 months at 6 percent, the borrower actually has only $940 to use—rather than $1,000. Hence, the true interest rate on $940 would be 6.4 percent. If the borrower must have $1,000, the lender may write the loan for an amount large enough to discount the interest and yet provide $1,000 to the borrower.

Table 15-2 shows the true interest rate of a $1,000 loan, with the interest computed by each of these methods.

TABLE 15-2

TRUE INTEREST RATES ON A $1,000 LOAN,
BY FOUR METHODS OF COMPUTING

Method of Computing Interest	Principal (12 mo.)	Interest (@ 6%)	Total to Repay	True Interest Rate
1. Flat rate of interest: paid in one sum at end of loan period------------	$1,000	$60	$1,060	6%
2. Added-on interest: principal repaid in equal monthly installments--------------------	$1,000	$60	$1,060	12%
3. Unpaid balance: $500 paid in 6 mos. $500 at end of 12 mos. ------	$1,000	$45	$1,045	6%
4. Discount--------------------------	$1,000	$60	$ 940	6.4

BUDGETS IN THE SWINE BUSINESS

A budget is a projection of records and accounts and a plan for organizing and operating ahead for a specific period of time. A short-time budget is usually for one year, whereas a long-time budget is for a period of years. The principal value of a budget is that it provides a working plan through which the operation can be coordinated. Changes in prices, droughts, and other factors make adjustments necessary. But these adjustments are more simply and wisely made if there is a written budget to use as a reference.

How to Set Up a Budget

It's unimportant whether a printed form (of which there are many good ones) is used or one made up on an ordinary ruled 8½″ × 11″ sheet placed sidewise. The important things are that (1) a budget is kept, (2) it be on a monthly basis, and (3) the operator be "comfortable" with whatever system or forms are to be used.

No budget is perfect. But it should be as good an estimate as can be made—despite the fact that it will be affected by such things as droughts, diseases, markets, and many other unpredictables.

A simple, easily kept, and adequate budget can be evolved with by using forms such as the three that follow (Tables 15-3, 15-4, and 15-5).

The Annual Cash Expense Budget should show the monthly breakdown of various recurring items—everything except the initial loan and capital improvements. It includes labor, feed, supplies, fertilizer, taxes, interest, utilities, etc.

The Annual Cash Income Budget is just what the name implies—an estimated cash income by months.

The Annual Cash Expense & Income Budget is a cash flow chart, obtained from the first two forms. It's a money "flow" summary by months. From this, it can be ascertained when, and how much, money will need to be borrowed, and the length of the loan along with a repayment schedule. It makes it possible to avoid tying up capital unnecessarily, thereby making for a saving in interest.

TABLE 15-3
ANNUAL CASH INCOME BUDGET[1]

_____ FOR 19____

(Name of farm)

Item	Total	Jan.	Feb.	Mar.	Apr.	May	June	July	Aug.	Sept.	Oct.	Nov.	Dec.
Labor hired													
Feed purchased													
Gas, fuel, grease													
Taxes													
Insurance													
Interest													
Utilities													
etc.													
Total													

[1]The Annual Cash Expense Budget should show the monthly breakdown of various recurring items—everything except the initial loan and capital improvements. It includes labor, feed, supplies, fertilizer, taxes, interest, utilities, etc.

TABLE 15-4

ANNUAL CASH INCOME BUDGET[1]

_____ FOR 19 _____

(Name of farm)

Item	Total	Jan.	Feb.	Mar.	Apr.	May	June	July	Aug.	Sept.	Oct.	Nov.	Dec.
500 feeder pigs													
430 bu. oats @ .70													
etc.													
Total													

[1] The Annual Cash Income Budget is just what the name implies—an estimated cash income by months.

TABLE 15-5

ANNUAL CASH EXPENSE & INCOME BUDGET (cash flow)[1]

_____ FOR 19_____

(Name of farm)

Item	Total	Jan.	Feb.	Mar.	Apr.	May	June	July	Aug.	Sept.	Oct.	Nov.	Dec.
Gross Income	25,670					1,000	1,000						
Gross Expense	13,910					575	2,405						
Difference	11,760					425	1,405						
Surplus (+) or Deficit (-)	+					+	-						

[1]The Annual Cash Expense & Income Budget is a cash flow budget, obtained from the first two forms. It's a money "flow" summary by months. From this, it can be ascertained when, and how much, money will need to be borrowed, and the length of the loan along with a repayment schedule. It makes it possible to avoid tying up capital unnecessarily, and to avoid unnecessary interest.

How to Figure Net Income

Table 15-5 will provide a gross income statement. However, there are other expenses that must be taken care of before net profit is determined; namely—

1. **Depreciation on buildings and equipment.**—It is suggested that the "useful life" of buildings and equipment be as follows, with depreciation accordingly: Buildings, 25 years; and machinery and equipment, 10 years. Sometimes a higher depreciation, or amortization, is desirable because it produces tax savings, and for protection against obsolescence due to scientific and technological developments.

2. **Interest on owner's money invested in farm and equipment.**—This should be computed at the going rate in the area, say 8 percent.

Here's an example of how this works:
Let's assume that on a given farm there was a gross income of $100,000 and a gross expense of $60,000, or a surplus of $40,000. Let's further assume that there are $40,000 worth of machinery, $30,000 worth of buildings, and $175,000 of the owner's money invested in farm and equipment. Here is the result:

```
Gross profit ............................................$40,000
Depreciation:
Machinery, $40,000 @ 10%....$ 4,000
Buildings, $30,000 @ 4%........$ 1,200
                                  $ 5,200
Interest $175,000 @ 8%..........  14,000
                                            $19,200
Return to labor and management.................$20,800
```

Some folks prefer to measure management by return on invested capital, and not wages. This approach may be accomplished by paying management wages first, then figuring return on investment.

Enterprise Accounts

Where a swine enterprise is diversified—for example, a farm producing feeder pigs, finishing hogs, and growing corn—enterprise accounts should be kept; in this case three different

accounts for three different enterprises. The reasons for keeping enterprise accounts are:

1. It makes it possible to determine which enterprises have been most profitable, and which least profitable.

2. It makes it possible to compare a given enterprise with competing enterprises of like kind, from the standpoint of ascertaining comparative performance.

3. It makes it possible to determine the profitableness of an enterprise at the margin (the last unit of production). This will give an indication as to whether to increase the size of a certain enterprise at the expense of an alternative existing enterprise when both enterprises are profitable in total.

ANALYZING A HOG BUSINESS; IS IT PROFITABLE?

Most people are in business to make money—and swine producers are people. In some areas, particularly near cities and where the population is dense, land values may appreciate so as to be a very considerable profit factor. Also, a tax angle may be important. But neither of these should be counted upon. The hog operation should make a reasonable return on the investment; otherwise, the owner should not be in the hog business.

The owner or manager of a hog establishment needs to analyze his business—to determine how well he's doing. With big operations, it's no longer possible to base such an analysis on the bank balance statement at the end of the year. In the first place, once a year is not frequent enough, for it is possible to go broke, without really knowing it, in that period of time. Secondly, a balance statement gives no basis for analyzing an operation—for ferreting out its strengths and weaknesses. In large hog enterprises, it is strongly recommended that progress be charted by means of monthly or quarterly closings of financial records.

Also, a hog producer must not only compete with other hogmen down the road, but he must compete with himself—with his record last year and the year before. He must work ceaselessly away at making progress, improving the end product, and lowering costs of production.

To analyze a hog business, two things are essential: (1) good records, and (2) yardsticks, or profit indicators, with which to measure an operation.

Profit indicators are a gauge for measuring the primary factors contributing to profit. In order for a hogman to determine how well he's doing, he must be able to compare his own operation with something else; for example, (1) his own historical 5-year average, (2) the average for the U.S. or for his particular area, or (3) the top 5 percent. The author favors the latter, for high goals have a tendency to spur superior achievement.

For purposes of illustrating, let us use the items listed in Table 15-1 as profit indicators. Like most profit indicators, they aren't perfect. But they will serve as useful guides. Also, some indicators may be added or deleted.

The important thing is that each hog operation have adequate profit indicators, and that these be applied as frequently as possible; in a growing-finishing operation, this may be done monthly with rate and efficiency of gains.

Feeder Pig Production Profit Indicators

Many factors determine the profitableness of feeder pig production. Certainly, a favorable per sow unit capital investment in land and buildings is a first requisite. Additionally, percent pig crop weaned and weaning weight are exceedingly important.

Of course, there are wide area differences, and no two hog farms are alike. Also, there are seasonal differences; for example, a drought will materially affect pastures.

Growing-Finishing Profit Indicators

Growing-finishing operators need to keep good records and make frequent analyses (at least once monthly) to determine how well they are doing. A determination of assets and liabilities at the end of the fiscal year is not good enough, primarily because it is available only once per year. Growing-finishing requires much feed; hence, feed records should be kept as current as possible at all times.

Grower-finisher producers are primarily interested in two questions; namely, (1) how well am I doing—profitwise, and (2) how do I compare with other similar operators? Table 15-1 (right hand column) gives some guidelines for answering these questions. It may be used in making an analysis of a specific finishing operation for determining (1) the strengths and weaknesses

within the unit, and (2) how it stacks up with similar operations. It is suggested that two additional evaluations be added to Table 15-1 (right column) when analyzing a finishing operation; namely, (1) rate of gain, and (2) efficiency of feed utilization.

Admittedly, profit indicators, such as those given in Table 15-1, are not perfect; simply because no two swine enterprises are the same. Nationally, there are wide area differences in climate, feeds, land costs, salaries and wages, and other factors. Nevertheless, indicators *per se* serve as a valuable yardstick. Through them, it is possible to measure how well a given operation is doing—to ascertain if it is out of line in any one category and, if so, the extent of same.

After a few years of operation, it is desirable that a grower-finisher operator evolve with his own yardstick and profit indicators, based on his own historical records and averages. Even with this, there will be year to year fluctuations due to seasonal differences, hog and feed price changes, disease outbreaks, changes in managers, wars and inflation, and other happenstances.

THE CORN-HOG RATIO

The corn-hog ratio refers to the number of bushels of corn required to equal in value 100 pounds of live hog. Thus, a corn-hog ratio of 13.8 means that price relationships are such that 13.8 bushels of corn equals in value 100 pounds of hogs. Usually the figures are computed on the basis of some central market, but farm prices may be used. Currently, corn-hog ratio of 13.8 may be accepted as normal; this figure is based on the average price relationship for the period 1940 to 1964.[4]

A high corn-hog ratio, one which is above 13.8, means cheap corn and high-priced hogs and likely profit to the producer—conditions that stimulate more breeding and feeding to heavier weights. On the other hand, a low ratio, one which is below 13.8, means high-priced corn and low-priced hogs—conditions that result in less breeding and feeding of swine. It is noteworthy, however, that the corn-hog ratio is a declining indicator of future hog production. This is so because (1) an

---

[4]Based on data from: *Livestock and Meat Statistics*, Consumer and Marketing Service, USDA, July 1963, and September 1965. Prior to the corn price support program, the corn-hog ratio averaged 11.4.

Hog - Corn Ratios 1940 - 1964

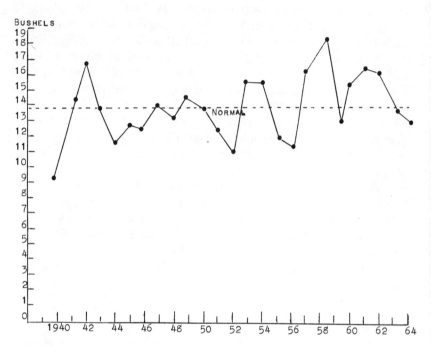

Fig. 15-1. The corn-hog ratio, 1940 to 1964. A corn-hog ratio of 13.8 is accepted as normal, with a higher figure than this favorable to the producer and a lower figure unfavorable to the producer. (Based on data from: *The Livestock and Meat Statistics*, Consumer and Marketing Service, USDA, July 1963, and September 1965.

estimated 5 percent of the nation's hog producers now market 33 percent of the hogs, which means that there are fewer of the small operators and "iners and outers" in the business; (2) big hog operators hold hog numbers to near capacity at all times, with little room for expansion or contraction in numbers according to prices; (3) with the prospect of favorable grain prices in the years ahead, producers are not inclined to put capital in hog facilities; (4) satisfactory farm labor for hog farms is hard to come by; (5) modern slotted-floor confinement-type farrowing and finishing units are costly, and producers are reluctant to enter the business without "going modern"; and (6) corn or other grain is now a smaller part of the total cost of production, and non-feed and fixed expenses a larger part.

COMPUTERS IN THE SWINE BUSINESS

Accurate and up-to-the-minute records and controls have taken on increasing importance in all agriculture, including the hog business, as the investment required to engage in farming has risen and profit margins have narrowed. Today's successful farmers must have, and use, as complete records as any other business. Also, records must be kept current.

Big and complex enterprises have outgrown hand record keeping. It's too time consuming, with the result that it doesn't allow management enough time for planning and decision making. Additionally, it does not permit an all-at-once consideration of the complex interrelationships which affect the economic success of the business. This has prompted a new computer technique known as linear programming.

Linear programming is similar to budgeting, in that it compares several plans simultaneously and chooses from among them the one likely to yield the highest returns. It is a way in which to analyze a great mass of data and consider many alternatives. It is not a managerial genie; nor will it replace decision-making managers. However, it is a modern and effective tool in the present age, when just a few dollars per head or per acre can spell the difference between profit and loss.

There is hardly any limit to what computers can do if fed the proper information. Among the difficult questions that they can answer for a specific farm are:

1. **How is the entire operation doing so far?** It is preferable to obtain quarterly or monthly progress reports; often making it possible to spot trouble before it's too late.

2. **What farm enterprises are making money; which ones are freeloading or losing?** By keeping records by enterprises—hogs, dairy, wheat, corn, etc.—it is possible to determine strengths and weaknesses; then either to rectify the situation or shift labor and capital to a more profitable operation. Through "enterprise analysis," some operators have discovered that one part of the farm business may earn $5, or more, per hour for labor and management, whereas another may earn only $1 per hour, and still another may lose money.

3. **Is each enterprise yielding maximum return?** By having profit or performance indicators in each enterprise, it is possible

to compare these (a) with the historical average of the same farm, or (b) with the same indicators of other farms.

4. How does this operation stack up with its competition? Without revealing names, the computing center (local, state, area, or national) can determine how a given operation compares with others—either the average, or the top (say 5 percent).

5. How can you plan ahead? By using projected prices and costs, computers can show what moves to make for the future— they can be a powerful planning tool. They can be used in determining when to plant, when to schedule farm machine use, etc.

6. How can income taxes be cut to the legal minimum? By keeping accurate record of expenses and figuring depreciations accurately, computers make for a saving in income taxes on most farms.

For providing answers to these questions, and many more, computer accounting costs an average of about 1 percent of the gross farm income. By comparison, it is noteworthy that city businesses pay double this amount.

There are three requisites for linear programming a farm; namely—

1. Access to a computer.

2. Computer know-how, so as to set the program up properly and be able to analyze and interpret the results.

3. Good records.

The pioneering computer services available to farmers were operated by universities, trade associations, and governments— most of them were on an experimental basis. Subsequently, others have entered the field, including commercial data processing firms, banks, machinery companies, feed and fertilizer companies, and farm suppliers. They are using it as a "service sell," as a replacement for the days of "hard sell."

Programmed farming is here to stay, and it will increase.

Computers in Ration Formulation

Ration formulation is only one use of computers in hog operations. As every hogman knows, many management decisions are involved in obtaining the highest net returns; and the bigger and the more complex the enterprise, the more important it is that the decisions be right.

Problems can be solved without the aid of a computer. But the machine has the distinct advantages of (1) speed, (2) coming up with answers to each of several problems simultaneously, and (3) offering the best single alternative, all factors considered. Among the possible uses of computers in rations, particularly on the larger operations, are:

1. Ration formulation.

2. How to determine the best ingredient buy.

3. The most profitable ration—the one that costs the least per pound of gain produced. In many cases, the cheapest ration will actually increase cost of gain. Also, rations that produce the most rapid gains may be too costly.

4. The most profitable kind of hogs—weight, sex, and grade —to feed in relation to available feeds and feed prices.

5. Seasonal differences in performance of hogs on a given farm.

6. As a means of forecasting profits or losses; with all-at-once consideration given to feeder prices, slaughter hog outlook, probable rate of gain, and interest and overhead costs.

7. As a means of keeping and updating the voluminous daily feed transfers from feed inventories, to mixed rations, to records for each lot of hogs. Accurate and current feed inventories are necessary for wise ingredient buying and for financing feed inventories; and accurate and current feed records by lots are important.

For additional information relative to the use of computers in ration formulation, the reader is referred to Chapter VI of this book, under the section headed, "How to Balance a Ration by the Computer Method."

HOG FUTURES TRADING

The biggest uncertainty in the hog business is the selling price of market hogs. The producer knows his cost of producing or purchasing feeder pigs; and from his past records, he is usually able to project, with reasonable accuracy, the costs of production to market time. But, unless he contracts ahead, he has no assurance of what they will bring when they're ready to go. Moreover, there is little flexibility in market time, for the reason that excess finish is costly, and unwanted by the consumer.

Now, live hog futures provide a means through which a hog feeder can fix his price at the outset of the feeding period. The Chicago Mercantile Exchange first offered live hog futures on February 28, 1966. Pork bellies and hams were traded on the futures market prior to this time; but trading in these commodities is of primary interest to packers and wholesale meat dealers, rather than hog producers.

The development of live hog futures requires that farmers, businessmen, and others be knowledgeable of what futures marketing involves and how it applies to the marketing of hogs. This section provides background information.

What Is Futures Trading?

Futures trading is not new. It is a well accepted, century-old procedure used in many commodities; for protecting profits, stabilizing prices, and smoothing out the flow of merchandise. For example, it has long been an integral part of the grain industry; grain elevators, flour millers, feed manufacturers, and others, have used it to protect themselves against losses due to price fluctuations. Also, a number of livestock products—frozen pork bellies, hams, hides, and tallow—were traded on the futures market before the advent of beef futures. Many of these operators prefer to forego the possibility of making a high speculative profit in favor of earning a normal margin or service charge through efficient operation of their business. They look to futures markets to provide (1) an insurance medium in the marketing field, and (2) the facilities and machinery for underwriting price risks.

Futures trading is a place where buyers and sellers meet on an organized market and transact business on paper, without the physical presence of the commodity. The exchange neither buys nor sells; rather, it provides the facilities, establishes rules, serves as a clearing house, holds the margin money deposited by both buyers and sellers, and guarantees delivery on all contracts. Buyers and sellers either trade on their own account or are represented by brokerage firms. Except for dealing in futures, and in paper contracts instead of live animals, futures trading on an exchange is very similar to terminal livestock markets. Hogmen need no introduction to the latter.

The unique characteristic of futures markets is that trading is in terms of contracts to deliver or to take delivery, rather

than on the immediate transfer of the physical commodity. In practice, however, very few contracts are held until the delivery date. The vast majority of them are cancelled by offsetting transactions made before the delivery date.

Many hogmen contract their feeder pigs for future delivery without the medium of an exchange. They contract to sell and deliver to a buyer a certain number and kind of pigs at an agreed upon price and place. Hence, the risk of loss from a decrease in price after the contract is shifted to the buyer; and, by the same token, the seller foregoes the possibility of a price rise. In reality, such contracting is a form of futures trading. Unlike futures trading on an exchange, however, actual delivery of the pigs is a must. Also, such privately arranged contracts are not always available, the terms may not be acceptable, and the only recourse to default on the contract is a lawsuit.

What Is a Futures Contract?

A futures contract is a standardized, legal, binding paper transaction in which the seller promises to make delivery and the buyer promises to take delivery on a specified quantity and type of a commodity at a specified location(s) during a specified future month. The buying and selling are done through a third party (the exchange clearing member) so that the buyer and seller remain anonymous; the validity of the contract is guaranteed by reputable and well financed exchange clearing members; and either buyer or seller can readily liquidate his position by simply offsetting sale or purchase.

The essential provisions of the live hog futures contract of the Chicago Mercantile Exchange follows:

> Delivery of 20,000 pounds of U.S.D.A. grade No. 1 and 2, barrows and gilts averaging 200 to 230 pounds (with certain permissible substitutions and allowances). Delivery to be made at Chicago; with delivery to St. Louis, Omaha, Sioux City, and St. Paul, at a 50¢ per cwt. discount, and delivery to Kansas City at a 75¢/cwt. discount.

The commission fee on each contract (20,000 pounds of No. 1 and 2 live hogs), covering both purchase and sale (called a round-turn) is $20 and a minimum margin, or cash deposit, of $300 is required. So, the total cost of hedging the 20,000 pounds of live

hogs is $20 plus the interest you forego on the $300 ($500 in delivery monthly) margin which you must deposit with the Exchange when you start the hedge.

How Does a Futures Contract Work?

Traditionally, futures contracts have been used for two purposes: (1) hedging and (2) speculating.

Hedging is an offsetting transaction by which purchases or sales of a commodity are counterbalanced by sales or purchases of an equivalent quantity of futures contracts in the same commodity.

Speculating is risk-taking by anyone who hopes to make a profit in the advances or declines in the price of the futures contract.

Hog producers are the primary hedgers in the live hog futures market. It is a way in which they can lessen risk. They hedge as price insurance in case hogs go down at the time it is expected that their finished animals will be ready to sell. Ordinarily, a hogman who hedges through futures is not likely to take a profit on both slaughter hogs and futures contracts. This bothers some hogmen, for they want "to have their cake and eat it too."

Speculators perform a very important function—that of assuming price risks. They make hedging possible. They buy or sell for future delivery, based on their judgment as to the direction and level of price between the current date and some future date. When a speculator buys a hog contract, he becomes an armchair hogman—one who doesn't have to feed or care for his hogs.

For purposes of illustrating how a hedge works, let's assume that we have a hog feeder with the following set of circumstances:

On April 1, he buys 91 feeder pigs weighing 50 pounds at $18 per head or 36 cents per pound. He plans to market these the following August, at an average weight of 220 pounds. He has kept good records in the past, from which he projects that feed, labor, equipment, capital, and miscellaneous costs required to finish these pigs to slaughter will total about $22 per head; and that he needs 18 cents per pound to cover the feeder pigs purchased plus all feedlot costs. Next, let us see what he can do by using the futures market to hedge his position.

If in April the August hogs futures are selling at 18 cents

per pound (see Box C in Table 15-6) he could assure himself of favorable returns on capital and labor by hedging. Thus, by selling an August futures contract he assures himself of a price of 18 cents next August. He also obligates himself either (1) to deliver the number, weight, and quality of hogs specified in the contract (with allowable substitutions) at 18 cents before the contract expires, or, as is true in nearly 99 percent of the grain hedges, (2) to buy an offsetting contract of the same futures month just before maturity and at the then current price (see Box D in Table 15-6).

TABLE 15-6

EXAMPLE OF A HOG FEEDER HEDGING

	Cash Transaction	Futures Transaction
April	A Buys 91 feeder pigs (50 lb.) at 36¢	C Sells August futures contract. One unit at 18¢
August	B Sells 91 U.S. No. 1 and 2 hogs at: 17¢ 18¢ 19¢	D Buys April futures contract. One unit at: 17¢ 18¢ 19¢

Normally, the respective cash market price and the futures market price in the delivery month will be very close together (compare Boxes D and B, Table 15-6).

For example, consider three different price situations in August: (1) where price expectations were realized (August cash price was 18 cents), (2) where prices were lower than expected (August cash price was 17 cents), and (3) where prices were higher than expected (August cash price was 19 cents). Assume in each case the hog feeder has hedged by transacting in the futures market. What would be the outcome?

1. If U.S. No. 1 and 2 hog prices in August are at 18 cents, the feeder would be in the same position as he would have been without hedging.

2. Where hog prices are 17 cents per pound in August he would have lost $2.20 per head in his feeding operation if he had not hedged. By hedging, however, he would cover his feeding

SWINE SCIENCE

costs by selling an August futures in April (at 18 cents). The cash and futures transaction in August would offset one another.

3. If hog prices in August are 19 cents per pound he would have gained $2.20 per head had he not hedged. By hedging, he again assured himself of 18 cents in August, and the August cash and futures transactions would cancel out any gains in that month.

Facts About Futures Contracts

Some pertinent facts about futures contracts follow:

1. A cardinal feature of any workable futures contract—whether it be grain, hogs, or any other commodity—is that there shall be maintained a solid connection with the commodity; that is, cash and futures must be tied together.

2. Any contract held until maturity must be delivered. This keeps the futures price in line with the cash price at the livestock market.

3. During the delivery month, the cash and futures market tend to come together at the point of delivery. If this were not so traders would quickly take advantage of the situation. For example, if prior to the termination of trading on August futures, the price of hogs on the terminal market was $5.00/cwt. below August futures, traders could buy hogs and sell futures, then deliver on the contract for a profit of $5.00/cwt. (less marketing and brokerage fees).

4. It is not good business to use the futures market as a selling hedge when the futures market is below the cash market.

5. A grower-finisher operator who buys feeder pigs and sells finished hogs on a regularly scheduled basis—perhaps monthly—throughout the year is doing his own hedging, **provided feeder prices roughly parallel slaughter hog prices.**

Advantages and Limitations of Live Hog Futures

Although some changes and refinements in live hog futures are inevitable as more experience is accumulated, they are serving a useful purpose, and they are here to stay. Before using them, however, a hogman should understand what they will and will not do for him.

Among the **advantages** of hog futures are:

1. Through hedging, they can provide price protection or insurance to hogmen against major breaks in the market.

2. They permit profits to be "locked in" any time that they become available during the feeding period.

3. They allow selectivity of the market time over the entire feeding period, rather than limit it to the one day that hogs are ready to go.

4. They make is possible for hogmen to obtain credit more easily.

5. They serve as (a) a price barometer for several months ahead and (b) a centralized point for disseminating prices.

6. They make for a more stable feeder pig market, with fewer peaks and valleys of price movements.

Like many good things in life, live hog futures are not perfect. They will not solve all the producer's price problems, they will not raise long-time price levels, nor will they cause people to eat more pork. But these are not disadvantages; they're facts.

Among the **limitations** of live hog futures are the following:

1. The hog inventory (the hogs on a particular farm, for example) may be at a location which would require costly transportation to the specified delivery point.

2. Some delivery months may not move exactly as the cash market does.

3. A change in the basis can mean a hedging loss as well as a hedging profit.

4. There is a relatively narrow range of time during which it is practical to hold slaughter hogs while waiting for a change in the basis (the basis is the spread between the cash price and the price of the futures).

5. The feeder must not forget to offset by purchase of another contract at the proper time; otherwise, he may find it necessary to deliver.

6. If the feeder sells futures for a greater amount than the finished weight of his hogs, he is engaged in speculation for the amount of the excess.

7. There are some costs in futures which must be considered; namely, commission ($20/contract) and interest on margin capital ($300; $500 in delivery month). These should be considered as costs of doing business; for the protection secured, the producer must pay a commission—much as he does for a life insurance policy.

8. Unless a feeder has maintained good and accurate records, and can project his costs with reasonable accuracy, he cannot

intelligently determine if a futures price is favorable for placing a hedge.

How to Go About Buying Hog Futures

Here is the "how and where" that a producer interested in buying hog futures must follow:

1. Have good and accurate records of costs.

2. Contact a stock brokerage firm that represents a company with membership in the exchange.

3. Open up a trading account with the broker, by signing an agreement with him authorizing him to execute trades.

4. Deposit with the broker the necessary margin money— $300; $500 in delivery month, for each contract desired. He will then maintain a separate account for the producer. The $20/ contract commission fee is due when the contract is fulfilled by either delivery or offsetting purchase or sale of another contract.

Maintain basis charts; showing the relationship between (a) local prices of feeders and slaughter hogs, and (b) live hog futures.

Some Futures Market Terms

Futures markets have a jargon and sign language of their own. It is not necessary that producers dealing in futures master many of them, but it will facilitate matters if they at least have a working knowledge of the following:

Pit.—The open auction of the exchange, where buyers and sellers transact business.

Speculators.—Persons who are willing to accept the risks associated with price changes.

Hedgers.—Persons who cannot afford risks, and who try to increase their normal margins through buying and selling of futures contracts.

Discount to the futures.—When the cash price is under the futures.

Premium.—When the cash price is above the futures.

Basis.—The spread between the cash price and the price of the futures.

Basis movement.—The change in the basis within a particular period of time; in one location, or from location to location at the same time.

Long position.—Buying a contract to sell later.

Short position.—Selling a contract to buy later.

Washout.—Offsetting a position taken earlier.

Limit order.—Placing limitations on orders given the brokerage firm.

Summary Relative to Hog Futures

Live hog futures may not stabilize slaughter hog prices, but it will stabilize profits. For the latter reason, it may develop into one of the more important hog marketing tools of the future, especially for larger and more specialized producers.

It will likely provide some degree of stability to the feeder pig market. This is so because those feeder pig producers who also have the necessary facilities for finishing hogs may now choose between (1) selling feeder pigs, or (2) finishing them out protected by hedging. Likewise, futures will impart increased price stability to the slaughter hog market provided sufficient large producers react to anticipated price levels, rather than current or past prices. In any case, it can be a profit stabilizer for the hog feeder who uses it effectively for hedging purposes. Additionally, live hog futures trading will likely encourage increased production and more specification production, and result in more orderly and efficient marketing, accompanied by reduced handling costs.

MANAGEMENT

According to Webster, *management is "the act, or art, of managing, handling, controlling or directing."*

Three major ingredients are essential to success in the hog business: (1) good hogs, (2) a sound feed and care program, and (3) good management.

Management gives point and purpose to everything else. The skill of the manager materially affects how well hogs are bought and sold, the health of the animals, the results of the rations,

the stress of the hogs, the rate of gain and feed efficiency, the performance of labor, the public relations of the establishment, and even the expression of the genetic potential of the hogs. Indeed, a manager must wear many hats—and he must wear each of them well.

The bigger and the more complicated the hog operation, the more competent the management required. This point merits emphasis because, currently, (1) bigness is a sign of the times, and (2) the most common method of attempting to "bail out" of an unprofitable hog venture is to increase its size. Although it's easier to achieve efficiency of equipment, labor, purchases, and marketing in big operations, bigness alone will not make for greater efficiency as some owners have discovered to their sorrow, and others will experience. Management is still the key to success. When in financial trouble, owners should have no illusions on this point.

In manufacturing and commerce, the importance and scarcity of top managers are generally recognized and reflected in the salaries paid to persons in such positions. Unfortunately, agriculture as a whole has lagged; and altogether too many owners still subscribe to the philosophy that the way to make money out of the hog business is to hire a manager "cheap," with the result that they usually get what they pay for—a "cheap **manager.**"

Traits of a Good Manager

There are established bases for evaluating many articles of trade, including hogs and grain. They are graded according to well-defined standards. Additionally, we chemically analyze feeds and conduct feeding trials. But no such standard or system of evaluation has evolved for managers, despite their acknowledged importance.

The author has prepared the Hog Manager Check List, given in Table 15-7, which (1) employers may find useful when selecting or evaluating a manager, and (2) managers may apply to themselves for self-improvement purposes. No attempt has been made to assign a percentage score to each trait, because this will vary among swine establishments. Rather, it is hoped that this check list will serve as a useful guide (1) to the traits of a good manager, and (2) to what the boss wants.

TABLE 15-7

HOG MANAGER CHECK LIST

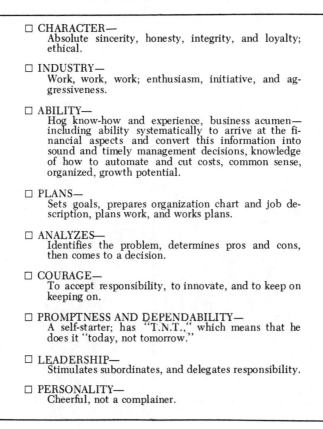

☐ CHARACTER—
Absolute sincerity, honesty, integrity, and loyalty; ethical.

☐ INDUSTRY—
Work, work, work; enthusiasm, initiative, and aggressiveness.

☐ ABILITY—
Hog know-how and experience, business acumen—including ability systematically to arrive at the financial aspects and convert this information into sound and timely management decisions, knowledge of how to automate and cut costs, common sense, organized, growth potential.

☐ PLANS—
Sets goals, prepares organization chart and job description, plans work, and works plans.

☐ ANALYZES—
Identifies the problem, determines pros and cons, then comes to a decision.

☐ COURAGE—
To accept responsibility, to innovate, and to keep on keeping on.

☐ PROMPTNESS AND DEPENDABILITY—
A self-starter; has "T.N.T.," which means that he does it "today, not tomorrow."

☐ LEADERSHIP—
Stimulates subordinates, and delegates responsibility.

☐ PERSONALITY—
Cheerful, not a complainer.

Organization Chart and Job Description

It is important that every worker know to whom he is responsible and for what he is responsible; and the bigger and the more complex the operation, the more important this becomes. This should be written down in an organization chart and a job description (as illustrated on pages 730 and 731).

Incentive Basis for the Help

Big farms must rely on hired labor, all or in part. Good help—the kind that everyone wants—is hard to come by; it's scarce, in strong demand, and difficult to keep. And the farm

ORGANIZATION CHART

on

PORKOPOLIS

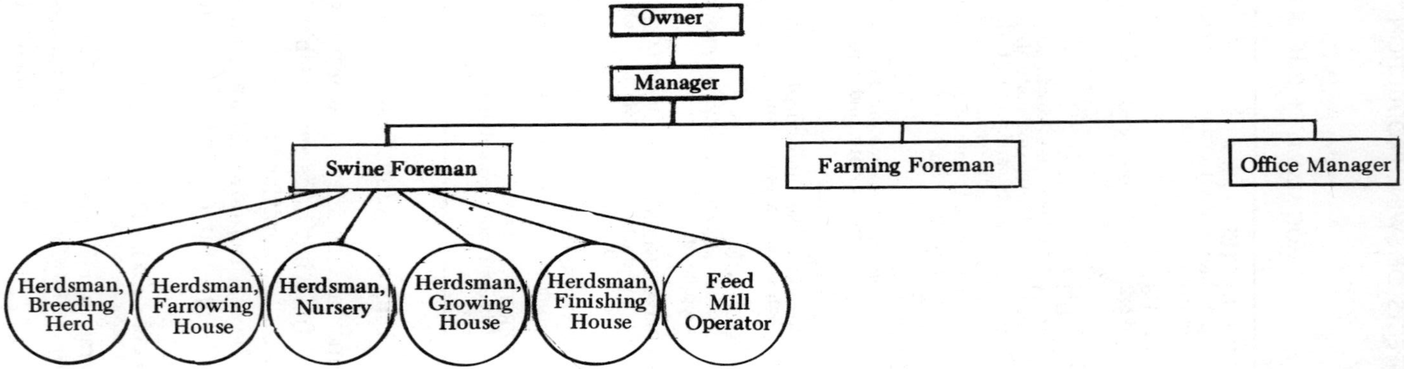

JOB DESCRIPTIONS

on

PORKOPOLIS

Owner	Manager	Swine Foreman	Farming Foreman	Office Manager	Herdsman, Breeding Herd	Etc.
Responsible for:	Responsible for:	Responsible for:	Responsible for:	Responsible for:	Responsible for:	
1. Making policy decisions. 2. Borrowing capital. 3. (List others)	1. Supervising all staff 2. Preparing proposed long-time plan 3. Budgets 4. (List others)	1. All swine operations 2. Directing his staff	1. Crop operations 2. Maintenance	1. Records 2. Budgets	1. Care of breeding herd 2. Buying herd boars 3. Production records	

manpower situation is going to become more difficult in the years ahead. There is need, therefore, for some system that will (1) give a big assist in getting and holding top-flight help, and (2) cut costs and boost profits. An incentive basis that makes hired help partners in profit is the answer.

Many manufacturers have long had an incentive basis. Executives are frequently accorded stock option privileges, through which they prosper as the business prospers. Common laborers may receive bonuses based on piecework or quotas (number of units, pounds produced). Also, most factory workers get overtime pay and have group insurance and a retirement plan. A few industries have a true profit-sharing arrangement based on net profit as such, a specified percentage of which is divided among employees. No two systems are alike. Yet, each is designed to pay more for labor, provided labor improves production and efficiency. In this way, both owners and laborers benefit from better performance.

Family-owned and family-operated farms have a built-in incentive basis; there is pride of ownership, and all members of the family are fully cognizant that they prosper as the business prospers.

Many different incentive plans can be, and are, used. There is no best one for all operations. The various plans given in Table 15-8 are intended as guides only.

The incentive basis chosen should be tailored to fit the specific operation; with consideration given to kind and size of operation, extent of owner's supervision, present and projected productivity levels, mechanization, and other factors. For most hog operations, the author favors a "production sharing and prevailing price" type of incentive, examples of which are given later in this section. (Also, see Tables 15-9 and 15-10.)

HOW MUCH INCENTIVE PAY?

After (1) reaching a decision to go on an incentive basis, and (2) deciding on the kind of incentive, it is necessary to arrive at how much to pay. Here are some guidelines that may be helpful in determining this:

1. Pay the going base, or guaranteed, salary; then add the incentive pay above this.

2. Determine the total stipend (the base salary plus incentive) to which you are willing to go.

TABLE 15-8

INCENTIVE PLANS FOR SWINE ESTABLISHMENTS

Types of Incentives	Pertinent Provisions of Some Known Incentive Systems in Use	Advantages	Disadvantages	Comments
1. Bonuses	A flat, arbitrary bonus; at Christmas time, year-end, or quarterly or other intervals. A tenure bonus such as (1) 5 to 10% of the base wage or 2 to 4 weeks additional salary paid at Christmas time or year-end, (2) 2 to 4 weeks vacation with pay, depending on length and quality of service, or (3) $3.00 to $20/week, set aside and to be paid if employee stays on the job a specified time.	It's simple and direct.	Not very effective in increasing production and profits.	
2. Equity-building plan	Employee is allowed to own a certain number of animals. These are usually fed without charge.	It imparts pride of ownership to the employee.	The hazard that the owner may feel that employee accords his animals preferential treatment; suspicioned if not proved.	

(Continued)

TABLE 15-8 (Continued)

Types of Incentives	Pertinent Provisions of Some Known Incentive Systems in Use	Advantages	Disadvantages	Comments
3. Production Sharing	50 cents to $1/pig marketed above 7 pigs/litter. 50 cents to $1/hundred lbs. of pork produced. $4 to $6 for every sow that weans 7 or more pigs. 25¢/cwt. of gain on finishing hogs.	It's an effective way to achieve higher production.	Net returns may suffer. For example, a higher rate of gain than is economical may be achieved by feeding finishing hogs more expensive feeds than are practical. This can be alleviated by (1) specifying the ration and (2) setting an upper limit on the gains to which the incentive will apply. If a high performance level already exists, further gains or improvements may be hard to come by.	Incentive payments for production above certain levels—for example, above 7 pigs weaned /litter—are more effective than paying for all pigs produced.
4. Profit Sharing: a. Percent of gross income	1% to 2% of the gross.		Percent of gross does not impart cost of production consciousness. Both (1) percent of gross income and (2)	There must be prior agreement on what constitutes gross or net receipts, as the case may be; and how it is figured.
b. Percent of net income	10% to 20% of the net after deducting all costs.	Net income sharing works better for managers, supervisors and foremen than for common labor-	percent of net income expose the books and	

(Continued)

TABLE 15-8 (Continued)

Types of Incentives	Pertinent Provisions of Some Known Incentive Systems in Use	Advantages	Disadvantages	Comments
4. Profit Sharing: (Continued)		ers; because fewer hazards are involved to opening up the books to them. It's an effective way to get hired help to cut costs. It's a good plan for a hustler.	accounts to workers, who may not understand accounting principles. This can lead to suspicion and distrust. Controversy may arise (1) over accounting procedure—for example, from the standpoint of the owner a fast tax write-off may be desirable on new equipment, but this reduces the net shared with the worker; and (2) because some owners are prone to overbuild and over-equip, thereby decreasing net.	
5. Production sharing and prevailing price	See Table 15-9, a proposed incentive basis for growing-finishing operations.	It embraces the best features of both production sharing and profit sharing, without the major disadvantages of each. It (1) encourages high productivity and likely	It is a bit more complicated than some other plans, and it requires more complete records.	When properly done, and all factors considered, this is the most satisfactory incentive basis for a swine enterprise.

(Continued)

TABLE 15-8 (Continued)

Types of Incentives	Pertinent Provisions of Some Known Incentive Systems in Use	Advantages	Disadvantages	Comments
		profits, (2) is tied in with prevailing prices, (3) does not necessitate opening the books, and (4) is flexible—it can be split between owner and employee on any basis desired, and the production part can be adapted to a sliding scale or escalator arrangement—for example, the incentive basis in feeder pig production can be higher for the 25 lbs. in excess of 375 lbs. weaned than for 25 lbs. in excess of 275 lbs.		

3. Before making any offers, always check the plan on paper to see (a) how it would have worked out in past years based on your records, and (b) how it will work out as you achieve the future projected production.

Let's take the following example:

A herdsman of a 400-sow herd is now producing an average of 275 pounds per litter at weaning. He is receiving a base salary of $400/month plus house, garden, and 400 pounds of dressed pork/year. The owner prefers a "production sharing and prevailing price" type of incentive.

Step by step, here is the procedure for arriving at an incentive arrangement based on increased production:

1. By checking with local sources, it is determined that the present salary of $400/month plus extras is the going wage; and, of course, the herdsman receives this regardless of what the year's pig production or price turns out to be—it's guaranteed.

2. A study of the records reveals that with a little extra care on the part of the herdsman—particularly in creep feeding—the average litter weaning weight can be boosted enough to permit paying him $500/month, or $100/month more than he's now getting. That's $1,200 more per year. This can be fitted into the incentive plan.

3. An average increase in weaning weight of 10 pounds per pig on a litter of 7 means 70 pounds more per litter. At 25 cents/pound, that's $17.50 more per litter, or $7,000 more income from the 400-sow herd. But let us assume that a part of the better creep care involved the use of $1,000 more for feed than was being spent. That still leaves a net gain of $6,000 ($7,000 − $1,000). With an 80:20 split on the $6,000 between owner and herdsman, the owner would get $4,800, and the herdsman $1,200.

REQUISITES OF AN INCENTIVE BASIS

Owners who have not previously had experience with an incentive basis are admonished not to start with any plan until they are sure of both their plan and their help. Also, it is well to start with a simple plan; then a change can be made to a more inclusive and sophisticated plan after experience is acquired.

Regardless of the incentive plan adopted for a specific operation, it should encompass the following essential features:

1. Good owner (or manager) and good workers. No incentive basis can overcome a poor manager. He must be a good supervisor and fair to his help. Also, on big establishments, he must prepare a written-down organization chart and job description so the help knows (a) to whom they are responsible, and (b) what their responsibilities are. Likewise, no incentive basis can spur employees who are not able, interested, and/or willing. This necessitates that employees must be selected with special care where they will be on an incentive basis. Hence, the three—good owner (manager), good employees, and good incentive—go hand in hand.

2. It must be fair to both employer and employees.

3. It must be based on and make for mutual trust and esteem.

4. It must compensate for extra performance, rather than substitute for a reasonable base salary and other considerations (house, utilities, and certain provisions).

5. It must be as simple, direct, and easily understood as possible.

6. It should compensate all members of the team, from top to bottom.

7. It must be put in writing, so that there will be no misunderstanding. If some production-sharing plan is used in a growing-finishing operation, it should stipulate the ration (or who is responsible for ration formulation), and the weight to which finishing hogs are to be carried. On a feeder pig production enterprise, it should stipulate the ration, the culling of sows, and other pertinent factors.

8. It is preferable, although not essential, that workers receive incentive payments (a) at rather frequent intervals rather than annually, and (b) immediately after accomplishing the extra performance.

9. It should give the hired help a certain amount of responsibility, from the wise exercise of which they will benefit through the incentive arrangement.

10. It must be backed up by good records; otherwise, there is nothing on which to base incentive payments.

11. It should be a two-way street. If employees are compensated for superior performance, they should be penalized (or,

under most circumstances, fired) for poor performance. It serves no useful purpose to reward the unwilling, the incompetent, and the stupid. No overtime pay should be given to an employee who must work longer because of slowness or correcting mistakes of his own making. Likewise, if the reasonable break-even point on a feeder pig production operation is an average of 280 pounds per litter at weaning and this production level is not reached because of obvious neglect (for example, not being on the job at farrowing time), the employee(s) should be penalized (or fired).

INDIRECT INCENTIVES

Normally, we think of incentives as monetary in nature— as direct payments or bonuses for extra production or efficiency. However, there are other ways of encouraging employees to do a better job. The latter are known as indirect incentives. Among them are: (1) good wages; (2) good labor relations; (3) adequate house plus such privileges as the use of the farm truck or car, payment of electric bill, use of a swimming pool, hunting and fishing, use of horse, and furnishing meat, milk, and eggs; (4) good buildings and equipment; (5) vacation time with pay, time off, sick leave; (6) group health; (7) security; (8) the opportunity for self-improvement that can accrue from working for a top man; (9) the right to invest in the business; (10) an all-expense-paid trip to a short course, show, or convention; and (11) year-end bonus for staying all year. These indirect incentives will be accorded to the help of more and more establishments, especially the big ones.

INCENTIVE BASIS FOR FEEDER PIG PRODUCERS

On feeder pig producing enterprises there is need for some system which will encourage caretakers to be good nursemaids to newborn pigs, though it may mean the loss of sleep. Additionally, there is need to do all those things which make for the maximum percent pig crop weaned at a heavy weight.

From the standpoint of the owner of a feeder pig producing enterprise, production expenses remain practically unchanged regardless of the efficiency of the operation. Thus, the investment in land, buildings and equipment, sow's feed, and labor differs very little with a change (up or down) in the percent pig crop

or the weaning weight of pigs; and income above a certain break-even point is largely net profit. Yet, it must be remembered that owners take all the risks; hence, they should benefit most from profits.

On a feeder pig operation, the author recommends that profits beyond the break-even point (after deducting all expenses) be split on an 80:20 basis. This means that every dollar made above a certain level is split, with the owner taking 80 cents and the employees getting 20 cents. Also, there is merit in an escalator arrangement; with the split changed to 70:30, for example, when a certain plateau of efficiency is reached. Moreover, that which goes to the employees should be divided on the basis of their respective contributions, all the way down the line; for example, 25 percent of it might go to the manager, 25 percent might be divided among the herdsmen, and 50 percent of it divided among the rest of the help.

TABLE 15-9

A PROPOSED INCENTIVE BASIS FOR FEEDER PIG PRODUCERS

Average pounds per litter weaned (lbs.)	Here's how it works
	On this particular operation, the break-even point is assumed to be an average of 275 pounds per litter weaned; and, of course, this is arrived at after including all costs of production factors.
225	
250	
275	
(break-even point)	
300	Pounds of litter weaned in excess of the break-even point are sold or evaluated at the going price.
325	
350	If an average of 350 pounds per litter is weaned, and if this is worth 30 cents per pound, that's $22.50 more net per sow. In a 400-sow herd, that's $9,000. With an 80:20 division, $7,200 would go to the owner, and $1,800 would be distributed among the employees.
375	
400	
425	
450	
475	
500	
	Or, if desired, and if there is an escalator arrangement, there might be an 80:20 split at 350 pounds, a 70:30 split at 375 pounds, and a 65:35 split at 400 pounds.

A true profit-sharing system on a feeder pig operation based on net profit has the disadvantages of (1) employees not benefiting when there are losses, as frequently happens in the hog business, and (2) management opening up the books, which may lead to gossip, misinterpretation, and misunderstanding. An in-

centive system based on major profit factors alleviates these disadvantages.

Gross income in feeder pig operations is determined primarily by (1) percent pig crop weaned, (2) weaning weight of pigs, and (3) price. The first two factors can easily be determined. Usually, enough pigs are sold to establish price; otherwise, the going price can be used.

The incentive basis proposed in Table 15-9 for feeder pig operations is simple, direct, and easily applied. As noted, it is based on average pounds of litter weaned per sow, which factor encompasses both percent pig crop and weaning weight.

INCENTIVE BASIS FOR GROWING-FINISHING OPERATORS

An incentive basis for growing-finishing help is needed for motivation purposes, just as it is in feeder pig production. It is the most effective way in which to lessen absenteeism, poor processing and mixing of feeds, irregular and careless feeding, unsanitary troughs and water, sickness, stress, and other profit-sapping factors.

The incentive basis for growing-finishing operations shown in Table 15-10 is simple, direct, and easily applied.

Whenever possible, the break-even points—(1) pounds feed/pound gain, and (2) daily rate of gain—should be arrived at from actual records accumulated by the specific operation, preferably over a period of years. Perhaps, too, they should be moving averages, based on 5 to 10 years, with older years dropped out and more recent years added from time to time; thereby reflecting improvement in efficiency and rate of gain due primarily to changing technology, rather than to the efforts of the caretakers.

With a new feeder operation, on which there are no historical records from which to arrive at break-even points of feed efficiency and rate of gain, it is recommended that the figures of other similar feeder operations be used at the outset. These can be revised as actual records on the specific finishing enterprise become available. It is important, however, that the new operation start an incentive basis, even though the break-even points must be arbitrarily assumed at the time.

Another incentive basis followed in a few large operations consists of the following: A certain percent (say 15 percent) of the net earnings set aside in a trust account, which is divided

TABLE 15-10

A PROPOSED INCENTIVE BASIS FOR GROWING-FINISHING OPERATIONS

Feed/lb. Gain	Daily Rate of Gain	Here's How It Works:
(lbs.)	(lbs.)	
4.5	1.5	On this particular growing-finishing operation, the break-
4.4	1.6	even points are assumed to be (1) 4.1 pounds of feed/
4.3	1.7	lb. gain, and (2) 1.9 lbs. daily gain.
4.2	1.8	
4.1 (Break-even	1.9	Feed saved and gains made in excess of the break-even
4.0 point)	2.0	points are computed at going prices.
3.9	2.1	
3.8	2.2	If the feed efficiency goes to 3.8 and the gain increases
3.7	2.3	to 2.2, and if feed costs $65.00 per ton and hogs are
3.6	2.4	worth 25 cents per pound, then these feed savings and
3.5	2.5	increased gains are worth—

Feed saved (lbs.)	Cost of feed/lb.	Value of feed saved/ lb. gain	Value of feed saved on 2.2 lbs. gain
0.3	3.25¢	0.975¢	2.145

Gains made lbs.	Per lb. mkt. value of gains	Value of increased daily gain
0.3	25¢	7.5¢

Increased profit/head/day:

		(cents)
	Feed	2.145
	Gain	7.5
		9.645

On pigs fed for 180 days, that's $17.36/head. With 1,000 hogs, that's $17,360 total. When divided on an 80:20 basis, that's $13,888 for the owner and $3,472 for the employees.

among and applied to the account of each employee according to salary and/or length of service, and paid to employees upon retirement or after a specified period of years. The main disadvantages to this incentive basis are that there may not be any net some years, that some employees do not want to wait that long for their added compensation, and that it opens up the books of the business.

Because of the high correlation between feed efficiency and rate of gain, the incentive basis previously recommended does result in an overlapping of measures. Nevertheless, both efficiency

and rate of gain are important profit indicators to hogmen. Because of the overlapping, however, some may prefer to choose one or the other of the measures, rather than both.

ESTATE PLANNING

Human nature being what it is, most farmers shy away from suggestions that someone help plan the disposition of their property and other assets. Also, they have a long-standing distrust of lawyers, legal terms and trusts, and, to them, the subject of taxes seldom makes for pleasant conversation.

If no plans are made, estate taxes and settlement costs often run considerably higher than if proper estate planning is done and a will is made to carry out these plans. Today, farming is big business; many farmers have more than $100,000 invested in land, animals, and equipment. Thus, it is not a satisfying thought to one who has worked hard to build and maintain a good farm during his lifetime to feel that his heirs will have to sell the farm to raise enough cash to pay Federal Estate and Inheritance Taxes. By using a good estate planning service, a farmer can generally save thousands of dollars for his family in estate and inheritance taxes and in estate settlement costs. For assistance, farmers should go to an estate planning specialist—an individual or company specializing in this work, or the trust department of a commercial bank.

Inheritance and Partnerships

Nothing pleases parents more than seeing their children succeed, and, generally speaking, having them take over the home farm makes for the ultimate in parental pride and satisfaction. Moreover, such an arrangement can make for a fine financial start in life for the young man who desires to carry on, provided, while the parents are still living, advantage is taken of the very considerable savings in federal inheritance taxes, as provided by law.

Regulations permit parents to make (1) one specific gift of $60,000 tax free, and (2) an annual tax-free gift, repeated for a number of years, of $6,000; and these gifts may be in the form of interest in the livestock operation. Thus, in the first year, it is possible to transfer a maximum interest of $66,000 in the hog farm to an heir without entailing the payment of any Federal

Inheritance Tax. It is necessary, however, to file a gift tax return. Frequently, even where it is the full intent and desire of the parents and the children that the latter continue with the farming operation, the gift tax provision is not considered. Then, upon death of the parents, the heir(s) may be required to raise such a large amount of cash to pay the inheritance taxes that a part or all of the operation may have to be liquidated.

A second logical step in this transfer is a partnership contract between the parents and their heir(s) recorded with the Clerk of Court in the county in which the farm is located. Appropriate counsel should be consulted in the preparation and recording of this agreement. Where the partnership contract is between the father and the heir, a provision should be included permitting the heir to purchase the father's share of the partnership for a fixed amount. The amount stipulated will then go into the father's estate. This will provide for proper and uninterrupted operation of the farm, because, upon the father's death, the partnership is legally terminated.

LIABILITY

Most farmers are in such financial position that they are vulnerable to damage suits. Moreover, the number of damage suits arising each year is increasing at an almost alarming rate, and astronomical damages are being claimed. Studies reveal that about 95 percent of the court cases involving injury result in damages being awarded.

Several types of liability insurance offer a safeguard against liability suits brought as a result of injury suffered by another person or damage to their property.

Comprehensive personal liability insurance protects a farm operator who is sued for alleged damages suffered from an accident involving his property or family. The kinds of situations from which a claim might arise are quite broad, including suits for injuries caused by animals, equipment, or personal acts.

Both workmen's compensation insurance and employer's liability insurance protect farmers against claims or court awards resulting from injury to hired help. Workmen's compensation usually costs slightly more than straight employer's liability insurance, but it carries more benefits to the worker. An injured employee must prove negligence by his employer before the

company will pay a claim under employer's liability insurance, whereas workmen's compensation benefits are established by state law and settlements are made by the insurance company without regard to who was negligent in causing the injury. Conditions governing participation in workmen's compensation insurance vary among the states.

HOG PRODUCERS AND INCOME TAXES

There are no tax rules and conditions dealing specifically with swine production as such. Rather, the tax treatment of a hog producer's receipts and expenditures is the same as that accorded to any other livestock business.

General tax information applicable to all livestock is fully covered in the section entitled "Tax Management and Reporting on the Livestock Farm" of *The Stockman's Handbook*, 4th ed., a book by the same author and publisher as this book. Hence, the reader is referred thereto.

QUESTIONS FOR STUDY AND DISCUSSION

1. Why have the business aspects of swine production become so important in recent years?
2. How can one acquire the needed training and experience in the business aspects of swine production?
3. Will the 10-sow owner be able to compete 20 years hence? Will the grower-finisher with 100 to 200 head on feed be able to compete?
4. Of what significance is the corn-hog ratio?
5. Discuss ways and means of automating a hog operation with a minimum of equipment.
6. Take your own farm, or one with which you are familiar, and develop a workable incentive basis for the help.
7. Using Tables 15-3, 15-4, and 15-5 as guides, develop a budget for the year ahead for your own farm, or for one with which you are familiar.
8. How may computers be used on a practical basis for (a) the commercial feeder pig operator, (b) the purebred hog breeder, and (c) the grower-finisher operator?
9. Assume a certain kind and size of hog operation—either pro-

ducing feeder pigs, raising and finishing market hogs, or
finishing purchased feeder pigs—then prepare a detailed report and request for credit.

10. Under what circumstances would you use hog futures?

SELECTED REFERENCE

Title of Publication	Author(s)	Publisher
Stockman's Handbook, The	M. E. Ensminger	The Interstate Printers & Publishers, Inc., Danville, Ill., 1970.

CHAPTER XVI

SELECTING, FITTING, AND SHOWING SWINE

Contents   Page

Through the years show-ring fashions in swine have fluctuated more radically than those in any other class of livestock. This story indicates better than voluminous words that, over a period of years, show-ring standards survive only when based on such utilitarian considerations as efficiency of production and selling price on a discriminating market. Breed fancy points and decisions made by judges are but passing fads when they conflict with the primary objective of producing swine, which is pork over the block.

ADVANTAGES OF SHOWING

Though not all exhibitors share equally in the many advan-

tages which may accrue from showing hogs, in general the following reasons may be advanced for exhibiting swine:

1. It serves as the best available medium for molding breed type.

2. It gives the breeder an opportunity to observe the impartial appraisal by a competent judge of his entries in comparison with others.

3. It offers an opportunity to study the progress being made within other breeds and classes of livestock.

4. It provides an excellent medium of advertising.

5. It gives breeders an opportunity to exchange ideas, thus serving as an educational event.

6. It offers an opportunity to sell a limited number of breeding animals.

7. It sets sale values for the animals back home, such values being based on the sale of show animals.

SELECTING SHOW ANIMALS

The first and most important assignment in preparation for the show is the selection of the prospective show animals. Unless the exhibitor has had considerable experience and is a good judge of hogs, it is well to secure the assistance and advice of a competent judge when selecting the animals that are to be fitted.

Selections should be made as far in advance of the show as is possible. In fact, the show-ring objective is usually kept in mind at the time matings are made and farrowing dates arranged. Selection is really a year-round job for the person who desires to exhibit a full herd. In general, all breeding animals intended for show, except those in the junior pig classes, should be selected at least four to six months in advance, thus allowing ample time for fitting and training. There is an unavoidable delay in selecting junior pigs and barrows.

As some animals may not develop properly, it is advisable to begin the fitting work with larger numbers in each class than it is intended to show, especially in the younger groups. In this manner, those animals which fail to respond may be culled out from time to time and a stronger show herd assembled.

Exhibitors may show (1) breeding animals or (2) barrows. When possible and when the classifications are available, it is desirable to show in both groups. In recent years, great em-

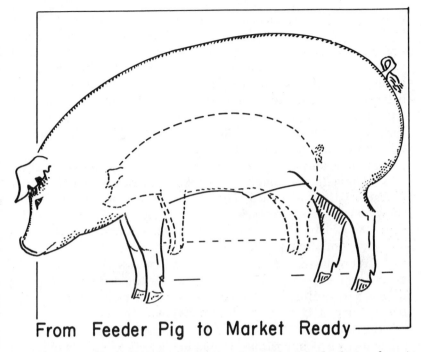

From Feeder Pig to Market Ready

Fig. 16-1. Selection of the prospective show animal is the first and most important assignment. Since this requires a projection into the future, no judging assignment is quite so difficult as that of selecting an animal for further development. (Drawing by R. F. Johnson)

phasis has been placed on barrow shows, and winning in a strong barrow show is looked upon as a fine accomplishment for the herd or breed which produced the champion. As the type of winning barrows generally reflects consumer demands, this is a good thing.

The exhibitor can enhance his chances of winning and of securing sufficient premium money to cover expenses by filling as many of the individual classes and groups as possible, and this applies to both breeding animals and barrows. Provided that the animals are good, it costs little more and is usually good economy to have a sizable and well balanced show herd.

Type

The most approved breeding animals in modern shows possess adequate size for age and are of meat type. They should be clean-cut about the head and neck; the back should be strong,

well arched, and of adequate width; the loin should be wide and the hams deep and smooth; the shoulders should be well laid and smooth; the sides should be long, deep, and smooth; the legs should be well placed and straight and the pasterns short and strong. With this splendid meat type, there should be a proper balance and blending of all parts, and the animal should be stylish and showy. An alert, active walk is a decided asset. Sex character, breediness, and adherence to distinctive breed characteristics is important in boars and sows.

In show barrows, special emphasis should be placed on trimness of middle and quality throughout as well as on the other characteristics mentioned. The ideal barrow when ready for the show must possess superior conformation, finish, and quality. There should be the maximum development in the high-priced cuts and a minimum of lardiness.

Group classes in both breeding and barrow classes should be as uniform as possible, for group placings are determined by the merits and uniformity of the entire group rather than on the basis of one or two outstanding individuals therein.

Further information relative to breed characteristics and other factors of importance in making selections can be obtained from Chapters III and IV.

Age and Show Classifications

It is also desirable to select hogs as large and heavy as possible within the respective age or weight classifications in order that they may show to the best possible advantage. Classifications for breeding animals are based on age, in keeping with the usual spring and fall farrowing dates. Barrow classifications are usually based on weight rather than age. The usual classifications for breeding animals and barrows are as follows:

1. **Breeding Swine.**—The classifications for breeding swine vary somewhat from fair to fair. The classifications shown in Table 16-1 were used at the Iowa State Fair and the Ohio State Fair, two of the great Corn Belt swine shows, in 1966.

The Junior Champion of each sex is selected from the first place winners in the Senior Pig and younger classes, whereas the Senior Champion is selected from the winners in the Junior Yearling and older class or classes. Show regulations differ relative to the stipulation of the groups; thus the exhibitor should

TABLE 16-1

HANDY SHOW CLASSIFICATION GUIDE FOR BREEDING SWINE

Class	Iowa State Fair	Ohio State Fair
Aged class	(No Aged class)	Farrowed on or after July 1 of the 3rd year prior to the show and before Dec. 31 of the 2nd year preceding the show.
Junior Yearling	Farrowed on or after Jan. 1 and before July 1 of the preceding year.	Farrowed on or after Jan. 1 and before June 30 of the year preceding the show.
Senior Pigs	(No Senior Pig class)	Farrowed on or after July 1 and before Dec. 31 of the year prior to the show.
Fall Pigs	Farrowed on or after July 1 of the preceding year and before Jan. 1 of the year shown.	(No Fall Pig class)
January Pigs	Farrowed on or after Jan. 1 and before Feb. 1 of the year shown.	Same as Iowa State Fair.
February Pigs	Farrowed on or after Feb. 1 and before March 1 of the year shown.	Same as Iowa State Fair.
March Pigs	Farrowed on or after Mar. 1 of the year shown.	Same as Iowa State Fair.
Certified Pair	A boar and a gilt from the same litter farrowed on or after Jan. 1 of the year shown, from a certified litter.	Same as Iowa State Fair.

study the rules of the particular show in which he desires to exhibit.

2. **Barrows.**[1]—The barrow classifications of the International Livestock Exposition, Chicago, are as follows:

a. By breeds (with similar classifications for each of the major breeds, and for purebreds of other breeds, crossbreds, and grades):

(1) Barrow, 190 to 209 pounds.

(2) Barrow, 210 to 224 pounds.

---

[1] In addition to individual classifications similar to those listed at the International Livestock Exposition, most shows also provide classes for pens of 3 barrows in each of the weight divisions, and for a champion pen.

(3) Barrow, 225 to 240 pounds.
(4) Champion Barrow, by breeds.
(5) Grand Champion Barrow over all breeds.
(6) Reserve Grand Champion Barrow over all breeds.

    b. Carcass contest, with each (1) **on hoof**, and (2) **dressed carcass** classes as follows:

(1) Barrow, 190 to 209 pounds.
(2) Barrow, 210 to 225 pounds.
(3) Champion Barrow on hoof.
(4) Champion dressed carcass.

    c. Truckload of 10 barrows (at least 6 of which must be barrows), any breed, cross or grade:

(1) Truckload, 190 and under 210 pounds.
(2) Truckload, 210 and under 225 pounds.
(3) Truckload, 225 and under 240 pounds.
(4) Champion truckload.

The weight divisions of different barrow shows vary considerably, thus making it imperative that the exhibitor study these carefully. In fact, the breeding program should be planned with this information in mind, because animals farrowed at the proper time may be better fitted and may reach the proper bloom for different weight divisions, if the breeding and feeding programs are properly synchronized.

Breeding

Animals selected for the show should always be of good ancestry, this being added assurance of satisfactory future development. Breeding animals should show the distinctive breed characteristics, but certain fancy points may be overlooked in selecting barrows. In fact, there are usually provisions for showing grade and crossbred barrows. Consideration is also given to breeding from the standpoint of filling the get-of-sire and produce-of-dam classes.

FEEDING AND HANDLING FOR THE SHOW

All animals intended for show purposes must be placed in proper condition, a process requiring great attention to details.

Keep the Animals Contented and Healthy; and Provide Exercise

Uncomfortable quarters, filthy wallows, annoyance by parasites (internal or external), improper handling, and unnecessary noise are the most common causes of discontentment. Prospective show animals should have the best quarters on the farm, and, above all, they should be kept cool, clean, and free from parasites. A certain amount of exercise is necessary in order to promote good circulation and to increase the thrift and vigor of the animal. Exercise tends to stimulate the appetite, making for greater feed consumption, and keeps the animals sound on their feet and legs. The run of a lush pasture always furnishes valuable exercise and excellent feed. In addition, it is usually well to walk mature sows or boars, thus forcing exercise. It is best to exercise show animals in the early morning or late evening, avoiding unnecessary handling in the heat of the day.

Segregate the Boars and Sows

Usually more individual attention can be given, especially in the matter of feeding, if show hogs are handled in small groups. With junior pigs, the boars should be separated from the gilts when the pigs are four months old. At the time young show boars begin to rant, usually when four to seven months of age, it is desirable that they be placed in isolated lots, preferably where they cannot see or hear other hogs. For the most part, show boars of all ages must be kept separate, but several sows of about the same age can be run together.

Some Suggested Rations

Any of the rations listed in Tables 6-19 through 6-24, of Chapter VI, for the respective classes and ages of swine, are suitable for use in fitting show animals of similar classification. In general, however, instead of self-feeding most experienced herdsmen feel that they can get superior bloom and condition by either (1) hand-feeding or (2) using a combination of hand-feeding and self-feeding (hand-feeding twice daily and allowing free access to a self-feeder). When hand-feeding, they also prefer mixing the ration with skimmed milk, buttermilk, or condensed buttermilk and feeding the entire ration in the form of a slop.

Adding milk to a ration that is already properly balanced does make for a higher protein content than necessary. On the other hand, most experienced herdsmen prefer using rations of higher protein content for fitting purposes. They feel they get more bloom that way. In general, however, when skimmed milk or buttermilk is used in slop-feeding, the protein feeds of the ration may be reduced by one-half without harm to the animal.

In fitting show barrows, it may be necessary to decrease or discontinue slop-feeding 2 to 4 weeks before the show to avoid paunchiness and lowering the dressing percentage.

When oatmeal (hulled oats) is not too high priced, many successful hog showmen, replace up to 50 percent of the grain (corn, wheat, barley, oats, and/or sorghum) in the ration with oatmeal. They do this especially when fitting hogs—both breeding animals and barrows—in the younger age groups. Oatmeal is highly palatable, lighter, and less fattening than corn.

Rules of Feeding

The general principles and practices of swine feeding have been fully covered in Chapter VI. The feeding of show hogs differs from the feeding of the rest of the herd primarily in that the former are fed for maximum development and bloom, with less attention being paid to economy from the standpoint of both feed and labor. It is to be noted, however, that it is a disadvantage to have the hogs excessively fat for modern shows, thus rendering possible harm to breeding animals and making barrows too lardy. Rather, a firm, smooth finish is desired.

The most successful herdsmen have worked out systems of their own as a result of years of practical experience and close observation. The beginner may well emulate their methods. Some rules of feeding show hogs as practiced by experienced herdsmen are:

1. **Practice economy, but avoid false economy.**—Although the ration should be as economical as possible, it must be remembered that proper condition is the primary objective, even at somewhat additional expense. Perhaps the most common mistake made in the fitting ration, especially of breeding animals, is the heavy feeding of corn or other grains.

2. **Hand-feeding versus self-feeding.**—Barrows are more often self-fed than breeding animals. Most experienced herdsmen

feel, however, that they can get superior bloom and condition by hand-feeding show animals. The majority prefer mixing the grain ration with skimmed milk, buttermilk, or condensed buttermilk, and feeding the entire ration in the form of a slop.

3. **Provide a variety of feeds.**—A good variety of feeds increases the palatability of the ration, thus increasing feed consumption. When fitting mature boars, many good herdsmen add a few raw eggs to the slop. A small amount of molasses adds to the palatability of a ration.

4. **Feed a balanced ration.**—A balanced ration will be more economical and will result in better growth and finish. Experienced herdsmen usually prefer a ration that is on the narrow side (high in proteins). For assistance in selecting a ration, the reader is referred to Chapter VI.

5. **Provide pasture.**—Valuable succulence may be provided through green, luxuriant pasture. This also provides necessary exercise.

6. **The ration must not be too bulky.**—Hogs cannot handle a great amount of bulk. Consumption of too much bulk will cause the animal to become paunchy and will lower the dressing percentage, a condition severely criticized in a show animal, especially a barrow.

7. **Feed regularly.**—Animals intended for show purposes should be fed with exacting regularity. In the early part of the fitting period, two feedings per day may be adequate. Later, the animals should be fed three to five times a day, especially when fitting rapidly growing pigs.

8. **Avoid sudden changes.**—Sudden changes in either the kind or amount of feed are apt to cause digestive disturbances. Any necessary changes should be gradual.

9. **Provide minerals.**—When a legume pasture is available and a part of the proteins in the ration are of animal origin (tankage, fish meal, milk, etc.), there may be no deficiency of minerals other than salt. However, access to a mineral mixture can be arranged at little cost and may be good protection with animals that are being crowded, especially junior pigs being fitted for the show. The chapter on feeding swine lists satisfactory mineral supplements.

EQUIPMENT FOR FITTING AND SHOWING HOGS

In the fitting, training, and grooming operations, the essential equipment consists of brushes, clipper, rasp, sharp knife, soap, canes or whips, and hurdles. In loading for the fair, all of these items should be included in the show box. In addition, most showmen take water buckets, light troughs, a sprinkling can, a fork and a broom, cresol dip, oil (and powder when white hogs or hogs with white spots are being shown), a saw, hammer, hatchet, a few nails, some rope, flashlight, blankets or a sleeping bag, and a limited and permissible supply of feed and bedding.

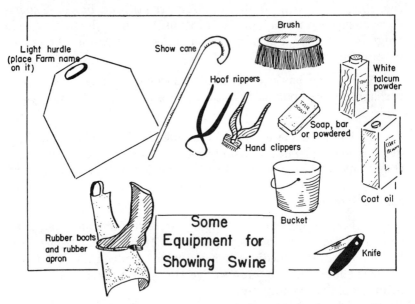

Fig. 16-2. The essential equipment for fitting and showing hogs. (Drawing by R. F. Johnson)

The show box, in which all smaller equipment is stored, is usually of durable wood construction, freshly painted, with a neat sign on the top or front giving the name and address of the exhibitor. In traveling by rail, barrels for water and a lantern are needed equipment for the show car. The feed taken to the show should be identical to the mix which was used at home.

TRAINING AND GROOMING THE ANIMAL

Most show rings are cursed with the presence of too many

squealing, scampering, unmanageable, and poorly groomed pigs. Such animals make an adverse impression on ringside spectators, annoy other exhibitors, and fail to catch the eye of the judge. When competition is keen, there may be several well-bred and beautifully fitted individuals of the right type in each class, with the result that the winner will be selected by a very narrow margin. Under such circumstances, proper training, grooming, and showing is often a deciding factor.

Fig. 16-3. Showmanship contest at the University of Connecticut being judged by Dr. Wesley Garrigus, University of Kentucky. Such contests sponsored by 4-H clubs, vocational agriculture, and college groups provide valuable training in the art of proper training, grooming, and showing. (Courtesy, University of Connecticut)

Training the Pig

Proper training of the pig requires time, patience, and persistence. Such schooling makes it possible for the judge to see

Fig. 16-4. Some essentials in training and grooming hogs for show. (Drawings by R. F. Johnson)

the animal to best advantage. Some herdsmen prefer to use the whip, whereas others use the conventional stockman's cane. The

pig should be trained to respond to either one or the other (cane or whip) but not to both. With mature boars, it is good protection to use a hand hurdle. However, the use of a hurdle in showing young animals is usually an admission of either a mean disposition or a lack of training.

Long before the show, the showman should study the individual animal, arriving at a decision as to the most advantageous pose. Then the animal should be trained to perfection so that he will execute the proper pose at the desired time. It is important that the pig be trained to stop when necessary, perhaps when the whip or cane is placed gently in front of his face. The direction of walking should be easily guided by merely placing the cane or whip alongside the animal's head.

The showman should avoid making a pet of the pig. Such an animal may display a nasty disposition when placed in the show ring, or it may slouch down when anyone comes near, including the judge.

Trimming the Feet

In order that the animal may stand squarely and walk properly and that the pasterns appear straight and strong, the toes and dew claws should be trimmed regularly. Moreover, long toes and dew claws are unsightly in appearance. Trimming can best be done with the animal lying on its side. Usually this position can best be acquired by merely stroking the animal's belly. With this procedure, tying and possible injury therefrom is unnecessary.

The practice of standing the animal on a hard surface and cutting off the ends of the toes with a hammer and chisel gives only temporary relief and is not recommended. The bottoms of the toes should be trimmed. Proper trimming can best be accomplished by using a small rasp and a knife.

The outside toes of the rear feet grow faster than the inside toes. In extreme cases this condition may result in crooked hind legs. This condition may be corrected by trimming the outside toes more frequently.

The toes should be trimmed regularly, with some animals as often as every six weeks. Too much trimming at any one time, however, may result in lameness. For this reason, it is not ad-

visable to work on the feet within two weeks before the show. In no case should trimming be so severe as to draw blood.

The dew claws should be cut back and dressed down neatly, making the pasterns appear short and straight.

Removing Tusks and Rings

Boars over one year of age usually have tusks of considerable size. These should be removed a month or two before the show. To remove the tusks, tie the animal to a post with a strong rope, draw up the upper jaw, and use a bolt clipper.

Rings should also be removed well in advance of fair time, allowing all soreness to disappear. Rings may be removed by securely tying the animal as for the removal of tusks and by cutting the rings with wire pliers or nippers.

Clipping

Clipping is usually done with hand clippers. It should be done a few days before the show. Many successful showmen prefer to use the clippers twice, about two weeks before the show and a second time the day before entering the ring. The usual practice is to clip the ears, both inside and outside, and to clip the tail. Clipping of the tail should begin above the switch and extend up to the tail head. The exact amount of switch to leave will vary somewhat with each individual, requiring judgment on the part of the showman.

It may also help to remove long hairs from about the head and jowl. The udder of a gilt will often show to better advantage if some of the hairs on the belly are carefully removed. In all trimming, it is important that the hair be gradually tapered off so that the clipped and unclipped areas blend nicely.

Washing

An occasional washing and brushing keeps the animal clean and makes the skin smooth and mellow. It also assists materially in shedding the coat of older animals. Lukewarm water, plenty of tar soap, and a fairly stiff brush will do the job. After the skin and hair have been dampened thoroughly, rub the hair with tar soap until a suds is formed and then work this lather into the hide with the hands and brush. Clean all parts of the body

thoroughly, using care not to get any of the water into the ears. A small amount of bluing in the water is helpful in bleaching out stained spots on white hogs. Following washing, the animal should be rinsed off in order to remove all traces of soap from the hair and skin. The animal should then be placed in a clean pen to dry.

Oiling

Oiling softens the skin and hair and gives the necessary bloom to the coat. It is most important that the oil be used sparingly and that it be evenly distributed over the body. For best results a light application of oil should be given the night before the show, using an oiled cloth or brush. Then give the animal a thorough grooming with a brush and a woolen rag just before entering the ring. This gives the necessary bloom. When the pig enters the ring, surplus oil should not be in evidence. Any clear, light vegetable oil is satisfactory for oiling purposes. Paraffin oil is low in cost and very satisfactory when mixed with small proportions of rubbing alcohol.

Oiling mature boars and sows that are in high condition may cause them to overheat more easily during warm weather. Under such conditions, some experienced showmen use no oil but sprinkle water over the animals before entering the ring, and then follow with the brush.

Powdering

White hogs or white spots on dark hogs are usually powdered with talcum powder or corn starch. The animal should first be thoroughly washed and allowed to dry. The powder should be dusted on before entering the ring. In order to be most effective, it should be evenly distributed.

MAKING FAIR ENTRIES

Well in advance of the show, the exhibitor should request that the fair manager or secretary forward a premium list and the necessary entry blanks. Usually, entries close from two to four weeks prior to the opening date of the show. All rules and regulations of the show should be studied carefully and followed to the letter—including requirements relative to entrance, reg-

istration certificates, vaccination, health certificates, pen fees, exhibition and helper's tickets, and other matters pertaining to the show. Most entry blanks for purebred hogs call for the following information: breed, sex, name and registration number of the entry, date farrowed, name and registration number of the sire and dam, a description of markings (such as ear notches), and the class in which the animal is to be shown. Entries should be made in all individual and group classes but not in breed specials or championship classes. It is not necessary to specify the identity of individuals constituting herds or groups, because, when the exhibitor has a choice, the winnings in the individual class will largely determine this.

PROVIDING HEALTH CERTIFICATES

Most fairs require that swine entering the exposition grounds be accompanied by a health certificate. Although the stipulations vary, perhaps the following provisions of the 1969 Iowa State Fair are rather typical.

1. **Hog cholera vaccination** required by one of the following methods:

a. Inactivated vaccine, not less than 21 days nor more than 6 months prior to entry date of exhibition, or

b. Modified live virus vaccine and anti-hog cholera serum or concentrate, not less than 21 days nor more than 1 year prior to entry date of exhibition.

2. **Brucellosis:**

a. All breeding swine 4 months of age and over must be negative to a brucellosis test conducted within 60 days of exhibition, or originate in a validated brucellosis free herd, date of last test and herd certificate number to be indicated on health certificate.

b. "Market Class Swine" can be moved from exhibition for further feeding when not meeting brucellosis requirements, on an affidavit which will be available by contacting the veterinary inspector in charge of exhibition.

SHIPPING TO THE FAIR

Show hogs should be shipped so that they arrive within the limitations imposed by the fair and a minimum of two days in

advance of showing. Because of the greater convenience and speed, most hauls are made by truck. With distances, however, show animals usually arrive in better condition if shipped by rail with a competent caretaker in charge who carefully feeds and waters enroute. With rail shipments, box cars are preferred to stock cars—the high-ceiling automobile cars being desirable in summer because they are cooler than standard cars.

The side doors of the box car should be left open and the openings protected with slatted panels. Usually, the hogs are placed in each end of the car, and the space in the center is reserved for the storing of feed and the necessary utensils and also as sleeping quarters for the caretaker. Whether shipping by truck or rail, public conveyances should always be thoroughly disinfected before loading hogs. Show hogs should not be crowded, and those of different age groups and sexes should be separated by suitable partitions. During warm weather, properly wetted sand makes the best bedding. In extremely hot weather, however, it may be desirable to ice the car, especially when heavily fitted mature animals are being transported. Regardless of the method of transportation, animals should be fed lightly (about a half ration) just prior to and during shipping. A heavy fill is likely to result in digestive disturbances and overheating in warm weather.

Rail shipments should be billed out to the exposition in keeping with the instructions given in the premium list. Free return is given on rail shipments of show hogs provided that (1) within 30 days after the close of the exposition or fair, they are returned to the point of origin via the same line or lines as the initial movement and (2) the bill of lading therefor is accompanied by a certification of the fair secretary or manager stating that the hogs were exhibited and have not changed ownership. Also, half rates may be obtained when transporting a car of hogs to more than one exposition, but the procedure is somewhat more complicated. Briefly, it consists in waybilling at the regular tariff rate to each point of exhibition, with the rate on the inbound charges later reduced by one-half upon complying with point number two above. Finally, when loading out from the last show for return to point of origin, the shipment is billed at one-half the tariff rates, provided that point number two is complied with in regard to the last show of the circuit. All half rates indicated

will apply only when the carrier's liability is limited to an evaluation of $15 on each hog.

PEN SPACE, FEEDING, AND MANAGEMENT AT THE FAIR

Most swine pens at fairs or exhibitions range from six to eight feet square. When it is not too hot and the hogs are used to each other, about the following numbers of the same sex can be accommodated in one pen: three to five junior pigs or barrows, two seniors, and two each of the older age groups— except that boars older than junior pigs had best be kept in separate pens. Sufficient pens should be obtained in order to avoid overcrowding, especially during warm weather. It is easier to keep the animals clean when there is ample space.

The advertising value of the exhibit will be enhanced through displaying a neat and attractive sign over the pens, giving the name and address of the breeder, farm, or ranch. It is also important that the pens and alleys be kept neat and attractive at all times, thus impressing spectators and cooperating with the management in putting on a good show.

Following a day of rest and light feeding after unloading at the show, normal feeding may be resumed provided that it is accompanied by normal exercise. Usually, the animals are fed twice daily, and, if possible, the exhibitors should feed outside the pens, preferably behind the exhibition building. Most exhibitors prefer to clean the pens thoroughly in the early morning, while the animals are confined within hurdles for feeding or are being taken for exercise. It is important that all animals receive sufficient and regular exercise—at least a half-hour walk daily—while they are on the fairgrounds.

The final washing may be given a day or two after arrival, but the coat should be brushed daily and oiled or powdered as the breed may require.

SHOWING THE PIG

Expert showmanship cannot be achieved through reading any set of instructions. Each show and each ring will be found to present unusual circumstances. However, there are certain

Pointers on Showing

1. Train early
2. Groom animal well
3. Dress neatly
4. Be prompt entering the ring
5. Don't crowd the judge
6. Keep in view
7. Always be showing your pig
8. Be calm, confident
9. Work in partnership with your animal
10. Be courteous
11. Avoid letting animals fight
12. Be a good sport

Fig. 16-5. Guiding principles adhered to by successful showmen. (Drawings by R. F. Johnson)

guiding principles that are always adhered to by the most successful showmen. Some of these are:

1. Train the animal long before entering the ring.

2. Have the animal carefully groomed and ready for the parade before the judge.

3. Dress neatly for the occasion.

4. Enter the ring promptly when the class is called.

5. Do not crowd the judge but keep your animal in a position of vantage at all times.

6. Avoid being smothered by the mob; keep in the open.

7. Keep one eye on the judge and the other on the pig. Center your attention entirely on showing the hog. The animal may be under the observation of the judge when you least suspect it.

8. Keep calm, confident, and collected. Remember that the nervous showman creates an unfavorable impression.

9. Work in close partnership with the animal.

10. Be courteous and respect the rights of other exhibitors.

11. Do not allow your hog to bite or fight other animals.

12. Be a good sport; win without bragging and lose without squealing.

AFTER THE FAIR IS OVER

Before an exhibitor can leave the show grounds, it is customary to require a signed release from the superintendent of the show. Immediately prior to that time, all of the equipment should be loaded, followed by loading of the hogs. The same care and precautions that applied in travel to the show should prevail in the return trip.

Because of the possible disease and parasite hazard resulting from contact with other herds and through transportation facilities, it is good protection to quarantine the show herd for a period of three weeks following return from the fair. The most prevalent swine disease around shows is hog "flu," a disease of the respiratory tract characterized by coughing. There is also the problem of letting them down in condition or reducing from the usual heavily fitted condition to breeding condition. To do the latter operation properly, especially with mature animals, requires great skill; for the manner in which animals are reduced in flesh often determines their fertility and future usefulness in the breeding herd as well as their possibility of "coming back" for future shows. Those who are most successful in this phase of management usually employ three methods—namely, (1) plenty of exercise, (2) added bulk in the ration, and (3) a gradual reduction of the concentrate allowance. In season, the animals should be allowed to exercise and forage on pasture. In addition, the concentrate ration should be made more bulky by adding such

feeds as oats, wheat bran, and ground alfalfa, and the feed allowance should be gradually reduced. With active, growing junior pigs, a slight reduction in the grain allowance will usually suffice in placing them in breeding condition.

QUESTIONS FOR STUDY AND DISCUSSION

1. Under what circumstances would you recommend that each, a purebred swine producer, a commercial swine producer, and a 4-H swine club member (a) should show, and (b) should not show hogs?

2. Take and defend either the affirmative or the negative position of each of the following statements:
   a. Fitting and showing does not harm animals.
   b. Livestock shows have been a powerful force in swine improvement.
   c. Too much money is spent on livestock shows.
   d. Unless all animals are fitted, groomed, and shown to the same degree of perfection, show-ring winnings are not indicative of the comparative quality of animals.

3. How may livestock shows be changed so that they (a) more nearly reflect consumer preference, and (b) make for greater swine improvement?

4. It is generally agreed that livestock shows abetted the radical shifts in swine types of the past—shifts which later proved to be detrimental. How could this have been averted?

SELECTED REFERENCES

Title of Publication	Author(s)	Publisher
Selecting, Fitting and Showing Swine	J. E. Nordby H. E. Lattig	The Interstate Printers & Publishers, Inc., Danville, Ill., 1961.
Stockman's Handbook, The	M. E. Ensminger	The Interstate Printers & Publishers, Inc., Danville, Ill., 1970.
Swine Production	C. E. Bundy R. V. Diggins	Prentice-Hall, Inc., Englewood Cliffs, N. J., 1956.

APPENDIX

SECTION I.—ENERGY TERMS AND FEED COMPOSITION[1]

In chart form, Figure I-1 shows the conventional energy system. Apparent digestible energy (DE), metabolizable energy (ME), and net energy (NE) are usually calculated by the conventional system.

Figure I-2 shows where the various energy fractions originate. Since some of the fecal energy is of metabolic origin and some of the urinary energy is of endogenous origin, the scheme shown in Fig. I-2"A" has been modified to give Figure I-2"B" which gives true digestible energy (TDE), true metabolizable energy (TME), and true net energy (TNE). Since the metabolic energy and endogenous energy are part of the net energy requirements under this scheme, these items are shown as part of the maintenance energy.

Energy Terms

A part of the confusion and disagreement over the calorie system stems from a lack of understanding of terms, and from the coining of numerous "pet" names. For this reason, under the

---

[1]The author gratefully acknowledges the authoritative help of Dr. Lorin E. Harris, Utah State University, in the preparation of this section.

heading, "Glossary of Energy Terms," the author has elected to present the terms, and brief definitions of each, after the monumental work of Harris.[2] Additionally, use of the calorie system necessitates a working knowledge of the metric system (see Appendix Section III).

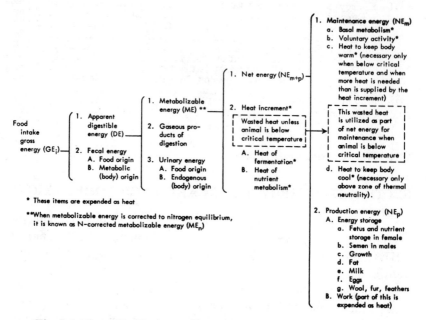

Fig. I-1. The utilization of energy, conventional scheme. (Courtesy, Dr. Lorin E. Harris, Utah State University)

---

[2] Lorin E. Harris, *Biological Energy Interrelationships and Glossary of Energy Terms*, National Academy of Sciences, NRC, Pub. No. 1411.

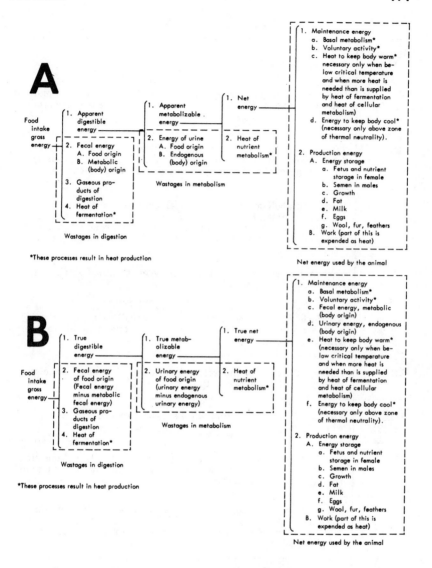

Fig. I-2. The utilization of energy (scheme to show where various portions originate). Since some of the fecal energy is of metabolic origin and some of the urinary energy is of endogenous origin, the scheme shown in Figure I-1"A" has been modified to give Figure I-1"B". Since the metabolic energy and endogenous energy are part of the net energy requirements under this scheme, these items are shown as part of the maintenance energy. (Courtesy, Dr. Lorin E. Harris, Utah State University)

GLOSSARY OF ENERGY TERMS

Abbrevi-ation	Term—Definition
DE	**Digestible Energy** (or apparent absorbed energy, or apparent energy of digested food) is the food intake gross energy minus fecal energy.
TDE	**True Digestible Energy** is the food intake gross energy minus fecal energy of food origin (FE minus FE_m) minus energy in gaseous products of digestion minus heat of fermentation.
BM	**Basal Metabolism** is the chemical change which occurs in the cells of an animal in the fasting and resting state when it uses just enough energy to maintain vital cellular activity, respiration, and circulation as measured by the basal metabolic rate.
CB	**Carbon Balance** is the relation between the food intake carbon and the carbon output.
cal	**A calorie** (cal, always written with a small c) is the amount of heat required to raise the temperature of one gram of water one degree centigrade.
EB	**Energy Balance** is the relation between the food intake gross energy and the energy output.
FHP	**Fasting Heat Production** is the heat produced by the animal while fasting.
FE	**Fecal Energy** is the gross energy of the feces. It consists of the energy content of the undigested food and the metabolic (body) fraction of the feces.
FE_m	**Fecal Energy, Metabolic,** is the amount of energy contained in the metabolic (body) fraction of feces (i.e., abraded intestinal mucosa, digestive fluids) that is not obtained from unabsorbed ration residues.
GPD	**Gaseous Products of Digestion** includes the combustible gases produced in the digestive tract incident to the fermentation of the ration. Methane makes up by far the major proportion of the combustible gases produced.
GE	**Gross Energy** (or heat of combustion) is the amount of heat, measured in calories, that is released when a substance is completely oxidized in a bomb calorimeter containing 25 to 30 at-

(Continued)

GLOSSARY (Continued)

Abbreviation	Term—Definition
	mospheres of oxygen. The gross energy of a feed, feces, urine, tissue, eggs, or other material is determined by burning them in a bomb calorimeter (see Fig. 6-5).
GE_1	**Gross Energy Intake** is the gross energy of the food consumed.
HF	**Heat of Fermentation** is the heat produced in the digestive tract as a result of microbial action.
HI	**Heat Increment** is the increase in heat production following consumption of feed when the animal is in a thermo-neutral environment.
HBC	**Heat to Keep Body Cool** is the extra energy expended by the animal when the temperature of the environment is above the animal's zone of thermal neutrality.
HBW	**Heat to Keep Body Warm** is the additional heat needed to keep the animal's body warm when the temperature of the environment is below the critical temperature.
HNM	**Heat of Nutrient Metabolism** is the heat produced as a result of the utilization of absorbed nutrients.
HP	**Heat Production (Total)** of an animal consuming food in a thermo-neutral environment is composed of the heat increment (heat of fermentation plus heat of nutrient metabolism) plus heat used for maintenance (basal metabolism plus voluntary activity). It can be estimated by three procedures; namely, (1) by measuring the quantity of oxygen an animal consumes (open circuit method), (2) by measuring directly the amount of heat produced by the animal (direct method), and (3) by the comparative slaughter technique. For the latter, two comparable animals are slaughtered, one at the beginning of the test period and the other at the end of the test period, and the energy content of each is determined. Then, the difference between these two values represents the amount of energy gained. The total heat production and energy utilization of a lactating animal are illustrated in Figure I-3.
kcal	A **kilocalorie** is 1,000 small calories.
Mcal	A **Megacalorie**, or a therm, is equivalent to 1,000 kilocalories or 1,000,000 calories.
$W^{0.75}$	**Metabolic Body Size** is defined as the weight of the animal raised to the three-fourths power.

(Continued)

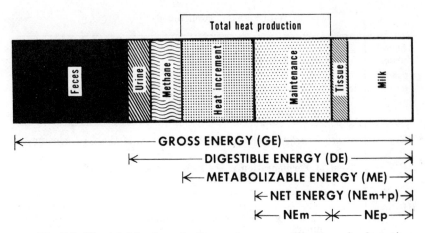

Fig. I-3. The total heat production and energy utilization of a lactating animal, adapted from data of W. P. Flatt. (Courtesy, Dr. Lorin E. Harris, Utah State University)

GLOSSARY (Continued)

Abbreviation	Term—Definition
ME	Metabolizable Energy is the food intake gross energy minus fecal energy, minus urinary energy, minus energy in the gaseous products of digestion.
TME	True Metabolizable Energy is the food intake gross energy minus fecal energy of food origin (FE minus FE_m), minus energy in gaseous products of digestion, minus heat of fermentation energy, minus urinary energy of food origin (UE minus UE_e).
ME_n	N-Corrected Metabolizable Energy is the food intake gross energy minus fecal energy, minus energy in the gaseous products of digestion, minus urinary energy; the total is then corrected for nitrogen retained or lost from the body.
TME_n	N-Corrected True Metabolizable Energy is the food intake gross energy minus fecal energy of food origin (FE minus FE_m), minus energy in gaseous products of digestion, minus heat of fermentation energy, minus urinary energy of food origin (UE minus UE_e); the total is then corrected for nitrogen retained or lost from the body.

(Continued)

GLOSSARY (Continued)

Abbreviation	Term—Definition
NE or NE$_{m+p}$	**Net Energy** is the difference between metabolizable energy and heat increment, and includes the amount of energy used either for maintenance only or for maintenance plus production.
NE$_m$	**Net Energy for Maintenance** is the fraction of net energy expended to keep the animal in energy equilibrium.
NE$_p$	**Net Energy for Production** is the fraction of net energy required in addition to that needed for maintenance that is used for work or for tissue gain (growth and/or fat production) or for the synthesis of a fetus, milk, eggs, wool, fur or feathers.
NE$_{egg}$	**Net Energy for Egg Production.**
NE$_{fat}$	**Net Energy for Fat Production.**
NE$_{fur}$	**Net Energy for Fur Production.**
NE$_{growth}$	**Net Energy for Growth.**
NE$_{milk}$	**Net Energy for Milk Production.**
NE$_{preg}$	**Net Energy for Pregnancy.**
NE$_{wool}$	**Net Energy for Wool Production.**
NE$_{work}$	**Net Energy for Work.**
	Note: These abbreviations could be used in feed composition tables or where more than one kind of production is being discussed.
TNE	**True Net Energy** is the intake gross energy minus the fecal energy of food origin (FE — FE$_m$) minus energy in gaseous products, minus heat of fermentation energy, minus urinary energy or direct food origin (UE — UE$_e$), minus heat of nutrient metabolism.
TNE$_m$	**True Net Energy for Maintenance** is the sum of the energy required for basal metabolism, voluntary activity, metabolic fecal energy (body origin), and endogenous urinary energy (body origin).
NB	**Nitrogen Balance** is the nitrogen in the food intake (NI) minus the nitrogen in the feces (FN), minus nitrogen in the urine (UN).
NCR	**Nutrient to Calorie Ratio.** There is acceptable evidence that the energy needs of animals and their requirements of the several nutrients are quantitatively correlated. This does not necessarily

(Continued)

GLOSSARY (Continued)

Abbreviation	Term—Definition
	mean a direct cause-and-effect relation, but it does mean that there is an optimum balance between them. For those nutrients that are needed to metabolize energy, it is logical to consider that the amount of energy metabolized "determines" their requirements. Hence, it is logical to express nutrients in weight per unit of energy needed. For example, it is suggested that the protein to calorie ratio should be expressed as grams of protein per 1000 kcal metabolizable energy (g protein/1000 kcal ME). If the ME is corrected for nitrogen retained or lost from the body then the abbreviation should be g protein/1000 kcal ME_n. This same dimension may easily be extended to other nutrients as g calcium/1000 kcal or mg riboflavin/1000 kcal, etc.
PFV	**Physiological Fuel Values** expressed in calories, are units used in the United States to measure food energy in human nutrition. It is similar to metabolizable energy.
UE	**Urinary Energy** is the gross energy of the urine.
UE_e	**Urinary Energy, Endogenous** is the amount of energy contained in the endogenous (body) fraction of the total urine.
VA	**Energy of Voluntary Activity** is the amount of energy needed by an animal to provide the energy required in getting up, standing, moving about to obtain food, grazing, drinking, lying down, etc.

Feed Composition

Nutrient compositions of feedstuffs are necessary for intelligent ration preparation, animal health, and feed efficiency. Table I-1 contains the most commonly used feeds for swine. It contains data, if available, for proximate composition, gross energy (GE), mineral, vitamin, and amino acid contents of feeds. Where available, apparent digestible protein, apparent digestible energy (DE), metabolizable energy (ME), and total digestible nutrients (TDN) are listed.

NRC NOMENCLATURE

The nomenclature of the feeds under which the analytical data are shown is based on the National Research Council (NRC)

scheme.[3] It is designed to give (to the extent that the information is available or applicable) a qualitative description of the product as to its: (1) origin or parent material, (2) species, variety, or kind, (3) the part actually eaten, (4) the process(es) and treatment(s) to which it has been subjected, (5) the stage of maturity, (6) cutting or crop, (7) grade or quality designations, and (8) classification.

Feeds of the same origin or parent material (and the same species, variety, or kind, if designated) have been subgrouped into the following feed classes: (1) dry forages and roughages, (2) pasture, range plants, and forages fed green, (3) silages, (4) energy feeds, (5) protein supplements, (6) minerals, (7) vitamins, and (8) additives. Classes are coded as indicated and are included in parentheses following the NRC names. Within each origin (and species, variety, or kind, if given) there may be feeds that belong to several classes. These classes are grouped in ascending numerical order of their class code number within origin or within origin and species. The scientific name precedes each group of feeds with the same scientific name.

Feeds in the dry state which contain more than 18 percent crude fiber are classified as forages and roughages. Products that contain 20 percent or more of protein are classified as protein supplements. Products with less than 20 percent protein are classified as energy feeds. (These guidelines are approximate and there is some overlapping.) The feeds have been classified in this way because each class has certain properties that are considered in balancing a ration. Fruits, nuts, and roots, have been classified as energy feeds because most of the by-product feeds from these subclasses furnish, primarily, energy to the animal.

To reduce the names to minimum printing or punch-card space requirement a system of abbreviations has been devised covering many of the terms involved in the eight components of the name. These are listed in this section under the heading, "Feed Term Abbreviations."

The system of naming is illustrated as follows:

Components
1. Origin ....Clover
2. Variety ....red

---

[3]Harris, Lorin E., Symposium on feeds and meats terminology. III. A system for naming and describing feedstuffs, energy terminology, and the use of such information in calculating diets. *J. Animal Sci.* 22:535-547, 1963.

3. Part eaten ....aerial pt
4. Process ....s-c
5. Maturity ....pre-blm
6. Cutting ....cut 1
7. Grade ....leafy
8. Classification ....(1)

The NRC name is written out in linear form with the components of the name separated by commas and without other punctuation. Commas are not included within the eight components so that the reader may readily recognize the entire component. The name would appear as:

Clover, red, aerial pt, s-c, pre-blm, cut-1,
leafy, (1)

This example would be read:

Clover, red, aerial part, sun-cured, pre-bloom,
first cutting, leafy. It is a dry roughage.

The Association of American Feed Control Officials (AAFCO) names, Canada Feeds Act (CFA) names, and other common names appear after the NRC names. Cross references (where necessary) have been included so the NRC name may be readily located.

Although care has been taken to include cross references, it is suggested that the entire list of feeds under a given origin be checked so that a feed is not missed.

An example of a feed which has different names is as follows:

Components
1. Origin ....Barley
3. Part ....flour by-prod mil-rn
8. Classification ....(4)

Other names:

Barley mill by-product (AAFCO)
Barley mixed feed (CFA)

Each feed has been given a six-digit reference number, the first of which indicates the feed classification. For the above example the Names and Feed reference number would appear as follows:

Barley, flour by-prod mil-rn, (4)
Barley mill by-product (AAFCO)
Barley mixed feed (CFA)
Ref no. 4-00-523

The analytical data are expressed in the metric system (with the exception of the bushel weights of the cereal grains) and are on an "as fed" as well as a "dry" basis. The NRC reference feed number may be used as an identification on electronic computers for linear programming.

It has not been possible to obtain apparent digestible energy (DE) and metabolizable energy (ME) values for all feedstuffs. In some of these cases, values have been estimated using the following formulae:

$$DE \text{ (kcal/kg)} = \frac{TDN \%}{100} \times 4409.2$$

$$ME \text{ (kcal/kg) for swine} = DE \text{ (kcal/kg)} \times \frac{96 - (0.202 \times protein \%)}{100}$$

The International Standards for vitamin A activity based on vitamin A and beta-carotene are as follows: One International Unit (IU) of vitamin A = one USP unit = vitamin A activity of 0.300 mcg of crystalline vitamin A alcohol, corresponding to 0.344 mcg of vitamin A acetate or 0.550 mcg of vitamin A palmitate. Beta-carotene is the standard for pro-vitamin A. One International Unit of vitamin A activity is equivalent to 0.6 mcg of beta-carotene or 1 mg of beta-carotene = 1667 IU of vitamin A. International Standards for vitamin A are based on the utilization by the rat of vitamin A and/or beta-carotene.

The vitamin A equivalent for carotene was calculated by assuming that 0.6 mcg of beta-carotene = one IU of vitamin A.

Because the various species do not convert carotene to vitamin A in the same ratio as rats, it is suggested that the following conversion rates be used:

CONVERSION OF BETA-CAROTENE TO VITAMIN A
FOR DIFFERENT SPECIES[1]

Species	Conversion mg beta-carotene to IU vitamin A	IU vitamin A activity (calculated from carotene)
	(mg) (IU)	(%)
Standard	1 = 1,667	100.
Swine	1 = 500	30.0
Beef cattle	1 = 400	24.0
Dairy cattle	1 = 400	24.0
Sheep	1 = 400-500	24.0-30.0
Horses		
Growth	1 = 555	33.3
Pregnancy	1 = 333	20.0
Poultry	1 = 1,667	100.
Rat	1 = 1,667	100.
Man	1 = 556	33.0

[1] Beeson, W. M., 1965. Relative potencies of vitamin A and carotene for animals. *Federation Proc.* 24:924-926.

Individual feed samples may vary widely from indicated averages because of influencing factors such as crop, variety, harvesting and storage conditions, and climate and soil pertinent to the locality where the feed was produced. Therefore, the values given should be used with judgment, often in conjunction with more specific information on hand about the feed.

FEED TERM ABBREVIATIONS

Abbreviation	Feed Term
AAFCO	Association of American Feed Control Officials
by-prod	by-product
Ca	calcium
Can	Canadian
c-bolt	coarse bolted
CFA	Canada Feeds Act
chop	chopped
c-sift	coarse sifted
comm	commercial
cond	condensed
CW	Canadian Western
dehy	dehydrated
digl	digestibility, digestible
distil	distillation, distillers
dry-mil	dry milled
dry-rend	dry rendered
equiv	equivalent
F	fluorine
fbr	fiber
f-grnd	fine ground
fm	foreign material (including seeds other than the principal product or grain)

(Continued)

FEED TERM ABBREVIATIONS (Continued)

Abbreviation	Feed Term
f-scr	fine screened
f-sift	fine sifted
g	gram
gr	grade
grnd	ground
hydro	hydrolyzed
ICU	International Chick Unit
insol	insoluble
IU	International Units
kcal	kilocalories
kg	kilogram
mech-extd	mechanically extracted, expeller extracted, hydraulic extracted, or old process
mcg	microgram
mg	milligram
mil-rn	mill run
mn	minimum
mx	maximum
N	nitrogen
No	Northern
P	phosphorus
precip	precipitated
proc	processed, processing
prot	protein
pt	part(s)
res	residue
s-c	sun-cured
shred	shredded
skim	skimmed
sol	solubles
solv-extd	solvent extracted
US	United States
w	with
wet-rend	wet rendered
wo	without
wt	weight

FORMULAS FOR ADJUSTING MOISTURE CONTENT

The majority of feed composition tables are on an "as fed" basis, while most of the National Research Council nutrient requirement tables are on an "approximate 90 percent dry matter" basis. Also, feeds contain varying amounts of dry matter. Hence, it would be much simpler if both feed composition and nutrient requirement tables were on a dry basis.

The significance of water content of feeds becomes obvious in the following examples. When using Total Digestible Nutrients (TDN) as a measure of energy value, some of the high-moisture tubers show almost the same feeding value per unit of their dry matter content as the cereal grains:

Feed	% Water	% Dry Matter	Energy Value (TDN) As Fed	Dry Matter Basis
Corn, grain	10	90	80	90
Barley, grain	10	90	77	85
Melons, whole	94	6	5	80
Potatoes, tubers	79	21	18	85
Apples, fruit	82	18	13	74

As shown, dry matter becomes a common denominator for the comparison for feeds, particularly as to energy value; but this applies to other nutrients, also.

The following formulas may be used for adjusting moisture contents:

From Dry to As Fed

To be used in converting the amounts of ingredients of a dry diet to a wet diet having a given percent of dry matter.[4]

Formula 1

$$\text{Parts of ingredient in wet diet} = \frac{\% \text{ ingredient in dry diet} \times \% \text{ dry matter wanted in diet}}{\% \text{ dry matter in ingredient}}$$

Total the parts and add enough water to make 100 parts (or 100 percent)

From Wet to Dry

To be used in calculating the amount of an ingredient that should be contained in a dry diet if the amount required in a wet diet having a given percent of dry matter is known.

Formula 2

$$\text{\% of ingredient in wet diet} = \frac{\% \text{ ingredient in wet diet}}{\% \text{ dry matter wanted in diet}} \times \frac{\% \text{ dry matter in ingredient}}{}$$

From Wet to Dry

To be used if the diet is on an as-fed basis and it is desired to change the amounts of the ingredients to a dry basis.

Formula 3

Parts on
wet basis = % ingredient in wet diet × % dry matter of ingredient

Perform this calculation for each ingredient; then add the products and divide each product by the sum of the products.

From Wet to Dry

To be used if the diet is on an as-fed basis and it is desired to compare the nutrient content of the diet with dry-basis requirements.

Formula 4

$$\text{\% nutrient in dry diet (total)} = \frac{\% \text{ nutrient in wet diet (total)}}{\% \text{ dry matter in diet (total)}}$$

---

[4]The term "dry diet" means a diet calculated on a dry (moisture-free) basis; "as fed" means a diet calculated to contain the amount of dry matter as it is fed to the animal.

TABLE I-1—COMPOSITION OF SOME COMMON SWINE FEEDS[a]

ALFALFA. Medicago sativa
Alfalfa, aerial pt, dehy grnd, mn 15 prot, (1)
Ref no 1-00-022

Feed name or analyses		As fed	Dry (Mean)
Dry matter	%	93.1	100.0
Ash	%	8.4	9.0
Crude fiber	%	26.4	28.4
Ether extract	%	2.3	2.5
N-free extract	%	40.8	43.8
Protein (N x 6.25)	%	15.2	16.3
Swine	dig prot %	7.0	7.5
Energy			
Swine	DE kcal/kg	1436.	1543.
Swine	ME kcal/kg	1331.	1430.
Swine	TDN %	32.	35.
Calcium	%	1.23	1.32
Chlorine	%	.44	.47
			Continued

Feed name or analyses		As fed	Dry (Mean)
Iron	%	.031	.033
Magnesium	%	.29	.31
Phosphorus	%	.22	.24
Potassium	%	2.33	2.50
Sodium	%	.07	.08
Cobalt	mg/kg	.180	.190
Copper	mg/kg	10.4	11.2
Iodine	mg/kg	.120	.129
Manganese	mg/kg	29.0	31.1
Selenium	mg/kg	.500	.540
Zinc	mg/kg	20.0	21.5
Carotene	mg/kg	102.0	109.5
Choline	mg/kg	1550.	1665.
Folic acid	mg/kg	1.54	1.65
Niacin	mg/kg	41.9	45.0
Pantothenic acid	mg/kg	20.9	22.4
Riboflavin	mg/kg	10.6	11.4
Thiamine	mg/kg	3.0	3.2
a-tocopherol	mg/kg	98.0	105.2
Vitamin B6	mg/kg	6.50	7.00
Vitamin K	mg/kg	9.90	10.60
			Continued

Feed name or analyses		As fed	Dry (Mean)
Vitamin A equiv	IU/g	170.0	182.5
Alanine	%	.80	.86
Arginine	%	.60	.64
Aspartic acid	%	1.70	1.82
Glutamic acid	%	1.50	1.61
Glycine	%	.70	.75
Histidine	%	.30	.32
Hydroxyproline	%	.60	.64
Leucine	%	1.10	1.18
Lysine	%	.60	.64
Methionine	%	.20	.21
Phenylalanine	%	.80	.86
Proline	%	.80	.86
Serine	%	.70	.75
Threonine	%	.60	.64
Tryptophan	%	.40	.43
Tyrosine	%	.40	.43
Valine	%	.70	.75

(1) dry forages and roughages
(2) pasture, range plants, and forages fed green
(3) silages
(4) energy feeds
(5) protein supplements
(6) minerals
(7) vitamins
(8) additives

[a] From the Feed Composition Table of the National Research Council Nutrient Requirements of Swine, with the permission of the National Research Council. Data and feed names were arranged for this book by Dr. Lorin E. Harris, Utah State University.

TABLE 1-1—COMPOSITION OF SOME COMMON SWINE FEEDS (Continued)

Alfalfa, aerial pt, dehy grnd, mn 17 prot, (1) — Ref no 1-00-023

Feed name or analyses		Mean	
		As fed	Dry
Dry matter	%	93.0	100.0
Ash	%	9.0	9.7
Crude fiber	%	24.3	26.1
Ether extract	%	3.0	3.2
N-free extract	%	38.9	41.8
Protein (N x 6.25)	%	17.9	19.2
Swine	dig prot %	8.3	8.9
Energy			
Swine	DE kcal/kg	1435.	1543.
Swine	ME kcal/kg	1322.	1421.
Swine	TDN %	32.	35.
Calcium	%	1.33	1.43
Chlorine	%	.46	.49
Iron	%	.046	.049
Magnesium	%	.29	.31
Phosphorus	%	.24	.26
Potassium	%	2.49	2.68
Sodium	%	.09	.10
Cobalt	mg/kg	.360	.390
Copper	mg/kg	9.9	10.6
Iodine	mg/kg	.150	.161
Manganese	mg/kg	29.0	31.2
Selenium	mg/kg	.600	.645
Zinc	mg/kg	16.0	17.2
Continued			

Feed name or analyses		Mean	
		As fed	Dry
Carotene	mg/kg	161.2	173.3
Choline	mg/kg	1518.	1632.
Folic acid	mg/kg	2.10	2.26
Niacin	mg/kg	45.8	49.2
Pantothenic acid	mg/kg	30.0	32.2
Riboflavin	mg/kg	12.3	13.2
Thiamine	mg/kg	3.5	3.8
a-tocopherol	mg/kg	128.0	137.6
Vitamin B_6	mg/kg	6.30	6.77
Vitamin K	mg/kg	8.70	9.35
Vitamin A equiv	IU/g	268.7	288.9
Alanine	%	.90	.97
Arginine	%	.70	.75
Aspartic acid	%	1.90	2.04
Glutamic acid	%	1.70	1.83
Glycine	%	.90	.97
Histidine	%	.40	.43
Isoleucine	%	.70	.75
Leucine	%	1.30	1.40
Lysine	%	.80	.86
Methionine	%	.20	.22
Phenylalanine	%	.80	.86
Proline	%	.90	.97
Serine	%	.70	.75
Threonine	%	.80	.86
Tryptophan	%	.40	.43
Tyrosine	%	.50	.54
Valine	%	.90	.97

Alfalfa, aerial pt, dehy grnd, mn 20 prot, (1) — Ref no 1-00-024

Feed name or analyses		Mean	
		As fed	Dry
Dry matter	%	93.1	100.0
Ash	%	10.3	11.1
Crude fiber	%	20.2	21.7
Ether extract	%	3.6	3.9
N-free extract	%	38.4	41.2
Protein (N x 6.25)	%	20.6	22.1
Swine	dig prot %	12.6	13.5
Energy			
Swine	DE kcal/kg	2217.	2381.
Swine	ME kcal/kg	2029.	2179.
Swine	TDN %	50.	54.
Calcium	%	1.52	1.63
Chlorine	%	.58	.62
Iron	%	.040	.043
Magnesium	%	.35	.38
Phosphorus	%	.27	.29
Potassium	%	2.52	2.71
Sodium	%	.86	.92
Cobalt	mg/kg	.320	.344
Copper	mg/kg	10.6	11.4
Iodine	mg/kg	.140	.150
Manganese	mg/kg	34.0	36.5
Selenium	mg/kg	.500	.537
Zinc	mg/kg	18.0	19.3
Continued			

Alfalfa, aerial pt, dehy grnd, mn 22 prot, (1)
Ref no 1-07-851

Feed name or analyses		Mean As fed	Dry
Dry matter	%	92.9	100.0
Ash	%	10.3	11.1
Crude fiber	%	18.5	19.9
Ether extract	%	3.7	4.0
N-free extract	%	37.9	40.8
Protein (N x 6.25)	%	22.5	24.2
Swine	dig prot %	13.7	14.8
Energy			
Swine	DE kcal/kg	2253.	2425.
Swine	ME kcal/kg	2052.	2209.
Swine	TDN %	51.	55.
Calcium	%	1.48	1.59
Chlorine	%	.52	.56
Iron	%	.045	.048
Magnesium	%	.34	.36
Phosphorus	%	.28	.30
Potassium	%	2.51	2.70
Sodium	%	.11	.12
Cobalt	mg/kg	.300	.323
Copper	mg/kg	11.1	11.9
Iodine	mg/kg	.200	.215
Manganese	mg/kg	37.0	39.8

Continued

Feed name or analyses		Mean As fed	Dry
Carotene	mg/kg	216.4	232.4
Choline	mg/kg	1618.	1738.
Folic acid	mg/kg	2.67	2.87
Niacin	mg/kg	54.7	58.7
Pantothenic acid	mg/kg	32.8	35.2
Riboflavin	mg/kg	15.5	16.6
Thiamine	mg/kg	3.9	4.2
a-tocopherol	mg/kg	147.0	157.9
Vitamin B6	mg/kg	7.90	8.48
Vitamin K	mg/kg	14.70	15.79
Vitamin A equiv	IU/g	360.7	387.4
Alanine	%	1.10	1.18
Arginine	%	.90	.97
Aspartic acid	%	2.10	2.26
Glutamic acid	%	2.10	2.26
Glycine	%	1.00	1.07
Histidine	%	.40	.43
Isoleucine	%	.80	.86
Leucine	%	1.50	1.61
Lysine	%	.90	.97
Methionine	%	.30	.32
Phenylalanine	%	1.10	1.18
Proline	%	1.00	1.07
Serine	%	.90	.97
Threonine	%	.90	.97
Tryptophan	%	.50	.54
Tyrosine	%	.70	.75
Valine	%	.10	.11

Feed name or analyses		Mean As fed	Dry
Selenium	mg/kg	.540	.581
Zinc	mg/kg	20.0	21.5
Carotene	mg/kg	252.5	271.7
Choline	mg/kg	1853.	1994.
Folic acid	mg/kg	3.00	3.23
Niacin	mg/kg	58.8	63.3
Pantothenic acid	mg/kg	33.0	35.5
Riboflavin	mg/kg	17.4	18.7
Thiamine	mg/kg	4.2	4.5
a-tocopherol	mg/kg	151.0	162.5
Vitamin B6	mg/kg	7.80	8.39
Vitamin K	mg/kg	8.50	9.15
Vitamin A equiv	IU/g	422.0	454.1
Alanine	%	1.30	1.40
Arginine	%	1.00	1.08
Aspartic acid	%	2.30	2.47
Glutamic acid	%	2.30	2.47
Glycine	%	1.10	1.18
Histidine	%	.50	.54
Isoleucine	%	.90	.97
Leucine	%	1.70	1.83
Lysine	%	1.00	1.08
Methionine	%	.40	.43
Phenylalanine	%	1.20	1.29
Proline	%	1.10	1.18
Serine	%	.90	.97
Threonine	%	1.00	1.08

Continued

(1) dry forages and roughages
(2) pasture, range plants, and forages fed green
(3) silages
(4) energy feeds
(5) protein supplements
(6) minerals
(7) vitamins
(8) additives

TABLE I-1—COMPOSITION OF SOME COMMON SWINE FEEDS (Continued)

Feed name or analyses		Mean As fed	Dry
Tryptophan	%	.60	.64
Tyrosine	%	.80	.86
Valine	%	1.20	1.29

Alfalfa, aerial pt, dehy, immature, (1)

Ref no 1-00-041

		As fed	Dry
Dry matter	%	91.1	100.0
Ash	%	10.9	12.0
Crude fiber	%	25.6	28.1
Ether extract	%	2.1	2.3
N-free extract	%	33.3	36.6
Protein (N x 6.25)	%	19.1	21.0
Swine	dig prot %	11.7	12.8
Energy			
Swine	DE kcal/kg	2009.	2205.
Swine	ME kcal/kg	1844.	2024.
Swine	TDN %	46.	50.

Feed name or analyses		Mean As fed	Dry

Alfalfa, hay, s-c grnd, (1)
Sun-cured alfalfa meal (AAFCO)
Ground alfalfa hay (AAFCO)

Ref no 1-00-111

		As fed	Dry
Dry matter	%	92.2	100.0
Ash	%	9.5	10.3
Crude fiber	%	25.8	28.0
Ether extract	%	2.3	2.5
N-free extract	%	37.8	41.0
Protein (N x 6.25)	%	16.7	18.2
Swine	dig prot %	7.7	8.4
Cellulose	%	22.1	24.0
Lignin	%	9.8	10.7
Energy	GE kcal/kg	4204.	4560.
Swine	DE kcal/kg	1382.	1499.
Swine	ME kcal/kg	1276.	1384.
Swine	TDN %	31.	34.
Calcium	%	1.24	1.35
Chlorine	%	.43	.47
Iron	%	.040	.050
Magnesium	%	.31	.34
Phosphorus	%	.28	.30
Potassium	%	2.27	2.46
Sodium	%	.18	.19
Cobalt	mg/kg	.220	.240
Copper	mg/kg	17.2	18.7

Continued

Feed name or analyses		Mean As fed	Dry
Manganese	mg/kg	42.9	46.5
Zinc	mg/kg	32.4	35.1
Carotene	mg/kg	96.3	104.5
Vitamin A equiv	IU/g	160.5	174.2

Alfalfa, leaves, s-c grnd, mn 20 prot mx 18 fbr, (1)
Alfalfa leaf meal, sun-cured (AAFCO)

Ref no 1-00-246

		As fed	Dry
Dry matter	%	88.8	100.0
Ash	%	9.5	10.7
Crude fiber	%	14.6	16.4
Ether extract	%	2.8	3.1
N-free extract	%	40.7	45.8
Protein (N x 6.25)	%	21.3	24.0
Swine	dig prot %	13.0	14.6
Energy	GE kcal/kg	3802.	4282.
Swine	DE kcal/kg	2192.	2469.
Swine	ME kcal/kg	2000.	2252.
Swine	TDN %	50.	56.
Calcium	%	2.11	2.38
Iron	%	.030	.034
Magnesium	%	.36	.41
Phosphorus	%	.26	.29
Potassium	%	1.80	2.02
Sulfur	%	.54	.61

Continued

Feed name or analyses		As fed (Mean)	Dry (Mean)
Manganese	mg/kg	42.9	48.3
Carotene	mg/kg	62.4	70.3
Vitamin A equiv	IU/g	104.0	117.2

ANIMAL. Scientific name not used

Animal, blood, dehy grnd, (5)
Blood meal (AAFCO)
Blood meal (CFA)

Ref no 5-00-380

		As fed (Mean)	Dry (Mean)
Dry matter	%	91.0	100.0
Ash	%	5.6	6.2
Crude fiber	%	1.0	1.1
Ether extract	%	1.6	1.8
N-free extract	%	2.8	3.1
Protein (N x 6.25)	%	79.9	87.8
Swine	dig prot %	62.3	68.5
Energy	GE kcal/kg	5210.	5726.
Swine	DE kcal/kg	2684.	2949.
Swine	ME kcal/kg	2101.	2309.
Swine	TDN %	61.	67.
Calcium	%	.28	.31
Iron	%	.376	.413

Continued

Feed name or analyses		As fed (Mean)	Dry (Mean)
Magnesium	%	.22	.24
Phosphorus	%	.22	.24
Potassium	%	.09	.10
Sodium	%	.32	.35
Copper	mg/kg	9.9	10.9
Manganese	mg/kg	5.3	5.8
Choline	mg/kg	757.	832.
Niacin	mg/kg	31.5	34.6
Pantothenic acid	mg/kg	1.1	1.2
Riboflavin	mg/kg	1.5	1.6
Arginine	%	3.50	3.85
Cystine	%	1.40	1.54
Histidine	%	4.20	4.62
Isoleucine	%	1.00	1.10
Leucine	%	10.30	11.32
Lysine	%	6.90	7.58
Methionine	%	.90	.99
Phenylalanine	%	6.10	6.70
Threonine	%	3.70	4.07
Tryptophan	%	1.10	1.21
Tyrosine	%	1.80	1.98
Valine	%	6.50	7.14

Animal, blood, spray dehy, (5)
Blood flour

Ref no 5-00-381

Feed name or analyses		As fed (Mean)	Dry (Mean)
Dry matter	%	91.0	100.0
Ash	%	4.8	5.3
Crude fiber	%	1.0	1.1
Ether extract	%	1.0	1.1
N-free extract	%	2.0	2.2
Protein (N x 6.25)	%	82.2	90.3
Swine	dig prot %	64.1	70.4
Energy			
Swine	DE kcal/kg	2608.	2866.
Swine	ME kcal/kg	2029.	2230.
Swine	TDN %	59.	65.
Calcium	%	.45	.49
Iron	%	.300	.330
Magnesium	%	.04	.04
Phosphorus	%	.37	.41
Potassium	%	.41	.45
Sodium	%	.33	.36
Cobalt	mg/kg	.100	.100
Copper	mg/kg	8.1	8.9
Manganese	mg/kg	6.4	7.0
Choline	mg/kg	279.	307.

Continued

(1) dry forages and roughages
(2) pasture, range plants, and forages fed green
(3) silages
(4) energy feeds
(5) protein supplements
(6) minerals
(7) vitamins
(8) additives

TABLE I-1—COMPOSITION OF SOME COMMON SWINE FEEDS (Continued)

Feed name or analyses		Mean As fed	Mean Dry
Niacin	mg/kg	28.6	31.4
Pantothenic acid	mg/kg	5.3	5.8
Riboflavin	mg/kg	4.2	4.6
Thiamine	mg/kg	.4	.4
Arginine	%	3.30	3.63
Histidine	%	4.80	5.28
Isoleucine	%	1.10	1.21
Leucine	%	10.60	11.65
Lysine	%	8.20	9.01
Methionine	%	1.00	1.10
Phenylalanine	%	5.60	6.15
Threonine	%	3.60	3.96
Tryptophan	%	1.00	1.10
Tyrosine	%	2.00	2.20
Valine	%	7.20	7.91

Continued

Animal carcass res, dry-rend dehy grnd, mx 4.4 P, (5)
Meat meal (AAFCO)
Meat scrap

Ref no 5-00-385

		As fed	Dry
Dry matter	%	93.5	100.0
Ash	%	25.2	27.0
Crude fiber	%	2.4	2.5
Ether extract	%	9.9	10.6
N-free extract	%	2.6	2.8

Continued

Feed name or analyses		Mean As fed	Mean Dry
Protein (N x 6.25)	%	53.4	57.1
Swine	dig prot %	47.5	50.8
Energy	GE kcal/kg	3181.	3402.
Swine	DE kcal/kg	3010.	3219.
Swine	ME kcal/kg	2543.	2720.
Swine	TDN %	68.	73.
Calcium	%	7.94	8.49
Chlorine	%	1.31	1.40
Iron	%	.044	.047
Magnesium	%	.27	.29
Phosphorus	%	4.03	4.31
Potassium	%	.55	.59
Sodium	%	1.68	1.80
Sulfur	%	.50	.53
Cobalt	mg/kg	.128	.137
Copper	mg/kg	9.7	10.4
Manganese	mg/kg	9.5	10.2
Biotin	mg/kg	.09	.10
Choline	mg/kg	1955.	2091.
Niacin	mg/kg	56.9	60.8
Pantothenic acid	mg/kg	4.8	5.1
Riboflavin	mg/kg	5.3	5.7
Thiamine	mg/kg	.2	.2
Vitamin B12	mcg/kg	51.1	54.6
Arginine	%	3.70	3.96
Cystine	%	.60	.64
Cysteine	%	.80	.86
Glutamic acid	%	8.10	8.66
Glycine	%	2.20	2.35

Continued

Feed name or analyses		Mean As fed	Mean Dry
Histidine	%	1.10	1.18
Isoleucine	%	1.90	2.03
Leucine	%	3.50	3.74
Lysine	%	3.80	4.06
Methionine	%	.80	.86
Phenylalanine	%	1.90	2.03
Serine	%	2.10	2.24
Threonine	%	1.80	1.92
Tryptophan	%	.30	.32
Tyrosine	%	.90	.96
Valine	%	2.60	2.78

Animal, carcass res w blood, dry- or wet-rend dehy grnd, mx 4.4 P, (5)
Meat meal tankage (AAFCO)
Digester tankage

Ref no 5-00-386

		As fed	Dry
Dry matter	%	92.0	100.0
Ash	%	21.4	23.3
Crude fiber	%	2.0	2.2
Ether extract	%	8.1	8.8
N-free extract	%	.6	.7
Protein (N x 6.25)	%	59.8	65.0
Swine	dig prot %	37.1	40.3
Lignin	%	3.0	3.3

Continued

Feed name or analyses		Mean As fed	Mean Dry
Energy			
Swine	DE kcal/kg	2475.	2690.
Swine	ME kcal/kg	2052.	2230.
Swine	TDN %	56.	61.
Calcium	%	5.94	6.46
Magnesium	%	.16	.17
Phosphorus	%	3.17	3.45
Potassium	%	.56	.61
Sodium	%	1.67	1.82
Cobalt	mg/kg	.200	.200
Copper	mg/kg	38.7	42.1
Manganese	mg/kg	19.1	20.8
Choline	mg/kg	2169.	2358.
Folic acid	mg/kg	1.50	1.60
Niacin	mg/kg	39.2	42.6
Pantothenic acid	mg/kg	2.4	2.6
Riboflavin	mg/kg	2.4	2.6
Arginine	%	3.60	3.91
Histidine	%	1.90	2.07
Isoleucine	%	1.90	2.07
Leucine	%	5.10	5.54
Lysine	%	4.00	4.35
Methionine	%	.80	.87
Phenylalanine	%	2.70	2.93
Threonine	%	2.40	2.61
Tryptophan	%	.70	.76
Valine	%	4.20	4.57

(1) dry forages and roughages
(2) pasture, range plants, and forages fed green

Feed name or analyses		Mean As fed	Mean Dry
Animal, carcass res w bone, dry-rend dehy grnd, mn 4.4 P, (5)			
Meat and bone meal (AAFCO)			
Meat and bone scrap			
Ref no 5-00-388			
Dry matter	%	94.0	100.0
Ash	%	29.1	31.0
Crude fiber	%	2.2	2.3
Ether extract	%	9.5	10.1
N-free extract	%	2.6	2.8
Protein (N x 6.25)	%	50.6	53.8
Swine	dig prot %	45.0	47.9
Energy			
Swine	DE kcal/kg	2859.	3042.
Swine	ME kcal/kg	2434.	2589.
Swine	TDN %	65.	69.
Calcium	%	10.57	11.25
Chlorine	%	.35	.37
Iron	%	.050	.053
Magnesium	%	1.13	1.20
Phosphorus	%	5.07	5.39
Potassium	%	1.46	1.55
Sodium	%	.73	.78
Cobalt	mg/kg	.183	.195

Continued

(3) silages
(4) energy feeds
(5) protein supplements

Feed name or analyses		Mean As fed	Mean Dry
Copper	mg/kg	1.5	1.6
Manganese	mg/kg	12.3	13.1
Choline	mg/kg	2189.	2329.
Niacin	mg/kg	47.8	50.8
Pantothenic acid	mg/kg	3.7	3.9
Riboflavin	mg/kg	4.4	4.7
Thiamine	mg/kg	1.1	1.2
Vitamin B_{12}	mcg/kg	44.8	47.7
Arginine	%	4.00	4.26
Cystine	%	.60	.64
Glutamic acid	%	11.00	11.70
Glycine	%	6.60	7.02
Histidine	%	.90	.96
Isoleucine	%	1.70	1.81
Leucine	%	3.10	3.30
Lysine	%	3.50	3.72
Methionine	%	.70	.74
Phenylalanine	%	1.80	1.92
Threonine	%	1.80	1.92
Tryptophan	%	.20	.21
Valine	%	2.40	2.55

Animal fat - see Animal-Poultry, fat; see Swine, lard

(6) minerals
(7) vitamins
(8) additives

TABLE I-1—COMPOSITION OF SOME COMMON SWINE FEEDS (Continued)

Animal, liver, dehy grnd, (5)
Animal liver meal (AAFCO)
Animal liver meal (CFA)
Liver meal

Ref no 5-00-389

Feed name or analyses		Mean As fed	Mean Dry
Dry matter	%	92.6	100.0
Ash	%	6.0	6.5
Crude fiber	%	1.3	1.4
Ether extract	%	15.1	16.3
N-free extract	%	3.7	4.0
Protein (N x 6.25)	%	66.5	71.8
Swine	dig prot %	64.4	69.6
Energy			
Swine	DE kcal/kg	3920.	4233.
Swine	ME kcal/kg	3195.	3450.
Swine	TDN %	89.	96.
Calcium	%	.50	.54
Iron	%	.063	.068
Phosphorus	%	1.25	1.35
Cobalt	mg/kg	.134	.144
Copper	mg/kg	89.3	96.4
Manganese	mg/kg	8.8	9.5
Biotin	mg/kg	.02	.02
Folic acid	mg/kg	5.56	6.00
Niacin	mg/kg	203.7	220.0
Pantothenic acid	mg/kg	45.2	48.8
			Continued

Feed name or analyses		Mean As fed	Mean Dry
Riboflavin	mg/kg	46.3	50.0
Thiamine	mg/kg	.2	.2
Vitamin B12	mcg/kg	501.5	541.6
Arginine	%	4.10	4.43
Cystine	%	.90	.97
Glutamic acid	%	8.10	8.75
Glycine	%	5.60	6.05
Histidine	%	1.50	1.62
Isoleucine	%	3.40	3.67
Leucine	%	5.40	5.83
Lysine	%	4.80	5.18
Methionine	%	1.30	1.40
Phenylalanine	%	2.90	3.13
Threonine	%	2.60	2.81
Tryptophan	%	.60	.65
Tyrosine	%	1.70	1.84
Valine	%	4.20	4.54

Animal, bone, cooked dehy grnd, mn 10 P, (6)
Feeding bone meal (CFA)

Ref no 6-00-397

		As fed	Dry
Dry matter	%	94.5	100.0
Ether extract	%	9.6	10.2
Protein (N x 6.25)	%	17.8	18.8
Calcium	%	25.82	27.32
			Continued

Feed name or analyses		Mean As fed	Mean Dry
Phosphorus	%	12.35	13.07
Fluorine	mg/kg	2000.00	2116.40

Animal, bone, steamed dehy grnd, (6)
Bone meal, steamed (AAFCO)

Ref no 6-00-400

		As fed	Dry
Dry matter	%	95.0	100.0
Ash	%	71.8	75.6
Crude fiber	%	2.0	2.1
Ether extract	%	3.2	3.4
Protein (N x 6.25)	%	12.1	12.7
Swine	dig prot %	9.4	9.9
Energy			
Swine	DE kcal/kg	660.	695.
Swine	ME kcal/kg	616.	649.
Swine	TDN %	15.	16.
Calcium	%	28.98	30.51
Iron	%	.084	.088
Magnesium	%	.64	.67
Phosphorus	%	13.59	14.31
Sodium	%	.46	.48
Cobalt	mg/kg	.100	.100
Copper	mg/kg	16.3	17.2
Manganese	mg/kg	30.4	32.0
Zinc	mg/kg	424.6	447.1
Niacin	mg/kg	4.2	4.4
			Continued

Feed name or analyses		Mean	
		As fed	Dry
Pantothenic acid	mg/kg	2.4	2.5
Riboflavin	mg/kg	.9	.9
Thiamine	mg/kg	.4	.4

Animal, bone phosphate, precip dehy, mn 17 P, (6)
Bone phosphate (AAFCO)

Ref no 6-00-406

		As fed	Dry
Dry matter	%	99.0	100.0
Ash	%	86.4	87.3
Ether extract	%	.3	.3
Protein (N x 6.25)	%	.4	.4
Calcium	%	28.00	28.28
Phosphorus	%	11.20	11.31

Feed name or analyses		Mean	
		As fed	Dry

ANIMAL—POULTRY. Scientific name not used

Animal-poultry, fat, heat-rend, mn 90 fatty acids mx 2.5 unsaponifiable matter mx 1 insol matter, (4)
Animal fat (AAFCO)

Ref no 4-00-409

		As fed	Dry
Dry matter	%	99.5	100.0
Ether extract	%	99.4	99.9
Energy	GE kcal/kg	9450.	9497.

Baking refuse - see also Bread, dehy

Feed name or analyses		Mean	
		As fed	Dry

BARLEY. Hordeum vulgare

Barley, grain, thresher-run, mn 48 wt mn 10 mx 20 fm, (4)

Ref no 4-08-159 Canada

		As fed	Dry
Dry matter	%	90.0	100.0
Ash	%	2.6	2.9
Crude fiber	%	4.5	5.0
Ether extract	%	.9	1.0
N-free extract	%	70.0	77.8
Protein (N x 6.25)	%	11.8	13.1
Swine	dig prot %	9.1	10.1
Energy	GE kcal/kg	4208.	4675.
Swine	DE kcal/kg	3214.	3571.
Swine	ME kcal/kg	3002.	3335.
Swine	TDN %	73.	81.

(1) dry forages and roughages
(2) pasture, range plants, and forages fed green
(3) silages
(4) energy feeds
(5) protein supplements
(6) minerals
(7) vitamins
(8) additives

TABLE 1-1—COMPOSITION OF SOME COMMON SWINE FEEDS (Continued)

Barley, grain, thresher-run, mn 48 wt mx 10 fm, (4)

Ref no 4-08-158 Canada

Feed name or analyses		As fed (Mean)	Dry (Mean)
Dry matter	%	90.0	100.0
Ash	%	2.8	3.1
Crude fiber	%	4.5	5.0
Ether extract	%	1.0	1.1
N-free extract	%	70.4	78.2
Protein (N x 6.25)	%	11.3	12.6
Swine dig prot	%	8.7	9.7
Energy GE	kcal/kg	4140.	4600.
Swine DE	kcal/kg	3214.	3571.
Swine ME	kcal/kg	3024.	3360.
Swine TDN	%	73.	81.

Barley, grain, thresher-run, mx 48 wt mn 10 mx 20 fm, (4)

Ref no 4-08-156 Canada

Feed name or analyses		As fed (Mean)	Dry (Mean)
Dry matter	%	90.0	100.0
Ash	%	2.8	3.1
Crude fiber	%	5.9	6.6
Ether extract	%	1.1	1.2
N-free extract	%	68.5	76.1
Protein (N x 6.25)	%	11.7	13.0
Swine dig prot	%	9.0	10.0
Energy			
Swine DE	kcal/kg	3174.	3527.
Swine ME	kcal/kg	2965.	3294.
Swine TDN	%	72.	80.

Barley, grain, thresher-run, mx 48 wt mx 10 fm, (4)

Ref no 4-08-155 Canada

Feed name or analyses		As fed (Mean)	Dry (Mean)
Dry matter	%	90.0	100.0
Ash	%	2.9	3.2
Crude fiber	%	5.1	5.7
Ether extract	%	.8	.9
N-free extract	%	69.4	77.1
Protein (N x 6.25)	%	11.8	13.1
Swine dig prot	%	9.1	10.1
Energy GE	kcal/kg	4140.	4600.
Swine DE	kcal/kg	3174.	3527.
Swine ME	kcal/kg	2952.	3280.
Swine TDN	%	72.	80.

Barley, grain, Can 1 feed mn 46 wt mx 4 fm, (4)

Ref no 4-00-531

Feed name or analyses		As fed (Mean)	Dry (Mean)
Dry matter	%	86.5	100.0
Ash	%	2.3	2.6
Crude fiber	%	4.8	5.6
Ether extract	%	1.9	2.2
N-free extract	%	66.1	76.4
Protein (N x 6.25)	%	11.4	13.2
Swine dig prot	%	8.9	10.3
Energy GE	kcal/kg	4599.	5317.
Swine DE	kcal/kg	3128.	3616.
Swine ME	kcal/kg	2918.	3374.
Swine TDN	%	71.	82.
Alanine	%	.41	.47
Arginine	%	.46	.53
Aspartic acid	%	.55	.64
Glutamic acid	%	2.37	2.74
Glycine	%	.42	.49
Histidine	%	.21	.24
Isoleucine	%	.32	.37
Leucine	%	.67	.78
Lysine	%	.35	.40
Methionine	%	.10	.12
Phenylalanine	%	.47	.54
Proline	%	.99	1.14
Serine	%	.41	.48

Continued

Feed name or analyses		Mean	
		As fed	Dry
Threonine	%	.32	.37
Tyrosine	%	.26	.30
Valine	%	.42	.49

Barley, grain, Can 2 feed mn 43 wt mx 10 fm, (4)

Ref no 4-00-532

		As fed	Dry
Dry matter	%	86.5	100.0
Ash	%	2.2	2.6
Crude fiber	%	5.0	5.7
Ether extract	%	1.9	2.2
N-free extract	%	66.1	76.4
Protein (N x 6.25)	%	11.4	13.1
Swine	dig prot %	8.8	10.2
Energy	GE kcal/kg	4599.	5317.
Swine	DE kcal/kg	3128.	3616.
Swine	ME kcal/kg	2921.	3377.
Swine	TDN %	71.	82.
Alanine	%	.40	.46
Arginine	%	.46	.53
Aspartic acid	%	.64	.74
Glutamic acid	%	2.40	2.78
Glycine	%	.40	.46
Histidine	%	.19	.22
Isoleucine	%	.36	.42

Continued

Feed name or analyses		Mean	
		As fed	Dry
Leucine	%	.67	.78
Lysine	%	.37	.43
Methionine	%	.10	.12
Phenylalanine	%	.50	.58
Proline	%	1.05	1.21
Serine	%	.40	.46
Threonine	%	.34	.39
Tyrosine	%	.24	.28
Valine	%	.50	.58

Barley, grain, gr 1 US mn 47 wt mx 1 fm, (4)

Ref no 4-00-535

		As fed	Dry
Dry matter	%	89.0	100.0
Ash	%	2.7	3.0
Crude fiber	%	6.0	6.7
Ether extract	%	1.9	2.1
N-free extract	%	66.4	74.6
Protein (N x 6.25)	%	12.1	13.6
Swine	dig prot %	9.4	10.6
Energy			
Swine	DE kcal/kg	3178.	3571.
Swine	ME kcal/kg	2962.	3328.
Swine	TDN %	72.	81.
Calcium	%	.24	.27

Continued

Feed name or analyses		Mean	
		As fed	Dry
Phosphorus	%	.36	.41
Thiamine	mg/kg	4.3	4.8

Barley, grain, gr 2 US mn 45 wt mx 2 fm, (4)

Ref no 4-00-536

		As fed	Dry
Dry matter	%	88.1	100.0
Ash	%	2.4	2.7
Crude fiber	%	5.6	6.3
Ether extract	%	1.8	2.0
N-free extract	%	66.7	75.7
Protein (N x 6.25)	%	11.7	13.3
Swine	dig prot %	9.2	10.4
Energy			
Swine	DE kcal/kg	3146.	3171.
Swine	ME kcal/kg	2935.	3332.
Swine	TDN %	71.	81.
Calcium	%	.05	.06
Phosphorus	%	.31	.35
Riboflavin	mg/kg	1.3	1.5
Thiamine	mg/kg	4.7	5.3

(1) dry forages and roughages
(2) pasture, range plants, and forages fed green
(3) silages
(4) energy feeds
(5) protein supplements
(6) minerals
(7) vitamins
(8) additives

793

TABLE 1-1—COMPOSITION OF SOME COMMON SWINE FEEDS (Continued)

Barley, grain, gr 3 US mn 43 wt mx 3 fm, (4)

Ref no 4-00-537

Feed name or analyses		Mean	
		As fed	Dry
Dry matter	%	88.0	100.0
Ash	%	1.8	2.1
Crude fiber	%	6.0	6.8
Ether extract	%	1.7	1.9
N-free extract	%	66.7	75.8
Protein (N x 6.25)	%	11.8	13.4
Swine	dig prot %	9.1	10.3
Energy			
Swine	DE kcal/kg	3104.	3527.
Swine	ME kcal/kg	2896.	3291.
Swine	TDN %	70.	80.
Calcium	%	.05	.06
Phosphorus	%	.34	.39

Barley, grain, gr 5 US mn 36 wt mx 6 fm, (4)
Barley grain, light

Ref no 4-00-540

Feed name or analyses		As fed	Dry
Dry matter	%	88.0	100.0
Ash	%	3.0	3.4
Crude fiber	%	10.0	11.4
Ether extract	%	2.4	2.7

Continued

Feed name or analyses		Mean	
		As fed	Dry
N-free extract	%	62.3	70.8
Protein (N x 6.25)	%	10.3	11.7
Swine	dig prot %	7.6	8.6
Energy			
Swine	DE kcal/kg	3142.	3571.
Swine	ME kcal/kg	2941.	3342.
Swine	TDN %	71.	81.

Barley, grain, Pacific coast, (4)

Ref no 4-07-939

Feed name or analyses		As fed	Dry
Dry matter	%	89.0	100.0
Ash	%	2.3	2.6
Crude fiber	%	6.2	7.0
Ether extract	%	2.2	2.5
N-free extract	%	68.5	77.0
Protein (N x 6.25)	%	9.7	10.9
Swine	dig prot %	7.5	8.4
Energy			
Swine	DE kcal/kg	3139.	3527.
Swine	ME kcal/kg	2944.	3308.
Swine	TDN %	71.	80.
Calcium	%	.06	.07
Phosphorus	%	.40	.45
Choline	mg/kg	937.	1054.
Niacin	mg/kg	44.1	49.6
Pantothenic acid	mg/kg	7.3	8.2

Continued

Feed name or analyses		Mean	
		As fed	Dry
Riboflavin	mg/kg	1.3	1.5
Thiamine	mg/kg	4.0	4.5

Barley, malt sprouts w hulls, dehy, mn 24 prot, (5)
Malt sprouts (AAFCO)

Ref no 5-00-545

Feed name or analyses		As fed	Dry
Dry matter	%	93.0	100.0
Ash	%	6.4	6.9
Crude fiber	%	14.0	15.1
Ether extract	%	1.4	1.5
N-free extract	%	44.9	48.3
Protein (N x 6.25)	%	26.2	28.2
Swine	dig prot %	20.7	22.3
Energy			
Swine	DE kcal/kg	1558.	1675.
Swine	ME kcal/kg	1406.	1512.
Swine	TDN %	35.	38.
Calcium	%	.22	.24
Magnesium	%	.18	.19
Phosphorus	%	.73	.78
Potassium	%	.21	.23
Manganese	mg/kg	31.7	34.1
Choline	mg/kg	1584.	1703.
Folic acid	mg/kg	.20	.20
Niacin	mg/kg	43.3	46.5
Pantothenic acid	mg/kg	8.6	9.2

Continued

(top left, continued table)

Feed name or analyses		Mean	
		As fed	Dry
Riboflavin	mg/kg	1.5	1.6
Thiamine	mg/kg	.7	.8

BARLEY, WESTERN. Hordeum vulgare

Barley, western, grain, gr 5 US mn 36 wt mx 4 fm, (4)

Barley, western, grain, light

Ref no 4-00-566

Feed name or analyses			Mean	
			As fed	Dry
Dry matter		%	88.6	100.0
Ash		%	3.3	3.7
Crude fiber		%	7.4	8.4
Ether extract		%	2.1	2.4
N-free extract		%	63.8	72.0
Protein (N x 6.25)		%	12.0	13.5
Swine	dig prot	%	8.9	10.0
Energy				
Swine		DE kcal/kg	2970.	3351.
Swine		ME kcal/kg	2770.	3126.
Swine		TDN %	67.	76.

(1) dry forages and roughages
(2) pasture, range plants, and forages fed green

BEET, SUGAR. Beta saccharifera

Beet, sugar, molasses, mn 48 invert sugar mn 79.5 degrees brix, (4)

Beet molasses (AAFCO)

Molasses (CFA)

Ref no 4-00-668

Feed name or analyses		Mean	
		As fed	Dry
Dry matter	%	77.0	100.0
Ash	%	8.2	10.6
Ether extract	%	.2	.3
N-free extract	%	61.9	80.4
Protein (N x 6.25)	%	6.7	8.7
Energy			
Calcium	%	.16	.21
Iron	%	.010	.010
Magnesium	%	.23	.30
Phosphorus	%	.03	.04
Potassium	%	4.77	6.20
Sodium	%	1.17	1.52
Cobalt	mg/kg	.400	.500
Copper	mg/kg	17.6	22.9
Manganese	mg/kg	4.6	6.0
Niacin	mg/kg	42.2	54.8
		Continued	

(3) silages
(4) energy feeds
(5) protein supplements

(top right, continued table)

Feed name or analyses		Mean	
		As fed	Dry
Pantothenic acid	mg/kg	4.6	6.0
Riboflavin	mg/kg	2.4	3.1

Beet, sugar, pulp, dehy, (4)

Dried beet pulp (AAFCO)

Dried beet pulp (CFA)

Ref no 4-00-669

Feed name or analyses			Mean	
			As fed	Dry
Dry matter		%	91.0	100.0
Ash		%	3.6	3.9
Crude fiber		%	19.0	20.9
Ether extract		%	.6	.7
N-free extract		%	58.7	64.5
Protein (N x 6.25)		%	9.1	10.0
Swine	dig prot	%	3.7	4.1
Lignin		%	8.0	8.8
Energy		GE kcal/kg	3837.	4217.
Swine		DE kcal/kg	2860.	3143.
Swine		ME kcal/kg	2688.	2954.
Swine		TDN %	65.	71.
Calcium		%	.68	.75
Iron		%	.030	.033
Magnesium		%	.27	.30
Phosphorus		%	.10	.11
Potassium		%	.21	.23
			Continued	

(6) minerals
(7) vitamins
(8) additives

TABLE I-1—COMPOSITION OF SOME COMMON SWINE FEEDS (Continued)

Feed name or analyses		Mean As fed	Mean Dry
Cobalt	mg/kg	.100	.100
Copper	mg/kg	12.5	13.7
Manganese	mg/kg	35.0	38.5
Zinc	mg/kg	.7	.8
Choline	mg/kg	829.	912.
Niacin	mg/kg	16.3	17.9
Pantothenic acid	mg/kg	1.5	1.6
Riboflavin	mg/kg	.7	.8
Thiamine	mg/kg	.4	.4
Vitamin D₃	ICU/g	1.0	1.0
Arginine	%	.30	.33
Histidine	%	.20	.22
Isoleucine	%	.30	.33
Leucine	%	.60	.66
Lysine	%	.60	.66
Phenylalanine	%	.30	.33
Threonine	%	.40	.44
Tryptophan	%	.10	.11
Tyrosine	%	.40	.44
Valine	%	.40	.44

Blood flour - see Animal blood, spray dehy

Blood meal - see Animal, blood, dehy grnd

Bone - see Animal

Feed name or analyses			Mean As fed	Mean Dry

Bone phosphate - see Animal, bone phosphate

Bran - see Wheat

BREAD. Scientific name not used

Bread, dehy, (4)

Ref no 4-07-944

Feed name or analyses			As fed	Dry
Dry matter		%	95.0	100.0
Ash		%	1.9	2.0
Crude fiber		%	.5	.5
Ether extract		%	1.0	1.1
N-free extract		%	80.6	84.8
Protein (N x 6.25)		%	11.0	11.6
Swine	dig prot	%	9.8	10.3
Energy				
Swine	DE kcal/kg		3686	3880
Swine	ME kcal/kg		3454	3636
Swine	TDN %		84.	88.
Calcium		%	.03	.03
Phosphorus		%	.10	.10

Feed name or analyses			Mean As fed	Mean Dry

Brewers dried grains - see Grains

Brewers dried yeast - see Yeast, brewers

Brown rice - see Rice, groats

BUCKWHEAT. Fagopyrum spp

Buckwheat, grain, (4)

Ref no 4-00-994

Feed name or analyses			As fed	Dry
Dry matter		%	88.0	100.0
Ash		%	1.8	2.0
Crude fiber		%	9.0	10.2
Ether extract		%	2.5	2.8
N-free extract		%	63.7	72.4
Protein (N x 6.25)		%	11.1	12.6
Swine	dig prot	%	8.0	9.1
Energy	GE kcal/kg		3967	4508
Swine	DE kcal/kg		3026	3439
Swine	ME kcal/kg		2829	3215
Swine	TDN %		69.	78.
Calcium		%	.11	.13

Continued

Feed name or analyses		Mean As fed	Dry
Phosphorus	%	.33	.38
Potassium	%	.45	.51
Cobalt	mg/kg	.060	.070
Copper	mg/kg	9.5	10.8
Manganese	mg/kg	33.7	38.3
Zinc	mg/kg	8.7	9.9
Niacin	mg/kg	17.8	20.2
Riboflavin	mg/kg	10.6	12.1
Thiamine	mg/kg	3.3	3.7
Arginine	%	.97	1.10
Histidine	%	.26	.30
Isoleucine	%	.35	.40
Leucine	%	.53	.60
Lysine	%	.62	.70
Methionine	%	.18	.20
Phenylalanine	%	.44	.50
Threonine	%	.44	.50
Tryptophan	%	.18	.20
Valine	%	.53	.60

Buckwheat, flour by-prod wo hulls, c-sift, mx 10 fbr, (5)

Buckwheat middlings, (AAFCO)

Ref no 5-00-991

Feed name or analyses		Mean As fed	Dry
Dry matter	%	89.0	100.0
Ash	%	4.7	5.3
Crude fiber	%	6.0	6.7
Ether extract	%	6.9	7.8
N-free extract	%	43.0	48.3
Protein (N x 6.25)	%	28.4	31.9
Swine	dig prot %	22.7	25.5
Energy			
Swine	DE kcal/kg	3178.	3571.
Swine	ME kcal/kg	2848.	3200.
Swine	TDN %	72.	81.
Phosphorus	%	1.02	1.15
Potassium	%	.98	1.10

Buttermilk - see Cattle

CALCIUM PHOSPHATE, DIBASIC

Calcium phosphate, dibasic, comm, (6)
Dicalcium phosphate (AAFCO)

Ref no 6-01-080

Feed name or analyses		Mean As fed	Dry
Dry matter	%	96.0	100.0
Calcium	%	22.20	23.13
Phosphorus	%	17.90	18.65
Fluorine	mg/kg	768.00	800.00

Cane molasses - see Sugarcane

Casein - see Cattle

(1) dry forages and roughages
(2) pasture, range plants, and forages fed green
(3) silages
(4) energy feeds
(5) protein supplements
(6) minerals
(7) vitamins
(8) additives

TABLE I-1—COMPOSITION OF SOME COMMON SWINE FEEDS (Continued)

Feed name or analyses		Mean As fed	Dry
CATTLE. Bos spp			
Cattle, whey, dehy, mn 65 lactose, (4)			
Dried whey (AAFCO)			
Whey, dried			
Ref no 4-01-182			
Dry matter	%	94.0	100.0
Ash	%	9.7	10.3
Ether extract	%	.8	.9
N-free extract	%	69.6	74.1
Protein (N x 6.25)	%	13.8	14.7
Swine	dig prot %	12.6	13.4
Energy			
Swine	DE kcal/kg	3432.	3651.
Swine	ME kcal/kg	3191.	3395.
Swine	TDN %	78.	83.
Calcium	%	.87	.93
Iron	%	.016	.017
Magnesium	%	.13	.14
Phosphorus	%	.79	.84
Cobalt	mg/kg	.094	.100
Copper	mg/kg	43.1	45.9
Manganese	mg/kg	4.6	4.9
Biotin	mg/kg	.40	.40
Choline	mg/kg	20.	21.

Continued

Feed name or analyses		Mean As fed	Dry
Folic acid	mg/kg	.90	1.00
Niacin	mg/kg	11.2	11.9
Pantothenic acid	mg/kg	47.7	50.8
Riboflavin	mg/kg	29.9	31.8
Thiamine	mg/kg	3.7	3.9
Arginine	%	.40	.43
Cystine	%	.30	.32
Histidine	%	.20	.21
Isoleucine	%	.90	.96
Leucine	%	1.40	1.49
Lysine	%	1.10	1.17
Methionine	%	.20	.21
Phenylalanine	%	.40	.43
Threonine	%	.80	.85
Tryptophan	%	.20	.21
Tyrosine	%	.30	.32
Valine	%	.70	.74

Feed name or analyses		Mean As fed	Dry
Cattle, buttermilk, cond, mn 27 total solids 0.055			
fat mx 0.14 ash per 1 solids, (5)			
Condensed buttermilk (AAFCO)			
Buttermilk, concentrated			
Buttermilk, condensed			
Buttermilk, evaporated			
Ref no 5-01-159			
Dry matter	%	29.0	100.0
Ash	%	3.4	11.9
Ether extract	%	2.5	8.6
N-free extract	%	12.4	42.6
Protein (N x 6.25)	%	10.7	36.9
Swine	dig prot %	9.9	34.3
Energy			
Swine	DE kcal/kg	959.	3307.
Swine	ME kcal/kg	850.	2930.
Swine	TDN %	22.	75.
Calcium	%	.44	1.52
Magnesium	%	.19	.66
Phosphorus	%	.26	.90
Potassium	%	.23	.79
Sodium	%	.31	1.07
Riboflavin	mg/kg	14.3	49.3

Cattle, buttermilk, dehy, feed gr mx 8 moisture mx 13 ash mn 5 fat, (5)
Dried buttermilk, feed grade (AAFCO)
Buttermilk, dried

Ref no 5-01-160

Feed name or analyses		As fed	Dry
Dry matter	%	93.0	100.0
Ash	%	9.6	10.8
Ether extract	%	5.8	6.2
N-free extract	%	45.2	48.6
Protein (N x 6.25)	%	32.0	34.4
Swine	dig prot %	29.8	32.0
Energy			
Swine	DE kcal/kg	3388.	3643.
Swine	ME kcal/kg	3015.	3242.
Swine	TDN %	77.	83.
Calcium	%	1.34	1.44
Magnesium	%	.48	.52
Phosphorus	%	.94	1.01
Potassium	%	.71	.76
Sodium	%	.95	1.02
Manganese	mg/kg	3.5	3.8
Biotin	mg/kg	.30	.30
Choline	mg/kg	1808.	1944.
Folic acid	mg/kg	.40	.40

Continued

(1) dry forages and roughages
(2) pasture, range plants, and forages fed green

Feed name or analyses		As fed	Dry
Niacin	mg/kg	8.6	9.2
Pantothenic acid	mg/kg	30.1	32.4
Riboflavin	mg/kg	31.0	33.3
Thiamine	mg/kg	3.5	3.8
Vitamin B6	mg/kg	2.40	2.60
Arginine	%	1.10	1.18
Histidine	%	.90	.97
Isoleucine	%	2.70	2.90
Leucine	%	3.40	3.66
Lysine	%	2.40	2.58
Methionine	%	.70	.75
Phenylalanine	%	1.50	1.61
Threonine	%	1.60	1.72
Tryptophan	%	.50	.54
Tyrosine	%	1.00	1.08
Valine	%	2.80	3.01

Cattle, casein, milk acid-precip dehy, mn 80 prot, (5)
Casein (AAFCO)
Casein, dried

Ref no 5-01-162

Feed name or analyses		As fed	Dry
Dry matter	%	90.0	100.0
Ash	%	3.3	3.7
Ether extract	%	.5	.6

Continued

(3) silages
(4) energy feeds
(5) protein supplements

Feed name or analyses		As fed	Dry
N-free extract	%	4.3	4.8
Protein (N x 6.25)	%	81.8	90.9
Swine	dig prot %	76.0	84.5
Energy			
Swine	DE kcal/kg	3532.	3924.
Swine	ME kcal/kg	2740.	3045.
Swine	TDN %	80.	89.
Calcium	%	.61	.68
Phosphorus	%	.99	1.10
Manganese	mg/kg	4.4	4.9
Choline	mg/kg	209.	232.
Folic acid	mg/kg	.40	.40
Niacin	mg/kg	1.3	1.4
Pantothenic acid	mg/kg	2.6	2.9
Riboflavin	mg/kg	1.5	1.7
Thiamine	mg/kg	.4	.4
Vitamin B6	mg/kg	.40	.50
Arginine	%	3.40	3.78
Cystine	%	.30	.33
Glycine	%	1.50	1.67
Histidine	%	2.50	2.78
Isoleucine	%	5.70	6.33
Leucine	%	8.60	9.55
Lysine	%	7.00	7.78
Methionine	%	2.70	3.00
Phenylalanine	%	4.60	5.11
Threonine	%	3.80	4.22

Continued

(6) minerals
(7) vitamins
(8) additives

TABLE 1-1—COMPOSITION OF SOME COMMON SWINE FEEDS (Continued)

Feed name or analyses		Mean	
		As fed	Dry
Tryptophan	%	1.00	1.11
Tyrosine	%	4.70	5.22
Valine	%	6.80	7.55
Cattle, milk, dehy, feed gr mx 8 moisture mn 26 fat, (5)			
Dried whole milk (AAFCO)			
Milk, whole, dried			
Ref no 5-01-167			
Dry matter	%	93.7	100.0
Ash	%	5.4	5.8
Crude fiber	%	.2	.2
Ether extract	%	26.4	28.2
N-free extract	%	36.4	38.9
Protein (N x 6.25)	%	25.2	26.9
Swine	dig prot %	24.4	26.1
Energy			
Swine	DE kcal/kg	5165.	5512.
Swine	ME kcal/kg	4679.	4994.
Swine	TDN %	117.	125.
Calcium	%	.89	.95
Chlorine	%	1.45	1.55
Iron	%	.017	.018
Phosphorus	%	.68	.72
Potassium	%	1.01	1.08
Sodium	%	.36	.38
			Continued

Feed name or analyses		Mean	
		As fed	Dry
Manganese	mg/kg	.4	.4
Biotin	mg/kg	.37	.39
Carotene	mg/kg	7.0	7.5
Niacin	mg/kg	8.4	9.0
Pantothenic acid	mg/kg	22.7	24.2
Riboflavin	mg/kg	19.6	20.9
Thiamine	mg/kg	3.7	3.9
Vitamin B6	mg/kg	4.63	4.94
Vitamin A equiv	IU/g	11.7	12.5
Vitamin D2	IU/g	.3	.3
Arginine	%	.90	.96
Histidine	%	.70	.75
Isoleucine	%	1.30	1.39
Leucine	%	2.50	2.67
Lysine	%	2.20	2.35
Methionine	%	.60	.64
Phenylalanine	%	1.30	1.39
Threonine	%	1.00	1.07
Tryptophan	%	.40	.43
Tyrosine	%	1.30	1.39
Valine	%	1.70	1.81

Feed name or analyses		Mean	
		As fed	Dry
Cattle, milk, fresh, (5)			
Milk, cattle, fresh			
Ref no 5-01-168			
Dry matter	%	12.0	100.0
Ash	%	.8	6.7
Ether extract	%	3.7	30.8
N-free extract	%	4.4	36.7
Protein (N x 6.25)	%	3.1	25.8
Swine	dig prot %	3.0	25.0
Energy			
Swine	DE kcal/kg	660.	5500.
Swine	ME kcal/kg	599.	4994.
Swine	TDN %	15.	125.
Choline	mg/kg	876.	7296.
Niacin	mg/kg	1.8	15.0
Pantothenic acid	mg/kg	8.1	67.5
Riboflavin	mg/kg	1.8	15.0
Thiamine	mg/kg	0.4	3.3
Arginine	%	.10	.83
Histidine	%	.10	.83
Isoleucine	%	.20	1.67
Leucine	%	.30	2.50
Lysine	%	.30	2.50
Methionine	%	.10	.83
Phenylalanine	%	.10	.83
Threonine	%	.10	.83
			Continued

Feed name or analyses		Mean	
		As fed	Dry
Tyrosine	%	.20	1.67
Valine	%	.20	1.67

Cattle, milk, skim dehy, mx 8 moisture, (5)
Dried skimmed milk, feed grade (AAFCO)
Milk, skimmed, dried

Ref no 5-01-175

Feed name or analyses		Mean	
		As fed	Dry
Dry matter	%	94.0	100.0
Ash	%	7.6	8.1
Crude fiber	%	.2	.2
Ether extract	%	.9	1.0
N-free extract	%	51.8	55.1
Protein (N x 6.25)	%	33.5	35.6
Swine	dig prot %	32.8	34.9
Energy	GE kcal/kg	3456.	3677.
Swine	DE kcal/kg	3784.	4026.
Swine	ME kcal/kg	3360.	3575.
Swine	TDN %	86.	92.
Calcium	%	1.26	1.34
Iron	%	.005	.005
Magnesium	%	.11	.12
Phosphorus	%	1.03	1.10
Potassium	%	1.67	1.78
Cobalt	mg/kg	.110	.117

Continued

(1) dry forages and roughages
(2) pasture, range plants, and forages fed green

Feed name or analyses		Mean	
		As fed	Dry
Copper	mg/kg	11.5	12.2
Manganese	mg/kg	2.2	2.3
Biotin	mg/kg	.33	.35
Choline	mg/kg	1426.	1517.
Folic acid	mg/kg	.62	.66
Niacin	mg/kg	11.5	12.2
Pantothenic acid	mg/kg	33.7	35.8
Riboflavin	mg/kg	20.1	21.4
Thiamine	mg/kg	3.5	3.7
a-tocopherol	mg/kg	9.2	9.8
Vitamin B_6	mg/kg	3.97	4.22
Vitamin B_{12}	mcg/kg	41.9	44.6
Vitamin D_2	IU/g	.4	.4
Arginine	%	1.20	1.28
Cystine	%	.50	.53
Glutamic acid	%	6.80	7.24
Glycine	%	.20	.21
Histidine	%	.90	.96
Isoleucine	%	2.30	2.45
Leucine	%	3.30	3.51
Lysine	%	2.80	2.98
Methionine	%	.80	.85
Phenylalanine	%	1.50	1.60
Threonine	%	1.40	1.49
Tryptophan	%	.40	.42
Tyrosine	%	1.30	1.38
Valine	%	2.20	2.34

(3) silages
(4) energy feeds
(5) protein supplements

Feed name or analyses		Mean	
		As fed	Dry

Chicken - see also Poultry, see Turkey

COCONUT. Cocos nucifera

Coconut, meats, mech-extd grnd, (5)
Coconut meal, expeller (AAFCO)
Copra meal, expeller (AAFCO)
Coconut meal, hydraulic (AAFCO)
Copra meal, hydraulic (AAFCO)

Ref no 5-01-572

Feed name or analyses		Mean	
		As fed	Dry
Dry matter	%	93.0	100.0
Ash	%	6.9	7.4
Crude fiber	%	12.0	12.9
Ether extract	%	6.6	7.1
N-free extract	%	47.2	50.7
Protein (N x 6.25)	%	20.4	21.9
Swine	dig prot %	14.9	16.0
Energy			
Swine	DE kcal/kg	3363.	3616.
Swine	ME kcal/kg	3080.	3312.
Swine	TDN %	76.	82.
Calcium	%	.21	.23

Continued

(6) minerals
(7) vitamins
(8) additives

TABLE I-1—COMPOSITION OF SOME COMMON SWINE FEEDS (Continued)

Feed name or analyses		As fed (Mean)	Dry (Mean)
Iron	%	.196	.211
Magnesium	%	.26	.28
Phosphorus	%	.61	.66
Potassium	%	1.12	1.20
Sodium	%	.04	.04
Cobalt	mg/kg	2.300	2.500
Copper	mg/kg	18.7	20.1
Manganese	mg/kg	55.4	59.6
Choline	mg/kg	920.	989.
Folic acid	mg/kg	1.30	1.40
Niacin	mg/kg	24.9	26.8
Pantothenic acid	mg/kg	6.6	7.1
Riboflavin	mg/kg	3.1	3.3
Thiamine	mg/kg	.7	.8

Coconut, meats, solv-extd grnd, (5)
Solvent extracted coconut meal (AAFCO)
Solvent extracted copra meal (AAFCO)

Ref no 5-01-573

Feed name or analyses		As fed (Mean)	Dry (Mean)
Dry matter	%	92.0	100.0
Ash	%	5.6	6.1
Crude fiber	%	15.0	16.3
Ether extract	%	1.8	2.0
N-free extract	%	48.3	52.5
Protein (N x 6.25)	%	21.3	23.1
Swine dig prot	%	15.5	16.9
			Continued

Feed name or analyses		As fed (Mean)	Dry (Mean)
Lignin	%	1.0	1.1
Energy			
Swine	DE kcal/kg	3123.	3395.
Swine	ME kcal/kg	2852.	3100.
Swine	TDN %	71.	77.
Calcium	%	.17	.18
Chlorine	%	.03	.03
Phosphorus	%	.61	.66
Riboflavin	mg/kg	13.2	14.3
Thiamine	mg/kg	.9	1.0

Copra - see Coconut

CORN. Zea mays

Corn, cobs, grnd, (1)
Ground corn cob (AAFCO)

Ref no 1-02-782

Feed name or analyses		As fed (Mean)	Dry (Mean)
Dry matter	%	90.4	100.0
Ash	%	1.5	1.7
Crude fiber	%	32.4	35.8
Ether extract	%	.5	.5
N-free extract	%	53.5	59.2
			Continued

Feed name or analyses		As fed (Mean)	Dry (Mean)
Protein (N x 6.25)	%	2.5	2.8
Swine	dig prot %	.0	.0
Energy	GE kcal/kg	3998.	4423.
Swine	DE kcal/kg	319.	353.
Swine	ME kcal/kg	305.	337.
Swine	TDN %	7.	8.
Calcium	%	.11	.12
Iron	%	.021	.023
Magnesium	%	.06	.07
Phosphorus	%	.04	.04
Potassium	%	.76	.84
Sulfur	%	.42	.47
Cobalt	mg/kg	.120	.130
Copper	mg/kg	6.6	7.3
Manganese	mg/kg	5.6	6.2
Carotene	mg/kg	.6	.7
Vitamin A equiv	IU/g	1.0	1.2

Corn, aerial pt, ensiled, (3)
Corn fodder silage

Ref no 3-02-822

Feed name or analyses		As fed (Mean)	Dry (Mean)
Dry matter	%	25.6	100.0
Ash	%	1.5	6.0
Crude fiber	%	6.4	25.1
Ether extract	%	.8	3.0
N-free extract	%	14.7	57.6
			Continued

Feed name or analyses		Mean	
		As fed	Dry
Protein (N x 6.25)	%	2.1	8.3
Calcium	%	.08	.33
Chlorine	%	.05	.18
Iron	%	.010	.020
Magnesium	%	.06	.24
Phosphorus	%	.06	.23
Potassium	%	.29	1.15
Sodium	%	.01	.03
Sulfur	%	.03	.11
Cobalt	mg/kg	.020	.090
Copper	mg/kg	2.6	10.1
Manganese	mg/kg	12.5	49.0
Zinc	mg/kg	5.4	20.9
Carotene	mg/kg	11.7	45.6
Vitamin A equiv	IU/g	19.5	76.0
Vitamin D₂	IU/g	.1	.4

Feed name or analyses		Mean	
		As fed	Dry
Corn, ears, grnd, (4)			
Corn and cob meal (AAFCO)			
Ear corn chop (AAFCO)			
Ground ear corn (AAFCO)			
Ref no 4-02-849			
Dry matter	%	87.0	100.0
Ash	%	1.6	1.8
Crude fiber	%	8.0	9.2
Ether extract	%	3.2	3.7
N-free extract	%	66.1	76.0
Protein (N x 6.25)	%	8.1	9.3
Swine	dig prot %	5.8	6.7
Energy			
Swine	DE kcal/kg	3107.	3571.
Swine	ME kcal/kg	2923.	3360.
Swine	TDN %	70.	81.
Calcium	%	.04	.05
Iron	%	.007	.008
Magnesium	%	.15	.17
Phosphorus	%	.27	.31
Potassium	%	.53	.61
Cobalt	mg/kg	.300	.300
Copper	mg/kg	7.7	8.8
Manganese	mg/kg	13.0	15.0

Feed name or analyses		Mean	
		As fed	Dry
Corn grain - see Corn, dent white; see Corn, dent yellow; see Corn, flint; see Corn, white			
Corn, grits by-prod, mn 5 fat, (4)			
Hominy feed (AAFCO)			
Hominy feed (CFA)			
Ref no 4-02-887			
Dry matter	%	90.6	100.0
Ash	%	2.5	2.8
Crude fiber	%	5.0	5.5
Ether extract	%	6.5	7.2
N-free extract	%	65.9	72.7
Protein (N x 6.25)	%	10.7	11.8
Swine	dig prot %	8.5	9.4
Energy			
Swine	GE kcal/kg	4275.	4702.
Swine	DE kcal/kg	3595.	3968.
Swine	ME kcal/kg	3365.	3714.
Swine	TDN %	82.	90.
Calcium	%	.05	.06
Iron	%	.006	.007
Magnesium	%	.24	.26
Phosphorus	%	.53	.58
Potassium	%	.67	.74

Continued

(1) dry forages and roughages
(2) pasture, range plants, and forages fed green
(3) silages
(4) energy feeds
(5) protein supplements
(6) minerals
(7) vitamins
(8) additives

TABLE I-1—COMPOSITION OF SOME COMMON SWINE FEEDS (Continued)

Feed name or analyses		Mean As fed	Dry
Sulfur	%	.03	.03
Cobalt	mg/kg	.060	.066
Copper	mg/kg	14.6	16.1
Manganese	mg/kg	14.6	16.1
Carotene	mg/kg	9.2	10.1
Niacin	mg/kg	51.1	56.2
Pantothenic acid	mg/kg	7.5	8.2
Riboflavin	mg/kg	2.0	2.2
Thiamine	mg/kg	7.9	8.7
Vitamin A equiv	IU/g	15.3	16.8

Corn, distil grains w sol, dehy, mn 75 orig solids, (5)
Corn distillers dried grains with solubles (AAFCO)

Ref no 5-02-843

Feed name or analyses		As fed	Dry
Dry matter	%	92.0	100.0
Ash	%	2.6	2.8
Crude fiber	%	9.0	9.8
Ether extract	%	9.3	10.1
N-free extract	%	43.7	47.5
Protein (N x 6.25)	%	27.4	29.8
Lignin	%	6.0	6.5
Energy	GE kcal/kg	4528.	4922.
Calcium	%	.09	.10
Iron	%	.020	.020
Magnesium	%	.06	.07
Phosphorus	%	.37	.40

Continued

Feed name or analyses		Mean As fed	Dry
Potassium	%	.09	.10
Sodium	%	.90	.98
Cobalt	mg/kg	.100	.100
Copper	mg/kg	44.7	48.6
Manganese	mg/kg	18.9	20.5
Biotin	mg/kg	.70	.80
Carotene	mg/kg	3.7	4.0
Choline	mg/kg	2471.	2686.
Niacin	mg/kg	66.9	72.7
Pantothenic acid	mg/kg	11.0	11.9
Riboflavin	mg/kg	8.6	9.3
Thiamine	mg/kg	2.9	3.2
Vitamin A equiv	IU/g	6.2	6.7
Vitamin D3	ICU/g	1.0	
Glycine	%	.50	.54
Leucine	%	2.20	2.39
Lysine	%	.70	.76
Methionine	%	.50	.54
Phenylalanine	%	1.70	1.85
Threonine	%	1.00	1.09
Tryptophan	%	.10	.11
Tyrosine	%	.60	.65
Valine	%	1.60	1.74

Feed name or analyses		Mean As fed	Dry

Corn, distil sol, dehy, (5)
Corn distillers dried solubles (AAFCO)

Ref no 5-02-844

Feed name or analyses		As fed	Dry
Dry matter	%	93.0	100.0
Ash	%	8.0	8.6
Crude fiber	%	4.0	4.3
Ether extract	%	9.1	9.8
N-free extract	%	45.0	48.4
Protein (N x 6.25)	%	26.9	28.9
Swine	dig prot %	16.1	17.3
Lignin	%	2.0	2.2
Energy			
Swine	DE kcal/kg	3300.	3548.
Swine	ME kcal/kg	2976.	3200.
Swine	TDN %	75.	81.
Calcium	%	.35	.38
Iron	%	.055	.059
Magnesium	%	.64	.69
Phosphorus	%	1.37	1.47
Potassium	%	1.74	1.87
Copper	mg/kg	82.7	88.9
Manganese	mg/kg	73.5	79.0
Biotin	mg/kg	1.50	1.60
Carotene	mg/kg	.7	.8
Choline	mg/kg	4818.	5179.
Folic acid	mg/kg	1.10	1.20

Continued

Feed name or analyses		Mean	
		As fed	Dry
Niacin	mg/kg	115.3	123.9
Pantothenic acid	mg/kg	20.9	22.5
Riboflavin	mg/kg	16.9	18.2
Thiamine	mg/kg	6.8	7.3
Vitamin A equiv	IU/g	1.2	1.3
Cystine	%	.60	.65
Glycine	%	1.10	1.18
Leucine	%	2.10	2.26
Lysine	%	.90	.97
Methionine	%	.60	.65
Phenylalanine	%	1.50	1.61
Threonine	%	1.00	1.07
Tryptophan	%	.20	.22
Tyrosine	%	.70	.75
Valine	%	1.50	1.61

Corn, germ wo sol, wet-mil solv-extd dehy grnd, (5)
Corn germ meal, solvent extracted, (wet-milled) (AAFCO)

Ref no 5-02-898

Dry matter	%	93.0	100.0
Crude fiber	%	12.0	12.9
Ether extract	%	2.0	2.2
Protein (N x 6.25)	%	18.0	19.4

Continued

Feed name or analyses		Mean	
		As fed	Dry
Calcium	%	.10	.11
Phosphorus	%	.40	.43
Choline	mg/kg	1800.	1936.
Folic acid	mg/kg	.20	.21
Niacin	mg/kg	35.1	37.7
Pantothenic acid	mg/kg	4.1	4.4
Riboflavin	mg/kg	4.1	4.4
Thiamine	mg/kg	1.0	1.1

Corn, gluten, wet-mil dehy, (5)
Corn gluten meal (AAFCO)
Corn gluten meal (CFA)

Ref no 5-02-900

Dry matter	%	91.0	100.0
Ash	%	2.4	2.6
Crude fiber	%	4.0	4.4
Ether extract	%	2.3	2.5
N-free extract	%	39.5	43.4
Protein (N x 6.25)	%	42.9	47.1
Energy			
Calcium	%	.16	.18
Iron	%	.040	.040
Magnesium	%	.05	.05
Phosphorus	%	.40	.44

Continued

Feed name or analyses		Mean	
		As fed	Dry
Potassium	%	.03	.03
Sodium	%	.10	.10
Cobalt	mg/kg	.100	.100
Copper	mg/kg	28.2	31.0
Manganese	mg/kg	7.3	8.0
Choline	mg/kg	330.	363.
Folic acid	mg/kg	.20	.20
Niacin	mg/kg	49.9	54.8
Pantothenic acid	mg/kg	10.3	11.3
Riboflavin	mg/kg	1.5	1.6
Thiamine	mg/kg	.2	.2
Arginine	%	1.40	1.54
Cystine	%	.60	.66
Glycine	%	1.50	1.65
Histidine	%	1.00	1.10
Isoleucine	%	2.30	2.53
Leucine	%	7.60	8.35
Lysine	%	.80	.88
Methionine	%	1.00	1.10
Phenylalanine	%	2.90	3.19
Threonine	%	1.40	1.54
Tryptophan	%	.20	.22
Tyrosine	%	1.00	1.10
Valine	%	2.20	2.42

(1) dry forages and roughages
(2) pasture, range plants, and forages fed green
(3) silages
(4) energy feeds
(5) protein supplements
(6) minerals
(7) vitamins
(8) additives

TABLE I-1—COMPOSITION OF SOME COMMON SWINE FEEDS (Continued)

CORN, DENT WHITE. Zea mays indentata

Corn, dent white, grain, (4)

Ref no 4-02-928

Feed name or analyses		As fed	Dry (Mean)
Dry matter	%	88.0	100.0
Ash	%	1.1	1.2
Crude fiber	%	2.0	2.3
Ether extract	%	3.7	4.2
N-free extract	%	72.6	82.5
Protein (N x 6.25)	%	8.6	9.8
Swine dig prot	%	6.9	7.8
Energy			
Swine	DE kcal/kg	3569.	4056.
Swine	ME kcal/kg	3354.	3812.
Swine	TDN %	81.	92.
Calcium	%	.04	.04
Phosphorus	%	.27	.31
Cobalt	mg/kg	.100	.100
Copper	mg/kg	5.8	6.6
Manganese	mg/kg	8.5	9.7
Zinc	mg/kg	23.6	26.8
Biotin	mg/kg	.10	.10
Carotene	mg/kg	.4	.4
Niacin	mg/kg	15.1	17.2
Pantothenic acid	mg/kg	3.9	4.4

Continued

Feed name or analyses		As fed	Dry (Mean)
Riboflavin	mg/kg	1.3	1.5
Thiamine	mg/kg	4.5	5.1
Vitamin A equiv	IU/g	.7	.7
Arginine	%	.26	.30
Cystine	%	.09	.10
Histidine	%	.18	.20
Isoleucine	%	.44	.50
Leucine	%	.88	1.00
Lysine	%	.26	.30
Methionine	%	.09	.10
Phenylalanine	%	.35	.40
Threonine	%	.35	.40
Tryptophan	%	.09	.10
Tyrosine	%	.44	.50
Valine	%	.35	.40

CORN, DENT YELLOW. Zea mays indentata

Corn, dent yellow, grain, gr 1 US mn 56 wt, (4)

Ref no 4-02-930

Feed name or analyses		As fed	Dry (Mean)
Dry matter	%	87.0	100.0
Ash	%	1.4	1.6
Crude fiber	%	2.0	2.3
Ether extract	%	3.8	4.4
N-free extract	%	70.9	81.5

Continued

Feed name or analyses		As fed	Dry (Mean)
Protein (N x 6.25)	%	8.9	10.2
Swine dig prot	%	7.1	8.2
Energy			
Swine	DE kcal/kg	3529.	4056.
Swine	ME kcal/kg	3317.	3813.
Swine	TDN %	80.	92.
Iron	%	.002	.002
Copper	mg/kg	4.2	4.8
Manganese	mg/kg	5.6	6.4

Corn, dent yellow, grain, gr 2 US mn 54 wt, (4)

Ref no 4-02-931

Feed name or analyses		As fed	Dry (Mean)
Dry matter	%	89.0	100.0
Ash	%	1.1	1.2
Crude fiber	%	2.0	2.2
Ether extract	%	3.9	4.4
N-free extract	%	73.1	82.2
Protein (N x 6.25)	%	8.9	10.0
Swine dig prot	%	7.1	8.0
Energy			
Swine	GE kcal/kg	3918.	4402.
Swine	DE kcal/kg	3610.	4056.
Swine	ME kcal/kg	3394.	3813.
Swine	TDN %	82.	92.
Calcium	%	.02	.02
Phosphorus	%	.31	.35
Carotene	mg/kg	1.8	2.0

Continued

Feed name or analyses		Mean	
		As fed	Dry
Niacin	mg/kg	26.3	29.5
Pantothenic acid	mg/kg	3.9	4.4
Riboflavin	mg/kg	1.3	1.5
Thiamine	mg/kg	3.6	4.0
Vitamin A equiv	IU/g	3.0	3.3
Arginine	%	.45	.51
Cystine	%	.09	.10
Histidine	%	.18	.20
Isoleucine	%	.45	.51
Leucine	%	.99	1.11
Lysine	%	.18	.20
Methionine	%	.09	.10
Phenylalanine	%	.45	.51
Threonine	%	.36	.40
Tryptophan	%	.09	.10
Valine	%	.36	.40

Corn, dent yellow, grain, gr 3 US mn 52 wt, (4)

Ref no 4-02-932

		As fed	Dry
Dry matter	%	86.0	100.0
Ash	%	1.0	1.2
Crude fiber	%	2.0	2.3
Ether extract	%	3.7	4.3
N-free extract	%	70.6	82.1

Continued

Feed name or analyses		Mean	
		As fed	Dry
Protein (N x 6.25)	%	8.7	10.1
Swine	dig prot %	7.0	8.2
Energy			
Swine	DE kcal/kg	3526.	4100.
Swine	ME kcal/kg	3314.	3854.
Swine	TDN %	80.	93.
Calcium	%	.02	.02
Iron	%	.002	.002
Phosphorus	%	.25	.29
Manganese	mg/kg	5.5	6.4

Corn, dent yellow, grain, gr 4 US mn 49 wt, (4)

Ref no 4-02-933

		As fed	Dry
Dry matter	%	87.0	100.0
Ash	%	1.0	1.2
Crude fiber	%	2.0	2.3
Ether extract	%	3.8	4.4
N-free extract	%	71.2	81.9
Protein (N x 6.25)	%	8.9	10.2
Swine	dig prot %	7.1	8.2
Energy			
Swine	DE kcal/kg	3529.	4056.
Swine	ME kcal/kg	3313.	3808.
Swine	TDN %	80.	92.

Continued

Feed name or analyses		Mean	
		As fed	Dry
Calcium	%	.04	.05
Magnesium	%	.17	.20
Phosphorus	%	.30	.34

Corn, dent yellow, grain, gr 5 US mn 46 wt, (4)

Ref no 4-02-934

		As fed	Dry
Dry matter	%	79.0	100.0
Ash	%	.9	1.1
Crude fiber	%	2.0	2.5
Ether extract	%	3.3	4.2
N-free extract	%	64.9	82.2
Protein (N x 6.25)	%	7.9	10.0
Swine	dig prot %	6.1	7.7
Energy			
Swine	DE kcal/kg	3135.	3968.
Swine	ME kcal/kg	2947.	3730.
Swine	TDN %	71.	90.

(1) dry forages and roughages
(2) pasture, range plants, and forages fed green
(3) silages
(4) energy feeds
(5) protein supplements
(6) minerals
(7) vitamins
(8) additives

TABLE 1-1—COMPOSITION OF SOME COMMON SWINE FEEDS (Continued)

Feed name or analyses		As fed	Dry (Mean)
Corn, dent yellow, grain, grnd cooked, (4)			
Ref no 4-07-953			
Dry matter	%	88.0	100.0
Crude fiber	%	2.1	2.4
Ether extract	%	4.0	4.5
Protein (N x 6.25)	%	9.2	10.5
Calcium	%	.02	.02
Phosphorus	%	.26	.30
Corn, dent yellow, grain, (4)			
Ref no 4-02-935			
Dry matter	%	86.0	100.0
Ash	%	1.1	1.3
Crude fiber	%	2.0	2.3
Ether extract	%	3.8	4.4
N-free extract	%	70.3	81.8
Protein (N x 6.25)	%	8.8	10.2
Swine	dig prot %	7.0	8.2
Energy	GE kcal/kg	3786.	4402.
Swine	DE kcal/kg	3488.	4056.
Swine	ME kcal/kg	3275.	3808.
Swine	TDN %	79.	92.
Calcium	%	.03	.03

Continued

Feed name or analyses		As fed	Dry (Mean)
Chlorine	%	.03	.04
Iron	%	.003	.003
Magnesium	%	.15	.17
Phosphorus	%	.27	.31
Potassium	%	.33	.38
Sodium	%	.01	.01
Sulfur	%	.12	.14
Cobalt	mg/kg	.100	.100
Copper	mg/kg	3.4	4.0
Manganese	mg/kg	4.1	4.8
Zinc	mg/kg	10.4	12.1
Biotin	mg/kg	.06	.07
Carotene	mg/kg	4.1	4.8
Choline	mg/kg	537.	625.
Folic acid	mg/kg	.20	.20
Niacin	mg/kg	22.9	26.6
Pantothenic acid	mg/kg	5.0	5.9
Riboflavin	mg/kg	1.1	1.3
Thiamine	mg/kg	4.0	4.6
Vitamin B6	mg/kg	7.20	8.40
Vitamin A equiv	IU/g	6.8	8.0
Cystine	%	.09	.10
Glycine	%	.43	.50
Methionine	%	.17	.20

Feed name or analyses		As fed	Dry (Mean)
CORN, FLINT. Zea mays indurata			
Corn, flint, grain, (4)			
Ref no 4-02-948			
Dry matter	%	89.0	100.0
Ash	%	1.3	1.5
Crude fiber	%	2.0	2.3
Ether extract	%	4.3	4.8
N-free extract	%	71.5	80.3
Protein (N x 6.25)	%	9.9	11.1
Swine	dig prot %	7.9	8.9
Energy			
Swine	DE kcal/kg	3610.	4056.
Swine	ME kcal/kg	3386.	3804.
Swine	TDN %	82.	92.
Iron	%	.003	.003
Phosphorus	%	.21	.24
Copper	mg/kg	11.6	13.0
Manganese	mg/kg	7.0	7.9
Niacin	mg/kg	15.8	17.8
Lysine	%	.27	.30
Methionine	%	.18	.20
Tryptophan	%	.09	.10

CORN, WHITE. Zea mays

Corn, white, grits by-prod, mn 5 fat, (4)
White hominy feed (AAFCO)
White hominy feed (CFA)
Hominy, white corn, feed
Corn, white, hominy feed

Ref no 4-02-990

Feed name or analyses		Mean	
		As fed	Dry
Dry matter	%	89.9	100.0
Crude fiber	%	4.7	5.2
Ether extract	%	5.7	6.3
Protein (N x 6.25)	%	10.8	12.0
Calcium	%	.05	.06
Phosphorus	%	1.00	1.10
Niacin	mg/kg	55.3	61.5
Pantothenic acid	mg/kg	6.7	7.5
Riboflavin	mg/kg	2.2	2.4
Thiamine	mg/kg	13.1	14.6

(1) dry forages and roughages
(2) pasture, range plants, and forages fed green

COTTON. Gossypium spp

Cotton, seed w some hulls, mech-extd grnd, mp
41 prot mx 14 fbr mn 2 fat, (5)
Cottonseed meal, 41% protein

Ref no 5-01-617

Feed name or analyses		Mean	
		As fed	Dry
Dry matter	%	94.0	100.0
Ash	%	6.2	6.6
Crude fiber	%	12.0	12.8
Ether extract	%	4.3	4.6
N-free extract	%	30.4	32.4
Protein (N x 6.25)	%	41.0	43.6
Swine	dig prot %	34.9	37.1
Energy Swine	GE kcal/kg	4600.	4893.
Swine	DE kcal/kg	2942.	3130.
Swine	ME kcal/kg	2565.	2729.
Swine	TDN %	67.	71.
Calcium	%	.16	.17
Iron	%	.030	.032
Magnesium	%	.56	.60
Phosphorus	%	1.20	1.28
Potassium	%	1.40	1.49
Sodium	%	.04	.04

Continued

(3) silages
(4) energy feeds
(5) protein supplements

Feed name or analyses		Mean	
		As fed	Dry
Cobalt	mg/kg	.150	.160
Copper	mg/kg	19.5	20.7
Manganese	mg/kg	21.5	22.9
Choline	mg/kg	2780.	2957.
Folic acid	mg/kg	2.30	2.45
Niacin	mg/kg	39.5	42.0
Pantothenic acid	mg/kg	14.0	14.9
Riboflavin	mg/kg	5.0	5.3
Thiamine	mg/kg	6.5	6.9
Arginine	%	4.25	4.52
Cystine	%	.85	.90
Glycine	%	2.05	2.18
Histidine	%	1.10	1.17
Isoleucine	%	1.60	1.70
Leucine	%	2.50	2.66
Lysine	%	1.70	1.81
Methionine	%	.65	.69
Phenylalanine	%	2.35	2.50
Threonine	%	1.45	1.54
Tryptophan	%	.65	.69
Valine	%	2.05	2.18

(6) minerals
(7) vitamins
(8) additives

TABLE I-1—COMPOSITION OF SOME COMMON SWINE FEEDS (Continued)

Cotton, seed w some hulls, pre-press solv-extd grnd, 41 prot, (5)
Cottonseed meal, pre-press solvent extracted, 41% protein

Ref no 5-07-872

Feed name or analyses		As fed (Mean)	Dry (Mean)
Dry matter	%	92.5	100.0
Ash	%	6.2	6.7
Crude fiber	%	12.0	13.0
Ether extract	%	1.4	1.5
N-free extract	%	31.9	34.5
Protein (N x 6.25)	%	41.0	44.3
Swine	dig prot %	34.8	37.6
Energy Swine	GE kcal/kg	4200.	4540.
Swine	DE kcal/kg	2692.	2910.
Swine	ME kcal/kg	2342.	2532.
Swine	TDN %	61.	66.
Calcium	%	.16	.17
Iron	%	.030	.032
Magnesium	%	.56	.60
Phosphorus	%	1.20	1.30
Potassium	%	1.40	1.51
Sodium	%	.04	.04
Cobalt	mg/kg	.150	.162
Copper	mg/kg	19.5	21.1
Manganese	mg/kg	21.5	23.2
Choline	mg/kg	2860.	3092.
Folic acid	mg/kg	2.30	2.49
Niacin	mg/kg	39.5	42.7
Pantothenic acid	mg/kg	14.0	15.1
Riboflavin	mg/kg	5.0	5.4
Thiamine	mg/kg	6.5	7.0
Arginine	%	4.25	4.59
Cystine	%	.85	.92
Glycine	%	2.05	2.22
Histidine	%	1.10	1.19
Isoleucine	%	1.60	1.73
Leucine	%	2.50	2.70
Lysine	%	1.70	1.84
Methionine	%	.65	.70
Phenylalanine	%	2.35	2.54
Threonine	%	1.45	1.57
Tryptophan	%	.65	.70
Valine	%	2.05	2.22

Continued

Cotton, seed w some hulls, solv-extd grnd, mn 41 prot mx 14 fbr mn 0.5 fat, (5)
Cottonseed meal, solvent extracted, 41% protein

Ref no 5-01-621

Feed name or analyses		As fed (Mean)	Dry (Mean)
Dry matter	%	91.5	100.0
Ash	%	6.2	6.8
Crude fiber	%	12.0	13.1
Ether extract	%	2.0	2.2
N-free extract	%	30.3	33.1
Protein (N x 6.25)	%	41.0	44.8
Swine	dig prot %	34.9	38.1
Energy	GE kcal/kg	4300.	4700.
Swine	DE kcal/kg	2703.	2954.
Swine	ME kcal/kg	2352.	2570.
Swine	TDN %	61.	67.
Calcium	%	.16	.17
Iron	%	.030	.033
Magnesium	%	.56	.61
Phosphorus	%	1.20	1.31
Potassium	%	1.40	1.53
Sodium	%	.04	.04
Cobalt	mg/kg	.150	.164
Copper	mg/kg	19.5	21.3
Manganese	mg/kg	21.5	23.5
Choline	mg/kg	2860.	3126.
Folic acid	mg/kg	2.30	2.51
Niacin	mg/kg	39.5	43.2
Pantothenic acid	mg/kg	14.0	15.3
Riboflavin	mg/kg	5.0	5.5
Thiamine	mg/kg	6.5	7.1
Arginine	%	4.25	4.64
Cystine	%	.85	.93
Glycine	%	2.05	2.24
Histidine	%	1.10	1.20
Isoleucine	%	1.60	1.75
Leucine	%	2.50	2.73

Continued

Feed name or analyses		Mean As fed	Dry
Lysine	%	1.70	1.86
Methionine	%	.65	.71
Phenylalanine	%	2.35	2.57
Threonine	%	1.45	1.58
Tryptophan	%	.65	.71
Valine	%	2.05	2.24

Cotton, seed wo hulls, pre-press solv-extd grnd, mn 50 prot, (5)

Cottonseed meal, pre-press solvent extracted, 50% protein

Ref no 5-07-874

		As fed	Dry
Dry matter	%	92.5	100.0
Ash	%	6.2	6.7
Crude fiber	%	8.5	9.2
Ether extract	%	1.2	1.3
N-free extract	%	26.6	28.8
Protein (N x 6.25)	%	50.0	54.0
Swine	dig prot %	45.0	48.6
Energy			
Swine	DE kcal/kg	3018.	3263.
Swine	ME kcal/kg	2569.	2777.
Swine	TDN %	68.	74.
Calcium	%	.16	.17

Continued

(1) dry forages and roughages
(2) pasture, range plants, and forages fed green

Feed name or analyses		Mean As fed	Dry
Iron	%	.011	.012
Magnesium	%	.46	.50
Phosphorus	%	1.01	1.09
Potassium	%	1.26	1.36
Sodium	%	.05	.05
Cobalt	mg/kg	2.000	2.162
Copper	mg/kg	18.0	19.4
Manganese	mg/kg	22.8	24.6
Zinc	mg/kg	73.3	79.2
Arginine	%	4.75	5.13
Cystine	%	1.00	1.08
Glycine	%	2.35	2.54
Histidine	%	1.25	1.35
Isoleucine	%	1.85	2.00
Leucine	%	2.80	3.03
Lysine	%	2.10	2.27
Methionine	%	.80	.86
Phenylalanine	%	2.75	2.97
Threonine	%	1.70	1.84
Tryptophan	%	.70	.76
Valine	%	2.05	2.22

(3) silages
(4) energy feeds
(5) protein supplements

Feed name or analyses		Mean As fed	Dry

CRAB. Callinectes sapidus, Cancer spp, Paralithodes camschatica

Crab, proc res, dehy grnd, mn 25 prot salt declared above 3 mx 7, (5)

Crab meal (AAFCO)

Ref no 5-01-663

		As fed	Dry
Dry matter	%	93.0	100.0
Ash	%	40.7	43.8
Crude fiber	%	11.0	11.8
Ether extract	%	1.8	1.9
N-free extract	%	8.4	9.1
Protein (N x 6.25)	%	31.1	33.4
Calcium	%	15.32	16.47
Iron	%	.44	.47
Magnesium	%	.88	.95
Phosphorus	%	1.59	1.71
Potassium	%	.45	.48
Sodium	%	.85	.91
Copper	mg/kg	32.8	35.3
Manganese	mg/kg	133.8	143.8
Pantothenic acid	mg/kg	6.6	7.1
Riboflavin	mg/kg	5.9	6.3

Continued

(6) minerals
(7) vitamins
(8) additives

TABLE 1-1—COMPOSITION OF SOME COMMON SWINE FEEDS (Continued)

Feed name or analyses		Mean As fed	Dry
Arginine	%	1.70	1.83
Histidine	%	.50	.54
Isoleucine	%	1.20	1.29
Leucine	%	1.60	1.72
Lysine	%	1.40	1.51
Methionine	%	.50	.54
Phenylalanine	%	1.20	1.29
Threonine	%	1.00	1.08
Tryptophan	%	.30	.32
Tyrosine	%	1.20	1.29
Valine	%	1.50	1.61

Defluorinated phosphate - see Phosphate, defluorinated

Dicalcium - see Calcium phosphate, dibasic, comm

Digester tankage - see Animal, carcass res w blood

Distillers grains - see Grains

Distillers grains with solubles - see Corn

Feed name or analyses		Mean As fed	Dry

Distillers solubles - see Corn

Farina - see Wheat, grits

Fat - see Animal-poultry; see Swine, lard

Feather meal - see Poultry, feathers

Feed flour - see Wheat, flour

Feeding bone meal - see Animal, bone, cooked

Feeding oat meal - see Oats, cereal by-prod, mx 4 fbr

FISH. Scientific name not used

Fish, sol, cond, mn 30 prot, (5)
Condensed fish solubles (AAFCO)

Ref no 5-01-969

Feed name or analyses		Mean As fed	Dry
Dry matter	%	51.0	100.0
Ash	%	10.0	19.6
Crude fiber	%	1.0	2.0
Ether extract	%	6.5	12.7
N-free extract	%	2.1	4.1
Protein (N x 6.25)	%	31.4	61.6
Swine	dig prot %	30.1	59.1
Energy			
Swine	DE kcal/kg	1956.	3836.
Swine	ME kcal/kg	1636.	3207.
Swine	TDN %	44.	87.
Calcium	%	.61	1.20
Iron	%	.03	.06
Magnesium	%	.02	.04
Phosphorus	%	.70	1.37
Potassium	%	1.75	3.43
Sodium	%	3.06	6.00
Copper	mg/kg	48.2	94.5
Manganese	mg/kg	11.9	23.3
Zinc	mg/kg	38.3	75.1

Continued

Feed name or analyses		Mean As fed	Mean Dry
Biotin	mg/kg	.2	.4
Choline	mg/kg	4028.	7899.
Niacin	mg/kg	168.7	330.8
Pantothenic acid	mg/kg	35.4	69.4
Riboflavin	mg/kg	14.5	28.4
Thiamine	mg/kg	5.5	10.8
Arginine	%	2.40	4.71
Cystine	%	1.70	3.33
Glycine	%	4.90	9.61
Histidine	%	2.50	4.90
Isoleucine	%	1.60	3.14
Leucine	%	2.50	4.90
Lysine	%	2.70	5.29
Methionine	%	1.00	1.96
Phenylalanine	%	1.40	2.75
Threonine	%	1.20	2.35
Tryptophan	%	.80	1.57
Tyrosine	%	.50	.98
Valine	%	1.60	3.14

(1) dry forages and roughages
(2) pasture, range plants, and forages fed green

Feed name or analyses		Mean As fed	Mean Dry
Fish, stickwater sol, cooked dehy, mn 60 prot, (5)			
Dried fish solubles (AAFCO)			
Fish solubles, dried			
Ref no 5-01-971			
Dry matter	%	92.0	100.0
Ash	%	15.8	17.2
Crude fiber	%	1.0	1.1
Ether extract	%	7.6	8.3
N-free extract	%	4.7	5.1
Protein (N x 6.25)	%	62.8	68.3
Swine	dig prot %	60.3	65.5
Energy			
Swine	DE kcal/kg	3408.	3704.
Swine	ME kcal/kg	2801.	3045.
Swine	TDN %	77.	84.
Choline	mg/kg	5223.	5677.
Niacin	mg/kg	231.1	252.3
Pantothenic acid	mg/kg	44.9	48.8
Riboflavin	mg/kg	7.7	8.4
Arginine	%	2.40	2.61
Histidine	%	2.60	2.83
Isoleucine	%	1.70	1.85
Leucine	%	2.70	2.93
Lysine	%	3.00	3.26

Continued

(3) silages
(4) energy feeds
(5) protein supplements

Feed name or analyses		Mean As fed	Mean Dry
Methionine	%	.90	.98
Phenylalanine	%	1.30	1.41
Threonine	%	1.20	1.30
Tryptophan	%	.70	.76
Tyrosine	%	.70	.76
Valine	%	1.90	2.07

FISH, ANCHOVY. Engraulis spp

Feed name or analyses		Mean As fed	Mean Dry
Fish, anchovy, whole or cuttings, cooked mech-extd dehy grnd, (5)			
Fish meal, anchovy			
Ref no 5-01-985			
Dry matter	%	93.0	100.0
Ash	%	19.0	20.4
Crude fiber	%	1.0	1.1
Ether extract	%	3.8	4.1
N-free extract	%	3.2	3.4
Protein (N x 6.25)	%	66.0	71.0
Swine	dig prot %	60.7	65.3
Energy			
Swine	DE kcal/kg	2994.	3219.
Swine	ME kcal/kg	2446.	2630.

Continued

(6) minerals
(7) vitamins
(8) additives

TABLE I-1—COMPOSITION OF SOME COMMON SWINE FEEDS (Continued)

Feed name or analyses		Mean	
		As fed	Dry
Swine	TDN %	68.	73.
Calcium	%	4.50	4.84
Phosphorus	%	2.85	3.06
Alanine	%	5.59	6.01
Arginine	%	4.46	4.79
Aspartic acid	%	7.86	8.45
Glutamic acid	%	9.98	10.73
Glycine	%	5.10	5.48
Histidine	%	1.84	1.98
Isoleucine	%	3.40	3.66
Leucine	%	7.01	7.54
Lysine	%	5.40	5.80
Methionine	%	2.19	2.35
Phenylalanine	%	2.48	2.67
Proline	%	2.30	2.47
Serine	%	3.54	3.80
Threonine	%	3.04	3.27
Tyrosine	%	1.77	1.90
Valine	%	3.54	3.80

FISH, HERRING. Clupea harengus harengus, Clupea harengus pallasi

Fish, herring, whole or cuttings, cooked mech-extd dehy grnd, (5)

Fish meal, herring

Ref no 5-02-000

Feed name or analyses		Mean	
		As fed	Dry
Dry matter	%	92.0	100.0
Ash	%	10.8	11.7
Ether extract	%	7.5	8.2
N-free extract	%	3.1	3.4
Protein (N x 6.25)	%	70.6	76.7
Swine	dig prot %	66.3	72.1
Energy			
Swine	DE kcal/kg	3650.	3968.
Swine	ME kcal/kg	2938.	3194.
Swine	TDN %	83.	90.
Calcium	%	2.94	3.20
Phosphorus	%	2.20	2.39
Manganese	mg/kg	9.9	10.8
Choline	mg/kg	4004.	4352.
Folic acid	mg/kg	2.40	2.60
Niacin	mg/kg	88.9	96.6
Pantothenic acid	mg/kg	11.4	12.4
Riboflavin	mg/kg	9.0	9.8

Continued

Feed name or analyses		Mean	
		As fed	Dry
Vitamin B₁₂	mcg/kg	218.7	237.7
Arginine	%	4.00	4.35
Cystine	%	1.60	1.74
Glycine	%	5.00	5.44
Histidine	%	1.30	1.41
Isoleucine	%	3.20	3.48
Leucine	%	5.10	5.54
Lysine	%	7.30	7.94
Methionine	%	2.00	2.17
Phenylalanine	%	2.60	2.83
Threonine	%	2.60	2.83
Tryptophan	%	.90	.98
Tyrosine	%	2.10	2.28
Valine	%	3.20	3.48

FISH, MENHADEN. Brevoortia tyrannus

Fish, menhaden, whole or cuttings, cooked mech-extd dehy grnd, (5)

Fish meal, menhaden

Ref no 5-02-009

		As fed	Dry
Dry matter	%	92.0	100.0
Ash	%	19.6	21.3
Crude fiber	%	1.0	1.1
Ether extract	%	7.7	8.4

Continued

Feed name or analyses		As fed	Dry
		Mean	
N-free extract	%	2.4	2.6
Protein (N x 6.25)	%	61.3	66.6
Swine dig prot	%	56.4	61.3
Energy			
Swine DE kcal/kg		3123.	3395.
Swine ME kcal/kg		2580.	2804.
Swine TDN	%	71.	77.
Calcium	%	5.49	5.97
Iron	%	.056	.061
Phosphorus	%	2.81	3.05
Copper	mg/kg	8.4	9.1
Manganese	mg/kg	25.7	27.9
Choline	mg/kg	3080.	3348.
Niacin	mg/kg	55.9	60.8
Pantothenic acid	mg/kg	8.8	9.6
Riboflavin	mg/kg	4.8	5.2
Thiamine	mg/kg	.7	.8
Arginine	%	4.00	4.35
Histidine	%	1.60	1.74
Isoleucine	%	4.10	4.46
Leucine	%	5.00	5.44
Lysine	%	5.30	5.76
Methionine	%	1.80	1.96
Phenylalanine	%	2.70	2.93
Threonine	%	2.90	3.15
Tryptophan	%	.60	.65

Continued

Feed name or analyses		As fed	Dry
		Mean	
Tyrosine	%	1.60	1.74
Valine	%	3.60	3.91

FISH, SARDINE. Clupea spp, Sardinops spp

Fish, sardine, whole or cuttings, cooked mech-
extd dehy grnd, (5)
Fish meal, sardine

Ref no 5-02-015

		As fed	Dry
		Mean	
Dry matter	%	93.0	100.0
Ash	%	15.7	16.9
Crude fiber	%	1.0	1.1
Ether extract	%	4.3	4.6
N-free extract	%	6.5	7.0
Protein (N x 6.25)	%	65.5	70.4
Swine dig prot	%	60.3	64.8
Energy			
Swine DE kcal/kg		2994.	3219.
Swine ME kcal/kg		2449.	2633.
Swine TDN	%	68.	73.
Calcium	%	4.90	5.27
Iron	%	.03	.03
Magnesium	%	.10	.11

Continued

Feed name or analyses		As fed	Dry
		Mean	
Phosphorus	%	2.77	2.98
Potassium	%	.33	.35
Sodium	%	.18	.19
Copper	mg/kg	20.2	21.7
Manganese	mg/kg	22.2	23.9
Choline	mg/kg	2959.	3181.
Niacin	mg/kg	62.0	66.7
Pantothenic acid	mg/kg	9.2	9.9
Riboflavin	mg/kg	5.9	6.3
Thiamine	mg/kg	.4	.4
Arginine	%	2.70	2.90
Cystine	%	.80	.86
Glycine	%	4.50	4.84
Histidine	%	1.80	1.94
Isoleucine	%	3.30	3.55
Leucine	%	4.70	5.05
Lysine	%	5.90	6.34
Methionine	%	2.00	2.15
Phenylalanine	%	2.60	2.80
Threonine	%	2.60	2.80
Tryptophan	%	.50	.54
Tyrosine	%	3.00	3.23
Valine	%	4.10	4.41

(1) dry forages and roughages
(2) pasture, range plants, and forages fed green
(3) silages
(4) energy feeds
(5) protein supplements
(6) minerals
(7) vitamins
(8) additives

TABLE I-1—COMPOSITION OF SOME COMMON SWINE FEEDS (Continued)

FISH, WHITE. Gadidae (family), Lophiidae (family), Rajidae (family)

Fish, white, whole or cuttings, cooked mech-
extd dehy grnd, mx 4 oil, (5)
White fish meal (CFA)
Fish, cod, meal
Fish, cusk, meal
Fish, haddock, meal
Fish, hake, meal
Fish, pollock, meal
Fish, monkfish, meal
Fish, skate, meal

Ref no 5-02-025

Feed name or analyses		Mean As fed	Dry
Dry matter	%	92.0	100.0
Ash	%	21.7	23.6
Crude fiber	%	1.0	1.1
Ether extract	%	4.4	4.8
N-free extract	%	1.6	1.8
Protein (N x 6.25)	%	63.2	68.7
Swine	dig prot %	58.1	63.2
Energy			
· Swine	DE kcal/kg	2921.	3175.
Swine	ME kcal/kg	2398.	2607.
Swine	TDN %	66.	72.

Continued

Feed name or analyses		Mean As fed	Dry
Calcium	%	7.87	8.55
Phosphorus	%	3.61	3.92
Manganese	mg/kg	14.3	15.5
Choline	mg/kg	8917.	9692.
Niacin	mg/kg	69.7	75.8
Pantothenic acid	mg/kg	8.8	9.6
Riboflavin	mg/kg	9.0	9.8
Thiamine	mg/kg	1.8	2.0

FLAX. Linum usitatissimum

Flax, seed, mech-extd grnd, mx 0.5 acid insol ash, (5)
Linseed meal (AAFCO)
Linseed meal (CFA)
Linseed oil meal, expeller extracted
Linseed oil meal, hydraulic extracted
Linseed meal, old process

Ref no 5-02-045

Feed name or analyses		Mean As fed	Dry
Dry matter	%	91.0	100.0
Ash	%	5.6	6.2
Crude fiber	%	9.0	9.9
Ether extract	%	5.2	5.7
N-free extract	%	35.8	39.4

Continued

Feed name or analyses		Mean As fed	Dry
Protein (N x 6.25)	%	35.3	38.8
Swine	dig prot %	31.8	34.9
Energy			
Swine	DE kcal/kg	3388.	3723.
Swine	ME kcal/kg	2988.	3284.
Swine	TDN %	77.	85.
Calcium	%	.44	.48
Iron	%	.017	.019
Magnesium	%	.58	.64
Phosphorus	%	.89	.98
Potassium	%	1.24	1.36
Sodium	%	.11	.12
Cobalt	mg/kg	.400	.500
Copper	mg/kg	26.4	29.0
Manganese	mg/kg	39.4	43.3
Carotene	mg/kg	.2	.2
Choline	mg/kg	1863.	2048.
Folic acid	mg/kg	2.90	3.20
Niacin	mg/kg	35.6	39.1
Pantothenic acid	mg/kg	17.8	19.6
Riboflavin	mg/kg	3.5	3.8
Thiamine	mg/kg	5.1	5.6
Vitamin A equiv	IU/g	.3	.3
Methionine	%	.70	.77

Flax, seed, solv-extd grnd, mx 0.5 acid insol ash, (5)
Solvent extracted linseed meal (AAFCO)
Solvent extracted linseed meal (CFA)
Linseed oil meal, solvent extracted

Ref no 5-02-048

Feed name or analyses		Mean	
		As fed	Dry
Dry matter	%	91.0	100.0
Ash	%	5.8	6.4
Crude fiber	%	9.0	9.9
Ether extract	%	1.7	1.9
N-free extract	%	39.3	43.2
Protein (N x 6.25)	%	35.1	38.6
Swine	dig prot %	31.6	34.7
Energy			
Swine	DE kcal/kg	2969.	3263.
Swine	ME kcal/kg	2619.	2878.
Swine	TDN %	67.	74.
Calcium	%	.40	.44
Iron	%	.033	.036
Magnesium	%	.60	.66
Phosphorus	%	.83	.91
Potassium	%	1.38	1.52
Sodium	%	.14	.15
Cobalt	mg/kg	.20	.20
Copper	mg/kg	25.7	28.2

Continued

Feed name or analyses		Mean	
		As fed	Dry
Manganese	mg/kg	37.6	41.3
Choline	mg/kg	1225.	1347.
Niacin	mg/kg	30.1	33.1
Riboflavin	mg/kg	2.9	3.2
Thiamine	mg/kg	9.5	10.4

Flax, seed screenings, mech-extd grnd, (5)
Flaxseed screenings meal (AAFCO)

Ref no 5-02-054

Feed name or analyses		Mean	
		As fed	Dry
Dry matter	%	91.0	100.0
Ash	%	6.7	7.4
Crude fiber	%	12.0	13.2
Ether extract	%	9.4	10.3
N-free extract	%	47.0	51.7
Protein (N x 6.25)	%	15.8	17.4
Energy	GE kcal/kg	4316.	4743.
Calcium	%	.37	.41
Phosphorus	%	.43	.47

GARBAGE. Scientific name not used

Garbage, cooked dehy, high fat, (4)

Ref no 4-07-863

Feed name or analyses		Mean	
		As fed	Dry
Dry matter	%	95.9	100.0
Ash	%	12.9	13.4
Crude fiber	%	20.0	20.8
Ether extract	%	23.7	24.7
N-free extract	%	22.0	22.9
Protein (N x 6.25)	%	17.5	18.2
Swine	dig prot %	6.3	6.6
Energy			
Swine	DE kcal/kg	3805.	3968.
Swine	ME kcal/kg	3512.	3662.
Swine	TDN %	86.	90.

Garbage, cooked dehy, low fat, (4)

Ref no 4-07-862

		As fed	Dry
Dry matter	%	92.3	100.0
Ash	%	14.1	15.3

Continued

(1) dry forages and roughages
(2) pasture, range plants, and forages fed green
(3) silages
(4) energy feeds
(5) protein supplements
(6) minerals
(7) vitamins
(8) additives

TABLE I-1—COMPOSITION OF SOME COMMON SWINE FEEDS (Continued)

Feed name or analyses		As fed	Dry (Mean)
Crude fiber	%	13.5	14.6
Ether extract	%	3.5	3.8
N-free extract	%	38.1	41.3
Protein (N x 6.25)	%	23.1	25.0
Swine dig prot	%	14.0	15.2
Energy			
Swine DE kcal/kg		2279.	2469.
Swine ME kcal/kg		2074.	2247.
Swine TDN	%	52.	56.

Garbage, hotel and restaurant, cooked wet grnd, (4)
Ref no 4-07-865

		As fed	Dry (Mean)
Dry matter	%	16.0	100.0
Ash	%	.9	5.7
Crude fiber	%	.5	3.3
Ether extract	%	4.0	24.9
N-free extract	%	8.1	50.8
Protein (N x 6.25)	%	2.4	15.3
Swine dig prot	%	2.2	13.5
Energy GE kcal/kg		853.	5330.
Swine DE kcal/kg		793.	4957.
Swine ME kcal/kg		767.	4605.
Swine TDN	%	19.	117.

Garbage, institutional, cooked wet grnd, (4)
Ref no 4-07-867

Feed name or analyses		As fed	Dry (Mean)
Dry matter	%	17.7	100.0
Ash	%	.9	5.3
Crude fiber	%	.5	2.8
Ether extract	%	2.6	14.8
N-free extract	%	11.1	62.5
Protein (N x 6.25)	%	2.6	14.6
Swine dig prot	%	2.3	12.8
Energy GE kcal/kg		853.	4820.
Swine DE kcal/kg		793.	4483.
Swine ME kcal/kg		738.	4169.
Swine TDN	%	19.	106.

Garbage, military, cooked wet grnd, (4)
Ref no 4-07-866

		As fed	Dry (Mean)
Dry matter	%	25.6	100.0
Ash	%	1.4	5.6
Crude fiber	%	.7	2.8
Ether extract	%	8.2	32.0
N-free extract	%	11.2	43.6
Protein (N x 6.25)	%	4.1	16.0
Swine dig prot	%	3.6	14.2

Continued

Feed name or analyses		As fed	Dry (Mean)
Energy			
Swine GE kcal/kg		1450.	5665.
Swine DE kcal/kg		1378.	5382.
Swine ME kcal/kg		1278.	4994.
Swine TDN	%	33.	128.

Garbage, municipal, cooked wet grnd, (4)
Ref no 4-07-864

		As fed	Dry (Mean)
Dry matter	%	16.6	100.0
Ash	%	1.4	8.6
Crude fiber	%	1.4	8.4
Ether extract	%	3.6	21.4
N-free extract	%	7.3	44.1
Protein (N x 6.25)	%	2.9	17.5
Swine dig prot	%	2.3	14.0
Energy GE kcal/kg		847.	5100.
Swine DE kcal/kg		635.	3825.
Swine ME kcal/kg		587.	3538.
Swine TDN	%	15.	91.

Grain sorghum - see Sorghum, grain variety

Left column

Feed name or analyses		Mean	
		As fed	Dry

GRAINS. Scientific name not used

Grains screenings - see also
Wheat, grain screenings

Grains, screenings, mn 70 grain mx 6.5 ash, (4)
Grain screenings (AAFCO)

Ref no 4-02-156

		As fed	Dry
Dry matter	%	90.0	100.0
Ash	%	5.7	6.3
Crude fiber	%	9.0	10.0
Ether extract	%	4.7	5.2
N-free extract	%	55.5	61.7
Protein (N x 6.25)	%	15.1	16.8
Swine	dig prot %	12.1	13.4
Energy			
Swine	DE kcal/kg	2579.	2866.
Swine	ME kcal/kg	2389.	2654.
Swine	TDN %	58.	65.
Calcium	%	.43	.48
Phosphorus	%	.39	.43

(1) dry forages and roughages
(2) pasture, range plants, and forages fed green

Middle column

Feed name or analyses		Mean	
		As fed	Dry

Grains, screenings, uncleaned, mn 12 grain mx 3 wild oats mx 17 buckwheat and large seeds mx 68 small weed seeds chaff hulls dust scourings noxious seeds, (4)
Uncleaned screenings (CFA)

Ref no 4-02-153

		As fed	Dry
Dry matter	%	91.5	100.0
Ash	%	7.7	8.4
Crude fiber	%	16.7	18.3
Ether extract	%	4.0	4.4
N-free extract	%	48.8	53.3
Protein (N x 6.25)	%	14.3	15.6
Swine	dig prot %	9.9	10.8
Energy			
Swine	DE kcal/kg	2461.	2690.
Swine	ME kcal/kg	2284.	2496.
Swine	TDN %	56.	61.
Calcium	%	.37	.40
Phosphorus	%	.41	.45
Alanine	%	.49	.54
Arginine	%	.61	.67
Aspartic acid	%	.74	.81
Glutamic acid	%	3.38	3.69
Glycine	%	.56	.61

Continued

(3) silages
(4) energy feeds
(5) protein supplements

Right column

Feed name or analyses		Mean	
		As fed	Dry
Histidine	%	.27	.30
Isoleucine	%	.41	.45
Leucine	%	.82	.90
Lysine	%	.38	.42
Methionine	%	.17	.19
Phenylalanine	%	.53	.58
Proline	%	1.05	1.15
Serine	%	.61	.67
Threonine	%	.40	.44
Tyrosine	%	.53	.58
Valine	%	.53	.58

Grains, brewers grains, dehy, mx 3 dried spent hops, (5)
Brewers dried grains (AAFCO)
Brewers dried grains (CFA)

Ref no 5-02-141

		As fed	Dry
Dry matter	%	92.0	100.0
Ash	%	3.6	3.9
Crude fiber	%	15.0	16.3
Ether extract	%	6.2	6.7
N-free extract	%	41.4	45.0
Protein (N x 6.25)	%	25.9	28.1
Swine	dig prot %	20.4	22.2

Continued

(6) minerals
(7) vitamins
(8) additives

TABLE I-1—COMPOSITION OF SOME COMMON SWINE FEEDS (Continued)

Feed name or analyses		Mean	
		As fed	Dry
Energy			
Swine	DE kcal/kg	1892.	2056.
Swine	ME kcal/kg	1708.	1856.
Swine	TDN %	43.	47.
Calcium	%	.27	.29
Iron	%	.025	.027
Magnesium	%	.14	.15
Phosphorus	%	.50	.54
Potassium	%	.08	.09
Sodium	%	.26	.28
Cobalt	mg/kg	.100	.100
Copper	mg/kg	21.3	22.2
Manganese	mg/kg	37.6	40.9
Choline	mg/kg	1587.	1725.
Folic acid	mg/kg	.22	.24
Niacin	mg/kg	43.4	47.2
Pantothenic acid	mg/kg	8.6	9.3
Riboflavin	mg/kg	1.5	1.6
Thiamine	mg/kg	.7	.8
Vitamin B6	mg/kg	.66	.72
Arginine	%	1.30	1.41
Histidine	%	.50	.54
Isoleucine	%	1.50	1.63
Leucine	%	2.30	2.50
Lysine	%	.90	.98
Methionine	%	.40	.43
Phenylalanine	%	1.30	1.41
Threonine	%	.90	.98
Tryptophan	%	.40	.43

Continued

Feed name or analyses		Mean	
		As fed	Dry
Tyrosine	%	1.20	1.30
Valine	%	1.60	1.74

Grains, distil grains, dehy, (5)
Distillers dried grains

Ref no 5-02-144

		As fed	Dry
Dry matter	%	91.6	100.0
Ash	%	3.1	3.4
Crude fiber	%	11.5	12.6
Ether extract	%	8.9	9.7
N-free extract	%	38.9	42.5
Protein (N x 6.25)	%	29.1	31.8
Swine	dig prot %	23.0	25.1
Energy			
Swine	DE kcal/kg	2020.	2205.
Swine	ME kcal/kg	1810.	1976.
Swine	TDN %	46.	50.
Calcium	%	.20	.22
Chlorine	%	.05	.05
Iron	%	.026	.028
Magnesium	%	.12	.13
Phosphorus	%	.55	.60
Potassium	%	.24	.26
Sodium	%	.05	.05
Sulfur	%	.45	.49
Cobalt	mg/kg	.041	.045

Continued

Feed name or analyses		Mean	
		As fed	Dry
Copper	mg/kg	21.5	23.5
Manganese	mg/kg	34.6	37.8
Carotene	mg/kg	7.7	8.4
Niacin	mg/kg	46.3	50.6
Pantothenic acid	mg/kg	11.5	12.6
Riboflavin	mg/kg	3.7	4.0
Thiamine	mg/kg	2.4	2.6
Vitamin A equiv	IU/g	12.8	14.0
Arginine	%	2.20	2.40
Histidine	%	1.10	1.20
Isoleucine	%	2.10	2.29
Leucine	%	3.20	3.49
Lysine	%	.80	.87
Methionine	%	.40	.44
Phenylalanine	%	1.80	1.96
Threonine	%	2.10	2.29
Tryptophan	%	.20	.22
Tyrosine	%	.90	.98
Valine	%	1.20	1.31

Groundnut - see Peanut

Hominy feed - see Corn, grits by-prod

Hydrolyzed poultry feathers - see Poultry, feathers

820

Feed name or analyses		Mean As fed	Dry

Lard - see Swine, lard

LIMESTONE. Scientific name not applicable

Limestone, grnd, mn 33 Ca, (6)
Limestone, ground (AAFCO)

Ref no 6-02-632

		As fed	Dry
Dry matter	%	100.0	100.0
Ash	%	95.8	95.8
Calcium	%	33.84	33.84
Iron	%	.330	.330
Phosphorus	%	.02	.02
Sodium	%	.06	.06
Manganese	mg/kg	279.6	279.6

Linseed meal - see Flax

Liver - see Animal, liver

(1) dry forages and roughages
(2) pasture, range plants, and
forages fed green

Feed name or analyses		Mean As fed	Dry

Maize - see Corn

Malt sprouts - see Barley, malt sprouts w hulls

Meat meal - see Animal, carcass res

Meat meal tankage - see Animal, carcass res w blood

Meat and bone meal - see Animal, carcass res w bone

Meat and bone scrap - see Animal, carcass res w bone

Meat scrap - see Animal, carcass res

Middlings - see Wheat, flour by-prod, f-sift, mx 4 fbr

Milk - see Cattle, milk

(3) silages
(4) energy feeds
(5) protein supplements

Feed name or analyses		Mean As fed	Dry

MILLET. Setaria spp

Millet, grain, (4)

Ref no 4-03-098

		As fed	Dry
Dry matter	%	90.0	100.0
Ash	%	3.2	3.5
Crude fiber	%	8.0	8.9
Ether extract	%	4.0	4.4
N-free extract	%	62.9	69.9
Protein (N x 6.25)	%	12.0	13.3
Swine	dig prot %	8.8	9.8
Energy			
Swine	DE kcal/kg	2897.	3219.
Swine	ME kcal/kg	2703.	3003.
Swine	TDN %	66.	73.
Calcium	%	.05	.06
Chlorine	%	.14	.16
Iron	%	.004	.005
Magnesium	%	.16	.18
Phosphorus	%	.28	.31
Potassium	%	.43	.48
Sodium	%	.04	.04
Sulfur	%	.13	.14

Continued

(6) minerals
(7) vitamins
(8) additives

TABLE I-1—COMPOSITION OF SOME COMMON SWINE FEEDS (Continued)

Feed name or analyses		Mean	
		As fed	Dry
Cobalt	mg/kg	.020	.022
Copper	mg/kg	21.6	24.0
Manganese	mg/kg	29.1	32.3
Zinc	mg/kg	13.9	15.4
Choline	mg/kg	789.	877.
Niacin	mg/kg	52.6	58.4
Pantothenic acid	mg/kg	7.4	8.2
Riboflavin	mg/kg	1.6	1.8
Thiamine	mg/kg	6.6	7.3

Milo - see Sorghum, milo

Molasses - see Beet, sugar, molasses; Citrus, syrup; Sugarcane, molasses.

Monosodium phosphate - see Sodium phosphate, monobasic

Oat middlings - see Oats, cereal by-prod, mx 4 fbr

Oat meal, feeding - see Oats, cereal by-prod

OATS. Avena sativa

Oats, hulls, (1)
Oat hulls (AAFCO)
Oat hulls (CFA)

Ref no 1-03-281

Feed name or analyses		Mean	
		As fed	Dry
Dry matter	%	93.0	100.0
Ash	%	6.0	6.5
Crude fiber	%	27.0	29.0
Ether extract	%	2.0	2.2
N-free extract	%	52.4	56.3
Protein (N x 6.25)	%	5.6	6.0
Swine	dig prot %	3.2	3.4
Cellulose	%	47.3	51.1
Lignin	%	13.1	14.2
Energy			
Swine	DE kcal/kg	1012.	1088.
Swine	ME kcal/kg	959.	1031.
Swine	TDN %	23.	25.
Calcium	%	.16	.17
Iron	%	.01	.01
Magnesium	%	.08	.09
Phosphorus	%	.19	.20
Potassium	%	.59	.63
Copper	mg/kg	5.1	5.5

Continued

Feed name or analyses		Mean	
		As fed	Dry
Manganese	mg/kg	18.5	20.0
Riboflavin	mg/kg	4.6	4.9
Arginine	%	.20	.22
Histidine	%	.10	.11
Isoleucine	%	.20	.22
Leucine	%	.30	.32
Lysine	%	.20	.22
Methionine	%	.10	.11
Phenylalanine	%	.20	.22
Threonine	%	.20	.22
Tryptophan	%	.10	.11
Tyrosine	%	.20	.22
Valine	%	.20	.22

Oats, cereal by-prod, mx 4 fbr, (4)
Feeding oat meal (AAFCO)
Oat middlings (CFA)

Ref no 4-03-303

Feed name or analyses		Mean	
		As fed	Dry
Dry matter	%	91.0	100.0
Ash	%	2.3	2.5
Crude fiber	%	4.0	4.4
Ether extract	%	5.8	6.4
N-free extract	%	63.1	69.3
Protein (N x 6.25)	%	15.8	17.4
Swine	dig prot %	13.3	14.6

Continued

Feed name or analyses		As fed (Mean)	Dry (Mean)
Energy			
Swine	DE kcal/kg	3210.	3527.
Swine	ME kcal/kg	2968.	3262.
Swine	TDN %	73.	80.
Calcium	%	.08	.09
Iron	%	.038	.042
Phosphorus	%	.49	.54
Manganese	mg/kg	44.0	48.4
Niacin	mg/kg	28.1	30.9
Pantothenic acid	mg/kg	23.1	25.4
Riboflavin	mg/kg	1.8	2.0
Thiamine	mg/kg	7.0	7.7
Arginine	%	.70	.77
Histidine	%	.30	.33
Lysine	%	.10	.11
Tyrosine	%	.91	1.00

Oats, grain, thresher-run, mx 34 wt mn 10 mx 20 fm, (4)

Ref no 4-08-161 Origin Canada

		As fed	Dry
Dry matter	%	90.0	100.0
Ash	%	3.5	3.9
Crude fiber	%	10.2	11.3
Ether extract	%	1.6	1.8

Continued

Feed name or analyses		As fed (Mean)	Dry (Mean)
N-free extract	%	63.1	70.1
Protein (N x 6.25)	%	11.4	12.7
Swine	dig prot %	9.6	10.7
Energy	GE kcal/kg	4320.	4800.
Swine	DE kcal/kg	2659.	2954.
Swine	ME kcal/kg	2483.	2759.
Swine	TDN %	60.	67.

Oats, grain, thresher-run, mx 34 wt mx 10 fm, (4)

Ref no 4-08-160 Origin Canada

		As fed	Dry
Dry matter	%	90.0	100.0
Ash	%	3.3	3.7
Crude fiber	%	10.3	11.4
Ether extract	%	1.6	1.8
N-free extract	%	63.4	70.4
Protein (N x 6.25)	%	11.4	12.7
Swine	dig prot %	9.6	10.7
Energy	GE kcal/kg	4410.	4900.
Swine	DE kcal/kg	2659.	2954.
Swine	ME kcal/kg	2483.	2759.
Swine	TDN %	60.	67.

Feed name or analyses		As fed (Mean)	Dry (Mean)

Oats, grain, (4)

Ref no 4-03-309

		As fed	Dry
Dry matter	%	89.0	100.0
Ash	%	3.2	3.6
Crude fiber	%	11.0	12.4
Ether extract	%	4.5	5.1
N-free extract	%	58.5	65.7
Protein (N x 6.25)	%	11.8	13.2
Swine	dig prot %	9.9	11.1
Cellulose	%	16.0	18.0
Lignin	%	8.9	10.0
Energy	GE kcal/kg	4187.	4704.
Swine	DE kcal/kg	2860.	3213.
Swine	ME kcal/kg	2668.	2998.
Swine	TDN %	65.	73.
Calcium	%	.10	.11
Iron	%	.007	.008
Magnesium	%	.17	.19
Phosphorus	%	.35	.39
Potassium	%	.37	.42
Sodium	%	.06	.07
Cobalt	mg/kg	.060	.070
Copper	mg/kg	5.9	6.6
Manganese	mg/kg	38.2	42.9

Continued

(1) dry forages and roughages
(2) pasture, range plants, and forages fed green
(3) silages
(4) energy feeds
(5) protein supplements
(6) minerals
(7) vitamins
(8) additives

TABLE I-1—COMPOSITION OF SOME COMMON SWINE FEEDS (Continued)

Feed name or analyses		Mean As fed	Mean Dry
Biotin	mg/kg	.30	.30
Choline	mg/kg	1073.	1206.
Folic acid	mg/kg	.40	.40
Niacin	mg/kg	15.8	17.8
Pantothenic acid	mg/kg	12.9	14.5
Riboflavin	mg/kg	1.6	1.8
Thiamine	mg/kg	6.2	7.0
a-tocopherol	mg/kg	5.9	6.6
Vitamin B6	mg/kg	1.2	1.3
Arginine	%	.71	.80
Cystine	%	.18	.20
Histidine	%	.18	.20
Isoleucine	%	.53	.60
Leucine	%	.89	1.00
Lysine	%	.36	.40
Methionine	%	.18	.20
Phenylalanine	%	.62	.70
Threonine	%	.36	.40
Tryptophan	%	.18	.20
Tyrosine	%	.53	.60
Valine	%	.62	.70

Oats grain - see also Oats, white; Oats, wild

Feed name or analyses		Mean As fed	Mean Dry
Oats, grain, gr sample US, (4)			
Ref no 4-03-310			
Dry matter	%	84.0	100.0
Ash	%	2.5	3.0
Crude fiber	%	10.0	11.9
Ether extract	%	4.8	5.7
N-free extract	%	56.0	66.7
Protein (N x 6.25)	%	10.7	12.7
Swine	dig prot %	9.0	10.7
Energy			
Swine	DE kcal/kg	2629.	3130.
Swine	ME kcal/kg	2455.	2923.
Swine	TDN %	60.	71.
Oats, grain, gr 1 US mn 34 wt mx 2 fm, (4)			
Ref no 4-03-313			
Dry matter	%	91.0	100.0
Ash	%	3.2	3.5
Crude fiber	%	12.0	13.2
Ether extract	%	4.8	5.3
N-free extract	%	58.9	64.7
Protein (N x 6.25)	%	12.1	13.3
Swine	dig prot %	10.2	11.2

Continued

Feed name or analyses		Mean As fed	Mean Dry
Energy			
Swine	DE kcal/kg	2768.	3042.
Swine	ME kcal/kg	2582.	2838.
Swine	TDN %	63.	69.
Calcium	%	.08	.09
Phosphorus	%	.30	.33
Oats, grain, gr 2 heavy US mn 36 wt mx 3 fm, (4)			
Oats, grain, heavy			
Ref no 4-03-315			
Dry matter	%	89.5	100.0
Ash	%	3.1	3.5
Crude fiber	%	9.8	10.9
Ether extract	%	4.0	4.5
N-free extract	%	60.5	67.6
Protein (N x 6.25)	%	12.1	13.5
Swine	dig prot %	10.1	11.3
Energy			
Swine	DE kcal/kg	2762.	3086.
Swine	ME kcal/kg	2577.	2879.
Swine	TDN %	63.	70.

Oats, grain, gr 2 US mn 32 wt mx 3 fm, (4)
Ref no 4-03-316

Feed name or analyses		Mean As fed	Mean Dry
Dry matter	%	89.0	100.0
Ash	%	2.9	3.3
Crude fiber	%	11.0	12.4
Ether extract	%	4.2	4.7
N-free extract	%	59.5	66.9
Protein (N x 6.25)	%	11.3	12.7
Swine dig prot	%	9.5	10.7
Energy			
Swine DE	kcal/kg	2746.	3086.
Swine ME	kcal/kg	2565.	2882.
Swine TDN	%	62.	70.
Calcium	%	.06	.07
Chlorine	%	.27	.30

Continued

Oats, grain, gr 3 US mn 30 wt mx 4 fm, (4)
Ref no 4-03-317

		Mean As fed	Mean Dry
Dry matter	%	91.0	100.0
Ash	%	3.4	3.7
Crude fiber	%	13.0	14.3

Continued

Feed name or analyses		Mean As fed	Mean Dry
Ether extract	%	4.6	5.1
N-free extract	%	57.9	63.6
Protein (N x 6.25)	%	12.1	13.3
Swine dig prot	%	10.2	11.2
Energy			
Swine DE	kcal/kg	2728.	2998.
Swine ME	kcal/kg	2545.	2797.
Swine TDN	%	62.	68.

Oats, grain, gr 4 US mn 27 wt mx 5 fm, (4)
Oats, grain, light
Ref no 4-03-318

		Mean As fed	Mean Dry
Dry matter	%	91.2	100.0
Ash	%	4.7	5.2
Crude fiber	%	15.1	16.5
Ether extract	%	4.5	4.9
N-free extract	%	54.9	60.2
Protein (N x 6.25)	%	12.0	13.2
Swine dig prot	%	10.1	11.1
Energy			
Swine DE	kcal/kg	2574.	2822.
Swine ME	kcal/kg	2404.	2633.
Swine TDN	%	58.	64.

Oats, groats, grnd cooked, (4)
Ref no 4-07-982

Feed name or analyses		Mean As fed	Mean Dry
Dry matter	%	91.0	100.0
Crude fiber	%	3.0	3.3
Ether extract	%	5.8	6.4
Protein (N x 6.25)	%	16.7	18.4
Calcium	%	.07	.08
Phosphorus	%	.43	.47

OATS, WHITE. Avena sativa

Oats, white, grain, Can 2 CW mn 36 wt mx 3 fm, (4)
Ref no 4-03-378

		Mean As fed	Mean Dry
Dry matter	%	86.5	100.0
Ash	%	3.0	3.5
Crude fiber	%	10.4	12.0
Ether extract	%	4.5	5.2
N-free extract	%	57.2	66.1
Protein (N x 6.25)	%	11.4	13.2
Swine dig prot	%	9.6	11.1

Continued

---

(1) dry forages and roughages
(2) pasture, range plants, and forages fed green
(3) silages
(4) energy feeds
(5) protein supplements
(6) minerals
(7) vitamins
(8) additives

TABLE 1-1—COMPOSITION OF SOME COMMON SWINE FEEDS (Continued)

Feed name or analyses		Mean	
		As fed	Dry
Energy	GE kcal/kg	4804.	5553.
Swine	DE kcal/kg	2669.	3086.
Swine	ME kcal/kg	2490.	2879.
Swine	TDN %	60.	70.
Alanine	%	.42	.48
Arginine	%	.50	.58
Aspartic acid	%	.69	.80
Glutamic acid	%	1.85	2.14
Glycine	%	.45	.52
Histidine	%	.19	.22
Isoleucine	%	.32	.37
Leucine	%	.64	.74
Lysine	%	.36	.42
Methionine	%	.03	.04
Phenylalanine	%	.45	.52
Proline	%	.51	.59
Serine	%	.07	.08
Threonine	%	.14	.16
Tyrosine	%	.15	.17
Valine	%	.51	.59

Oats, white, grain, Can 2 feed mn 28 wt mx 22 fm, (4)

Ref no 4-03-379

		As fed	Dry
Dry matter	%	86.5	100.0
Ash	%	2.9	3.4

Continued

Feed name or analyses		Mean	
		As fed	Dry
Crude fiber	%	10.4	12.0
Ether extract	%	4.4	5.1
N-free extract	%	57.8	66.8
Protein (N x 6.25)	%	11.0	12.7
Swine	dig prot %	9.2	10.7
Energy	GE kcal/kg	4804.	5553.
Swine	DE kcal/kg	2669.	3086.
Swine	ME kcal/kg	2496.	2885.
Swine	TDN %	60.	70.
Alanine	%	.42	.48
Arginine	%	.47	.54
Aspartic acid	%	.67	.78
Glutamic acid	%	1.94	2.24
Glycine	%	.42	.48
Histidine	%	.15	.17
Isoleucine	%	.22	.26
Leucine	%	.59	.68
Lysine	%	.27	.31
Methionine	%	.10	.12
Phenylalanine	%	.40	.46
Proline	%	.54	.62
Serine	%	.45	.52
Threonine	%	.28	.33
Tyrosine	%	.23	.27
Valine	%	.31	.36

Feed name or analyses		Mean	
		As fed	Dry

Oats, white, grain, Can 3 CW mn 34 wt mx 6 fm, (4)

Ref no 4-03-380

		As fed	Dry
Dry matter	%	86.5	100.0
Ash	%	2.9	3.4
Crude fiber	%	10.5	12.1
Ether extract	%	4.6	5.3
N-free extract	%	57.5	66.5
Protein (N x 6.25)	%	11.0	12.7
Swine	dig prot %	9.2	10.7
Energy	GE kcal/kg	4804.	5553.
Swine	DE kcal/kg	2669.	3086.
Swine	ME kcal/kg	2496.	2885.
Swine	TDN %	60.	70.
Alanine	%	.41	.47
Arginine	%	.51	.59
Aspartic acid	%	.72	.83
Glutamic acid	%	1.82	2.10
Glycine	%	.43	.50
Histidine	%	.16	.18
Isoleucine	%	.24	.28
Leucine	%	.60	.70
Lysine	%	.29	.34
Methionine	%	.10	.11
Phenylalanine	%	.42	.49
Proline	%	.47	.54
Serine	%	.45	.52

Continued

Left section

Feed name or analyses		Mean As fed	Dry
Threonine	%	.29	.34
Tyrosine	%	.23	.27
Valine	%	.36	.42

OATS, WILD. Avena fatua

Oats, wild, grain, (4)

Ref no 4-03-394

		As fed	Dry
Dry matter	%	89.0	100.0
Ash	%	4.6	5.2
Crude fiber	%	15.0	16.9
Ether extract	%	5.6	6.3
N-free extract	%	52.0	58.4
Protein (N x 6.25)	%	11.7	13.2
Swine	dig prot %	10.0	11.2
Energy			
Swine	DE kcal/kg	2512.	2822.
Swine	ME kcal/kg	2343.	2633.
Swine	TDN %	57.	64.

Middle section

Feed name or analyses		Mean As fed	Dry

OYSTERS. Crassostrea spp, Ostrea spp

Oysters, shells, f-grnd, mn 33 Ca, (6)
Oyster shell flour (AAFCO)

Ref no 6-03-481

		As fed	Dry
Dry matter	%	100.0	100.0
Ash	%	80.8	80.8
Protein (N x 6.25)	%	1.0	1.0
Calcium	%	38.05	38.05
Iron	%	.290	.290
Magnesium	%	.30	.30
Phosphorus	%	.07	.07
Potassium	%	.10	.10
Sodium	%	.21	.21
Manganese	mg/kg	133.3	133.3

Paddy rice - see Rice, grain w hulls

Right section

Feed name or analyses		Mean As fed	Dry

PEA. Pisum spp

Pea, seed, grnd, (5)

Ref no 5-03-598

		As fed	Dry
Dry matter	%	91.0	100.0
Ash	%	3.7	4.1
Crude fiber	%	9.0	9.9
Ether extract	%	1.9	2.1
N-free extract	%	53.9	59.2
Protein (N x 6.25)	%	22.5	24.7
Swine	dig prot %	19.3	21.2
Energy			
Swine	DE kcal/kg	3531.	3880.
Swine	ME kcal/kg	3213.	3531.
Swine	TDN %	80.	88.
Calcium	%	.17	.19
Phosphorus	%	.50	.55
Potassium	%	1.03	1.12
Choline	mg/kg	649.	713.
Niacin	mg/kg	17.2	18.9
Pantothenic acid	mg/kg	4.6	5.1
Riboflavin	mg/kg	.8	.9
Thiamine	mg/kg	1.8	2.0

(1) dry forages and roughages
(2) pasture, range plants, and forages fed green
(3) silages
(4) energy feeds
(5) protein supplements
(6) minerals
(7) vitamins
(8) additives

TABLE I-1—COMPOSITION OF SOME COMMON SWINE FEEDS (Continued)

Feed name or analyses		Mean	
		As fed	Dry
PEANUT. Arachis hypogaea			
Peanut, kernels, mech-extd grnd, mx 7 fbr, (5)			
Peanut meal (AAFCO)			
Peanut oil meal (CFA)			
Peanut oil meal, expeller extracted			
Ref no 5-03-649			
Dry matter	%	92.0	100.0
Ash	%	5.7	6.2
Crude fiber	%	11.0	12.0
Ether extract	%	5.9	6.4
N-free extract	%	23.6	25.6
Protein (N x 6.25)	%	45.8	49.8
Swine	dig prot %	43.0	46.8
Energy			
Swine	DE kcal/kg	3772.	4100.
Swine	ME kcal/kg	3244.	3526.
Swine	TDN %	86.	93.
Calcium	%	.17	.18
Magnesium	%	.33	.36
Phosphorus	%	.57	.62
Potassium	%	1.15	1.25
Manganese	mg/kg	25.5	27.7
Choline	mg/kg	1683.	1829.
Niacin	mg/kg	169.0	183.7
Continued			

Feed name or analyses		Mean	
		As fed	Dry
Pantothenic acid	mg/kg	48.2	52.3
Riboflavin	mg/kg	5.3	5.8
Thiamine	mg/kg	7.3	7.9
Arginine	%	4.69	5.10
Histidine	%	1.00	1.09
Isoleucine	%	2.00	2.17
Leucine	%	3.10	3.37
Lysine	%	1.30	1.41
Methionine	%	.60	.65
Phenylalanine	%	2.30	2.50
Threonine	%	1.40	1.52
Tryptophan	%	.50	.54
Valine	%	2.20	2.39
Peanut, kernels, solv-extd grnd, mx 7 fbr, (5)			
Solvent extracted peanut meal (AAFCO)			
Groundnut oil meal, solvent extracted			
Peanut oil meal, solvent extracted			
Ref no 5-03-650			
Dry matter	%	92.0	100.0
Ash	%	4.5	4.9
Crude fiber	%	13.0	14.1
Ether extract	%	1.2	1.3
N-free extract	%	25.9	28.2
Protein (N x 6.25)	%	47.4	51.5
Swine	dig prot %	44.5	48.4
Continued			

Feed name or analyses		Mean	
		As fed	Dry
Energy			
Swine	DE kcal/kg	3408.	3704.
Swine	ME kcal/kg	2920.	3174.
Swine	TDN %	77.	84.
Calcium	%	.20	.22
Magnesium	%	.04	.04
Phosphorus	%	.65	.71
Manganese	mg/kg	29.0	31.5
Choline	mg/kg	2000.	2174.
Niacin	mg/kg	170.1	184.9
Pantothenic acid	mg/kg	53.0	57.6
Riboflavin	mg/kg	11.0	12.0
Thiamine	mg/kg	7.3	7.9
Arginine	%	5.90	6.41
Histidine	%	1.20	1.30
Isoleucine	%	2.00	2.17
Leucine	%	3.70	4.02
Lysine	%	2.30	2.50
Methionine	%	.40	.43
Phenylalanine	%	2.70	2.93
Threonine	%	1.50	1.63
Tryptophan	%	.50	.54
Tyrosine	%	1.80	1.96
Valine	%	2.80	3.04

PHOSPHATE, DEFLUORINATED

Phosphate, defluorinated grnd, mn 1 pt F per 100 pt P, (6)
Phosphate, defluorinated (AAFCO)
Defluorinated phosphate (CFA)

Ref no 6-01-780

Feed name or analyses		As fed	Mean Dry
Dry matter	%	99.8	100.0
Calcium	%	33.00	33.07
Iron	%	.920	.922
Phosphorus	%	18.00	18.04
Potassium	%	.09	.09
Sodium	%	3.95	3.96
Fluorine	mg/kg	1800.00	1803.61

PLANT. Scientific name not used

Plant, charcoal, (6)
Charcoal, vegetable

Ref no 6-03-727

Feed name or analyses		As fed	Mean Dry
Dry matter	%	90.0	100.0
Ash	%	9.6	10.6
Calcium	%	4.70	5.22
Iron	%	.410	.455
Phosphorus	%	.03	.03
Cobalt	mg/kg	.200	.222
Copper	mg/kg	.1	.1
Manganese	mg/kg	.1	.1

POTATO. Solanum tuberosum

Potato meal - see Potato, tubers, dehy grnd

Potato, proc res, dehy, (4)
Potato by-product, dried
Potato pomace, dried
Potato pulp, dried
Potato waste, dried

Ref no 4-03-775

Feed name or analyses		As fed	Mean Dry
Dry matter	%	88.6	100.0
Ash	%	4.2	4.7
Crude fiber	%	6.1	6.9
Ether extract	%	.4	.4
N-free extract	%	70.2	79.3
Protein (N x 6.25)	%	7.7	8.7
Swine	dig prot %	5.7	6.4
Energy			
Swine	DE kcal/kg	3399.	3836.
Swine	ME kcal/kg	3202.	3614.
Swine	TDN %	77.	87.
Calcium	%	.15	.17
Iron	%	.035	.040
Magnesium	%	.09	.10
Phosphorus	%	.12	.13
Potassium	%	1.05	1.17
Sodium	%	.06	.07
Copper	mg/kg	15.4	17.1

Continued

(1) dry forages and roughages
(2) pasture, range plants, and forages fed green
(3) silages
(4) energy feeds
(5) protein supplements
(6) minerals
(7) vitamins
(8) additives

TABLE 1-1—COMPOSITION OF SOME COMMON SWINE FEEDS (Continued)

Feed name or analyses		Mean As fed	Mean Dry
Manganese	mg/kg	31.5	35.0
Riboflavin	mg/kg	1.1	1.2

Potato, tubers, cooked, (4)

Ref no 4-03-784

Feed name or analyses		Mean As fed	Mean Dry
Dry matter	%	22.5	100.0
Ash	%	1.2	5.2
Crude fiber	%	.7	3.0
Ether extract	%	.1	.3
N-free extract	%	18.3	81.5
Protein (N x 6.25)	%	2.2	10.0
Swine	dig prot %	1.6	7.0
Energy			
Swine	DE kcal/kg	863.	3836.
Swine	ME kcal/kg	811.	3606.
Swine	TDN %	20.	87.
Calcium	%	.01	.04
Chlorine	%	.06	.26
Iron	%	.002	.009
Magnesium	%	.03	.13
Phosphorus	%	.05	.22
Potassium	%	.48	2.13
Sodium	%	.02	.09
Sulfur	%	.02	.09
Copper	mg/kg	3.7	16.4
Manganese	mg/kg	8.8	39.1
Continued			

Feed name or analyses		Mean As fed	Mean Dry
Niacin	mg/kg	11.0	48.8
Pantothenic acid	mg/kg	6.4	28.4
Riboflavin	mg/kg	.2	.9
Thiamine	mg/kg	1.5	6.7

Potato, tubers, dehy grnd, (4)
Potato meal

Ref no 4-07-850

Feed name or analyses		Mean As fed	Mean Dry
Dry matter	%	90.3	100.0
Ash	%	11.9	13.2
Crude fiber	%	1.4	1.6
Ether extract	%	.5	.6
N-free extract	%	70.5	78.1
Protein (N x 6.25)	%	5.9	6.5
Swine	dig prot %	5.0	5.6
Energy			
Swine	DE kcal/kg	3345.	3704.
Swine	ME kcal/kg	3168.	3508.
Swine	TDN %	76.	84.
Calcium	%	.07	.08
Chlorine	%	.36	.40
Phosphorus	%	.20	.22
Potassium	%	1.97	2.18
Manganese	mg/kg	2.9	3.2

Feed name or analyses		Mean As fed	Mean Dry

POULTRY. Scientific name not used

Poultry, feathers, hydro dehy grnd, mn 75 of prot dig, (5)
Hydrolyzed poultry feathers (AAFCO)

Ref no 5-03-795

Feed name or analyses		Mean As fed	Mean Dry
Dry matter	%	91.0	100.0
Crude fiber	%	3.2	3.5
Crude fiber	%	.0	.0
Ether extract	%	2.4	2.6
N-free extract	%	.0	.0
Protein (N x 6.25)	%	85.4	93.9
Swine	dig prot %	60.2	66.2
Energy			
Swine	DE kcal/kg	2728.	2998.
Swine	ME kcal/kg	2100.	2308.
Swine	TDN %	62.	68.
Calcium	%	.41	.45
Phosphorus	%	.49	.54
Choline	mg/kg	1091.	1199.
Niacin	mg/kg	20.8	22.8
Pantothenic acid	mg/kg	8.8	9.7
Riboflavin	mg/kg	2.0	2.2
Vitamin B$_{12}$	mcg/kg	78.3	86.0
Alanine	%	4.34	4.77
Continued			

Feed name or analyses		Mean	
		As fed	Dry
Arginine	%	6.24	6.86
Aspartic acid	%	6.20	6.81
Cystine	%	3.78	4.15
Glutamic acid	%	8.95	9.84
Glycine	%	7.14	7.85
Histidine	%	.56	.62
Isoleucine	%	4.34	4.77
Leucine	%	7.89	8.67
Lysine	%	1.78	1.96
Methionine	%	.56	.62
Phenylalanine	%	4.40	4.84
Proline	%	10.40	11.43
Threonine	%	4.61	5.07
Tryptophan	%	.62	.68
Tyrosine	%	2.54	2.79
Valine	%	7.14	7.85

Primary dried yeast - see Yeast, primary

Feed name or analyses		Mean	
		As fed	Dry

RAPE. Brassica spp

Rape, seed, mech-extd grnd, (5)
Rapeseed oil meal, expeller extracted
Rapeseed meal, expeller extracted

Ref no 5-03-870

		As fed	Dry
Dry matter	%	93.6	100.0
Ash	%	6.0	6.4
Crude fiber	%	13.7	14.6
Ether extract	%	6.3	6.7
N-free extract	%	30.6	32.7
Protein (N x 6.25)	%	37.1	39.6
Swine	dig prot %	30.4	32.5
Energy			
Swine	DE kcal/kg	3054.	3263.
Swine	ME kcal/kg	2687.	2871.
Swine	TDN %	69.	74.
Calcium	%	.60	.64
Phosphorus	%	.97	1.04
Choline	mg/kg	6295.	6725.
Niacin	mg/kg	149.8	160.0
Pantothenic acid	mg/kg	8.6	9.2
Riboflavin	mg/kg	3.6	3.8

Continued

Feed name or analyses		Mean	
		As fed	Dry
Thiamine	mg/kg	1.7	1.8
Alanine	%	1.72	1.84
Arginine	%	2.08	2.22
Aspartic acid	%	2.69	2.87
Glutamic acid	%	6.59	7.04
Glycine	%	1.91	2.04
Histidine	%	.98	1.05
Isoleucine	%	1.52	1.62
Leucine	%	2.63	2.81
Lysine	%	1.79	1.91
Methionine	%	.77	.82
Phenylalanine	%	1.52	1.63
Proline	%	2.33	2.49
Serine	%	1.65	1.76
Threonine	%	1.67	1.78
Tryptophan	%	.38	.41
Tyrosine	%	.88	.94
Valine	%	1.95	2.08

(1) dry forages and roughages
(2) pasture, range plants, and forages fed green
(3) silages
(4) energy feeds
(5) protein supplements
(6) minerals
(7) vitamins
(8) additives

TABLE I-1—COMPOSITION OF SOME COMMON SWINE FEEDS (Continued)

Feed name or analyses		Mean	
		As fed	Dry
Rape, seed, solv-extd grnd, (5)			
Rapeseed oil meal, solvent extracted			
Rapeseed meal, solvent extracted			
Ref no 5-03-871			
Dry matter	%	90.3	100.0
Ash	%	6.5	7.2
Crude fiber	%	13.8	15.3
Ether extract	%	2.4	2.7
N-free extract	%	28.2	31.2
Protein (N x 6.25)	%	39.4	43.6
Swine	dig prot %	32.3	35.8
Energy			
Swine	DE kcal/kg	2747.	3042.
Swine	ME kcal/kg	2396.	2653.
Swine	TDN %	62.	69.
Calcium	%	.40	.44
Phosphorus	%	.90	1.00
Choline	mg/kg	6073.	6725.
Niacin	mg/kg	144.5	160.0
Pantothenic acid	mg/kg	8.3	9.2
Riboflavin	mg/kg	3.4	3.8
Thiamine	mg/kg	1.6	1.8
Alanine	%	1.69	1.87
Arginine	%	2.16	2.39
Aspartic acid	%	2.64	2.93
Glutamic acid	%	6.63	7.34
			Continued

Feed name or analyses		Mean	
		As fed	Dry
Glycine	%	1.88	2.08
Histidine	%	1.05	1.16
Isoleucine	%	1.43	1.58
Leucine	%	2.63	2.91
Lysine	%	2.09	2.32
Methionine	%	.76	.84
Phenylalanine	%	1.49	1.65
Proline	%	2.41	2.67
Serine	%	1.65	1.83
Threonine	%	1.65	1.83
Tryptophan	%	.48	.53
Tyrosine	%	.83	.92
Valine	%	1.90	2.10

RAPE, ARGENTINE. Brassica napus

Rape, Argentine, seed, mech-extd grnd, (5)

		Mean	
		As fed	Dry
Ref no 5-07-869			
Dry matter	%	93.2	100.0
Ash	%	6.7	7.2
Crude fiber	%	14.9	16.0
Ether extract	%	7.0	7.5
N-free extract	%	32.7	35.1
Protein (N x 6.25)	%	31.9	34.2
Swine	dig prot %	26.1	28.0
			Continued

Feed name or analyses		Mean	
		As fed	Dry
Energy			
Swine	DE kcal/kg	3041.	3263.
Swine	ME kcal/kg	2709.	2907.
Swine	TDN %	69.	74.
Calcium	%	.70	.75
Phosphorus	%	.99	1.06
Choline	mg/kg	6524.	7000.
Niacin	mg/kg	155.6	167.0
Pantothenic acid	mg/kg	9.2	9.9
Riboflavin	mg/kg	3.9	4.2
Thiamine	mg/kg	1.8	1.9
Arginine	%	1.54	1.65
Histidine	%	.80	.86
Isoleucine	%	1.42	1.53
Leucine	%	2.15	2.31
Lysine	%	1.28	1.37
Methionine	%	.38	.41
Phenylalanine	%	1.26	1.35
Threonine	%	1.29	1.38
Tryptophan	%	.31	.33
Valine	%	1.74	1.87

Rape, Argentine, seed, solv-extd grnd, (5)

Ref no 5-07-868

		As fed	Dry
Dry matter	%	92.0	100.0
Ash	%	6.6	7.2
			Continued

Feed name or analyses		Mean	
		As fed	Dry
Crude fiber	%	8.6	9.3
Ether extract	%	1.0	1.1
N-free extract	%	35.7	38.8
Protein (N x 6.25)	%	40.1	43.6
Swine	dig prot %	32.9	35.8
Energy			
Swine	DE kcal/kg	2798.	3042.
Swine	ME kcal/kg	2441.	2653.
Swine	TDN %	63.	69.
Calcium	%	.61	.66
Phosphorus	%	.86	.93
Choline	mg/kg	6524.	7000.
Niacin	mg/kg	155.6	167.0
Pantothenic acid	mg/kg	9.2	9.9
Riboflavin	mg/kg	3.9	4.2
Thiamine	mg/kg	1.8	1.9
Arginine	%	2.15	2.34
Histidine	%	1.03	1.12
Isoleucine	%	1.51	1.64
Leucine	%	2.65	2.88
Lysine	%	2.06	2.24
Methionine	%	.51	.55
Phenylalanine	%	1.63	1.77
Threonine	%	1.65	1.79
Tryptophan	%	.45	.49
Valine	%	2.07	2.25
			Continued

(1) dry forages and roughages
(2) pasture, range plants, and
    forages fed green

Feed name or analyses		Mean	
		As fed	Dry

Rape, Canada, seed, cooked pre-press solv-extd, Can 1 mx 1 fat, (5)
Canada rapeseed pre-press solvent extracted meal (CFA)

Ref no 5-08-135

		As fed	Dry
Dry matter	%	92.0	100.0
Ash	%	7.2	7.8
Crude fiber	%	9.3	10.1
Ether extract	%	1.1	1.2
N-free extract	%	33.9	36.8
Protein (N x 6.25)	%	40.5	44.0
Swine	dig prot %	34.2	37.2
Energy			
Swine	DE kcal/kg	2637.	2866.
Swine	ME kcal/kg	2296.	2496.
Swine	TDN %	60.	65.
Calcium	%	.66	.72
Phosphorus	%	.93	1.01
Alanine	%	1.48	1.61
Arginine	%	1.90	2.06
Aspartic acid	%	2.31	2.51
Glutamic acid	%	5.78	6.28
Glycine	%	1.66	1.80
Histidine	%	.93	1.01
			Continued

(3) silages
(4) energy feeds
(5) protein supplements

Feed name or analyses		Mean	
		As fed	Dry
Isoleucine	%	1.24	1.35
Leucine	%	2.31	2.51
Lysine	%	1.82	1.98
Methionine	%	.65	.71
Phenylalanine	%	1.31	1.42
Proline	%	2.10	2.28
Serine	%	1.44	1.57
Threonine	%	1.44	1.57
Tryptophan	%	.41	.45
Tyrosine	%	.73	.79
Valine	%	1.66	1.80

Rape, Canada, seed, cooked mech-extd grnd, Can 1 mx 6 fat, (5)
Canada rapeseed meal (CFA)

Ref no 5-08-136

		As fed	Dry
Dry matter	%	94.0	100.0
Ash	%	6.8	7.2
Crude fiber	%	15.5	16.5
Ether extract	%	7.0	7.4
N-free extract	%	29.5	31.4
Protein (N x 6.25)	%	35.2	37.5
Swine	dig prot %	29.3	31.2
			Continued

(6) minerals
(7) vitamins
(8) additives

TABLE 1-1—COMPOSITION OF SOME COMMON SWINE FEEDS (Continued)

(continuation of preceding feed)

Feed name or analyses		As fed	Dry
Energy			
Swine	DE kcal/kg	2942.	3130.
Swine	ME kcal/kg	2601.	2767.
Swine	TDN %	67.	71.
Calcium	%	.71	.76
Phosphorus	%	1.00	1.06
Choline	mg/kg	7000.	7448.
Niacin	mg/kg	167.	178.
Pantothenic acid	mg/kg	9.9	10.5
Riboflavin	mg/kg	4.2	4.5
Thiamine	mg/kg	1.9	2.0
Alanine	%	1.48	1.57
Arginine	%	1.79	1.90
Aspartic acid	%	2.31	2.46
Glutamic acid	%	5.68	6.04
Glycine	%	1.65	1.75
Histidine	%	.85	.90
Isoleucine	%	1.31	1.39
Leucine	%	2.27	2.41
Lysine	%	1.54	1.64
Methionine	%	.66	.70
Phenylalanine	%	1.32	1.40
Proline	%	2.01	2.14
Serine	%	1.42	1.51
Threonine	%	1.44	1.53
Tryptophan	%	.33	.35
Tyrosine	%	.76	.81
Valine	%	1.67	1.78

RAPE, POLISH. Brassica campestris

Rape, Polish, seed, mech-extd grnd, (5)

Ref no 5-07-871

Feed name or analyses		As fed	Dry
Dry matter	%	94.0	100.0
Ash	%	6.4	6.8
Crude fiber	%	14.6	15.5
Ether extract	%	6.6	7.0
N-free extract	%	34.3	36.5
Protein (N x 6.25)	%	32.1	34.2
Swine	dig prot %	26.3	28.0
Energy			
Swine	DE kcal/kg	3067.	3263.
Swine	ME kcal/kg	2732.	2907.
Swine	TDN %	69.	74.
Calcium	%	.67	.71
Phosphorus	%	.94	1.00
Choline	mg/kg	6063.	6450.
Niacin	mg/kg	142.9	152.0
Pantothenic acid	mg/kg	8.1	8.6
Riboflavin	mg/kg	3.1	3.3
Thiamine	mg/kg	1.6	1.7
Arginine	%	1.72	1.83
Histidine	%	.89	.95
Isoleucine	%	1.37	1.46
Leucine	%	2.15	2.29
Lysine	%	1.58	1.68
Methionine	%	.46	.49
Phenylalanine	%	1.24	1.32
Threonine	%	1.34	1.43
Tryptophan	%	.31	.33
Valine	%	1.72	1.83

Continued

Rape, Polish, seed, solv-extd grnd, (5)

Ref no 5-07-870

Feed name or analyses		As fed	Dry
Dry matter	%	92.0	100.0
Ash	%	6.6	7.2
Crude fiber	%	8.6	9.3
Ether extract	%	1.0	1.1
N-free extract	%	35.7	38.8
Protein (N x 6.25)	%	40.1	43.6
Swine	dig prot %	32.9	35.8
Energy			
Swine	DE kcal/kg	2798.	3042.
Swine	ME kcal/kg	2441.	2653.
Swine	TDN %	63.	69.
Calcium	%	.61	.66
Phosphorus	%	.86	.93
Choline	mg/kg	5934.	6450.
Niacin	mg/kg	139.8	152.0
Pantothenic acid	mg/kg	7.9	8.6

Continued

Feed name or analyses		Mean As fed	Dry
Riboflavin	mg/kg	3.0	3.3
Thiamine	mg/kg	1.6	1.7
Arginine	%	2.36	2.57
Histidine	%	1.12	1.22
Isoleucine	%	1.66	1.80
Leucine	%	2.79	3.03
Lysine	%	2.26	2.46
Methionine	%	.56	.61
Phenylalanine	%	1.63	1.77
Threonine	%	1.75	1.90
Tryptophan	%	.47	.51
Valine	%	2.14	2.33
			Continued

RICE. Oryza sativa

Rice, bran w germ, dry-mil, mx 13 fbr CaCO3 declared above 3 mn, (4)
Rice bran (AAFCO)

Ref no 4-03-928

Dry matter	%	91.0	100.0
Ash	%	10.9	12.0
Crude fiber	%	11.0	12.1
Ether extract	%	15.1	16.6
			Continued

(1) dry forages and roughages
(2) pasture, range plants, and forages fed green

Feed name or analyses		Mean As fed	Dry
N-free extract	%	40.5	44.5
Protein (N x 6.25)	%	13.5	14.8
Swine	dig prot %	10.2	11.2
Energy			
Swine	DE kcal/kg	3256.	3578.
Swine	ME kcal/kg	3028.	3328.
Swine	TDN %	74.	81.
Calcium	%	.06	.07
Iron	%	.019	.021
Magnesium	%	.95	1.04
Phosphorus	%	1.82	2.00
Potassium	%	1.74	1.91
Copper	mg/kg	13.0	14.3
Manganese	mg/kg	417.8	459.2
Zinc	mg/kg	29.9	32.9
Biotin	mg/kg	4.20	4.60
Choline	mg/kg	1254.	1378.
Niacin	mg/kg	303.2	333.2
Pantothenic acid	mg/kg	23.5	25.8
Riboflavin	mg/kg	2.6	2.9
Thiamine	mg/kg	22.4	24.6
Arginine	%	.50	.55
Cystine	%	.11	.11
Histidine	%	.20	.22
Isoleucine	%	.40	.44
Leucine	%	.60	.66
Lysine	%	.50	.55
			Continued

(3) silages
(4) energy feeds
(5) protein supplements

Feed name or analyses		Mean As fed	Dry
Phenylalanine	%	.40	.44
Threonine	%	.40	.44
Tryptophan	%	.10	.11
Valine	%	.60	.66

Rice, brown - see Rice, groats

Rice, grain w hulls, grnd, (4)
Ground rough rice (AAFCO)
Ground paddy rice (AAFCO)

Ref no 4-03-938

Dry matter	%	89.0	100.0
Ash	%	4.5	5.0
Crude fiber	%	9.0	10.1
Ether extract	%	1.9	2.1
N-free extract	%	66.4	74.6
Protein (N x 6.25)	%	7.3	8.2
Swine	dig prot %	5.5	6.2
Energy	GE kcal/kg	3066.	3445.
Swine	DE kcal/kg	2511.	2821.
Swine	ME kcal/kg	2367.	2660.
Swine	TDN %	57.	64.
Calcium	%	.04	.04
			Continued

(6) minerals
(7) vitamins
(8) additives

TABLE I-1—COMPOSITION OF SOME COMMON SWINE FEEDS (Continued)

Feed name or analyses		Mean	
		As fed	Dry
Magnesium	%	.14	.16
Phosphorus	%	.26	.29
Potassium	%	.34	.38
Folic acid	mg/kg	.4	.4
Niacin	mg/kg	30.3	34.1
Riboflavin	mg/kg	1.1	1.3
Thiamine	mg/kg	2.8	3.1
Arginine	%	.53	.60
Histidine	%	.09	.10
Isoleucine	%	.27	.30
Leucine	%	.53	.60
Lysine	%	.27	.30
Phenylalanine	%	.27	.30
Threonine	%	.18	.20

Rice, groats, grnd, (4)
Ground brown rice (AAFCO)
Rice grain without hulls, ground

Ref no 4-03-935

		As fed	Dry
Dry matter	%	89.0	100.0
Ash	%	.7	.8
Crude fiber	%	1.0	1.1
Ether extract	%	1.2	1.3
N-free extract	%	77.6	87.2

Continued

Feed name or analyses		Mean	
		As fed	Dry
Protein (N x 6.25)	%	8.5	9.6
Swine	dig prot %	7.3	8.2
Energy			
Swine	DE kcal/kg	3846.	4321.
Swine	ME kcal/kg	3619.	4066.
Swine	TDN %	87.	98.
Calcium	%	.04	.04
Iron	%	.004	.005
Magnesium	%	.05	.06
Phosphorus	%	.18	.20
Potassium	%	.12	.14
Sodium	%	.04	.05
Copper	mg/kg	4.3	4.8
Manganese	mg/kg	4.3	4.8
Niacin	mg/kg	17.1	19.2
Riboflavin	mg/kg	.3	.3
Thiamine	mg/kg	1.1	1.2

Rice, groats, polished, (4)
Rice, white, polished

Ref no 4-03-942

		As fed	Dry
Dry matter	%	89.0	100.0
Ash	%	.5	.6
Crude fiber	%	.4	.4

Continued

Feed name or analyses		Mean	
		As fed	Dry
Ether extract	%	.4	.4
N-free extract	%	80.4	90.4
Protein (N x 6.25)	%	7.3	8.2
Swine	dig prot %	6.2	7.0
Energy			
Swine	GE kcal/kg	3604.	4049.
Swine	DE kcal/kg	3784.	4252.
Swine	ME kcal/kg	3569.	4010.
Swine	TDN %	86.	97.
Calcium	%	.03	.03
Iron	%	.002	.002
Magnesium	%	.02	.02
Phosphorus	%	.12	.14
Potassium	%	.13	.15
Copper	mg/kg	2.9	3.3
Manganese	mg/kg	10.9	12.3
Zinc	mg/kg	1.8	2.0
Choline	mg/kg	907.	1019.
Niacin	mg/kg	14.1	15.8
Pantothenic acid	mg/kg	3.3	3.7
Riboflavin	mg/kg	.6	.7
Thiamine	mg/kg	.6	.7
a-tocopherol	mg/kg	3.6	4.0
Vitamin B6	mg/kg	.4	.4
Arginine	%	.36	.40
Cystine	%	.09	.10
Glycine	%	.71	.80
Histidine	%	.18	.20
Isoleucine	%	.45	.51
Leucine	%	.71	.80

Continued

Feed name or analyses		Mean	
		As fed	Dry
Lysine	%	.27	.30
Methionine	%	.27	.30
Phenylalanine	%	.53	.60
Threonine	%	.36	.40
Tryptophan	%	.09	.10
Tyrosine	%	.62	.70
Valine	%	.53	.60

Rice, polishings, dehy, (4)
Rice polishings (AAFCO)
Rice polish (CFA)

Ref no 4-03-943

		As fed	Dry
Dry matter	%	90.0	100.0
Ash	%	8.0	8.9
Crude fiber	%	3.0	3.3
Ether extract	%	13.2	14.7
N-free extract	%	54.0	60.0
Protein (N x 6.25)	%	11.8	13.1
Swine	dig prot %	10.3	11.4
Energy			
Swine	DE kcal/kg	3916.	4351.
Swine	ME kcal/kg	3658.	4064.
Swine	TDN %	89.	99.
Calcium	%	.04	.04

Continued

(1) dry forages and roughages
(2) pasture, range plants, and forages fed green

837

Feed name or analyses		Mean	
		As fed	Dry
Magnesium	%	.65	.72
Phosphorus	%	1.42	1.58
Potassium	%	1.17	1.30
Sodium	%	.11	.12
Biotin	mg/kg	.60	.70
Choline	mg/kg	1307.	1452.
Niacin	mg/kg	531.7	590.7
Pantothenic acid	mg/kg	58.3	64.8
Riboflavin	mg/kg	1.8	2.0
Thiamine	mg/kg	19.7	21.9
Arginine	%	.50	.56
Cystine	%	.10	.11
Histidine	%	.10	.11
Isoleucine	%	.30	.33
Leucine	%	.50	.55
Lysine	%	.50	.55
Phenylalanine	%	.30	.33
Threonine	%	.30	.33
Tryptophan	%	.10	.11

Rough rice - see Rice, grain w hulls

(3) silages
(4) energy feeds
(5) protein supplements

Feed name or analyses		Mean	
		As fed	Dry

RYE. Secale cereale

Rye, grain, (4)

Ref no 4-04-047

		As fed	Dry
Dry matter	%	89.0	100.0
Ash	%	1.7	1.9
Crude fiber	%	2.0	2.2
Ether extract	%	1.6	1.8
N-free extract	%	71.8	80.7
Protein (N x 6.25)	%	11.9	13.4
Swine	dig prot %	9.6	10.8
Energy			
Swine	DE kcal/kg	3300.	3708.
Swine	ME kcal/kg	3079.	3460.
Swine	TDN %	75.	84.
Calcium	%	.06	.07
Iron	%	.008	.009
Magnesium	%	.12	.13
Phosphorus	%	.34	.38
Potassium	%	.46	.52
Sodium	%	.02	.02
Copper	mg/kg	7.8	8.8
Manganese	mg/kg	66.9	75.2

Continued

(6) minerals
(7) vitamins
(8) additives

TABLE I-1—COMPOSITION OF SOME COMMON SWINE FEEDS (Continued)

Feed name or analyses		Mean As fed	Dry
Zinc	mg/kg	30.5	34.3
Biotin	mg/kg	.06	.07
Folic acid	mg/kg	.60	.70
Niacin	mg/kg	1.2	1.3
Pantothenic acid	mg/kg	6.9	7.7
Riboflavin	mg/kg	1.6	1.8
Thiamine	mg/kg	3.9	4.4
a-tocopherol	mg/kg	15.0	17.4
Arginine	%	.53	.60
Cystine	%	.18	.20
Histidine	%	.27	.30
Isoleucine	%	.53	.60
Leucine	%	.71	.80
Lysine	%	.45	.51
Methionine	%	.18	.20
Phenylalanine	%	.62	.70
Threonine	%	.36	.40
Tryptophan	%	.09	.10
Tyrosine	%	.27	.30
Valine	%	.62	.70

Screenings - see Flax, seed screenings; see Grains, screenings; see Wheat, grain screenings

SESAME. Sesamum indicum

Sesame, seed, mech-extd grnd, (5)
Sesame oil meal, expeller extracted

Ref no 5-04-220

Feed name or analyses		Mean As fed	Dry
Dry matter	%	93.0	100.0
Ash	%	9.3	10.0
Crude fiber	%	5.0	5.4
Ether extract	%	5.1	5.5
N-free extract	%	25.7	27.6
Protein (N x 6.25)	%	47.9	51.5
Swine dig prot	%	45.0	48.4
Energy Swine	DE kcal/kg	3526.	3792.
Swine	ME kcal/kg	3019.	3246.
Swine	TDN %	80.	86.
Calcium	%	2.03	2.18
Phosphorus	%	1.29	1.39
Manganese	mg/kg	48.0	51.6
Choline	mg/kg	1533.	1648.
Pantothenic acid	mg/kg	6.4	6.9
Riboflavin	mg/kg	3.7	4.0
Thiamine	mg/kg	2.9	3.1

Shorts - see Wheat, flour by-prod, c-sift, mx 7 fbr

Skimmed milk - see Cattle, milk, skim

SODIUM PHOSPHATE, MONOBASIC

Sodium, phosphate, monobasic, NaH2PO4·H2O, tech, (6)
Monosodium phosphate (AAFCO)

Ref no 6-04-288

Feed name or analyses		Mean As fed	Dry
Dry matter	%	96.7	100.0
Ash	%	96.7	100.0
Phosphorus	%	21.80	22.46
Sodium	%	32.3	33.4
		120.00	124.10

SODIUM TRIPOLYPHOSPHATE

Feed name or analyses	Mean As fed	Mean Dry
Sodium, tripolyphosphate, comm, (6)		
Sodium tripolyphosphate (AAFCO)		
Ref no 6-08-076		
Dry matter %	96.0	100.0
Phosphorus %	24.94	25.98

SORGHUM, GRAIN VARIETY. Sorghum vulgare

Sorghum grain - see Sorghum, grain variety; see Sorghum, milo

Feed name or analyses	Mean As fed	Mean Dry
Sorghum, grain variety, grain, mn 6 mx 9 prot, (4)		
Ref no 4-08-138		
Dry matter %	88.0	100.0
Ash %	2.0	2.3
Crude fiber %	1.9	2.2
		Continued

(1) dry forages and roughages
(2) pasture, range plants, and forages fed green

Feed name or analyses	Mean As fed	Mean Dry
Ether extract %	2.6	3.0
N-free extract %	74.4	84.6
Protein (N x 6.25) %	7.0	7.9
Alanine %	.61	.69
Arginine %	.26	.29
Aspartic acid %	.48	.54
Cysteine %	.10	.11
Glutamic acid %	1.36	1.54
Glycine %	.26	.29
Histidine %	.16	.18
Isoleucine %	.26	.30
Leucine %	.68	.77
Lysine %	.18	.20
Methionine %	.09	.10
Phenylalanine %	.34	.39
Proline %	.52	.59
Serine %	.30	.34
Threonine %	.23	.26
Tyrosine %	.14	.16
Valine %	.35	.40

(3) silages
(4) energy feeds
(5) protein supplements

Feed name or analyses	Mean As fed	Mean Dry
Sorghum, grain variety, grain, mn 9 mx 12 prot, (4)		
Ref no 4-08-139		
Dry matter %	88.0	100.0
Ash %	1.9	2.2
Crude fiber %	2.1	2.4
Ether extract %	2.6	2.9
N-free extract %	71.1	80.8
Protein (N x 6.25) %	10.3	11.7
Lignin %	1.1	1.3
Alanine %	.97	1.10
Arginine %	.33	.38
Aspartic acid %	.70	.79
Cysteine %	.14	.16
Glutamic acid %	2.24	2.54
Glycine %	.32	.37
Histidine %	.23	.26
Isoleucine %	.43	.49
Leucine %	1.41	1.60
Lysine %	.22	.25
Methionine %	.13	.15
Phenylalanine %	.53	.60
Proline %	.84	.96
Serine %	.44	.50
		Continued

(6) minerals
(7) vitamins
(8) additives

TABLE 1-1—COMPOSITION OF SOME COMMON SWINE FEEDS (Continued)

Feed name or analyses		Mean As fed	Mean Dry
Threonine	%	.32	.37
Tyrosine	%	.22	.25
Valine	%	.53	.60

Sorghum, grain variety, grain, mn 12 mx 15 prot, (4)

Ref no 4-08-140

Feed name or analyses		As fed	Dry
Dry matter	%	88.0	100.0
Ash	%	2.3	2.6
Crude fiber	%	1.8	2.0
Ether extract	%	1.5	1.7
N-free extract	%	71.0	80.7
Protein (N x 6.25)	%	11.4	13.0
Alanine	%	1.17	1.33
Arginine	%	.39	.43
Aspartic acid	%	.81	.92
Cystine	%	.18	.20
Glutamic acid	%	2.59	2.94
Glycine	%	.35	.40
Histidine	%	.26	.29
Isoleucine	%	.49	.56
Leucine	%	1.77	2.01
Lysine	%	.23	.26
Methionine	%	.14	.16
Phenylalanine	%	.62	.70
Proline	%	.97	1.10

Continued

Feed name or analyses		As fed	Dry
Serine	%	.51	.58
Threonine	%	.37	.42
Tyrosine	%	.26	.29
Valine	%	.61	.69

Sorghum, grain variety, grain, (4)

Ref no 4-04-383

Feed name or analyses			As fed	Dry
Dry matter		%	89.0	100.0
Ash		%	1.8	2.0
Crude fiber		%	2.0	2.2
Ether extract		%	3.0	3.4
N-free extract		%	71.1	79.9
Protein (N x 6.25)		%	11.1	12.5
Swine	dig prot	%	7.9	8.9
Energy				
Swine	DE kcal/kg		3414.	3836.
Swine	ME kcal/kg		3192.	3587.
Swine	TDN	%	77.	87.
Calcium		%	.04	.05
Magnesium		%	.17	.19
Phosphorus		%	.31	.35
Potassium		%	.34	.38
Sodium		%	.04	.05
Cobalt		mg/kg	2.800	3.100
Copper		mg/kg	9.6	10.8
Manganese		mg/kg	14.5	16.3

Continued

Feed name or analyses		Mean As fed	Mean Dry
Zinc	mg/kg	13.7	15.4
Biotin	mg/kg	2.60	2.90
Choline	mg/kg	678.	761.
Folic acid	mg/kg	.20	.20
Niacin	mg/kg	43.1	48.4
Pantothenic acid	mg/kg	11.1	12.5
Riboflavin	mg/kg	1.3	1.5
Thiamine	mg/kg	4.1	4.6
Vitamin B_6	mg/kg	5.30	5.90
Arginine	%	.36	.40
Cystine	%	.18	.20
Histidine	%	.27	.30
Isoleucine	%	.53	.60
Leucine	%	1.42	1.60
Lysine	%	.27	.30
Phenylalanine	%	.45	.51
Threonine	%	.27	.30
Tryptophan	%	.09	.10
Tyrosine	%	.36	.40
Valine	%	.53	.60

SORGHUM, MILO. Sorghum vulgare

Sorghum, milo, grain, (4)

Ref no 4-04-444

Feed name or analyses		As fed	Dry
		Mean	
Dry matter	%	89.0	100.0
Ash	%	1.7	1.9
Crude fiber	%	2.0	2.2
Ether extract	%	2.8	3.1
N-free extract	%	71.6	80.4
Protein (N x 6.25)	%	11.0	12.4
Swine	dig prot %	7.8	8.8
Energy	GE kcal/kg	3906.	4389.
Swine	DE kcal/kg	3453.	3880.
Swine	ME kcal/kg	3229.	3628.
Swine	TDN %	78.	88.
Calcium	%	.04	.04
Magnesium	%	.20	.22
Phosphorus	%	.29	.33
Potassium	%	.35	.39
Sodium	%	.01	.01
Cobalt	mg/kg	.100	.100
Copper	mg/kg	14.1	15.8
Manganese	mg/kg	12.9	14.5

Continued

Feed name or analyses		As fed	Dry
		Mean	
Choline	mg/kg	678.	761.
Niacin	mg/kg	42.7	48.0
Pantothenic acid	mg/kg	11.4	12.8
Riboflavin	mg/kg	1.2	1.3
Thiamine	mg/kg	3.9	4.4
Vitamin B_6	mg/kg	4.10	4.60
Arginine	%	.36	.40
Cystine	%	.18	.20
Histidine	%	.27	.30
Isoleucine	%	.53	.60
Leucine	%	1.42	1.60
Lysine	%	.27	.30
Methionine	%	.09	.10
Phenylalanine	%	.45	.51
Threonine	%	.27	.30
Tryptophan	%	.09	.10
Tyrosine	%	.36	.40
Valine	%	.53	.60

Soy - see Soybean

SOYBEAN. Glycine max

Soybean, oil, (4)

Ref no 4-07-983

Feed name or analyses		As fed	Dry
		Mean	
Dry matter	%	100.0	100.0
Ether extract	%	100.0	100.0

Soybean, seed, mech-extd grnd, mx 7 fbr, (5)
Soybean meal (AAFCO)
Soybean meal, expeller extracted
Soybean meal, hydraulic extracted
Soybean oil meal, expeller extracted
Soybean oil meal, hydraulic extracted

Ref no 5-04-600

Feed name or analyses		As fed	Dry
		Mean	
Dry matter	%	90.0	100.0
Ash	%	5.7	6.3
Crude fiber	%	6.0	6.7
Ether extract	%	4.7	5.2
N-free extract	%	29.8	33.1

Continued

(1) dry forages and roughages
(2) pasture, range plants, and forages fed green
(3) silages
(4) energy feeds
(5) protein supplements
(6) minerals
(7) vitamins
(8) additives

TABLE 1-1—COMPOSITION OF SOME COMMON SWINE FEEDS (Continued)

Feed name or analyses		As fed	Dry
Protein (N x 6.25)	%	43.8	48.7
Swine	dig prot %	39.4	43.8
Energy	GE kcal/kg	4332.	4813.
Swine	DE kcal/kg	3476.	3862.
Swine	ME kcal/kg	2996.	3329.
Swine	TDN %	79.	88.
Calcium	%	.27	.30
Iron	%	.016	.018
Magnesium	%	.25	.28
Phosphorus	%	.63	.70
Potassium	%	1.71	1.90
Sodium	%	.24	.27
Cobalt	mg/kg	.200	.200
Copper	mg/kg	18.0	20.0
Manganese	mg/kg	32.3	35.9
Biotin	mg/kg	.30	.30
Choline	mg/kg	2673.	2970.
Folic acid	mg/kg	6.60	7.30
Niacin	mg/kg	30.4	33.8
Thiamine	mg/kg	4.0	4.4
Arginine	%	2.60	2.89
Cystine	%	.60	.67
Glycine	%	2.50	2.78
Histidine	%	1.10	1.22
Isoleucine	%	2.80	3.11
Leucine	%	3.60	4.00
Lysine	%	2.70	3.00
Methionine	%	.80	.89
Phenylalanine	%	2.10	2.33
Threonine	%	1.70	1.89
Tryptophan	%	.60	.67
Tyrosine	%	1.40	1.56
Valine	%	2.20	2.44

Continued

Soybean, seed, solv-extd grnd, mx 7 fbr, (5)

Solvent extracted soybean meal (AAFCO)
Soybean meal, solvent extracted
Soybean oil meal, solvent extracted

Ref no 5-04-604

Feed name or analyses		As fed	Dry
Dry matter	%	89.0	100.0
Ash	%	5.8	6.5
Crude fiber	%	6.0	6.7
Ether extract	%	.9	1.0
N-free extract	%	30.5	34.3
Protein (N x 6.25)	%	45.8	51.5
Swine	dig prot %	41.7	46.9
Energy	GE kcal/kg	4198.	4719.
Swine	DE kcal/kg	3300.	3708.
Swine	ME kcal/kg	2825.	3174.
Swine	TDN %	75.	84.
Calcium	%	.32	.36
Iron	%	.012	.013
Magnesium	%	.27	.30
Phosphorus	%	.67	.75
Potassium	%	1.97	2.21
Sodium	%	.34	.38
Cobalt	mg/kg	.100	.100
Copper	mg/kg	36.3	40.8
Manganese	mg/kg	27.5	30.9
Choline	mg/kg	2743.	3083.
Folic acid	mg/kg	.70	.80
Niacin	mg/kg	26.8	30.1
Pantothenic acid	mg/kg	14.5	16.3
Riboflavin	mg/kg	3.3	3.7
Thiamine	mg/kg	6.6	7.4
Arginine	%	3.20	3.60
Histidine	%	1.10	1.24
Isoleucine	%	2.50	2.81
Leucine	%	3.40	3.82
Lysine	%	2.90	3.26
Methionine	%	.60	.67
Phenylalanine	%	2.20	2.47
Threonine	%	1.70	1.91
Tryptophan	%	.60	.67
Tyrosine	%	1.40	1.57
Valine	%	2.40	2.70

Continued

Feed name or analyses		Mean	
		As fed	Dry

Soybean, seed wo hulls, solv-extd grnd, mx 3 fbr, (5)
Soybean meal, dehulled, solvent extracted (AAFCO)
Soybean oil meal, dehulled, solvent extracted

Ref no 5-04-612

		As fed	Dry
Dry matter	%	89.8	100.0
Ash	%	5.6	6.2
Crude fiber	%	2.8	3.1
Ether extract	%	.8	.9
N-free extract	%	29.7	33.1
Protein (N x 6.25)	%	50.9	56.7
Swine	dig prot %	46.3	51.6
Energy			
Swine	DE kcal/kg	3405.	3792.
Swine	ME kcal/kg	2881.	3208.
Swine	TDN %	77.	86.
Calcium	%	.26	.29
Phosphorus	%	.62	.69
Potassium	%	2.02	2.24
Manganese	mg/kg	45.5	50.6
Choline	mg/kg	2761.	3068.
Niacin	mg/kg	21.6	24.0
			Continued

Feed name or analyses		Mean	
		As fed	Dry
Riboflavin	mg/kg	3.1	3.4
Thiamine	mg/kg	2.4	2.7

SUGARCANE. Saccharum officinarum

Sugarcane, molasses, dehy, (4)
Cane molasses, dried
Molasses, cane, dried

Ref no 4-04-695

		As fed	Dry
Dry matter	%	96.0	100.0
Ash	%	8.0	8.3
Crude fiber	%	5.0	5.2
Ether extract	%	1.0	1.0
N-free extract	%	71.7	74.8
Protein (N x 6.25)	%	10.3	10.7
Swine	dig prot %	7.3	7.6
Energy	GE kcal/kg	3087.	3212.
Swine	DE kcal/kg	2878.	2998.
Swine	ME kcal/kg	2700.	2812.
Swine	TDN %	65.	68.

Feed name or analyses		Mean	
		As fed	Dry

Sugarcane, molasses, mn 48 invert sugar mn 79.5 degrees brix, (4)
Cane molasses (AAFCO)
Molasses, cane

Ref no 4-04-696

		As fed	Dry
Dry matter	%	75.0	100.0
Ash	%	8.1	10.8
Ether extract	%	.1	.1
N-free extract	%	63.6	84.8
Protein (N x 6.25)	%	3.2	4.3
Energy	GE kcal/kg	3086.	4114.
Swine	DE kcal/kg	2464.	3285.
Swine	ME kcal/kg	2343.	3124.
Swine	TDN %	56.	75.
Calcium	%	.89	1.19
Iron	%	.019	.025
Magnesium	%	.35	.47
Phosphorus	%	.08	.11
Potassium	%	2.38	3.17
Copper	mg/kg	59.6	79.4
Manganese	mg/kg	42.2	56.3
Choline	mg/kg	876.	1167.
Niacin	mg/kg	34.3	45.7
Pantothenic acid	mg/kg	38.3	51.1
			Continued

(1) dry forages and roughages
(2) pasture, range plants, and forages fed green
(3) silages
(4) energy feeds
(5) protein supplements
(6) minerals
(7) vitamins
(8) additives

TABLE I-1—COMPOSITION OF SOME COMMON SWINE FEEDS (Continued)

Feed name or analyses		As fed	Dry
Riboflavin	mg/kg	3.3	4.4
Thiamine	mg/kg	.9	1.2

SUNFLOWER. Helianthus spp

Sunflower, seed wo hulls, mech-extd grnd, (5)
Sunflower meal (AAFCO)
Sunflower oil meal, without hulls, expeller extracted

Ref no 5-04-738

		As fed	Dry
Dry matter	%	93.0	100.0
Ash	%	6.8	7.3
Crude fiber	%	13.0	14.0
Ether extract	%	7.6	8.2
N-free extract	%	24.6	26.4
Protein (N x 6.25)	%	41.0	44.1
Swine	dig prot %	33.7	36.2
Energy			
Swine	DE kcal/kg	3116.	3351.
Swine	ME kcal/kg	2715.	2919.
Swine	TDN %	71.	76.
Calcium	%	.43	.46
Phosphorus	%	1.04	1.12
Potassium	%	1.08	1.16
Manganese	mg/kg	22.9	24.6
			Continued

Feed name or analyses		As fed	Dry
Lysine	%	2.00	2.15
Methionine	%	1.60	1.72

Sunflower, seed wo hulls, solv-extd grnd, (5)
Sunflower meal (AAFCO)
Sunflower oil meal, without hulls, solvent extracted

Ref no 5-04-739

		As fed	Dry
Dry matter	%	93.0	100.0
Ash	%	7.7	8.3
Crude fiber	%	11.0	11.8
Ether extract	%	2.9	3.1
N-free extract	%	24.6	26.5
Protein (N x 6.25)	%	46.8	50.3
Swine	dig prot %	42.1	45.3
Energy			
Swine	DE kcal/kg	3034.	3263.
Swine	ME kcal/kg	2604.	2800.
Swine	TDN %	69.	74.
Riboflavin	mg/kg	3.1	3.3

Feed name or analyses		As fed	Dry

SWINE. Sus scrofa

Swine, lard, (4)
Ref no 4-04-790

		As fed	Dry
Dry matter	%	100.0	100.0
Ether extract	%	100.0	100.0
Protein (N x 6.25)	%	.0	.0
Energy	GE kcal/kg	9020.	9020.

Tankage - see Animal, carcass res w blood

WHEAT. Triticum spp

Wheat, bran, dry-mil, (4)
Wheat bran (AAFCO)
Bran (CFA)

Ref no 4-05-190

		As fed	Dry
Dry matter	%	89.0	100.0
Ash	%	6.1	6.9
Crude fiber	%	10.0	11.2
			Continued

Feed name or analyses		As fed	Dry
			Mean
Ether extract	%	4.1	4.6
N-free extract	%	52.8	59.3
Protein (N x 6.25)	%	16.0	18.0
Swine	dig prot %	12.2	13.7
Energy	GE kcal/kg	4052.	4554.
Swine	DE kcal/kg	2512.	2822.
Swine	ME kcal/kg	2321.	2608.
Swine	TDN %	57.	64.
Calcium	%	.14	.16
Iron	%	.017	.019
Magnesium	%	.55	.62
Phosphorus	%	1.17	1.32
Potassium	%	1.24	1.39
Sodium	%	.06	.07
Cobalt	mg/kg	1.000	1.100
Copper	mg/kg	12.3	13.8
Manganese	mg/kg	115.7	130.0
Choline	mg/kg	988.	1110.
Folic acid	mg/kg	1.80	2.00
Niacin	mg/kg	209.2	235.1
Pantothenic acid	mg/kg	29.0	32.6
Riboflavin	mg/kg	3.1	3.5
Thiamine	mg/kg	7.9	8.9
a-tocopherol	mg/kg	10.8	12.1
Arginine	%	1.00	1.12
Cystine	%	.30	.34
Glycine	%	.90	1.01

Continued

Feed name or analyses		As fed	Dry
			Mean
Histidine	%	.30	.34
Isoleucine	%	.60	.67
Leucine	%	.90	1.01
Lysine	%	.60	.67
Methionine	%	.10	.11
Phenylalanine	%	.50	.56
Threonine	%	.40	.45
Tryptophan	%	.30	.34
Tyrosine	%	.40	.45
Valine	%	.70	.79

Wheat endosperm - see Wheat, grits

Wheat, flour, c-bolt, feed gr mx 2 fbr, (4)
Wheat feed flour, mx 1.5 fbr (AAFCO)
Feed flour, mx 2.0 fbr (CFA)

Ref no 4-05-199

		As fed	Dry
Dry matter	%	89.0	100.0
Ash	%	2.1	2.4
Crude fiber	%	3.0	3.4
Ether extract	%	2.9	3.3
N-free extract	%	65.0	73.1

Continued

Feed name or analyses		As fed	Dry
			Mean
Protein (N x 6.25)	%	15.8	17.8
Swine	dig prot %	14.6	16.4
Energy			
Swine	DE kcal/kg	3610.	4056.
Swine	ME kcal/kg	3336.	3748.
Swine	TDN %	82.	92.
Calcium	%	.03	.03
Iron	%	.002	.002
Phosphorus	%	.28	.31
Copper	mg/kg	4.6	5.2
Manganese	mg/kg	44.9	50.5
Niacin	mg/kg	41.8	47.0
Pantothenic acid	mg/kg	.9	1.0
Thiamine	mg/kg	5.9	6.6
Arginine	%	.40	.45
Histidine	%	.30	.34
Isoleucine	%	.60	.67
Leucine	%	.90	1.01
Lysine	%	.30	.34
Methionine	%	.11	.12
Phenylalanine	%	.60	.67
Threonine	%	.30	.34
Tryptophan	%	.11	.12
Tyrosine	%	.20	.22
Valine	%	.50	.56

(1) dry forages and roughages
(2) pasture, range plants, and forages fed green
(3) silages
(4) energy feeds
(5) protein supplements
(6) minerals
(7) vitamins
(8) additives

TABLE I-1—COMPOSITION OF SOME COMMON SWINE FEEDS (Continued)

Feed name or analyses		Mean	
		As fed	Dry

Wheat, flour by-prod, c-sift, mx 7 fbr, (4)
Wheat shorts, mx 7 fbr (AAFCO)
Shorts, mx 8 fbr (CFA)

Ref no 4-05-201

		As fed	Dry
Dry matter	%	90.0	100.0
Ash	%	3.9	4.3
Crude fiber	%	5.0	5.6
Ether extract	%	4.2	4.7
N-free extract	%	58.5	65.0
Protein (N x 6.25)	%	18.4	20.4
Swine	dig prot %	15.4	17.1
Energy			
Swine	DE kcal/kg	3168.	3520.
Swine	ME kcal/kg	2912.	3235.
Swine	TDN %	72.	80.
Calcium	%	.11	.12
Iron	%	.010	.011
Magnesium	%	.26	.29
Phosphorus	%	.76	.84
Potassium	%	.85	.94
Sodium	%	.07	.08
Cobalt	mg/kg	.100	.100
Copper	mg/kg	9.2	10.3
Manganese	mg/kg	104.5	116.1
Choline	mg/kg	928.	1093.
Niacin	mg/kg	94.6	105.1

Continued

Feed name or analyses		Mean	
		As fed	Dry
Pantothenic acid	mg/kg	17.6	19.6
Riboflavin	mg/kg	2.0	2.2
Thiamine	mg/kg	15.8	17.6
a-tocopherol	mg/kg	29.9	33.2

Wheat, flour by-prod, f-sift, mx 4 fbr, (4)
Wheat red dog, mx 4.0 fbr (AAFCO)
Middlings, mx 4.5 fbr (CFA)

Ref no 4-05-203

		As fed	Dry
Dry matter	%	89.0	100.0
Ash	%	2.5	2.8
Crude fiber	%	2.0	2.2
Ether extract	%	3.6	4.0
N-free extract	%	63.0	70.8
Protein (N x 6.25)	%	18.0	20.2
Swine	dig prot %	16.0	18.0
Energy			
Swine	DE kcal/kg	3212.	3609.
Swine	ME kcal/kg	2952.	3317.
Swine	TDN %	73.	82.
Calcium	%	.08	.09
Iron	%	.006	.007
Magnesium	%	.29	.33
Phosphorus	%	.52	.58
Potassium	%	.60	.67
Sodium	%	.66	.74

Continued

Feed name or analyses		Mean	
		As fed	Dry
Copper	mg/kg	4.4	4.9
Manganese	mg/kg	37.6	42.3
Niacin	mg/kg	52.6	59.1
Pantothenic acid	mg/kg	13.6	15.3
Riboflavin	mg/kg	1.5	1.7
Thiamine	mg/kg	18.9	21.2
a-tocopherol	mg/kg	57.6	64.7
Arginine	%	1.00	1.12
Histidine	%	.40	.45
Isoleucine	%	.70	.79
Leucine	%	1.20	1.35
Lysine	%	.60	.67
Methionine	%	.10	.11
Phenylalanine	%	.50	.56
Threonine	%	.50	.56
Tryptophan	%	.20	.22
Tyrosine	%	.50	.56
Valine	%	.80	.90

Wheat, flour by-prod, mil-rn, mx 9.5 fbr, (4)
.... eat r: run (AAFCO)

Ref no 4-05-206

		As fed	Dry
Dry matter	%	90.0	100.0
Ash	%	5.2	5.8
Crude fiber	%	8.0	8.9
Ether extract	%	4.0	4.4

Continued

Feed name or analyses		Mean	
		As fed	Dry
N-free extract	%	57.5	63.9
Protein (N x 6.25)	%	15.3	17.0
Swine	dig prot %	12.2	13.6
Energy	GE kcal/kg	3951.	4390.
Swine	DE kcal/kg	3168.	3520.
Swine	ME kcal/kg	2934.	3260.
Swine	TDN %	72.	80.
Calcium	%	.09	.10
Iron	%	.009	.010
Magnesium	%	.51	.57
Phosphorus	%	1.02	1.13
Potassium	%	1.28	1.42
Sodium	%	.22	.24
Cobalt	mg/kg	.200	.200
Copper	mg/kg	18.7	20.8
Manganese	mg/kg	102.7	114.1
Choline	mg/kg	981.	1090.
Niacin	mg/kg	112.0	124.4
Pantothenic acid	mg/kg	13.2	14.7
Riboflavin	mg/kg	2.4	2.7
Thiamine	mg/kg	15.2	16.9

Feed name or analyses		Mean	
		As fed	Dry

Wheat, grain, thresher-run, mn 55 mx 60 wt mx 5 fm, (4)

Ref no 4-08-165 Canada

		As fed	Dry
Dry matter	%	88.0	100.0
Ash	%	1.6	1.8
Crude fiber	%	2.6	2.9
Ether extract	%	1.2	1.4
N-free extract	%	66.7	75.8
Protein (N x 6.25)	%	15.8	18.0
Swine	dig prot %	14.6	16.6
Energy	GE kcal/kg	4224.	4800.
Swine	DE kcal/kg	3530.	4012.
Swine	ME kcal/kg	3262.	3707.
Swine	TDN %	80.	91.

Wheat, grain, thresher-run, mn 60 wt mx 5 fm, (4)

Ref no 4-08-164 Canada

		As fed	Dry
Dry matter	%	88.0	100.0
Ash	%	1.8	2.0
Crude fiber	%	2.2	2.5
Ether extract	%	1.4	1.6

Continued

Feed name or analyses		Mean	
		As fed	Dry
N-free extract	%	69.1	78.5
Protein (N x 6.25)	%	13.6	15.4
Swine	dig prot %	12.5	14.2
Energy	GE kcal/kg	4174.	4743.
Swine	DE kcal/kg	3569.	4056.
Swine	ME kcal/kg	3316.	3768.
Swine	TDN %	81.	92.

Wheat, grain, Pacific coast, (4)

Ref no 4-08-142

		As fed	Dry
Dry matter	%	89.2	100.0
Ash	%	1.9	2.1
Crude fiber	%	2.7	3.0
Ether extract	%	2.0	2.2
N-free extract	%	72.8	81.6
Protein (N x 6.25)	%	9.9	11.1
Swine	dig prot %	9.1	10.2
Energy			
Swine	DE kcal/kg	3618.	4056.
Swine	ME kcal/kg	3388.	3798.
Swine	TDN %	82.	92.
Calcium	%	.12	.14
Phosphorus	%	.30	.34
Niacin	mg/kg	59.1	66.3

Continued

(1) dry forages and roughages
(2) pasture, range plants, and forages fed green

(3) silages
(4) energy feeds
(5) protein supplements

(6) minerals
(7) vitamins
(8) additives

TABLE 1-1—COMPOSITION OF SOME COMMON SWINE FEEDS (Continued)

Feed name or analyses		As fed (Mean)	Dry (Mean)
Pantothenic acid	mg/kg	11.5	12.9
Riboflavin	mg/kg	1.1	1.2
Thiamine	mg/kg	4.9	5.5
Wheat, grain, (4)			
Ref no 4-05-211			
Dry matter	%	89.0	100.0
Ash	%	1.6	1.8
Crude fiber	%	3.0	3.4
Ether extract	%	1.7	1.9
N-free extract	%	70.0	78.6
Protein (N x 6.25)	%	12.7	14.3
Swine	dig prot %	11.7	13.2
Energy Swine	GE kcal/kg	4001.	4495.
Swine	DE kcal/kg	3520.	3955.
Swine	ME kcal/kg	3277.	3682.
Swine	TDN %	80.	90.
Calcium	%	.05	.06
Iron	%	.005	.006
Magnesium	%	.16	.18
Phosphorus	%	.36	.41
Potassium	%	.52	.58
Sodium	%	.09	.10
Cobalt	mg/kg	.080	.090
Copper	mg/kg	7.2	8.1
Manganese	mg/kg	48.8	54.8

Continued

Feed name or analyses		As fed (Mean)	Dry (Mean)
Zinc	mg/kg	13.7	15.4
Biotin	mg/kg	.10	.10
Choline	mg/kg	830.	933.
Folic acid	mg/kg	.40	.40
Niacin	mg/kg	56.6	63.6
Pantothenic acid	mg/kg	12.1	13.6
Riboflavin	mg/kg	1.2	1.3
Thiamine	mg/kg	4.9	5.5
a-tocopherol	mg/kg	15.5	17.4
Arginine	%	.71	.80
Cystine	%	.18	.20
Glycine	%	.89	1.00
Histidine	%	.27	.30
Isoleucine	%	.53	.60
Leucine	%	.89	1.00
Lysine	%	.45	.51
Methionine	%	.18	.20
Phenylalanine	%	.62	.70
Threonine	%	.36	.40
Tryptophan	%	.18	.20
Tyrosine	%	.45	.51
Valine	%	.53	.60

Wheat grain - see also Wheat, durum; Wheat, hard red spring; Wheat, hard red winter; Wheat, red spring; Wheat, soft; and Wheat, soft red winter

Feed name or analyses		As fed (Mean)	Dry (Mean)
Wheat, grain screenings, (4)			
Ref no 4-05-216			
Dry matter	%	89.0	100.0
Ash	%	3.2	3.6
Crude fiber	%	7.0	7.9
Ether extract	%	3.0	3.4
N-free extract	%	60.7	68.2
Protein (N x 6.25)	%	15.0	16.9
Swine	dig prot %	12.0	13.5
Cellulose	%	5.0	5.6
Lignin	%	7.0	7.9
Energy Swine	DE kcal/kg	2772.	3114.
Swine	ME kcal/kg	2567.	2884.
Swine	TDN %	63.	71.
Calcium	%	.08	.09
Phosphorus	%	.36	.40
Manganese	mg/kg	28.6	32.1

Wheat, grain screenings - see also Grains, screenings

Feed name or analyses		As fed	Dry
			Mean

Wheat, grits, cracked f-scr, (4)
Farina
Wheat endosperm

Ref no 4-07-852

Feed name or analyses		As fed	Dry
Dry matter	%	88.0	100.0
Ash	%	1.2	1.4
Crude fiber	%	.3	.3
Ether extract	%	1.1	1.2
N-free extract	%	74.4	84.5
Protein (N x 6.25)	%	11.1	12.6
Swine	dig prot %	9.8	11.2
Energy			
Swine	DE kcal/kg	3414.	3880.
Swine	ME kcal/kg	3193.	3628.
Swine	TDN %	77.	88.
Arginine	%	.60	.68
Cystine	%	.30	.34
Histidine	%	.30	.34
Isoleucine	%	1.10	1.25
Leucine	%	1.70	1.93
Lysine	%	.40	.45
Methionine	%	.20	.23
Phenylalanine	%	.60	.68
Threonine	%	.40	.45

Continued

Feed name or analyses		As fed	Dry
			Mean
Tryptophan	%	.30	.34
Valine	%	.60	.68

Wheat, germ, grnd, mn 25 prot 7 fat, (5)
Wheat germ meal (AAFCO)
Ref no 5-05-218

Feed name or analyses		As fed	Dry
Dry matter	%	90.0	100.0
Ash	%	4.3	4.8
Crude fiber	%	3.0	3.3
Ether extract	%	10.9	12.1
N-free extract	%	45.6	50.7
Protein (N x 6.25)	%	26.2	29.1
Swine	dig prot %	23.6	26.2
Energy			
Swine	GE kcal/kg	4206.	4673.
Swine	DE kcal/kg	3770.	4189.
Swine	ME kcal/kg	3397.	3774.
Swine	TDN %	86.	95.
Calcium	%	.07	.08
Iron	%	.011	.012
Phosphorus	%	1.04	1.16
Copper	mg/kg	8.8	9.8
Manganese	mg/kg	134.9	149.9
Choline	mg/kg	3010.	3344.
Folic acid	mg/kg	2.00	2.20
Niacin	mg/kg	47.3	52.6

Continued

Feed name or analyses		As fed	Dry
			Mean
Pantothenic acid	mg/kg	11.2	12.4
Riboflavin	mg/kg	5.1	5.7
Thiamine	mg/kg	27.9	31.0
α-tocopherol	mg/kg	132.7	147.4
Arginine	%	1.60	1.78
Cystine	%	.50	.56
Histidine	%	.50	.56
Isoleucine	%	1.20	1.33
Leucine	%	1.10	1.22
Lysine	%	1.60	1.78
Methionine	%	.30	.33
Phenylalanine	%	.80	.89
Threonine	%	.80	.89
Tryptophan	%	.30	.33
Valine	%	1.10	1.22

WHEAT, DURUM. Triticum durum

Wheat, durum, grain, Can 4 CW mn 56 wt mx 2.5 fm, (4)

Ref no 4-05-225

		As fed	Dry
Dry matter	%	86.5	100.0
Ash	%	1.6	1.8

Continued

---

(1) dry forages and roughages
(2) pasture, range plants, and forages fed green
(3) silages
(4) energy feeds
(5) protein supplements
(6) minerals
(7) vitamins
(8) additives

TABLE I-1—COMPOSITION OF SOME COMMON SWINE FEEDS (Continued)

Feed name or analyses		Mean As fed	Mean Dry
Crude fiber	%	2.3	2.6
Ether extract	%	1.7	1.9
N-free extract	%	67.5	78.0
Protein (N x 6.25)	%	13.6	15.7
Swine dig prot	%	12.4	14.4
Energy Swine	GE kcal/kg	4804.	5553.
Swine	DE kcal/kg	3508.	4056.
Swine	ME kcal/kg	3256.	3764.
Swine	TDN %	79.	92.

Wheat, durum, grain, (4)

Ref no 4-05-224

Feed name or analyses		Mean As fed	Mean Dry
Dry matter	%	89.5	100.0
Ash	%	1.8	2.0
Crude fiber	%	2.2	2.5
Ether extract	%	2.0	2.2
N-free extract	%	70.1	78.3
Protein (N x 6.25)	%	13.4	15.0
Swine dig prot	%	12.4	13.8
Energy Swine	DE kcal/kg	3630.	4056.
Swine	ME kcal/kg	3376.	3772.
Swine	TDN %	82.	92.
Calcium	%	.15	.17
Iron	%	.004	.005
Phosphorus	%	.40	.45

Continued

Feed name or analyses		Mean As fed	Mean Dry
Copper	mg/kg	7.7	8.6
Manganese	mg/kg	28.7	31.9
Folic acid	mg/kg	.39	.44
Thiamine	mg/kg	6.3	7.0

WHEAT, HARD RED SPRING. Triticum aestivum

Wheat, hard red spring, grain, (4)

Ref no 4-05-258

Feed name or analyses		Mean As fed	Mean Dry
Dry matter	%	86.5	100.0
Ash	%	1.7	2.0
Crude fiber	%	3.0	3.4
Ether extract	%	1.9	2.2
N-free extract	%	66.0	76.3
Protein (N x 6.25)	%	13.9	16.1
Swine dig prot	%	12.8	14.8
Energy Swine	DE kcal/kg	3470.	4012.
Swine	ME kcal/kg	3220.	3723.
Swine	TDN %	79.	91.
Calcium	%	.05	.06
Iron	%	.005	.006
Phosphorus	%	.41	.47
Copper	mg/kg	10.6	12.3
Manganese	mg/kg	62.2	71.9

Continued

Feed name or analyses		Mean As fed	Mean Dry
Choline	mg/kg	778.	899.
Folic acid	mg/kg	.42	.48
Niacin	mg/kg	57.8	66.8
Pantothenic acid	mg/kg	13.5	15.6
Riboflavin	mg/kg	1.1	1.3
Thiamine	mg/kg	5.2	6.0
Arginine	%	.60	.70
Cystine	%	.17	.20
Histidine	%	.17	.20
Isoleucine	%	.69	.80
Leucine	%	.95	1.10
Lysine	%	.35	.40
Methionine	%	.17	.20
Phenylalanine	%	.78	.90
Threonine	%	.35	.40
Tryptophan	%	.17	.20
Tyrosine	%	.78	.90
Valine	%	.69	.80

WHEAT, HARD RED WINTER. Triticum aestivum

Wheat, hard red winter, grain, (4)

Ref no 4-05-268

Feed name or analyses		Mean As fed	Mean Dry
Dry matter	%	89.1	100.0
Ash	%	1.8	2.0

Continued

Feed name or analyses		As fed	Dry
			Mean
Crude fiber	%	2.7	3.0
Ether extract	%	1.6	1.8
N-free extract	%	70.0	78.6
Protein (N x 6.25)	%	13.0	14.6
Swine	dig prot %	11.9	13.4
Energy			
Swine	GE kcal/kg	3552.	3991.
Swine	DE kcal/kg	3575.	4012.
Swine	ME kcal/kg	3324.	3731.
Swine	TDN %	81.	91.
Calcium	%	.05	.06
Magnesium	%	.10	.11
Phosphorus	%	.40	.45
Potassium	%	.51	.57
Cobalt	mg/kg	.100	.100
Copper	mg/kg	4.5	5.1
Manganese	mg/kg	38.8	43.6
Choline	mg/kg	734.	825.
Folic acid	mg/kg	.40	.40
Niacin	mg/kg	50.9	57.2
Pantothenic acid	mg/kg	12.5	14.1
Riboflavin	mg/kg	1.0	1.1
Thiamine	mg/kg	6.2	7.0
Vitamin B6	mg/kg	4.10	4.60

Wheat red dog - see Wheat, flour by-prod, f-sift, mx 4 fbr

(1) dry forages and roughages
(2) pasture, range plants, and forages fed green

WHEAT, RED SPRING. Triticum aestivum

Wheat, red spring, grain, Can 4 No mn 56 wt mx 2.5 fm, (4)

Ref no 4-05-282

Feed name or analyses		As fed	Dry
			Mean
Dry matter	%	86.5	100.0
Ash	%	1.5	1.7
Crude fiber	%	2.4	2.8
Ether extract	%	1.7	2.0
N-free extract	%	66.8	77.2
Protein (N x 6.25)	%	14.1	16.3
Swine	dig prot %	13.0	15.0
Energy	GE kcal/kg	4804.	5553.
Swine	DE kcal/kg	3508.	4056.
Swine	ME kcal/kg	3252.	3760.
Swine	TDN %	80.	92.

(3) silages
(4) energy feeds
(5) protein supplements

WHEAT, SOFT. Triticum aestivum

Wheat, soft, grain, (4)

Ref no 4-05-284

Feed name or analyses		As fed	Dry
			Mean
Dry matter	%	90.0	100.0
Ash	%	1.8	2.0
Crude fiber	%	2.3	2.6
Ether extract	%	1.7	1.9
N-free extract	%	73.4	81.5
Protein (N x 6.25)	%	10.8	12.0
Swine	dig prot %	9.9	11.0
Energy			
Swine	DE kcal/kg	3650.	4056.
Swine	ME kcal/kg	3416.	3796.
Swine	TDN %	83.	92.
Calcium	%	.09	.10
Iron	%	.005	.006
Magnesium	%	.10	.11
Phosphorus	%	.30	.33
Potassium	%	.40	.44
Copper	mg/kg	9.7	10.8
Manganese	mg/kg	51.3	57.0
Choline	mg/kg	788.	876.

Continued

(6) minerals
(7) vitamins
(8) additives

TABLE I-1—COMPOSITION OF SOME COMMON SWINE FEEDS (Continued)

Feed name or analyses		Mean	
		As fed	Dry
Niacin	mg/kg	59.2	65.8
Pantothenic acid	mg/kg	12.8	11.5
Riboflavin	mg/kg	1.2	1.3
Thiamine	mg/kg	4.8	5.3
Vitamin B6	mg/kg	4.80	5.30

WHEAT, SOFT RED WINTER. Triticum aestivum

Wheat, soft red winter, grain, (4)

Ref no 4-05-294

		As fed	Dry
Dry matter	%	89.1	100.0
Ash	%	1.8	2.0
Crude fiber	%	2.2	2.5
Ether extract	%	1.6	1.8
N-free extract	%	72.5	81.4
Protein (N x 6.25)	%	11.0	12.3
Swine	dig prot %	10.1	11.3
Energy Swine	GE kcal/kg	3516	3951
Swine	DE kcal/kg	3614	4056
Swine	ME kcal/kg	3379	3792
Swine	TDN %	82.	92.
Calcium	%	.09	.10
Magnesium	%	.10	.11
Phosphorus	%	.29	.33
Potassium	%	.39	.44

Continued

Feed name or analyses		Mean	
		As fed	Dry
Copper	mg/kg	9.8	11.0
Manganese	mg/kg	38.2	42.9
Choline	mg/kg	779.	875.
Folic acid	mg/kg	.40	.40
Niacin	mg/kg	57.4	64.5
Pantothenic acid	mg/kg	11.4	12.8
Thiamine	mg/kg	5.3	5.9
Vitamin B6	mg/kg	4.60	5.30
Arginine	%	.36	.40
Cystine	%	.18	.20
Histidine	%	.09	.10
Lysine	%	.80	.90
Tryptophan	%	.27	.30
Tyrosine	%	.36	.40

Whey - see Cattle, whey

White hominy feed - see Corn, white, grits by-prod

White rice - see Rice, groats, polished

Feed name or analyses		Mean	
		As fed	Dry

YEAST. Saccharomyces cerevisiae

Yeast, brewers saccharomyces, dehy grnd, mn 40 prot, (7)

Brewers dried yeast (AAFCO)

Ref no 7-05-527

		As fed	Dry
Dry matter	%	93.0	100.0
Ash	%	6.4	6.9
Crude fiber	%	3.0	3.2
Ether extract	%	1.1	1.2
N-free extract	%	37.9	40.8
Protein (N x 6.25)	%	44.6	47.9
Swine	dig prot %	39.2	42.2
Energy Swine	GE kcal/kg	3958.	4255.
Swine	DE kcal/kg	3076.	3307.
Swine	ME kcal/kg	2654.	2854.
Swine	TDN %	70.	75.
Calcium	%	.13	.14
Iron	%	.010	.010
Magnesium	%	.23	.25
Phosphorus	%	1.43	1.54
Potassium	%	1.72	1.85
Sodium	%	.07	.08
Cobalt	mg/kg	.200	.200
Copper	mg/kg	33.0	35.5

Continued

Feed name or analyses		As fed	Mean Dry
Manganese	mg/kg	5.7	6.1
Zinc	mg/kg	38.7	41.6
Choline	mg/kg	3885.	4177.
Folic acid	mg/kg	9.70	10.40
Niacin	mg/kg	447.5	481.1
Pantothenic acid	mg/kg	109.8	118.0
Riboflavin	mg/kg	35.0	37.6
Thiamine	mg/kg	91.7	98.6
Vitamin B_6	mg/kg	43.30	46.60
Arginine	%	2.20	2.36
Cystine	%	.50	.54
Glycine	%	1.70	1.83
Histidine	%	1.10	1.18
Isoleucine	%	2.10	2.26
Leucine	%	3.20	3.44
Lysine	%	3.00	3.22
Methionine	%	.70	.75
Phenylalanine	%	1.80	1.93
Threonine	%	2.10	2.26
Tryptophan	%	.50	.54
Tyrosine	%	1.50	1.61
Valine	%	2.30	2.47

Feed name or analyses		As fed	Mean Dry
Yeast, primary saccharomyces, dehy, mn 40 prot,			
(7)			
Dried yeast (AAFCO)			
Primary dried yeast (AAFCO)			
Ref no 7-05-533			
Dry matter	%	93.0	100.0
Ash	%	8.0	8.6
Crude fiber	%	3.0	3.2
Ether extract	%	1.0	1.1
N-free extract	%	33.0	35.5
Protein (N x 6.25)	%	48.0	51.6
Swine	dig prot %	42.2	45.4
Energy	GE kcal/kg	4426.	4758.
Swine	DE kcal/kg	2860.	3075.
Swine	ME kcal/kg	2448.	2632.
Swine	TDN %	65.	70.
Calcium	%	.36	.39
Iron	%	.028	.030
Magnesium	%	.36	.39
Phosphorus	%	1.72	1.85
Manganese	mg/kg	3.7	4.0
Biotin	mg/kg	1.60	1.70
Folic acid	mg/kg	31.00	33.30
Niacin	mg/kg	300.1	322.6

Continued

Feed name or analyses		As fed	Mean Dry
Pantothenic acid	mg/kg	311.3	334.6
Riboflavin	mg/kg	38.7	41.6
Thiamine	mg/kg	6.4	6.9
Arginine	%	2.60	2.80
Cystine	%	.50	.54
Histidine	%	5.60	6.02
Isoleucine	%	3.60	3.87
Leucine	%	3.72	4.00
Lysine	%	3.80	4.08
Methionine	%	1.00	1.08
Phenylalanine	%	2.50	2.69
Threonine	%	2.50	2.69
Tryptophan	%	.40	.43
Valine	%	3.20	3.44

(1) dry forages and roughages
(2) pasture, range plants, and forages fed green
(3) silages
(4) energy feeds
(5) protein supplements
(6) minerals
(7) vitamins
(8) additives

SECTION II.—ANIMAL UNITS

An animal unit is a common animal denominator, based on feed consumption. It is assumed that one mature cow or one mature horse represents an animal unit. The comparative (to a mature cow or a mature horse) feed consumption of other age groups or classes of animals determines the proportion of an animal unit which they represent. For example, it is generally estimated that the ration of one mature cow or one mature horse will feed five hogs raised to 200 pounds. For this reason, the "animal units/head" on this class and age of animals is 0.2. The following table gives the animal units for different classes and ages of livestock:

TABLE II-1

ANIMAL UNITS

Type of Livestock	Animal Units per Head
Horse	1
Cow	1
Bull	1
Young cattle over 1 year old	0.5
Calf	0.25
Colt	0.5
Brood sow or boar	0.4
Hog raised to 200 pounds	0.2
Ewe or ram	0.14
Lamb	0.07
Poultry (per 100)	1
Chickens raised (per 200)	1

SECTION III.—WEIGHTS AND MEASURES

METRIC AND AVOIRDUPOIS SYSTEMS[1]

From time to time, stockmen and those who counsel with stockmen have need to refer to such weights and measures as follows:

---

[1] For additional conversion factors, or for greater accuracy, see *Misc. Publ. 233*, The National Bureau of Standards.

Length

Unit	Is Equal To	
Metric System 1 millimicron (mμ)	.000000001 meter	(U.S.) .00000003937 in.
1 micron (μ)	.000001 meter	.00003937 in.
1 millimeter (mm)	.001 meter	.03937 in.
1 centimeter (cm)	.01 meter	.3937 in.
1 decimeter (dm)	.1 meter	3.937 in.
1 meter (m)	1 meter	39.37 in.; 3.28083 ft.; 1.09361 yds.
1 hectometer (hm)	100 meters	328 ft., 1 in.; 19.8838 rods
1 kilometer (km)	1,000 meters	3,280 ft., 10 in.; 0.621372 mi.
U.S. System 1 inch (in.)		(metric) 2.54 centimeters
1 hand[1]	4 in.	
1 foot (ft.)	12 in.	30.48 cm; .304801 meter
1 yard (yd.)	3 feet	.914402 meter
1 fathom[2]	6.08 feet	1.828804 meters
1 rod (rd.), pole, or perch	16½ ft.; 5½ yd.	5.029210 meters
1 furlong	220 yd.; 40 rods	201.168 meters
1 mile	5,280 ft.; 1,760 yd.; 320 rods; 8 furlongs	1.60941 kilometers; 1,609.35 m
1 knot or nautical mile	6,080 ft.; 1.15 land miles	
1 league (land)	3 miles (land)	
1 league (nautical)	3 miles (nautical)	

[1]Used in measuring height of horses.
[2]Used in measuring depth at sea.

CONVERSIONS

To Change	To	Multiply By
inches	centimeters	2.54001
feet	meters	.30480
meters	inches	39.37
miles	kilometers	1.60935
kilometers	miles	.62137

Surface or Area

Unit	Is Equal To	
Metric System 1 sq. millimeter (mm²)	.000001 m²	(U.S.) .00155 sq. in.
1 sq. centimeter (cm²)	.001 m²	.155 sq. in.
1 sq. decimeter (dm²)	.01 m²	15.50 sq. in.
1 sq. meter (m²)	1 centare (ca)	1,550 sq. in.; 10.76 sq. ft.; 1.196 sq. yd.
1 are (a)	100 m²	119.6 sq. yds.
1 hectare (ha)	10,000 m²	2.47 acres
1 sq. kilometer (km²)	1,000,000 m²	247.1 acres; .386 sq. mi.
U.S. System 1 sq. inch (sq. in.)	1 inch x 1 inch	(metric) 6.452 cm²
1 sq. foot (sq. ft.)	144 sq. in.	.09290341 m²
1 sq. yard (sq. yd.)	1,296 sq. in.; 9 sq. ft.	.836307 m²
1 sq. rod (sq. rd.)	272.25 sq. ft.; 30.25 sq. yd.	25.29301 m²
1 rood	40 sq. rods	10.117 ares
1 acre (A)	43,560 sq. ft.; 4,840 sq. yd. 160 sq. rd.; 4 roods	4,046.87 m²; 0.405 hectare
1 sq. mile (sq. mi.)	640 acres	2.58998 sq. km.; 259 ha
1 township	36 sections; 6 miles square	

CONVERSIONS

To Change	To	Multiply By
square inches	square centimeters	6.452
square centimeters	square inches	.155
square yards	square meters	.836
square meters	square yards	1.196

Volume

Unit	Is Equal To		
Liquid and Dry:			
Metric System		(U.S.)	
		(liquid)	(dry)
1 milliliter (ml)	.001 liter	.271 dram (fl.)	.0610250 cu. in.
1 centiliter (cl)	.01 liter	.338 oz (fl.)	.610 cu. in.
1 deciliter (dl)	1 liter	3.38 ozs. (fl.)	
1 liter (l)	1,000 cc.	1.057 qts. (fl.)	.908102 qt.
1 hectoliter (hl)	100 liter	26.418 gals.	2.83782 bu.
1 kiloliter (kl)	1,000 liter	264.18 gals.	1,308 cu. yds.
U.S. System Liquid:		(ounces) (cu. in.)	(metric)
1 teaspoon (t.)	60 drops	1/6	
1 dessert spoon	2 t.		
1 tablespoon (T.)	3 t.	½	
1 gill (gi.)	½ c.	4 7.22	118.29 ml
1 cup (c.)	16 T.	8 14.44	236.58 ml
1 pint (pt.)	2 c.	16 28.88	.47 liter
1 quart (qt.)	2 pts.	32 57.75	.95 liter
1 gallon (gal.)	4 qts.	8.34 lbs. 231	3.79 liter
1 barrel	31½ gals.		
1 hogshead	2 barrels		
Dry: 1 pint (pt.)	½ qt.	33.6	.550599 liter
1 quart (qt.)	2 pts.	67.20	1.101198 liter
1 peck (pk.)	8 qts.	537.61	8.810958 liter
1 bushel (bu.)	4 pecks	2,150.42	35.2383 liter
Solid: **Metric System** 1 cu. millimeter (mm^3)	.001 cc		

(Continued)

Volume (Continued)

Unit	Is Equal To	
1 cu. centimeter (cc)	1,000 mm	.061
1 cu. decimeter (dm³)	1,000 cc	61.023
1 cu. meter (m³)	1,000 dm³	1.308 cu. yd.
U.S. System 1 cubic inch (cu. in.)		16.387 cc
1 board foot (bd. ft.)	144 cu. in.	2,359.8 cc
1 cubic foot (cu. ft.)	1,728 cu. in.	.028 m³
1 cubic yard (cu. yd.)	27 cu. ft.	.765 m³
1 cord	128 cu. ft.	3.625 m³

CONVERSIONS

To Change	To	Multiply by
ounces (fluid)	cubic cemtimeters	29.57
cu. centimeters	ounces (fluid)	.034
quarts	liters	.946
liters	quarts	1.057
cu. inches	cu. centimeters	16.387
cu. centimeters	cu. inches	.061
cu. yards	cu. meters	.765
cu. meters	cu. yards	1.308

Weight

Unit	Is Equal To	
Metric System 1 microgram (mcg)	.001 mg	(U.S.)
1 milligram (mg)	.001 gram	.015432356 grain
1 centigram (cg)	.01 gram	.15432356 grain
1 decigram (dg)	.1 gram	1.5432356 grains
1 gram (g)	1,000 mg	.03527396 oz.
1 dekagram (dkg)	10 grams	5.643833 drams
1 hectogram (hg)	100 grams	3.527396 oz.
1 kilogram (kg)	1,000 grams	35.274 oz.; 2.2046223 lb.
1 ton	1,000 kg	2,204.6 lb.; 1.102 tons (short); 0.984 ton (long)
U.S. System 1 grain (gr.)	.03657143 dram	(metric) 64.798918 mg; .064798918 g
1 dram	.063 oz.	1.771845 g
1 ounce (oz.)	16 drams	28.349527 g
1 pound (lb.)	16 oz.	453.5924 g; 0.4536 kg
1 hundredweight (cwt.)	100 lb.	45.36 kg
1 ton (tn.) (short)	2,000 lb.	907.18486 kg; 0.907 (metric) ton
1 ton (tn.) (long)	2,200 lb.	1,016.05 kg; 1.016 (metric) ton
1 part per million (ppm)	1 microgram/gram 1 mg/l 1 mg/kg	.4535924 mg/lb. .907 g/ton .0001% .013 oz./gal.
1 percent (%) (1 part in 100 parts)	10,000 ppm 10 g/l	1.28 oz./gal. 8 lbs./100 gal.

CONVERSIONS

To Change	To	Multiply by
grains	milligrams	64.799
ounces (dry)	grams	28.35
pounds	grams	454
pounds (dry)	kilograms	.45359
kilograms	pounds	2.20462
mg/lb.	ppm	2.20462
ppm	grams/ton	.90718
grams/ton	ppm	1.1
mg/lb.	grams/ton	2
grams/ton	mg/lb.	.5
grams/lb.	grams/ton	2,000
grams/ton	grams/lb.	.0005
grams/ton	lbs./ton	.0022
lbs./ton	grams/ton	453.65924
grams/ton	%	.00011
%	grams/ton	9,072

Weights and Measures per Unit

Unit	Is Equal To
Volume per unit area:	
1 liter/hectare	0.107 gal./acre
1 gal./acre	9.354 liters/hectare
Weight per unit area:	
1 kilogram/cm²	14.22 lb./sq. inch
1 kilogram/hectare	0.892 lb./acre
1 lb./sq. in.	0.0703 kilogram/cm²
1 lb./acre	1.121 kilograms/hectare
Area per unit weight:	
1 cm²/kg	0.0703 sq. in./lb.
1 sq. in/lb.	14.22 cm²/kg

Temperature

One Centigrade (C) degree is 1/100 the difference between the temperature of melting ice and that of water boiling at standard atmospheric pressure.

One Fahrenheit (F) degree is 1/180 of the difference between the temperature of melting ice and that of water boiling at standard atmospheric pressure.

To Change	To	Multiply by
Degrees Centigrade	Degrees Fahrenheit	9/5 and add 32
Degrees Fahrenheit	Degrees Centigrade	subtract 32, then multiply by 5/9

WEIGHTS AND MEASURES OF COMMON FEEDS

In calculating rations and mixing concentrates, it is usually necessary to use weights rather than measures. However, in practical feeding operations it is often more convenient for the farmer to measure the concentrates. Table III-1 will serve as a guide in feeding by measure.

TABLE III-1

WEIGHTS AND MEASURES OF COMMON FEEDS

Feed	Approximate Weight	
	(lbs. per quart)	(lbs. per bushel)
Alfalfa meal	.6	19
Barley	1.5	48
Beet pulp (dried)	.6	19
Brewers grain (dried)	.6	19
Buckwheat	1.6	50
Buckwheat bran	1.0	29
Corn, husked ear	—	70
Corn, cracked	1.6	50
Corn, shelled	1.8	56
Corn meal	1.6	50
Corn-and-cob meal	1.4	45
Cottonseed meal	1.5	48
Cowpeas	1.9	60
Distillers grain (dried)	.6	19
Fish meal	1.0	35
Gluten feed	1.3	42
Linseed meal (old process)	1.1	35
Linseed meal (new process)	.9	29
Meat scrap	1.3	42
Molasses feed	.8	26
Oats	1.0	32
Oats, ground	.7	22
Oat middlings	1.5	48
Peanut meal	1.0	32
Rice bran	.8	26
Rye	1.7	56
Soybeans	1.8	60
Tankage	1.6	51
Velvet beans, shelled	1.8	60
Wheat	1.9	60
Wheat bran	.5	16
Wheat middlings, standard	.8	26
Wheat screenings	1.0	32

SECTION IV.—GESTATION TABLE

The swine producer who has information relative to breeding dates can easily estimate parturition dates from Table IV-1.

TABLE IV-1

GESTATION TABLE

Date Bred	Sow 114 Days (date due)	Date Bred	Sow 114 Days (date due)
Jan. 1	April 25	July 5	Oct. 27
Jan. 6	April 30	July 10	Nov. 1
Jan. 11	May 5	July 15	Nov. 6
Jan. 16	May 10	July 20	Nov. 11
Jan. 21	May 15	July 25	Nov. 16
Jan. 26	May 20	July 30	Nov. 21
Jan. 31	May 25	Aug. 4	Nov. 26
Feb. 5	May 30	Aug. 9	Nov. 31
Feb. 10	June 4	Aug. 14	Dec. 6
Feb. 15	June 9	Aug. 19	Dec. 11
Feb. 20	June 14	Aug. 24	Dec. 16
Feb. 25	June 19	Aug. 29	Dec. 21
Mar. 2	June 24	Sept. 3	Dec. 26
Mar. 7	June 29	Sept. 8	Dec. 31
Mar. 12	July 4	Sept. 13	Jan. 5
Mar. 17	July 9	Sept. 18	Jan. 10
Mar. 22	July 14	Sept. 23	Jan. 15
Mar. 27	July 19	Sept. 28	Jan. 20
April 1	July 24	Oct. 3	Jan. 25
April 6	July 29	Oct. 8	Jan. 30
April 11	Aug. 3	Oct. 13	Feb. 4
April 16	Aug. 8	Oct. 18	Feb. 9
April 21	Aug. 13	Oct. 23	Feb. 14
April 26	Aug. 18	Oct. 28	Feb. 19
May 1	Aug. 23	Nov. 2	Feb. 24
May 6	Aug. 28	Nov. 7	Mar. 1
May 11	Sept. 2	Nov. 12	Mar. 6
May 16	Sept. 7	Nov. 17	Mar. 11
May 21	Sept. 12	Nov. 22	Mar. 16
May 26	Sept. 17	Nov. 27	Mar. 21
May 31	Sept. 22	Dec. 2	Mar. 26
June 5	Sept. 27	Dec. 7	Mar. 31
June 10	Oct. 2	Dec. 12	April 5
June 15	Oct. 7	Dec. 17	April 10
June 20	Oct. 12	Dec. 22	April 15
June 25	Oct. 17	Dec. 27	April 20
June 30	Oct. 22		

SECTION V.—ALL-TIME TOP SALES

Swine producers and students frequently like to refer to the great sales in history. Presented herewith are the record sales, both for individual animals and for consignment sales.

TABLE V-1

ALL-TIME TOP INDIVIDUAL SALES

Breed	Year of Sale	Identity of Animal	Sex	Price ($)	Private Treaty or Auction	Seller	Purchaser
American Landrace	1958	Maebrook Betty 11th	Sow	3,000	Private Treaty	Arnold Moore, Columbia, Mo.	Seminole Farms, Donalsonville, Ga.
	1958	Bruntown Conquest	Boar	6,000	Private Treaty	Perry Phillips, Columbia, Mo., Robert Moore, Noblesville, Ind.	Harold Milliman, Crozet, Va.
Berkshire	1941	Pomeroy Falcon Second	Boar	2,500	Auction	Pomeroy Farms, Barrington, Ill.	W. S. Ridgly, Decatur, Ill.
	1958	Ramaco Mainstay	Boar	1,750	Auction	Ramaco Farms, Manitowoc, Wis.	Sir William Farm, Hillsdale, N.Y.
	1964	Kleins Success 2nd cl	Boar	3,000	Private	Milo Wolrob, Mt. Vernon, Ia.	Larry Powers, Alva, Okla.
	1965	Ramaco Charter Ann	Sow	1,100	Auction	Ramaco Farm, Manitowoc, Wis.	Albert Thuron, Yorkville, Ill.
	1965	PAW Hi Class	Gilt	900	Auction	Allen Wagner, Marissa, Ill.	Stanley White, Lamesa, Texas
Chester White	1944	Portage Model	Boar	3,200	Auction	Portage Farms, Woodville, Ohio	Robert Naetke, Clarion, Ia.
	1944	Lisle Ridglydale	Boar	3,400	Auction	Lisle Farms, Lisle, Ill.	Ridglydale Farms, Decatur, Ill.
	1954	The Key	Boar	2,000	Auction	Ruben Schreyer, New Ulm, Minn.	Geo. W. Corron, McComb, Ohio
	1965	Champion boar at Nat. Barrow Show, Austin, Minn.	Boar	4,050	Auction	KOK Farms, Sullivan, Ill.	Parkison & Rodibaugh, Rensselaer, Ind.
	1965	Champion at Nat. Barrow Show, Austin, Minn.	Gilt	1,050	Auction	KOK Farms, Sullivan, Ill.	Chester Home Farms, Waterloo, Wisc.
Duroc	1919	Jackson's Orion King #134009A	Boar	32,000	Private Treaty	Ira Jackson	H. L. White
	1946	Taswell Ace	Boar	4,250	Auction	Taswell Farms, Washington, Ill.	Wynn Farm Co., Wynnburg, Tenn.
	1948	Red Velvet	Boar	4,000	Private Treaty	Bryan Jackson, Galveston, Ind.	H. Y. Patter, Jacksonville, Ill.
	1949	Johnson's Leader	Boar	2,600	Auction	Earl Young, Gibson City, Ill.	Earnest Johnson, Prophetstown, Ill.
	1951	The Master #275983	Boar	3,400	Auction	M. W. Wiltse, St. Charles, Minn.	F. L. Bossingham, Stanford, Ill.
	1951	Cherry Velvet #270683	Boar	3,050	Auction	Patter Farms, Jacksonville, Ill	H. F. Anderson, Des Moines, Ia.
	1951	The Captain #122749	Boar	4,000	Private Treaty	J. C. McKee & Son, Rio, Ill.	Old McDonnell Farm, Yorkville, Ill.
	1951	Fenmar Masterpiece #259652	Boar	3,500	Private Treaty	C. R. Beard, Frankfort, Ind.	Fenmar Farms, Orion, Ill.
	1952	Perfection Kind	Boar	2,500		Klein & Neubauer, Iowa Falls, Ia.	Gregor Vaske, Dyersville, Ia.

(Continued)

TABLE V-1 (Continued)

Breed	Year of Sale	Identity of Animal	Sex	Price ($)	Private Treaty or Auction	Seller	Purchaser
	1952	Triumph's Heritage	Boar	2,500		Elmer Hoge, Walnut, Ill.	Tracy Bros., Williamsville, Ill.
	1953	The Foundation	Boar	2,600	Auction	J. W. Simpson & Son, Edgerton, Mo.	Martin Katter & Son Wapakoneta, Ohio.
	1954	The Clipper	Boar	2,500	Auction	Ora Staley, Paris, Ill.	Tracy Bros., Williamsville, Ill.
	1955	Champion Clipper	Boar	4,000	Auction	Tracy Bros., Williamsville, Ill.	K-A Ranch, Clarksdale, Miss.
	1958	Kayward Constructor	Boar	5,000	Private Treaty	J. L. Lewis Versailles, Ohio	Kayward Farm, Iowa City, Ia.
	1959	Royal Future	Boar	4,100	Auction	O. W. Long Elnora, Ind.	Clarence Chappell, Belvidere, N.C.
	1959	Kayward Centennial	Boar	4,050	Auction	Juhl Bros., Luverne, Minn.	Kayward Farm, Iowa City, Ia.
	1960	Modern Star	Boar	3,000	Private Treaty	Melvin Feik & Son, LaMoille, Ill.	Oral W. Long, Elnora, Ind.
	1960	Super Charm Jr.	Boar	3,000	Private Treaty	J. L. Lewis & Son, Versailles, Ohio	Kee-Wah-Din Farms, Montrose, Mich.
	1961	Great Star	Boar	3,000	Private Treaty	Donald Kremer, Monticello, Ind.	Joe Metzger & Sons, South Whitley, Ind.
	1962	Mr. X	Boar	3,150	Auction	Wm. Urban & Sons, Prophetstown, Ill.	Earl Martin & Son, DeKalb, Mo.
	1963	Champs Special Lady	Gilt	3,525	Auction	Earl Martin & Son, DeKalb, Mo.	Clarence Chappell & Son, Belvidere, N.C.
	1963	Dynamite	Boar	4,150	Auction	Strowold Farms, Boling Green, Mo.	Earl Martin & Sons, DeKalb, Mo.
	1964	Ramrod	Boar	3,659	Auction	Wm. Urban & Sons, Prophetstown, Ill.	Earl Martin & Son, DeKalb, Mo.
	1965	Congress Champion	Boar	5,125		Thompson Farms, Sesser, Ill.	Robert F. Johnson, Cash, Ark.
Hampshire	1920	Cherokee Roller #66671	Boar	10,000	Private Treaty	C. S. Boynton, Pleasant Plains, Ill.	Seth T. Hadley, Danville, Ind.
	1920	Venus #113072	Sow	4,000	Auction	F. R. Pierce, Mt. Vernon, S. Dak.	Mrs. Jos. Kotrba, Mitchell, S. Dak.
	1947	Comprest #338339	Boar	8,000	Private Treaty	Parkfield Farm, Toluca, Ill.	C. E. Wilson, Oxford, Mich.
	1948	Tru-Mold #364119	Boar	8,500	Private Treaty	Fruehauf Farms, Cedar Rapids, Ia.	Chardon Farms, Grays Lake, Ill.
	1949	Carmen Jane #904428	Sow	2,575	Auction	Mullady Farms, Elgin, Ill.	Model Farms, Mundelein, Ill.
	1951	Zehr's Glory #483113	Boar	4,500	Private Treaty	Lester Zehr & Sons, Pontiac, Ill.	Martin's Rock River Farm, Byron, Ill.
	1951	Wester Packer #433139	Boar	4,000	Private Treaty	James B. Nance & Sons, Alamo, Tenn.	Model Farms, Mundelein, Ill.
	1951	Great Western	Boar	3,050	Auction	Cecil Wilson, Lenox, Ia.	Model Farms, Mundelein, Ill.
	1951	Executive #420157	Boar	3,000	Auction	Cecil Wilson, Lenox, Ia.	P. L. Benshoof, Webster City, Ia.
	1952	Lochinvar Lil	Sow	5,000	Auction	Mullady Farms, Elgin, Ill.	P. L. Benshoof, Webster City, Ia.
	1953	Great Western	Boar	10,200	Auction	Model Farms, Mundelein, Ill.	Martin's Rock River Farm, Byron, Ill.

(Continued)

TABLE V-1 (Continued)

Breed	Year of Sale	Identity of Animal	Sex	Price ($)	Private Treaty or Auction	Seller	Purchaser
	1953	Carmen's Image	Sow	2,050	Auction	Model Farms, Mundelein, Ill.	Murrell Belanger, Lowell, Ind.
	1953	Jubilee Medal	Boar	3,025	Auction	B. Behrens & Son, Walnut, Ill.	Walsh Bros., Beloit, Wis.
	1956	Future Design Image	Boar	6,000	Auction	Ralph Wilson, Burlington, Wis.	Treasure Acres, Blairsburg, Ia.
	1957	Transmitter Eagle	Boar	3,800	Auction	Ralph Wilson, Burlington, Wis.	Chinguapin Farms, Tryon, N.C.
	1958	Look-Ahead	Boar	5,700	Auction	Lettow Bros., Alden, Ia.	Cedar Point Farms, Easton, Md.
	1959	Golden Comet	Boar	5,000	Private Treaty	Allen Lang & Son, Brooklyn, Ia.	Sandra-Lin Stock Farm, Ft. Worth, Tex.
	1964	Miss Tribute 5-6	Gilt	1,700	Auction	J. Rodibaugh, Rensselaer, Ind.	Raymond Randall, Jr., Oskaloosa, Ia.
	1965	Buster Tab	Boar	4,000	Auction	Wm. G. Nash & Sons, Sharpsville, Ind.	Carr Bros., McNabb, Ill.
	1966	Miss Buster Tab	Gilt	2,050	Auction	Shady Side Farm, Powell, Ohio	M. J. Pate & Sons, Staley, N.C.
	1966	Top Climax	Boar	4,100	Auction	Wm. G. Nash & Sons, Sharpsville, Ind.	Wayland Givens, Owensboro, Ky.
OIC	1963	T-Ayr-Sally	Sow	225	Auction	Thos. E. Hendricks, Cloverdale, Ind.	Arthur Perkins, Greencastle, Ind.
	1965		Boar	400	Auction	Ricky Toms, Boonsboro, Md.	Edward Ness, Columbia City, Ind.
Poland China	1919	The Clansman #92964	Boar	15,000	Private Treaty	Silver Brook Farm, Muncie, Ind.	Wm. Wrigley, Jr., Lake Geneva, Wis.
	1919	Designer #93699	Boar	30,000	Private Treaty	Wm. Ferguson, Scribner, Neb.	D.C. Lonergan & Sons, Florence, Neb.
	1920	Fashion Girl #219444	Sow	17,200	Auction	L. H. Glover, Grandview, Mo.	F. R. McDermand, Kansas City, Mo.
	1920	Kramers Kind #219443	Sow	14,600	Private Treaty	T. E. Thompson, Franklin, Ind.	Arlington Farms, Indianapolis, Ind.
	1959	Famous	Boar	1,750 (½ int.)	Private Treaty	O. A. Anderson, Leland, Ill.	Harvey Richardson, Elmore City, Okla.
	1961	Super Sire	Boar	3,800	Auction	Prewitt & Orr, Tipton, Ind.	O. W. Anderson & Sons, Leland, Ill.
Spotted	1950	Hit Parade	Boar	4,050	Auction	Clifford Goff, Burwell, Neb.	Ridgedale Farms, Decatur, Ill.
Yorkshire	1958	Oakdale Toastmaster 2N	Boar	2,300	Auction	Cerny Bros., Dorchester, Neb.	Sir William Farm, Hillsdale, N.Y.
	1959	CJP Cooperdale Champ 200N	Boar	2,400	Auction	C. J. Cooper & Sons, Hartley, Ia.	Smith Concrete Prod., Leco Feeds, Kinco Feeds, Kinston, N.C.
	1966		Female	1,500	Auction	Lloyd Michals, St. Peter, Minn.	C. J. Cooper & Sons, Hartley, Ia.
	1966	Mr. Forty Four	Boar	4,400	Auction	Wm. Hickey, Carthage, Ind.	Reno Thomas, Brooks End Farm, Beavertown, Pa.

TABLE V-2

ALL-TIME TOP CONSIGNMENT SALES

Breed	Year of Sale	Number of Animals	Average Price	Seller
			(dollars)	
Chester White	1965	31 boars & gilts	685	Parkison & Rodibaugh, Rensselaer, Ind.
	1966	114 bred sows	192	Rudasill Farms, Mexico, Mo.
Duroc	1920	50	2,000	E. M. Kern, Stanton, Neb.
	1965	166	290	National Duroc Congress, Des Moines, Ia.
Hampshire	1958	30	654	National Barrow Show, Austin, Minn.
	1963	30	796	National Barrow Show
	1964	30	528	National Barrow Show
	1965	30	860	National Barrow Show
	1966	98	565	National Winter Hampshire Type Conference
Landrace	1953	103	2,600	England
Poland China	1920	40	3,112	L. H. Glover, Kansas City, Mo.
Yorkshire	1966	133	400	American Yorkshire Club Type Conference Sale

SECTION VI.—BREED REGISTRY ASSOCIATIONS

A breed registry association consists of a group of breeders banded together for the purposes of: (1) recording the lineage of their animals, (2) protecting the purity of the breed, (3) encouraging further improvement of the breed, and (4) promoting the interest of the breed. A list of the swine registry associations is given in Table VI-1.

TABLE VI-1
SWINE REGISTRY ASSOCIATIONS

Breed	Association	Secretary and Address
American Landrace	American Landrace Assn., Inc.	Eugene G. Benedict, Exec. Secy., P.O. Box 111, Culver, Ind. 46511
Berkshire	American Berkshire Assn.	Gene Mason, Secy., 601 W. Monroe St., Springfield, Ill. 62704
Chester White	Chester White Swine Record Assn.	Larry L. Rus, Secy., Rochester, Ind. 46975
Duroc	United Duroc Swine Registry	Bruce Henderson, Secy., 237-239 N. Monroe, Peoria, Ill. 61602
English Large Black	National Large Black Swine Breeders' Assn.	R. L. Teeter, Pres., Rt. 1, Midland, N.C. 28107
Hampshire	Hampshire Swine Registry	Harold Boucher, Secy., 1111 Main St., Peoria, Ill. 61606
Hereford	National Hereford Hog Record Assn.	Mrs. Sylvia Schulte, Secy.-Treas. Norway, Ia. 52318
Inbred Breeds	Inbreed Livestock Registry Assn.	George W. Slater, Pres., Rt. 4, Box 207, Noblesville, Ind. 46060
OIC (Ohio Improved Chester)	OIC Swine Breeders' Assn. Inc.	Thomas R. Hendricks, Secy.-Treas., Box 111, Greencastle, Ind. 46135
Poland China	Poland China Record Assn.	C. W. Mitchell, Secy., 501 E. Losey St., Galesburg, Ill. 61401
Red Berkshire	Kentucky Red Berkshire Swine Record Assn.	Hogan Teater, Secy., Lancaster, Ky. 40444
Spotted	National Spotted Swine Record, Inc.	Duane Fort, Sec., West Main Street, Bainbridge, Ind. 46105
Tamworth	Tamworth Swine Assn.	Erwin Mahrenholz, Secy., R.R. #2, Cederville, Ohio 45314
Wessex Saddleback	Wessex Saddleback Swine Assn.	A. M. McCracken, Secy., 4010 Clinton Ave., Des Moines, Ia. 50310
Yorkshire	American Yorkshire Club, Inc.	Wilbur L. Plager, Secy., Box 878, Lafayette, Ind. 47902

SECTION VII.—BREED MAGAZINES

The livestock magazines publish news items and informative articles of special interest to swine men. Also, many of them employ field representatives whose chief duty it is to assist in the buying and selling of animals.

In the compilation of the list herewith presented (see Table VII-1) no attempt was made to list the general livestock magazines of which there are numerous outstanding ones. Only those magazines which are devoted exclusively to swine are included.

TABLE VII-1

SWINE MAGAZINES

Breed	Publication	Address
General	National Hog Farmer	1999 Shepard Rd., St. Paul, Minn. 55116
American Landrace	American Landrace, The	313 S. Glenstone, Springfield, Mo. 65802
Berkshire	Berkshire News	601 W. Monroe St., Springfield, Ill. 62704
Chester White	Chester White Journal	Rochester, Ind. 46975
Duroc	Duroc News	237 N. Monroe St., Peoria, Ill. 61603
Hampshire	American Hampshire Herdsman	1111 Main St., Peoria, Ill. 61606
OIC	OIC News	Greencastle, Ind.
Poland China	Poland China World	501 E. Losey St., Galesburg, Ill. 61401
Spotted	Spotted News	Alamo Bldg., Greencastle, Ind.
Tamworth	Tamworth News	Lacona, Ia. 50139
Yorkshire	Yorkshire Journal	1001 South Street, Lafayette, Ind. 46225

SECTION VIII.—STATE COLLEGES OF AGRICULTURE

The stockman can obtain a list of available bulletins and circulars and other information regarding livestock, by writing to his state agricultural college. A list of the State Agricultural Colleges (land-grant institutions have an *) follows:

State	Address
Alabama	*Auburn University, Auburn.
	Tuskegee Institute, Tuskegee.
Alaska	*University of Alaska, Palmer.
Arizona	*University of Arizona, Tucson.
	Arizona State University, Tempe.
Arkansas	*University of Arkansas, Fayetteville.
	Arkansas State College, State College.
California	*University of California, Davis.
	California State Polytechnic College, San Luis Obispo.
	California State Polytechnic College, Kellogg-Voorhis, Pomona.
	Chico State College, Chico.
	Fresno State College, Fresno.

State	Address
Colorado	*Colorado State University, Fort Collins.
Connecticut	*University of Connecticut, Storrs.
Delaware	*University of Delaware, Newark.
Florida	*University of Florida, Gainesville. Florida A & M University, Tallahassee.
Georgia	*University of Georgia, Athens.
Hawaii	*University of Hawaii, Honolulu.
Idaho	*University of Idaho, Moscow.
Illinois	*University of Illinois, Urbana. Southern Illinois University, Carbondale. Illinois State University, Normal. Western Illinois University, Macomb.
Indiana	*Purdue University, Lafayette.
Iowa	*Iowa State University, Ames.
Kansas	*Kansas State University, Manhattan.
Kentucky	*University of Kentucky, Lexington. Berea College, Berea. Eastern Kentucky University, Richmond. Morehead State University, Morehead. Murray State University, Murray. Western Kentucky State University, Bowling Green.
Louisiana	*Louisiana State University, University Station, Baton Rouge. Frances T. Nicholls State College, Thibodaux. Grambling College, Grambling. Louisiana Polytechnic Institute, Ruston. McNeese State College, Lake Charles. Northeast Louisiana State College, Monroe. Northwestern State College of Louisiana, Natchitoches. Southeastern Louisiana State College, Hammond. Southern University and A & M College, Baton Rouge. University of Southwestern Louisiana, Lafayette.
Maine	*University of Maine, Orono.
Maryland	*University of Maryland, College Park.
Massachusetts	*University of Massachusetts, Amherst.
Michigan	*Michigan State University, East Lansing. Michigan Emmanual Missionary College, Berrien Springs.
Minnesota	*University of Minnesota, St. Paul.
Mississippi	*Mississippi State University, State College.
Missouri	*University of Missouri, Columbia.
Montana	*Montana State University, Bozeman.
Nebraska	*University of Nebraska, Lincoln.
Nevada	*University of Nevada, Reno.
New Hampshire	*University of New Hampshire, Durham.
New Jersey	*Rutgers University, New Brunswick.
New Mexico	*New Mexico State University, University Park.
New York	*Cornell University, Ithaca.
North Carolina	*North Carolina State University, Raleigh. Agricultural and Technical College of North Carolina, Greensboro. Pembroke State College, Pembroke.
North Dakota	*North Dakota State University, Fargo.

State	Address
Ohio	*Ohio State University, Columbus.
Oklahoma	*Oklahoma State University, Stillwater.
	Panhandle A & M College, Goodwell.
Oregon	*Oregon State University, Corvallis.
Pennsylvania	*Pennsylvania State University, University Park.
	Delaware Valley Col. Sci. & Agr., Doylestown.
Puerto Rico	*University of Puerto Rico, Rio Piedras.
Rhode Island	*University of Rhode Island, Kingston.
South Carolina	*Clemson University, Clemson.
South Dakota	*South Dakota State University, University Station, Brookings.
Tennessee	*University of Tennessee, Knoxville.
	Middle Tennessee State University, Murfreesboro.
	Tennessee A & I State University, Nashville.
	Tennessee Polytech Institute, Cookeville.
Texas	*Texas A & M University, College Station.
	Abilene Christian College, Abilene.
	Prairie View A & M College, Prairie View.
	Sul Ross State College, Alpine.
	Texas A&I University, Kingsville.
	Texas Technological College, Lubbock.
Utah	*Utah State University, Logan.
	Brigham Young University, Provo.
Vermont	*University of Vermont, Burlington.
Virginia	*Virginia Polytechnic Institute, Blacksburg.
	Virginia State College, Petersburg.
Washington	*Washington State University, Pullman.
West Virginia	*West Virginia University, Morgantown.
Wisconsin	*University of Wisconsin, Madison.
	Wisconsin State University, River Falls.
Wyoming	*University of Wyoming, Laramie.

IN CANADA

Province	Address
Alberta	University of Alberta, Edmonton.
British Columbia	University of British Columbia, Vancouver.
Manitoba	University of Manitoba, Winnipeg.
New Brunswick	University of New Brunswick, Fredericton.
Nova Scotia	University of Nova Scotia, Truro.
Ontario	University of Guelph, Guelph.
Quebec	Faculty d'Agriculture, University of Laval, Quebec City.
	Macdonald College, St. Anne de Bellevue, Montreal.
Saskatchewan	University of Saskatchewan, Saskatoon.

INDEX